LOCAL COMPUTER NETWORKS

IFIP In-Depth Symposium on
Local Computer Networks
Florence, Italy, 19-21 April, 1982

sponsored by
International Federation for Information Processing (IFIP)

co-sponsored by
Associazione Italiana Calcolo Automatico (AICA)
Progetto Finalizzato Informatica —
Consiglio Nazionale delle Ricerche (PFI - CNR)

organized by
IFIP TC 6, Working Group 6.4 (Local Computer Networks)
OLTECO — Olivetti Telecomunicazioni

program committee
M. Bazewich (Poland), A. Danthine (Belgium), D. Davies (UK),
L. Fratta (Italy), G. Hopkins (USA), F. Konigshofer (Austria),
K. Kümmerle (Switzerland), G. Le Moli (Italy), R. Metcalfe (USA),
N. Naffah (France), Y. Nakagome (Japan), W. Jensen (Sweden),
E. Raubold (Germany), P. Ravasio (Italy), J. Shoch (USA),
F. Telbisz (Hungary), A. West (Switzerland)

organizing committee
L. Mercurio, G. P. Bracchi, R. Falugi, A. R. Meo

The Symposium was held under the auspices of the
Municipality of Florence

NORTH-HOLLAND PUBLISHING COMPANY
AMSTERDAM • NEW YORK • OXFORD

LOCAL COMPUTER NETWORKS

Proceedings of the IFIP TC 6 International In-Depth Symposium on
Local Computer Networks
Florence, Italy, 19-21 April, 1982

edited by

PIERCARLO RAVASIO
Ing. C. Olivetti & C.S.p.A.
Centro Studi
Ivrea, Italy

GREG HOPKINS
The MITRE Corporation
Bedford, MA, U.S.A.

and

NAJAH NAFFAH
INRIA
Le Chesnay, France

1982

NORTH-HOLLAND PUBLISHING COMPANY
AMSTERDAM • NEW YORK • OXFORD

ISBN: 0 444 86386 9

Published by:

NORTH-HOLLAND PUBLISHING COMPANY – AMSTERDAM • NEW YORK • OXFORD

Sole distributors for the U.S.A. and Canada:

ELSEVIER SCIENCE PUBLISHING COMPANY, INC.
52 Vanderbilt Avenue
New York, N.Y. 10017

PRINTED IN THE NETHERLANDS

PREFACE

The technology developments surrounding local area networks over the last three years have been dramatic. This conference addresses a number of the current issues in LAN design, performance analysis, protocols, gateway development, distributed operating systems, standards, and network applications. We are sure you will find that these technical presentations reflect the rapid pace of LAN development.

Although we are finally seeing general purpose ring, bus, and digital PBX products enter the marketplace to satisfy user requirements, an important question remains to be asked in the field of LAN's. What is required before LAN's reach wide commercial acceptance? Generally most of the features inhibiting LAN development are pragmatic, and not highly technical, engineering issues.

Probably the most serious issues center around network installation and maintenance procedures. LAN's offer architecturally simple solutions to an organization's heterogeneous, mixed vendor communications requirements. Yet the dependence on this common channel requires more elaborate network monitoring and control procedures which are not necessary on networks built from individual point-to-point connections. Network monitoring and installation support tools are currently unfulfilled marketing promises. Real-time performance analysis capabilities are not found in current LAN products. Fault isolation techniques, built in test equipment, and fault tolerant network interface designs have also rarely been addressed. Even more practical considerations such as fire law restrictions, installation techniques, and adherence to regulations concerning RF signal emanations have not been resolved. Although LAN's exacerbate these problems, they also offer promising opportunities to solve network reliability and monitoring problems.

A closely related topic still in its early development is network management. Many of the LAN's in existence today are based on distributed access control techniques but centralized network management functions appear to be a necessity. Tools will be required to monitor loading, perform network accounting, support access control, monitor connectivity, and generally control the day-to-day operation of the network. Organizations must also accept the responsibility of developing an in-house group to operate and maintain the LAN, rather than relying on outside vendors for complete support.

Local networks will not exist in a vacuum, but rather a large variety of different local networks will be internetworked to solve corporate communications problems. Significant technical issues remain to be resolved before effective internetworks can be developed. Gateway design, protocol conversion, service mapping and address resolution, internetwork standards and regulations are all open issues. A widely accepted but poorly followed maxim is that protocols used for LAN's must be designed with internetworking as a fundamental requirement. Yet we continually see "home-brew" protocols being introduced which make internetworking difficult or impossible and gateway performance poor.

The development of standards is also important to the acceptance of LAN's. Standards should result from the careful synthesis of a number of proven alternatives rather than designed in committee without any proven implementations to support the engineering claims. The impact of these standards on computer manufacturers should be understood so that the operating system support is feasible. The development and acceptance of a high-speed parallel interface standard is critical to the growth of mixed vendor distributed systems. Further, these interfaces must allow for the multiplexing of a large amount of application program I/O over the high-speed port.

Finally, the greatest opportunities for LAN market acceptance are with the development of local network applications. Most of the current LAN offerings are aimed at shared terminal access to a number of host processors or primitive file transfer capabilities between machines of the same manufacturer. Effective network operating systems and distributed data base management systems are generally not available. As LAN developers we have once again designed from bottom-up. Most of the design emphasis has been on media and media access considerations. With this limited perspective, the integration of LAN's is difficult.

In summary, the pace of LAN technology has been rapid but the opportunities for further development are even more dramatic. The growth of the LAN marketplace and our hope of general purpose LAN's supporting a wide variety of manufacturer's equipment require system level perspective and the solution to a number of pragmatic problems.

Greg Hopkins
Najah Naffah
Piercarlo Ravasio

WELCOME ADDRESS

At the beginning of the IFIP TC 6 International Symposium on Local Computer Networks I would like to first congratulate TC 6 for outstanding activities and, in particular, for having launched this Symposium on Local Computer Networks. Data Communications at all levels is a subject of utmost relevance for our society.

The rapid development of informatics and simultaneously of worldwide data communications facilities have opened new possibilities which we are only beginning to apprehend. All of us experiment daily the benefits of such developments, even if we can hardly imagine how they will transform our world during the years to come.

The importance of telecommunications is well recognized throughout the world and, as you know, the United Nations decided that next year will be the World Communications Year, dedicated to the development of communications infra-structures.

For several years, the IFIP TC 6 is actively working to advanced the development of telecommunications theory, methodology and applications. It is therefore contributing already significantly to these developments. The area of local networks is, of course, of fundamental importance and I am glad to see so much energy put by TC 6 and, in particular, by WG 6.4 in the organization of such Symposia. I regret very much not to be able to attend this event. I wish the organizers of this Symposium every success for the coming three days and hope the participants will benefit from the fine technical programme which has been prepared by the Programme Committee.

With my best regards to the Symposium organizers and participants as well as to all TC 6 and WG 6.4 members who contributed to the success of this event.

P.B. Bobillier

TABLE OF CONTENTS

VLSI - APPLICATION FOR LCN

LOCAL COMPUTER NETWORKS
P.C. Ravasio, G. Hopkins and N. Naffah (editors)
North-Holland Publishing Company
© IFIP, 1982

C I C S 81
COMMUNICATIONS INTEGRATED CIRCUITS

Gérard MICHEL

Centre National d'Etudes des Télécommunications
Chemin du Vieux Chêne
B.P. 42
38240 MEYLAN - FRANCE

In this paper, the specifications for two integrated circuits,
a transceiver and a controller are described. These circuits are
currently being designed for use in distributed process control
or in office automation. Our main aims in drawing up the specifications were : to provide digital speech transmission and to
facilitate design at the transport level.

INTRODUCTION

The specifications for specialized integrated circuits to be used in local network
communications systems have been worked out with the following criteria in mind :
- The ability to transport digital speech samples as well as computer data.
- Ease of programmation on the upper communication levels.

According to the first criteria such a system will be interesting in distributing
process control applications having real time constraints. With regard to these options, we have not adopted the functional characteristics given in the Ethernet
specifications (1,2), and those used in the Cambridge ring (3). These two examples
are given as they are the most significant among numerous other techniques (4).

Very fruitful ideas have emerged from discussion with the French researchers working on the KAYAK project (5), with regard to programmation of the upper communication levels.

The primary characteristics of the system are described in the second section and
the services provided to the users are listed in section three.

In section four, the communication access protocol and the frame format are described.

Section five deals with the architecture of the circuits which is given only in
terms of interconnected functional blocks.

PRIMARY CHARACTERISTICS

Physical characteristics :

* The data rate is 8 Million bits/second on a broadcast medium which will first be
a coaxial cable, then an optical fiber.

* The maximum distance between two stations is two kilometers and the maximum number of stations possible is 256.

* At each station, the system uses two integrated circuits : a transceiver and a controller.

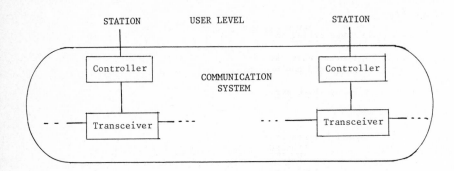

Functional characteristics :

* This communication system covers the three lower levels of the ISO model (6).

* It allows packet transmissions. The length of the packets is variable, with a data field ranging from one to 256 bytes. A destination address field also has a variable length of from one to 16 bytes.

* The addresses are logical and the list of the addresses to be recognized by the communication system is dynamically defined by the user level. Adresses can either be added to or taken away from this list.

* The access protocol is based on priority allocation technique applied to a broadcast medium. Each packet has one byte priority field. When the medium is free, the packet having the highest priority is transferred. In the event of equal priority, the physical position is taken into account.

* Some traffic rate analysis services are provided by the communication system.

* The packets are stamped by the communication system. The stamp value is an ever increasing integer value. It is therefore a global variable in this system. Such a feature is very useful : it helps solve synchronization problems in distributed systems.

* Transmission error recovery : the users do not receive erroneous packets. A transmitter user learns that a transfer has not succeeded after several attempts tried automatically by the communication system. The stamp value does not change in this case.

* In órder to facilitate the transport of the digital speech samples, a user can give : first, the parameters of the packet (data field length, address field content) and then, the data. The communication system automatically frames the packets and transmits them.

THE SERVICES PROVIDED TO A USER

U >... is used to describe the services requested by a user and
U <... the communication system's calls to a user.

Address management :

     U > Add (<u>byte string</u> Address) : <u>boolean</u> Address-table-is-saturated.

The Communication System tells the user if the address table is saturated. In this
way, the user knows the address has not been stored.

     U > Take-away (<u>byte string</u> Address)

Block transmission :

     U > Transmit (<u>struct</u> frame
          (<u>integer</u> priority : <u>integer</u> Adlength ;
           <u>byte string</u> Address ; <u>byte</u> string Data)) :
        Struct Trans-status
          (<u>integer</u> stamp ; <u>integer</u> Rec-Number ;
          <u>boolean</u> Recbufsat ; <u>type</u> error persistent-error)

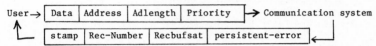

* Priority $\in \{0, 255\}$; Adlength $\in \{1, 16\}$; stamp $\in \{0, 10^9\}$
* Rec-Number is the number of receivers which have recognized the address field and
have not found any transmission errors.
The Rec-Number value $\in \{0, 1, 2, 3, 4$ or more $\}$
* Recbufsat tells if a packet has been refused due to a buffer saturation.
* Persistent-error indicates that after four attempts, the packet has not been ac-
cepted.
Type-error = $\{$ CRC error, Alignment-error, Stamp-value-error $\}$

Receiving a frame :

U < Receive (<u>struct</u> frame
     (<u>integer</u> priority ; <u>integer</u> Adlength ;
      <u>byte string</u> Address ; <u>byte</u> string Data)
    Struct recstatus
     (<u>integer</u> stamp ; <u>integer</u> Rec-Number ;
     <u>boolean</u> will-be-retransmitted))

Communication System→ | Will-be-retransmitted | Rec-Number | Stamp |
         | Data | Address | Adlength | Priority |——→ User

Automatic framing :

    U > Aut-framing (<u>byte string</u> Address ; <u>integer</u> Datalength).

In this case, the data are given separately. This will be used for digital speech
sample transmission.

    U > Data-to-be-transmitted (<u>bit</u> Data)

When the specified Datalength is reached, a packet is transmitted. This service can be stopped :

>   U > Stop-Aut-Framing.

Automatic "Deframing" :

>   U > Deframing (<u>byte</u> <u>string</u> Address)

In this case the data are delivered to the user.

>   U > Data-to-be-received (<u>bit</u> Data)

This service can be stopped :

>   U > Stop-Aut-Deframing.

Traffic Analysis :

U > Thresholds (% Upper-T ; % Lower-T)
The user is warned that either the Upper or the Lower threshold is being crossed by receiving either :
U < Upper-T-crossed or U < Lower-T-crossed.

<u>Stamp value</u> will return to zero after having reached its maximum value. The user will be told that has happened by receiving the message :
>   U < Stamp-reset.

Connection-Disconnection :

>   U > Connection.
>   U > Disconnection.
The communication System will tell the user what was the cause of the disconnection.
>   U < Disconnection (<u>type Dis-cause</u> Dis-cause) among the three possible "Dis-cause", i.e. { dis-request, error-received, wrong-local-selection }

COMMUNICATION MEDIUM ACCESS PROTOCOL.

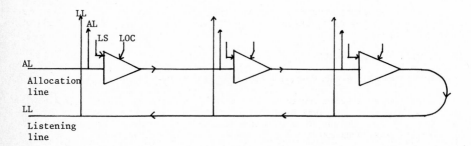

At each station connection, there is a two-to-one selector which lets either the local signal (LS) or the Allocation line signal (A1) go through, controlled by the LOC signal.

When a packet must be transmitted by a station, let PLOC be this packet :

* Wait for the start flag of a packet Q on the allocation line.

* If the priority field of this packet Q has a value less than the priority field of the packet PLOC, the packet PLOC is transmitted, via LS.

* Listening to LL and comparing it with PLOC one knows whether PLOC has been sent.

The priority field comparison between Q and PLOC is processed on the fly, without any computing delay.

The frame format on the listening line is the following :

Flag	PreReNb	Prior	Stamp	Adlength	Address	Data	CRC	Flag
1	1	1	4	1	1 to 16	1 to 256	2	1

Byte Nb

The field semantic is obvious except for PreReNb or Previous Receiver Number, i.e. the number of receivers which have accepted the previous packet, without errors, and recognized the field address. This field is also built on the fly by these receivers.

When a transmission error is detected an error indication packet will be sent, with the maximum value in the priority field, immediatly following the erroneous packet.

We shall now discuss the problem of first packet generation : at each station, there exists an empty frame generator, EFG. EFG is said to be active if no flag has been recognized on AL during one millisecond. This is a kind of watchdog to start or to restart if a failure occurs.

An active EFG generates "empty" frames, with the lowest possible value in the priority field. An empty frame is sent just after the end of each frame on LL or just after EFG is said to be active.

EFG is said to be inactive if a flag is recognized on AL.

Owing to the algorithm chosen to realize the communication access protocol, the "speech" packets, having a very high priority, will be transmitted with a minimum waiting delay.

ARCHITECTURE OF THE CIRCUIT.

The controller and the receiver have been sketched on the following diagram.

The user hardware interface, with the controller, is composed of GPIB (IEEE488) Interface, which is the standard parallel interface used for all the digital integrated circuits we designed. This interface is used to transmit all the requests described in section three.

Serial Input and Output are used to transmit data directly and the controller automatically manages the packets.

Transceiver and controller can be disconnected. The transceiver power is supplied by the cable. When they are disconnected, the transceiver automatically provides a correct connection control module output.

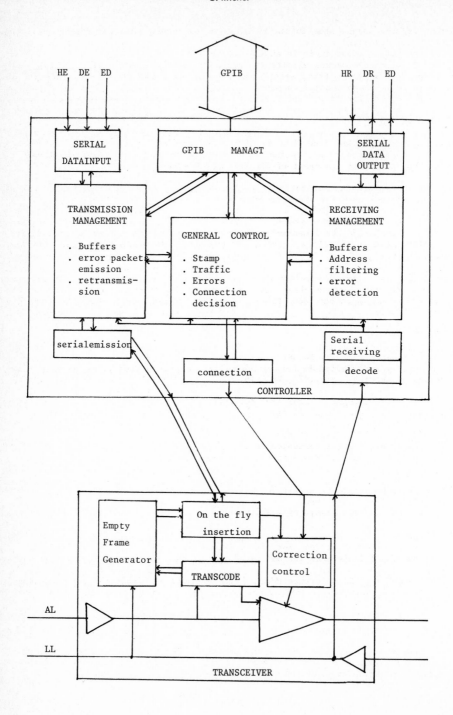

Concerning the stamp value initialization, at the moment that transceiver and con-
troller are connected :
- The controller knows it is in an Init state.
- The first emitted packet elicits a stamp error from the other controllers.
- Using "Init state", "Stamp error" and the current stamp value just found in the
error packet, the controller computes and brings up to date the stamp value.
-Then the controller is in "not init state" and the packet is retransmitted.

CONCLUSION.

In this paper we have described an integrated communication system allowing very
low cost local network realization. Some original features have been developped to
solve the problem of transport of digital speech samples.

Some services, such as automatic framing and traffic analysis make the control of
this system very easy for speech transmission.

Likewise, a powerful error recovery mechanism leads to very simple user interface
control. Lastly, the stamp mechanism facilitates the realization of synchronization
primitives at upper levels of communication in the distributed systems using this
local network technique.

The integrated circuits specification phase is now completed and we are entering
the detailed architecture phase. These circuits will be designed in HMOS at the
Centre National d'Etudes des Télécommunications (Microelectronics Research) in
Grenoble/France.

BIBLIOGRAPHY.

1- R.M. METCALFE and D.R. BOGGS
   Ethernet : Distributed Packet switching for local computer networks. Communications of the ACM. July 1976, Vol. 19, Nb 7, pp 395-404.

2- D.I.X. The Ethernet. A local Area Network.
   Datalink layer and Physical layer specifications. Version 1.0, Sept. 1980.

3- M.V. WILKES and D.J. WHEELER.
   The Cambridge digital communication ring
   Proceedings of the LACN Symposium, May 1979.

4- M. ELDESSOUKY
   Access protocols for a packet switched broadcast Channel. Technical Note
   NT/RDS/RGM/118, Juin 1980.
   CNET PARIS-A. 92131 ISSY-LES-MOULINEAUX.

5- NAFFAH N.
   KAYAK / A national project for office automation.
   International conference for Data Processing, Berlin, Octobre 1980.

6- ZIMMERMANN H. "OSI Reference Model - the Isomodel of Architecture for open Systems Interconnection". IEEE Transactions on communication COM.28 4 (April
   1980).

VOICE TRANSMISSION ON LCN

LOCAL COMPUTER NETWORKS
P.C. Ravasio, G. Hopkins and N. Naffah (editors)
North-Holland Publishing Company
© IFIP, 1982

Using Local Area Networks
for Carrying Online Voice

by

Danny Cohen[1]
USC / ISI

Abstract

The use of local area network technology for local online interactive voice communication has recently attracted the interest of many researchers around the world, e.g., [31], [44] and [48].

Digital local handling of voice communication is not new in a non-packet mode. TDM connections for digitized voice have been in use for long time by the phone companies, on trunks like T1 and T2.

The new research is focused on the application of local **packet switching** networks for voice communication.

This paper argues that the major issue is the compatibility with long haul packet voice communication and not the technology required for achieving the performance needed to support locally a large number of interactive voice connections.

Local packet voice may be used either for support of local communication (intra-office) or as an access/distribution mechanism for long haul (inter-office) communication system. There are other applications for real-time packet voice (e.g., voice messages, [10]). However, the human communication is the major application.

The paper discusses issues in digital voice communication, packet voice communication, and local and long haul networking. Against this background the paper suggests that the long haul compatibility should become the prime design objective for using local networks for interactive voice communication.

As a public service the paper includes a bibliography on the subject of packet voice and on other related issues.

---

[1]Mailing address: 4676 Admiralty Way, Marina del Rey, California, 90291, USA.

This research is supported by the Defense Advanced Research Projects Agency under Contract No. MDA903 81 C 0335. Views and conclusions contained in this article are the author's and should not be interpreted as representing the official opinion or policy of DARPA, the U.S. Government, or any person or agency connected with them.

Digital Voice Communication

The most important ("classic") tradeoff in digitized voice communication is between processing and data-rate which is measured in bits/second. This data rate is commonly (and slightly erroneously) referred to as "bandwidth". Obviously, when considering this tradeoff one must assume that the same signal quality is achieved. Typically, the more processing is applied the lower data rate is required for communicating signals of the same quality.

Another important tradeoff is between signal quality and data rate, assuming constant processing. Typically, the higher the data rate is, the better the signal is, given the same amount of processing.

The relation among these qualities can easily be stated in words: The communication of more data and more processing of this data yield better quality of the voice communication. Unfortunately, there is no simple way to quantify these features precisely (i.e., numerically).

Only the data rate can be measured and quantitatively (numerically) described, by bits/second. Computations may be described by MIPS (Millions Instructions Per Second) but this measure may be very misleading. From a system point of view the number of ICs needed to implement the computation may be a better measure, especially if the ICs are weighted appropriately (by cost, size, etc). The quality measure is a very sore point. There is no absolute objective measure of voice communication quality. However, there are two widely-used quality measures, the DRT (Diagnostic Rhyme Test), and the PAR (Paired Acceptability Rating) score. Both give only partial quality measures (i.e., comparison) without the use of a any objective measuring algorithm, but applies subjective judgment by people [28].

Typical phone-quality connections require data rates of 64,000b/s. The process of conversion between analog waveforms and their digital representation, PCM (Pulse Code Modulation), requires at least A/D and D/A converters and some provisions for signal conditioning (e.g., various filters). The basic PCM can be handled by about two ICs only. It is worth mentioning that there is nothing sacred about this date rate which represents 8KHz sampling with 8bit/sample, in a logarithmic scale. However, occasionally on telephone connections an LSB is "stolen" from samples for the T1 signalling. Typically this loss does not yield a noticeable degradation of the audio communication.

By applying more processing the data rate may be reduced from 64,000b/s. The use of CVSD (Continuously Varying Slope Delta modulation) typically results in data rates of 32,000 or 16,000b/s. The extra processing required by the CVSD scheme does not increase the IC count and therefore may be considered as being free. Unfortunately, there is a certain quality loss associated with the CVSD vocoding.

More advanced vocoding techniques, like LPC (Linear Prediction Coding), may reduce the data rate further, to 9,600 and 2,400b/s. This further reduction requires the use of additional 5 (about) ICs, at least this is the case today (1981). In addition to this extra processing penalty the acoustic compatibility with the general phone system may be severely damaged (tandeming problems) and the LPC connection is restricted mainly to human sounds.

It is important to be aware that LPC cannot be tandemed with regular telephone lines since the LPC makes a great use of the fundamental frequencies which are in the low part of the spectrum and is totally discarded by the phone system.

Since PCM, CVSD and LPC are the major vocoding techniques in actual use (in the USA) we use them in this paper as representative of the vocoding technology. Readers interested in this area are encouraged to learn about some of the many other vocoding techniques like ADPCM, channel vocoders, cepstral and homomorphic vocoders and more.

A most reasonable vocoding scheme for local networks is PCM which is compatible with both the telephone trunks (both the analog and the digital ones) and with any sophisticated acoustic vocoding scheme like LPC. This is obviously possible only if the local network is capable of delivering the required performance.

Another important aspect of voice communication is the ability to detect automatically silence periods, and to turn the communication on and off according to the level (or lack) of voice activity.

This is another instance of data-rate/processing tradeoff. The additional processing required for estimating the voice activity (silence detection) results in substantial communication data rate saving, especially since in a full duplex connection the average use of each unit is less than 50%, [4].

Luckily, silence detection can be accomplished by a single IC, which in many cases may be integrated into the packages already in use.

Readers interested in vocoding are advised to see [2], [6], [14], [16], [17], [18], [19], [26], [27], [29], [32], [35], [36], [37], [38], [43], [50], [51], [52], [53], [54] and [55].

Packet Voice Communication

For several years packet speech experiments are conducted both on short and long haul networks. The long haul packet speech systems typically implement some sort of speech compression since the raw 64,000b/s is too taxing for the long haul networks. One may tend to confuse the packet speech issue and the speech compression issues, because they typically appear together in these systems.

The most important single issue in packet speech over long haul networks is the need to cope with the high variance of the network performance. This is common issue to all systems where the variance of performance is significant. Most local networks, if properly engineered, do not suffer from this problem.

Another issue which is typical of the long haul nets is the need to conserve data rate, either just in order to reduce the cost which otherwise may be prohibitively high - or in order to fit into the performance envelope offered by that network. The raw PCM (64,000b/s) connection which is trivial for most of the local network technologies is still very high for most (all?) the long haul store and forward packet switching networks, except satellite links.

This need to conserve data rate suggests both silence detection and speech compression, which is often referred to as "narrow band vocoding". The silence detection reduces the transmission duty cycle, whereas the speech compression reduces the peak data rate requirement. Both are important.

Silence detection achieves only a reduction factor of 2 to 3 whereas speech compression may achieve a factor of 20 to 30. Silence detection is nearly free (one or less IC) and may be handled even without any protocol simply by lack of transmission during silence periods. Hence it is very simple both for the hardware and the software.

In contrast, the use of efficient speech compression vocoding requires more hardware, higher level of compatibility among the communicating parties and more complicated software and protocols.

The optimal choice of vocoding scheme (including the silence detection feature) depends, obviously, on the overall system performance and cost parameters. Where data rate is more abundant the need to conserve it is less crucial, and vice versa.

One of the differences between online speech communication and other data communication systems is the way in which lost packets are handled. For online speech, unlike file transfer, for example, timely continuity is as important as data integrity. Therefore, in many cases no effort is made to recover lost packets, and therefore data is not regularly acknowledged, and discovered losses are not reported to the sender.

Ignoring lost packets is the right strategy if the recovery introduces delays which damage the communication quality more than the loss itself. But, if this is not so, there is no reason to tolerate any damage to the data integrity, and lost packets should be retransmitted just as done for file transfer.

One may expect that lost packet be ignored over slow long haul networks, but be retrieved over fast local nets.

Delay variance may cause gaps in the delivery of the speech at the destination. In order to encounter this problem several strategies were devised, all based on the concept that the speech bursts are delayed for a short time at the destination before starting to play them back in order to be able to smooth delay variance [7], [20].

While handling such strategy it is important to distinguish between "coming out of silence" and arrival of packets after a loss, in the former case the playback should be delayed, but not so in the latter. Therefore, it is important to signal silence if no transmission occurs during silence periods.

Part of the quality of an interactive online speech communication is the short delay between the time an utterance is spoken by the talker and the time it is played to the listener. The shorter this delay is - the better is the human interaction, but the larger it is - the easier are the requirements on the communication system.

The total end-to-end delay is the total of the processing time, the packetization period and the transmission delay. Therefore, it makes sense to keep these periods short in order to minimize the total end-to-end delay needed for the improvement of the quality of the voice interaction.

This strategy suggests that the packetization period be kept small, in order to reduce the total end-to-end delay. However, since the number of packets required for communicating a given data rate is inversely proportional to their length (which is proportional to the packetization period) the very same strategy which advocated shorter packetization delay causes the use of a larger number of packets.

The load on the communication system grows as these packets get shorter. This is caused by the requirement for a fixed packet overhead (i.e., independent of packet length) which results in the increase of the data to be communicated as the packets get short, even though the effective data rate (the "payload") is constant.

The increase in the number of packets causes also increased delays due to collisions and queues. For most networks, local or long-haul, delays grow with the number of packets, for a constant effective data-rate.

Therefore, short packet periods are not necessarily the proper strategy for reducing the total end-to-end delay. For any situation (network and the load on it) and a given data rate there is an optimal packet size, which may sometimes be derived analytically, or be found experimentally by trial and error techniques.

When several networks are used in tandem, the best strategy is for all of them to use the same packetization period. The concept of depacketization and repacketization of voice in "gateways" leaves a lot to be desired.

Very important work has been done in order to improve the utilization of local networks for voice communication by using techniques like clever retransmission algorithms aggregation and multiplexing.

It is safe to assume that on high performance local networks the optimal packet size [40] is shorter than on long haul slower networks. It is also safe to assume that when such faster local networks are used on both sides of long haul network(s) the delay cause by the latter networks is the dominant component of the overall delay.

Therefore, when local and long haul networks are combined, the packetization period should be mainly aimed at the improvement of the long haul network performance, without necessarily paying too much attention to the parameters of the high performance local network.

Aggregation, multiplexing and concentration techniques can be used for reducing the number of packets without increasing the packetization period. These techniques apply to both local and long haul networks.

The benefits of using these techniques were both proven analytically [31] and verified by various experiments and simulations.

To sum it all up, several issues such as the optimal packetization period, silence detection, vocoding depend on the network performance, and significantly differ between different networks in general, and in particular between different classes of networks, like the local and the long haul ones.

When different networks are interconnected for real-time voice communication a the overall optimal communication scheme is not necessarily the one which optimizes the utility of the high performance local networks.

Summary

Local packet voice may be used either for support of local communication (intra-office) or as an access/distribution mechanism for long haul (inter-office) communication system.

The paper argues that getting online voice service over high performance local networks is relatively simple and can be done in any of many ways (as reported in many papers) and that the major issue in using local networks is the compatibility with the long haul packet voice networks.

When an intra-office communication system is designed the major design objective should not be just the optimization of the intra-office voice handling but the compatibility with the external phone system. The pursuit of high fidelity voice over the office intercom is secondary to the ability to use the same system for cross-town, cross-country and inter-continental phone calls.

The paper suggests that similar approach applies also to packet speech.

References on Packet Voice and Closely Related Issues

[1] Arthurs, E. and Stuck, B.W., "A Theoretical Traffic Performance Analysis of an Integrated Voice-Data Virtual Circuit Packet-Switch", IEEE Transaction on Communications COM-27, (7), July 1979, 1104-1111.

[2] Berouti, M. and Makhoul, J., "An Embedded-Code Multirate Speech Transform Coder", in International Conference on Acoustics, Speech and Signal Processing, 356-359, Denver, Co., April 1980.

[3] Bially, T., Gold B. and Seneff, S., "A Technique for Adaptive Voice Flow Control in Integrated Packet Networks", IEEE transaction on Communications COM-28, (3), March 1980, 325-333.

[4] Brady, P.T., "A Technique for Investigating On-Off Patterns in Speech", Bell System Technical Journal 44, 1965.

[5] Brady, P.T., "Effects of Transmission Delay on conversational behavior on echo-free telephone circuits", Bell System Technical Journal 55, 1971.

[6] Buzo, A., Gray, A.H. Jr., Gray, R.M. and Markel, J.D., "Speech Coding based upon Vector Quantization", IEEE transaction on Acoustics, Speech and Signal Processing ASSP-28, (5), October 1980, 562-574.

[7] Cohen, D., "Issues in Transnet Packetized Voice Communication", in Proceedings of the 5th Data Communication Symposium, 6/10-13, September 1977.

[8] Cohen, D., "A Protocol for Packet-Switching Voice Communication", Computer Networks, September 1978.

[9] Cohen, D., "Flow Control for Real-Time Applications", Computer Communication Review, January 1980.

[10] Cohen, D., "VMS - Voice Message System", in Proceedings of the International Conference on Computer Message Systems, 17-28, Ottawa, April 1981.

[11] Cohen, D., "Packet communication of online speech", in Proceedings of the National Computer Conference, 1981.

[12] Cohen, D., "The Servant's Dilemma", Datamation, November 1981.

[13] Cohen, D., "Network Voice Conferencing Protocol - NVCP", NSC note 113. Available from ISI, 4676 Admiralty Way, Marina del Ray, California, 90291.

[14] Cole, R., "A Proposed LPC Analysis System for the SPS-41", 1974. NSC note 46. Available from ISI, 4676 Admiralty Way, Marina del Ray, California, 90291.

[15] Coviello, G.J., "Comparative discussion of Circuit - vs. Packet-switched Voice", IEEE Transaction on Communications COM-27, (8), August 1979, 1153-1159.

[16] Cox, R.V. and Crochiere, R.E., "Multiple User Variable Rate Codings for TASI and Packet Transmission Systems", IEEE Transaction on Communications COM-28, (3), March 1980, 334-344.

[17] Dhadesugoor, V.F., Ziegler, C. and Schilling, D.L., "Delta modulators in Packet Voice Networks", IEEE Transaction on Communications COM-28, (1), January 1980, 33-51.

[18] Flanagan, J.L., Speech Analysis, Synthesis, and Prediction, Springer-Verlag, New York, 1972.

[19] Flanagan, J.L., Schroeder, M.R., Atal B.S., Crochiere, R.E., Jayant, N.S., and Tribolet, J.S., "Speech Coding", IEEE Transaction on Communications COM-27, (4), April 1979, 710-737.

[20] Forgie, J.W., "Speech Transmission in Packet-Switched Store-and-Forward Networks", in Proceedings of the NCC, 137-142, 1975.

[21] Forgie, J., Nemeth A., "An Efficient Packetized Voice/Data Network Using Statistical Flow Control", in Proceedings of the ICC, Chicago, June 1977.

[22] Frank, H. and Gitman I., "Economic Analysis of Integrated DOD Voice and Data Networks", NAC Report for ARPA, September 1978.

[23] Frank, H. and Gitman I., "Study shows packet switching best for voice traffic, too", Data Communications, March 1979, 43-62.

[24] Gitman, I. and Frank H., "Economic Analysis of Integrated Voice and Data Networks: A Case Study", Proceedings of the IEEE; Special Issue on Packet Communication Networks 66, November 1978, 1549-1570.

[25] Gold, B., "Digital Speech Networks", Proceedings of the IEEE 65, December 1977, 1636-1658.

[26] Gold, B., "Multiple Rate Channel Vocoding", in EASCON Conference Record, 1978.

[27] Gray, A.H. Jr., and Markel J.D., "Quantization and Bit-Allocation in Speech Processing", IEEE transaction on Acoustics, Speech and Signal Processing ASSP-25, (6), December 1976, 459-473.

[28] Huggins, A.W.G., et al., "Speech-Quality Testing of Some Variable-Frame-Rate (VFR) Linear-Predictive (LPC) Vocoders", Journal of the Acoustical Society of America 62, August 1977, 430-434.

[29] Jayant, N.S., "Digital coding of speech waveforms: PCM, DPCM and DM quantizers", in Proceedings of the IEEE, 1974.

[30] Jayant, N.S., "Effects of Packet Losses in Waveform-Coded Speech", in ICCC-80, Atlanta, October 1980.

[31] Johnson, D.H. and O'Leary G.C., "A Local Access Network for Packetized Digital Voice Communications", in Proceedings of the National Telecommunication Conference, 13.4.1-5, 1979.

[32] Lim, J.S., Oppenheim A.V., "Enhancement and Bandwidth Compression of Noisy Speech", Proceedings of the IEEE 67, December 1978, 1586-1604.

[33] Lincoln Laboratory, "Network speech system implications of packetized speech", MIT - Lincoln Laboratory, Lexington, Ma., Technical Report ESD-TR-77-178, September 1976.

[34] Lincoln Laboratory, "Wideband Integrated Voice/Data Technology", MIT - Lincoln Laboratory, Information Processing Techniques Program Semiannual Summary ESD-TR-78-203, March 1978. AD-060714/3.

[35] Magill, D.T., "Adaptive Speech Compression for Packet Communication Systems, National Telecommunications Conference.", in Proceedings of the National Telecommunications Conference, Conference Record, Volume 2, 29D/1-5, Atlanta, Ga., 1973.

[36] Makhoul, J., et al., "Natural Communications with Computers: Speech Compression Research at BBN", BBN Report No. 2976 NTIS No. AD/A 003478/5GA, December 1974. Vol. II.

[37] Markel, J.D., Gray A.H., Jr., Linear Prediction of Speech, Springer-Verlag, New York, 1976.

[38] Markel, J.D., "Highlights of a Group Effort in Algorithmic Development for Packet Switched Voice Networks", National Computer Conference, 1981.

[39] McAuliffe, D, "An Integrated Approach to Communication Switching", in Proceedings of the ICC, Toronto, June 1978.

[40] Minoli, D., "Optimum packet length for packet voice communication", IEEE Transaction on Communication COM-27, (3), March 1979, 607-611.

[41] O'Leary, G.C., "Local Access Area Facilities for Packet Voice", in Proceedings of the ICCC-80, 281-286, Atlanta, October 1980.

[42] O'Leary, G.C., Blankenship P.E., Tierney J., and Feldman J.A., "A modular approach to packet voice terminal hardware design", National Computer Conference, 1981.

[43] Rabiner, L.R., and Schafer R.W., Digital Processing of Speech Signals, Prentice-Hall, Englewood Cliffs, N.J., 1978.

[44] Ravasio, P.C., Mapcogliese, A., and Novarese R., "Voice Transmission over an Ethernet Backbone", in these Proceedings.

[45] Ross, M., Tabbot A. and Waite J., "Design Approaches and Performance Criteria for Voice/Data Switching", in Proceedings of the IEEE, September 1977.

[46] Ross, M.J., Sidlo C.M., "Approaches to the Integration of Voice and Data Telecommunication", in Proceedings of the NTC, Washington, D.C., November 1979.

[47] Rudin, H., "Studies on the the Integration of Circuit and Packet Switching", in Proceedings of the ICC, Toronto, June 1978.

[48] Shoch, J.F., "Carrying voice traffic through an Ethernet local network - a general overview", in Proceedings of the IFIP WG 6.4 International Workshop on local-area Computer Networks, Xerox-PARC, Zurich, August 1980. Xerox-PARC Technical Report, Aug. 1980.

[49] Sproull, R.F. and Cohen D., "High Level Protocols", Proceedings of the IEEE 66, November 1978, 1371-1386.

[50] Tierney, J.T. and Malpass M.L., "Enhanced CVSD - An Embedded Speech Coder for 64-16 kbps", in Proceedings of the IEEE International Conference on Acoustics, Speech and Signal Processing, Atlanta, Ga., March 1981.

[51] Tremain, T., et al., "Implementation of Two Real- Time Narrowband Speech Algorithms", IEEE Eastcon, September 1978, 698-708.

[52] Un, C. and Magill D.T., "The Residual Excited Linear Prediction Vocoder with Transmission Rate below 9.6 Kbs", IEEE transaction on Acoustics, Speech and Signal Processing COM-23, (12), December 1975.

[53] Viswanathan, R., Makhoul J., "Quantization Properties of Transmission Parameters in Linear Predictive Systems", IEEE Transaction on Acoustics, Speech and Signal Processing ASSP-23, June 1975, 309-321.

[54] Viswanathan, R., et al., "Variable Frame Rate Narrowband Speech Transmission Over Fixed Rate Noisy Channels", in Proceedings of the EASCON '77, Washington, September 1977. Paper 23.

[55] Webber, S.A., Harris C.J., and Flanagan J.L., "Use of Variable Quality Coding and Time Interval Modification in Packet Transmission of Speech", Bell System Technical Journal 56, October 1977, 1569-1573.

[56] Weinstein, C.J., "Fractional Speech Loss and Talker Activity Model for TASI and for Packet-switched voice", IEEE transaction on Communications COM-26, (8), August 1978, 1253-1257.

[57] Weinstein, C.J., McLaughlin A.J. and Bially T., "Efficient multiplexing of Voice and Data in Integrated Digital Networks", in Proceedings of the International Conference on Communication, 21.1.1-7, Seattle, June 1980.

LOCAL COMPUTER NETWORKS
P.C. Ravasio, G. Hopkins and N. Naffah (editors)
North-Holland Publishing Company
© IFIP, 1982

CARTHAGE : A MULTISERVICE LOCAL NETWORK

ON A FIBER OPTICS LOOP

Jean Luc FAVRE

Centre Commun d'Etudes de Télédiffusion et Télécommunications

RENNES - FRANCE

The goal of the CARTHAGE project is to provide the future offices of the C.C.E.T.T. (Common Research Center in Broadcasting and Telecommunications) with a multiservice local network.

This network will be able to serve a 500-persons community and carry information kind as video, data and voice.

The services provided by it will be such as electronic mail, telematics services, switched and broadcast television, etc...

1 - INTRODUCTION

The CARTHAGE network has been designed in order to take very seriously into account the set of existing terminals in a firm. We assume that these firms dispose of telephone sets, asynchronous and synchronous computer terminals, videotex terminals, fac-simile terminals, data bases organised on computers with connection protocol like X25.

The videocommunication capability will be limited, in a first step to the control of a switching unit connecting TV-channels between laboratories and meeting rooms.

In addition, if the first role of the local network is to convey homogeneously all the data handled in the offices, the fundamental capability of implementing gateways towards the public networks should not be forgotten; these capabilities have been considered at the beginning of the design.

2 - SERVICES HANDLED BY THE NETWORK

2-1. VOIVE

This kind of services is perfectly described by the features of the last generation of PABX; let us give as examples automatic call-basic, call privacy, leave messages,...

2-2. DATA

These services are provided by the computer-based systems; they connect classical terminals to data bases via appropriate protocoles (X25, X28, X29...).

2-3. PICTURES

The goal of this service is to interconnect a pictures production center to
different laboratories or laboratories to meeting rooms.

3 - NETWORK STRUCTURE

The medium used by the network is made of a bundle of fiber optics; one fiber is
dedicated to the voice and data traffic when the others are reserved for video-
communications. The switching unit of pictures traffic is controlled via a
signalling channel carried by the data fiber. All the terminals are star-connected
to a cluster unit (or termals controller); all the clusters are ring-connected
by the fiber optics. A specific controller (loop controller) ensures the loop
and supervisory functions.

In addition, the gateway functions are distributed amongst the clusters, but they
can be also gathered in the loop controller.

The figure 1 shows the general organization of the network :

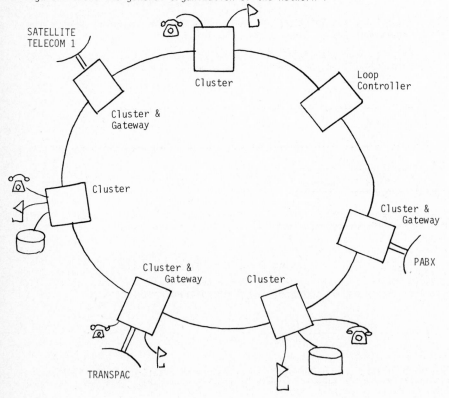

4 - INFORMATION FRAME STRUCTURE

The CARTHAGE data loop uses a TDM technique; the information frame
conveyed on it is made of 128 time slots of 1 µs each. Hence, the loop throughput
is 8 Mbit/s. Twenty basic frames are linked together to make a multiframe :

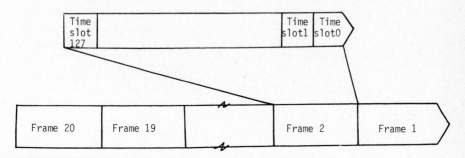

Each station increases the frame propagation time around the loop by an addi-
tionnal delay of 2 µs.

Endly the basic frame is divided into two areas, each addressing specific needs :
a sub-frame "PACKET" and a sub-frame "CIRCUIT" :

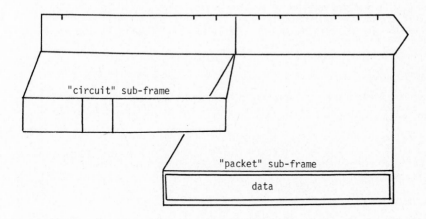

The sub-frame "PACKET", with a size of 32, 64 or 96 bytes, offers an instantaneous throughput of 2, 4 or 6 Mbit/s, when the sub-frame "CIRCUIT" offers
throughputs within a range of 2400 bit/s - 64 Kbits/s; for instance, a 6400
bit/s "CIRCUIT" channel is represented by two time-slots a multiframe.

4-1. HANDLING OF THE "PACKET" SUB-FRAME

The PACKET/CIRCUIT resource sharing is made very convenient by the variable size of the packet resource.

The "PACKET" resource carries all the packet-like data and is used for, by example, X25-servers interconnection, the broadcasting using DIDON technique, the signalling exchange to allocate the two basic resources etc...

The access to the "PACKET" resource is made via a TOKEN technique : each packet holds a label which determines whether the packet is full or empty of information; when a station has a packet to send, it expects an "empty" packet in which it puts its data in and marks it "full". Endly, in order to prevent a station from monopolizing the use of the "PACKET" resource, the access lies on a speech-right-rule.

4-2. HANDLING OF THE "CIRCUIT" SUB-FRAME

The "CIRCUIT" sub-frame offers throughputs within a range of 2400 bit/s - 64 Kbit/s. This resource is allocated by a process implemented in the loop controller, which holds the map of all the available time slots of the multiframe. The telephone service stands as a good example of a consumer of this kind of resource, and so is the connection of terminals to a computer. However, the difference between the moduli of transmission (nx 1200 bit/s, px 3200 bit/s) makes a speed conversion necessary.

5 - SERVICES PROVIDED BY THE NETWORK

It has been seen that the network offers two basic resources : the "PACKET" and the "CIRCUIT" resources. The basic services follow this sharing and are, in connection mode, the virtual circuit and the actual circuit and, in connection-less mode, the datagram and broadcast.

6 - PROTOCOLS

Let us see now the different protocols implemented on the loop in order to provide the services described previously. Let us analyze the different layers of the OSI Reference Model :

6-1. PHYSICAL LAYER

This layer provides the network with all the bit-transmission and reception mechanisms. The code is NRZ.

6-2. DATA LINK LAYER

This layer provides the network with the data framing and the error detection and recovery.

Considering the "PACKET" resource, it encapsulates the information within the format :

acknowledgement	CRC	data	sequencing number	source address	destination address	token

Let us detail the different fields :

TOKEN   This field has several meanings regarding the different functions of
            the packet :

    EMPTY - the PACKET resource is free
    FULL - the PACKET resource is full and the TO-ADDRESS is to be matched by
        all stations
    LAST-PACKET - indicates to the addresse that the packet is the last of the
        transaction (limited by the speech-right-rule)
    RESERVATION - indicates that the data are not significant, but that the
        ACKNOLEDGEMENT field is.
    DIDON - indicates that the packet is used in a broadcastgoal and is struc
        tured following the DIDON standard.

In addition, the TOKEN field is able to indicate the size of the PACKET resource
(32, 64 or 96 bytes).

TO-ADDRESS   This field contains the address of the addressee of the
                    packet; this address is made with a loop-address concatena-
                    ted with an "on-the-loop" address. This allows a very easy
                    implementation of the gateway to an other CARTHAGE-loop by
                    solving this problem at the level 2.

SOURCE-ADDRESS   Same as the DESTINATION-ADDRESS, but regarding the sender.

SEQUENCING NUMBER   This field contains the number of the packet.

DATA   This field contains the bytes of information.

CRC   This field contains a cyclic redundancy check sequence.

ACKNOWLEDGEMENT   This field contains :
                    - the sequencing number of the acknowledged packet;
                    - the flow control code of the addressee station :
                    . RR - station ready to receive more packet
                    . RNR - station no more ready to receive additional
                         packets;
                    . REJ - packet errored; must be retransmitted.

In a first step, we have only implemented a point-to-point protocol of transmission. The broadcast with acknowledgement is for further study.

6-3. NETWORK LAYER

This layer ensures the routing of information. The field used in the routing
process depends on the service :

- datagram   : addressee's address enclosed in the DATA field

- broadcast   : no field present at the level 3

- virtual circuit : reference enclosed in the DATA field

- actual circuit : connection matrix.

This last feature (connection matrix) is commonly used in telephone technology; each cluster is equipped wich two types of matrix (or memory) : a frame-connection matrix and a multi-frame-connection matrix. The frame-memory is used to transmit and receive the contents of a time-slot a basic-frame (64 Kbits/s).
The multi-frame matrix memories the time-slots allocated within the multi-frame.

6-4. TRANSPORT LAYER

This layer ensures the independance of the network-means by respect with upper layers; it chooses the kind of resource, depending on the quality of service (throughput, error rate,...); for the connection mode, it provides the network with the multiservice signalling channel.

The primitives employed by signalling channel are :

TYPE	FUNCTION	PARAMETERS
CALL REQUEST	To establish a call	. Addressee's address . Caller's address . Throughput . Circuit type - virtual - actual - TDM - Video - ... . My-reference
CALL RESPONSE	To accept a call	. Your-reference . My-reference
RESET REQUEST	To purge the circuit	. My-reference
RESET RESPONSE	To confirm the purge	. My-reference
LIBERATION REQUEST	To end a connection	. My-reference . Cause of liberation
LIBERATION RESPONSE	To confirm a liberation	. My-reference

The reference concept replaces the logical link concept. In fact, in the public data networks (like TRANSPAC), the network itself translates during the data transfer phase the logical link numbers between the two endpoints.

In the local networks, the two endpoints speak to each other, and nobody has to
do the translation. The data exchange uses the references exchanged during the
connection phase. This reference exchange is made via an intermediate process,
which needs to know all the resource requests on the network. This also avoids
reference collisions (as it does with logical link numbers in X25).

Besides, the set-up of a video-connection should be considered as a particular
example of connection; a special cluster unit acts as a video switching unit and
connects together input lines to output lines (exactly as a PABX does with
telephone lines). In the future, it will be possible, with a truly multiservice
signalling channel, to set-up an audio and video communication within the same
call.

7 - ARCHITECTURE OF THE DIFFERENT ELEMENTS

7-1. CLUSTER ARCHITECTURE

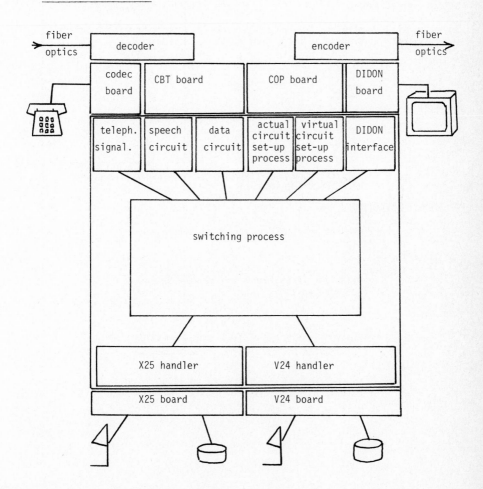

The different boards are detailed below :

CBT-BOARD   : - synchronization handling on the fiber optics
                 - transmission and reception of data according with
                   the connection matrices
                 - interface with processor and telephone via CODEC-Board.

CODEC-BOARD   : - handling of 4 telephone sets

ASV8-BOARD   : - handling of 8 asynchronous terminals (V24)

COP-BOARD   : - access to the PACKET resource
                 - handling of level 1 and 2 of the PACKET protocol

MX25-BOARD   : - processor board which allows two X25 links

The different software modules are :

ACTUAL CIRCUIT PROCESS :

                 - handles the connection between clusters and intermediate
                   process in charge of actual circuits set-up

VIRTUAL CIRCUIT PROCESS :

                 - same, with virtual circuit

DATA CIRCUIT :
                 - handles multiframe connection matrix and data exchanges
                   on actual circuits

SPEECH CIRCUITS :

                 - handles frame connection matrix and speech exchanges
                   on actual circuits

TELEPHONE SIGNALLING :

                 - handles the local telephone signalling

SWITCHING PROCESS :

                 - establish links inside the cluster between
                   software units

X25 HANDLER   :

                 - ensures levels 1-2-3 of X25 for connection with
                   X25 servers or terminals

V24 HANDLER   :

                 - ensures asynchronous terminals connection

7-2. LOOP CONTROLLER

This unit ensures the re-synchronization of the frame and the allocation of the
CIRCUIT resource. It distributes also the speech rights and supervises the loop.

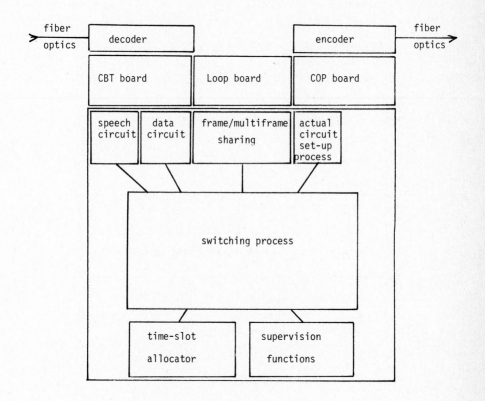

7-3. VIDEO SWITCHING UNIT

This unit has the same architecture as the cluster has, and, in addition, is able to handle videocommunication.

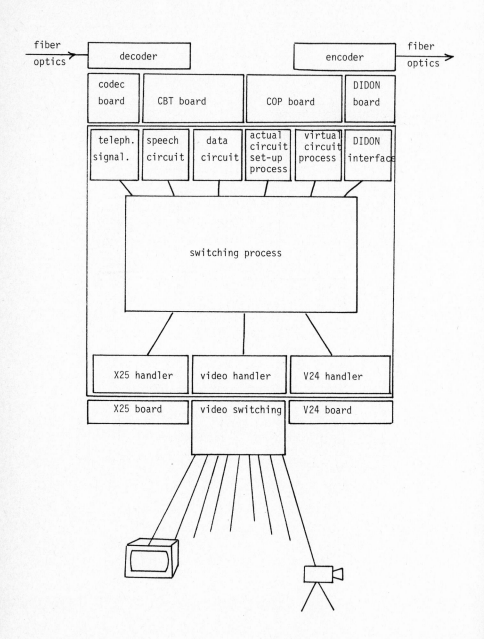

7-4. TRANSPAC GATEWAY

This function is provided by a specific cluster. The basic service of TRANSPAC being the virtual circuit, this unit supports also the intermediate process for virtual circuit set-up.

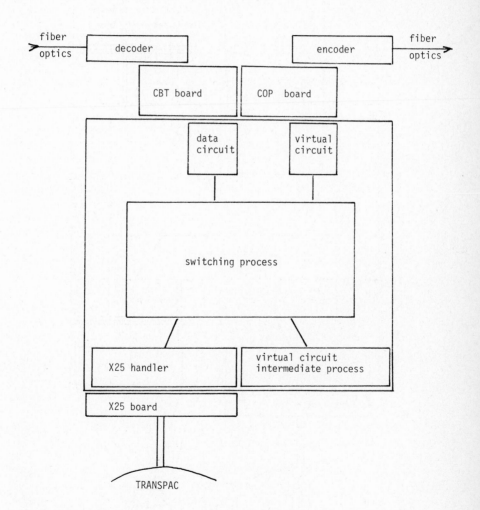

7-5. <u>PABX GATEWAY</u>

This gateway lies on a particular cluster and supports also the intermediate
process for actual circuit set-up (as a basic service of public telephone
network).

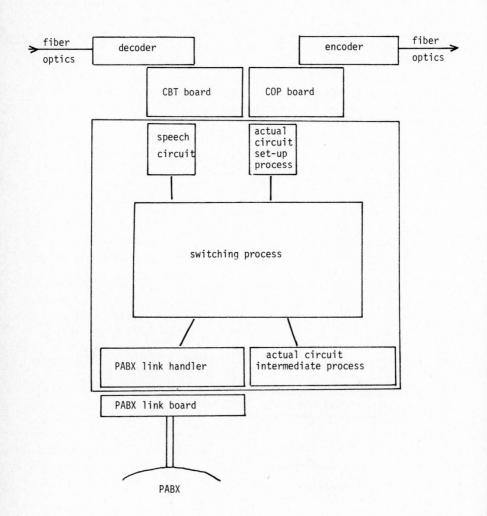

7-6. SATELLITE GATEWAY

This unit is implemented in order to interconnect remote local networks via TELECOM-1 satellite. In a first step, this link will convey circuits.

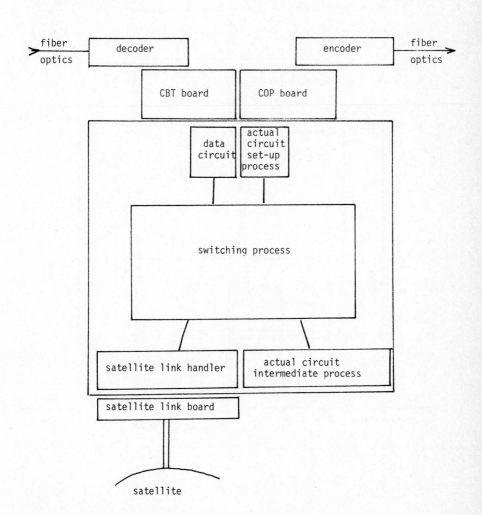

7-7. <u>CARTHAGE GATEWAY</u>

The way the address fields have been implemented makes easy the interconnection between several CARTHAGE networks : indeed, two COP Boards, each one connected to a network are able to make the communication :

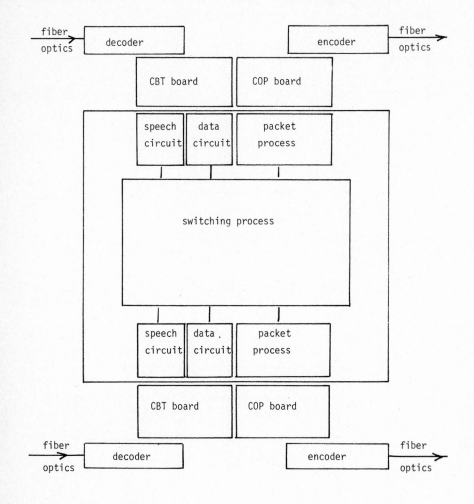

8 - SAFETY

The CARTHAGE network is designed in order to convey all the types of data
exchanged inside company facilities : a failure of this equipement may have some
catastrophic consequences on its working. So, during the design phase a specific
effort has been made towards modularity : the different units of the network are
built with the same elements and the units that are unique on the loop, such as
the loop controller and the gateways for instance, are duplicated for safety
reasons.

In addition, the fiber optics itself have been doubled and each cluster unit
provided with an automatic sensor which extracts the signal from the valid
fiber.

Besides, the loop controller achieves supervision functions during the life of
the network and is able, for example, to stop a chattering station, to stop
remotely any station, etc...

9 - FUTURE

The future developments led on CARTHAGE will be :

- toward a true multiservice signalling channel.

- toward a more accurate integration of the video functions in the network.

LOCAL COMPUTER NETWORKS
P.C. Ravasio, G. Hopkins and N. Naffah (editors)
North-Holland Publishing Company
© IFIP, 1982

VOICE TRANSMISSION OVER AN ETHERNET BACKBONE

P.C. Ravasio
R. Marcogliese
R. Novarese
OLTECO - Olivetti Telecommunications

ABSTRACT

This paper reports results of simulation studies performed in OLTECO about voice and data transmission using an Ethernet backbone. The second section presents the basic principle applied for voice transmission and an overview of problems arising in using packet switching networks for the transmission of digitized voice. In section three the basic protocol used to handle real time voice flow, and a brief description of a prototype implementation are given. In the fourth section an outline of our simulation model is presented. Finally, in sections five and six discussion on results and conclusions follow.

1 INTRODUCTION

The aim of this paper is to describe a set of studies performed on the possibility of using an Ethernet type of local network to implement an integrated communication system able to carry voice and data. The system, described in section two, can be connected to PABXs and Public Switched Telephone Networks (PSTN). There exists a clear trend in integrating all the communication requirements of an office environment; the second generation digital PABXs allow voice and data communication, studies on the possibility of using packet switching networks to transport voice are going on /COH 80/, /COH 79a/, /COH 79b/; studies are also going on the possibility to use CSMA/CD access schemes for the same purpose /OLA 80/, /OLA 81/. Using a packet switching local network to carry voice flow a delay is introduced in the voice call. Thus problems arise when connections to external world (PABX, PSTN) are required because of the presence of echo paths in those systems.

In this first design we have not considered the possibility of using voice compression or silence suppression techniques to optimize the use of the bandwidth. In section 3 we present the two alternative approaches we have implemented in our research laboratory, while in section 4 and 5 we present the simulator of the system and the obtained results. The simulation experiments reproduced environments with only telephones connected to the network and with both voice and data terminals sharing the same subnet.

2 SYSTEM OVERVIEW

The system, figure 1, uses a Ethernet type of local network /MET 75/ as a communication subsystem; the terminals are connected by means of Network Interface Modules (NIM).

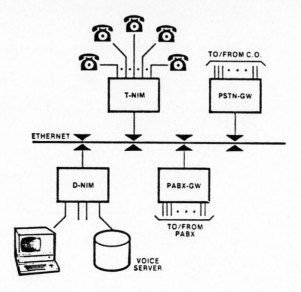

Figure 1. General Structure of DCS

We implemented several types of NIMs which allow the connection of different kinds of equipment. For the sake of simplicity, in this paper let us divide the modules into two classes: the data-NIM (D-NIM) which connects data equipments, and the telephone-NIM (T-NIM) which clusters telephones.
The system is connected to the external world by gateways, in figure 1 we have shown only those which are relevant to this study: the PABX-GW, towards an existing PABX, and the PSTN-GW towards the Central Office that is part of the PSTN.

The overall system will therefore be able to support complex office automation systems in which integrated data and voice communication is needed. It is out of the scope of this paper to give a rationale for the need of such asystem, but it can easily be imagined mostly when sophisticated voice handlingsystems such as voice recognizer, voice data-base, voice synthesizers systems will be available. A deeper view of the voice part of the communicationsubsystem is given in figure 2. The system is composed of 5 basic modules which are listed in the figure. The functions of each module are:

1) Ethernet tranceiver. It performs the connection of a NIM to the coax cable. It is fully compatible with the Ethernet DIX specs /DIX 80/.
2) Analog line interface circuit (ALIC), this module handles up to 8 standard two wire analog telephones. It is responsible for conversion of voice from analog to digital, for connection to the processing unit and for handling the telephone
3) Digital Line Interface Circuit (DLIC). This is the dual of the ALIC for the digital telephone set.
4) Trunk Interface Module (TIM). This module is responsible for the handling of the trunk connection. It is a more sophisticated version of the ALIC and performs the full set of the BORSCHT (Battery feed, Overload

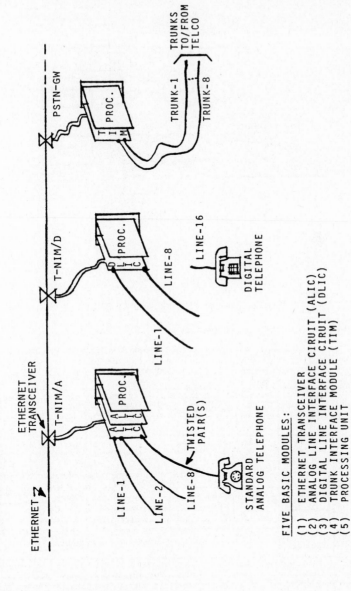

Figure 2. Overall Hardware Architecture

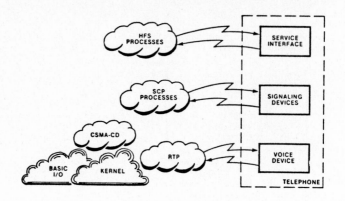

Figure 3.   Basic T-NIM Software Structure

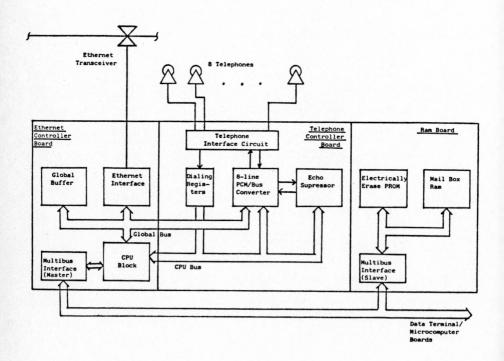

Figure 4.   T-NIM/A Internal Connections (tentative)

protection, Ringing, Supervision, Codec and filter, Hybrid, Testing) function.
5) The processing unit responsible for the handling of the overall system. It supports the software structure summarized in figure 3.

A conceptual scheme of the T-NIM is given in figure 4. The T-NIM behaviour is briefly described below. The ALIC transforms the analog voice signal into PCM sample, the samples are stored in a global buffer through an internal T1 bus and when a packet is formed, the Ethernet interface is activated in order to transmit it. This function is performed by a Real Time Protocol (RTP) which is all hardware implemented. A more detailed description of RTP is given in section 3. The T-NIM is also responsible for the handling ofall the dialling process and for the tone generation: the T-NIM can be regarded therefore as a small switching system which haules up to 16 telephoneslocally and allows the expansion through the network.
The processing unit manages the system, handles high-level features, system diagnosis and testing functions, implements a Signaling and Control Protocol (SCP) for the call processing both locally and through the Ethernet.

In our research lab we have prototypes of the T-NIM/A and the T-NIM/D. Gateways are still under design. We have, of course, our own tranceiver and several types of D-NIMs.

2.1 PACKETIZED VOICE TRANSMISSION: AN OVERVIEW

The fundamental mechanism needed for packetized voice transmission is voice digitalization. It is well known that it is possible and cost effective to digitize the analog voice signal coming out of a microphone. Most of the new PABXs are based on a digital switch of the voice among different instruments /MEL 80/, /MEL 78/. The voice switching is normally based on TDM techniques. Following the rapidly increasing success of PSNs (Packet Swiched Network), many studies have been started /COH 80/ on the possibility of using Packet Switcing techniques to carry voice flow. One of the most popular voice digitalization technique is the Pulse Code Modulation (PCM). According to this technique, the analog voice signal is sampled at a rate of 8 kHz. For each sampling point, values of the signal are evaluated and collected. The possible collected values range from -127 to +127, therefore, 8 bits are needed to represent the value of the signal at a given moment. The resulting rate for the digitized voice is therefore 8 kbytes/sec or 64kbps.

2.2 PACKETIZATION DELAY AND PACKET RATE

The voice transmission on a packet switching network is based on the following principles: the samples of digitized voice are collected and stored; when a certain amount of samples are collected, a packet containing all the stored samples is sent onto the network. At the other end of the network a peer entity receives the packet, stores it and delivers to its own transducer the voice samples at rate 64 kbps.

The first very obvious note is that the packet transmission of voice has an intrinsic delay: the packetization delay. This delay is exactly equal to the number of collected sample multiplied by 125 usec (the sampling period). We will refer to the number of samples contained in a packet as the packet size. This quantity is expressed in either number of bytes or time. This delay can be

large or small, according to the size of packets, but the basic point is that
it exists and must be carefully considered mostly when closed echo paths can be
present in the overall system. We will also use the expression packet rate, it
is the frequency corresponding to a period equal to the packetization delay.

2.3 A FIRST PROBLEM: THE TRANSMISSION DELAY

     Unfortunately the packetization delay is not the only source of delay in
a packetized voice transmission system. In fact, when a packet is sent on a
packet switching network, it experiences a transmission delay. This delay is
due to different causes (delay in getting the line, delay on store and forward
nodes, delay due to the medium and to the transmission characteristics of the
network, delay due to routing and error recovery mechanisms, and so on) which
may or may not coexist in a particular network. For example the value of the
medium delay may be very large with satellite connections while it is
negligible in local networks.

     Moreover, the transmission delay is not a constant value as the
packetization delay is, but it depends on the load of the network, the chosen
route in a complex network, and so on. But this is not all, for some types of
network it is not deterministic (e.g. Ethernet), moreover it may be not
bounded.

     The voice transmission algorithms over a packet switching network must
take into account the effect of both the packetization and the transmission
delay. We will see that several techniques can be used to overcome the delay
problem. General principles to be applied are the following:

- reduce to a minimum the maximum transmission delay
- reduce as much as possible the delay variance
- deal with lost packets and with discarded packets.

     The third point introduces a new argument in our discussion: the
discarded packets. Several studies have shown that a certain amount of lost
packets does not affect the quality of transmitted voice /JAY 80/. The range of
acceptable percentage of lost packets varies according to different authors
from 1% to 5%. The latter value requires that some techniques (interpolation)
be used in order to have a good recovery from lost packets. In some kinds of
network the packet transmission delay is not predictable (Ethernet backoff
algorithm) but a voice packet arriving after a certain period time badly
influences the following traffic flow. Consequently, when a delay greater than
a predefined threshold is experienced, we must resynchronize the arriving
packets by using a discarding policy. Mechanisms to handle this situation must
be inserted in order to have consistent protocols.

2.4 PROBLEMS CAUSED BY THE DELAY

     Why is the problem of delay central in packetized voice transmission? The
main troubles caused by the delay are related to:

- quality and interactivity of voice communication
- echos.

Several papers show that when the delay exceedes a threshold, the interaction between the speakers becomes very poor. The threshold value depends on many factors, /BRA 70/, for esample in the absence of echos, the allowed delay ranges from 200 msec to 1200 msec on a call. We point out that those values are measured in a PSTN environment. This means that the calls were among distant cities. Psycologically a user may suffer a big delay on long distances or overseacalls, the same degree of acceptability is to be prooved in a local environment. But delay is more troublesome with echo. We have already pointed out how the 4 to 2 wire and the 2 to 4 wire conversions may be sources of echos due to the imperfect balancing of impedance at the conversion points (some energy is reflected back!).

When no delay is present, echos can be considered as side tones (your voice in the loudspeaker is repeated a few microseconds after your speech, and you cannot fill it); but when a measurable delay is present between your speech and the echo you can be aware of it. When the delay exceedes a threshold from 50 msec (unbalanced net) to 80 msec, echos degrade the voice quality unacceptably /EML 63/.

2.5 DIGITAL VOICE COMMUNICATION: WASTE OF BANDWIDTH?

As we have shown in the previous section, digitized voice takes 64 Kbps for each speaker. This means that in a limited bandwidth network it is almost impossible to carry voice channels unless compression techniques are used in order to limit the bandwidth needed for each call. In a local network the bandwidth can be of some tens of Mbps allowing the handling of some voice calls. For example, in a 10 Mbps network, the upper limit of voice channels is easily calculated: the number of simultaneous calls is as follows

$$NC = \frac{\text{Avail. Bandwidth}}{2 * \text{PCM frequency}} = \frac{10^{**}7}{128*10^{**}3} = 78 \text{ bidirectional calls}$$

Which results in a theoretical upper bound equal to 78 bidirectional calls or 156 contemporary active telephones.

But a 64 bps of PCM carry a huge amount of redundant information. The greatest one is silence. It has been measured that on each call, the real voice activity for each speaker varies from 35% to 45% of the total call time /BRA 67/. This implies that if we can perform some silence suppression technique, or at least if we can reuse the bandwidth wasted by silence, the capacity of our channel can be more than doubled.

Moreover, there are techniques for voice digitalization in the frequency domain (LPC and similar) which allow for digitized voice which take a considerably less amount of bandwidth. There are some results which show that voice can be "compressed" up to 2.4 Kbps with good quality. Unfortunately these techniques are today still expensive and have not been considered in our study, they will become very interesting in the near future.

The algorithms for voice compression, since they work on a certain amount of collected voice samples, introduce a new delay to be considered to build a compressed packet.

3 VOICE TRANSMISSION PROTOCOLS ON ETHERNET: POSSIBILITIES AND PROBLEMS

In this section we will describe two very simple protocols which allow voice transmission through Ethernet.
We assume that the reader is familiar with Ethernet like networks and has knowledge on the CSMA/CD class of protocols.

We will give a quick overview of problems arising from carrying real time voice over an Ethernet backbone. The most important problem to solve is the delay. The Ethernet CSMA/CD access scheme has been deeply investigated during recent years and main results are /TOB 79/, /SHO 80/:

a) Ethernet performs better with large rather then with small packet length.
b) Ethernet is not delay bounded, but in practice, with low load, the delay is very small.
c) Ethernet does not provide any error recovery, but the error rate is very small (10^{-9}).
d) CSMA/CD is not a real time protocol

On the other hand, the Real Time Voice Flow (RTVF) is characterized by the following statements:

a) packets length must be kept small to prevent the packetization delay from growing
b) the requirements on the delay are very strong
c) it is "error resistant" that is a small percentage of lost or erroneous packets do not affect the correctness of voice flow.

On preliminary analysis it seems that the two sets of requirements are not compatible. Nevertheless, the following considerations can be made:
- in an actual environment the average data load is very low: measurement over a 3 Mbps coaxial cable at Xerox Park showed an average data load less than 4% and a peak value less than 30% /SHO 79/,
- the curves of delay versus load are very good in the low load region
- channel utilization could be controlled by a user layer protocol.

3.1 ETHERNET: RTP PROTOCOL OUTLINES

The basic idea is to use a "pure Ethernet" backbone to transmit packetized voice (we use the word "pure Ethernet" to mean a backbone fully compatible with the DIX specs). Its implementation in this case is the following:
- up to the data link layer we use the pure Ethernet scheme
- above the data link layer we add a protocol to intelligently handle the line; we refer to this protocol as RTP (Real Time Protocol)
- above the RTP there is the Signalling and Control Protocol (SCP), whose function is to handle the status of telephone, connections, tone generation, to perform accounting and maintenance functions, the control of simultaneously active calls and so on. We will not discuss the SCP here, but it is simple and takes about 8 Kbytes RAM to be implemented.

The basic RTP receiving algorithm is the following:
1. receive voice packets from the line
2. store voice packets in a buffer pool
3. when three packets are present in the buffer pool, start the delivery of

   voice samples to the codec
4. continue to deliver voice samples at a constant rate to the codec
5. if the buffers are empty, deliver the last packet again and report the event
   to the upper layer
6. if that event occurs too many times, the communication will be cut
7. as soon as another packet comes, restart the delivery of new samples to the
codec.
   From the transmitting side the algorithm is the following:
1. collect a voice packet
2. send the packet onto the channel to the destination T-NIM
3. if you cannot get the line within a delay of three packets then apply the
   discarding policy and try to transmit again; report the event to the upper
   layer
4. if the discard event occurs too many times then communication will be cut.

   The SCP will not start a communication when the line is too busy,
therefore, a discarded packet event is not usual and is to be considered a case
of overload or at least an indication of a potential overload condition.

   We mentioned before a "discarding policy" mechanism to be applied when an
overload condition occurs. According to the transmission algorithms, a
discarding decision can occur only when three packets are ready to be sent.
Therefore the T-NIM has some information on which it bases the discarding
policy. The trivial alternative is to discard the oldest packet; a smarter
policy is to merge the packets and from two packets generate a third "alternate
packet". The alternate packet is built in such a way as to lose a minimum
amount of information. One method is to discard samples which are equal,
another is to discard odd samples in one packet and even samples in the other.
Discarding policies are still under study. We are aware that the implemented
one is very crude.

3.1.1 LINE UTILIZATION - PACKET LENGTH AND DELAY TRADEOFF

   This protocol scheme introduces an almost constant transmission delay in
the voice communication path. This delay is exactly equal to three times the
packetization delay. The probability that a T-NIM cannot get the line in a
three time packet delay can be, given some load conditions, very small. In any
case it is compatible with the acceptable percentage of lost packets.

   According to the previous discussion on the delay, in order to have it as
small as possible, it is useful to have small voice packet length /MIN 79/.
This is still more important when three packets delay overhead is introduced to
compensate the delay variance. But if we make the packet length too small two
problems arise, the first is related to the Ethernet overhead and the need to
send, in any case, a packet whose length is greater than the line round trip
delay. Moreover the line utilization will collapse in the case that too small
packets are sent with high rate. The collision probability becomes high and the
maximum throughput becomes very small. If in order to save the bandwidth a
compression policy is used on a constant packet rate, the packet size could
become too small to be accepted by Ethernet. On the other hand, if the
compression policy is used with constant packet size, it results in a growth of
packetization delay.

   According to us, the only mechanism that can be successfully used in this
case is silence suppression. And a tradeoff must be found among the three

following factors:
- packet length must be set to a value which allows a minimum transmission delay respecting Ethernet characteristics and constraints,
- compression must be used in such a way that the packetization delay does not increase over a certain threshold and the compressed packet length is consistent with Ethernet constraints
- line throughput cannot be as good as in the case of data transmission, but RTP must reach the best throughput value achievable with the resulting packet length.

3.1.2 SYNCHRONIZATION PHENOMENON

We explain such a phenomenon that we have found with an example: suppose there are 20 active telephones and suppose the packet delay to be 8 msec; suppose there is also data equipment trying to get the line. Line requests coming from the telephones are randomly distributed over the 8 msec period, but suppose they are uniformly distributed. This means that there is a packet ready to be sent every 400 usecs (4000 bits time). If for some reason telephone "i" is delayed more than 400 usecs, it is sure, using Ethernet scheme, to collide with telephone "i+1" and so on. The presence of long data packets are, from this point of view, a trouble over the voice path, for they make the transmission delay bigger and they force the T-NIMs into a "synchronous request situation". In this case T-NIMs collide at least once. The simulation results show how, in such a case, the line throughput collapses. The synchronization phenomenon can be avoided by maintaining the line on a low load or by making the T-NIM transmission algorithm more complex by introducing a further random delay before transmitting.

3.1.3 AN OVERVIEW OF THE IMPLEMENTATION

We implemented a T-NIM which exactly uses the RT protocol in order to transmit voice over an Ethernet cable. The T-NIM handles up to eigth telephones. The basic hardware structure is composed of six buffers for each telephone. The six buffers are used for both the input stream (three buffers) and the output stream (three buffers).

The SCP sets the connection between the two telephones according to its policies. When the connection is set, the SCP prepares in a separate "header buffer" the header of the packet. The header is the standard Ethernet header in which the type field specifies that the packet is a voice packet. The codecs generate the stream of samples and store them in the first available position in the buffer pool.

After the first buffer is full, a transmission request is sent to Ethernet and the transmission mechanism is started. The packet is made up of the stored header and the content of the buffer. Meanwhile, the samples that the codec is still producing are stored in the next buffers. When all three buffers are full, the second packet is thrown away and an interrupt is generated to report the event.

From the receiving side, the receiver checks the type field of the incoming frame. When the packet is a voice packet, the correct input buffer is selected, the voice samples are decapsulated from the Ethernet envelope and put in the buffer. When the third buffer becomes full, the delivery of samples to

the codec begins, and ends at the end of the call. A mechanism to handle
jittering among codec clocks is also provided.

    The existing lab prototypes consist of four boards to handle eigth
telephones. Up to now no optimization has been made, but we forecast that the
T-NIM can be incorporated on two boards.

3.2 THE MULTIFRAME VOICE PROTOCOL

    The multiframe voice protocol (MVP) has been designed in order to solve
the problems described in the previous sections /RAV 81/, /RAV 81a/.

    The basic idea is that since every T-NIM handles more than one telephone,
we can reduce the number of collisions by making a single request to the line
to transmit all the voice samples collected by the T-NIM.

    In this case the packet format is the following:

```
/ p/ da/ sa/ ty/da(j1)/d(z1,w1)/da(j2)/d(z2,w1)/.../crc/
--------------------------------------------------------
```


- p the Ethernet defined preamble
- da the DIX specs destination multicast address, and will be recognized by all
  the T-NIMs
- sa the DIX specs source address
- ty the DIX specs type field
- da(j) the DIX specs destination address of the destination T-NIM
- d(z,w) a voice stream of the call extablished between the z telephone of sa
  T-NIM and the w telephone of da(j) T-NIM
- crc the DIX specs check field, it is held only for compatibility reasons.
Each $d(z,w)$ is strictly related to the immediately preceding da(j).

    A T-NIM monitors the line, when a voice packet (multicast addess and type
field) is seen, it checks all the da(j) fields and receives the data of the
portion of the multiframe starting with the da(j) field which matches its own
name. The synchronization on the da(j) fields is quite easy since every d(z,w)
field has a constant length. The p, da, sa, ty fields are called "common
header", while the field da(j) is referred to as "inner header".

    The advantage of this protocol is that it reduces considerably the amount
of collisions that can occur. This is a good result because in the previous
case the voice flow requires to access the line with an almost constant rate
equal to 1 over the voice packet length expressed in msec. This results in an
huge amount of contentions among T-NIMs, even when T-NIMs are asynchronous.

3.2.1 MVP: AN OVERVIEW

    MVP behaviour is quite similar to the behaviour of the "pure Ethernet"
voice protocol. The biggest difference is that a T-NIM collects samples from

all the active telephones and, once it gets the line it generates packets
containing the collected packets of all the active calls. We will refer to
these packets as big-pack.

As far as the buffering policies are concerned, they are exactly the same
implemented on the Ethernet voice protocol. The codecs of a single T-NIM are
all synchronous. The packets for each call are collected at the same moment. At
the beginning of a call, a part of a packet can be discarded in order to reach
a synchronism among all the active telephones.

This protocol acts as a set of Ethernet voice protocols working in
parallel. The generated packet will be exactly equal to that of the previous
case, but the transmission algorithm is a bit more sophisticated:

```
Generate a common header k (see above)
FOR i:=1 STEP 1 TO active calls DO
APPEND inner header(i)
PUT packet(i) in big-pack(k)
OD
IF cannot get the line in three packets delay THEN
apply discarding policy;
```

The utilization of a "common header" and an "inner header" is an
interesting application of the multicast address on Ethernet. In some sense we
define the class of T-NIMs, and inside that class the "inner header" defines a
new addressing scheme.

The receiving algorithm is the following:

```
WHEN da eq multicast for T-NIM DO
   FOR i:=1 STEP 1 TO number of telephones DO
      IF da(i) eq my address THEN
      recover d(i,w)
      ELSE discard d(i,w)
      FI
   OD
OD
```

The recover d(i,w) procedure is exactly the receiving algorithm described in
the previous section.

3.2.2 MVP DISCUSSION

The MVP protocol does not change the panorama in which we are working. It
is fully Ethernet compatible, and it still suffers from the problem of the
unbounded transmission delay. Moreover, if there is only one active telephone
per T-NIM, it is exactly the RTP of the previous section.

Using this protocol,the resulting traffic pattern is more "friendly" and
the advantages are:

- the number of transmission requests is highly reduced, the packet size is
  bigger

- the number of collisions is reduced, the synchronization phenomenon is less likely to occur: this provides for a better line utilization
- the Ethernet overhead is highly reduced, 26 envelope bytes defined dy DIX specs transport more information than before (note that in the case of 8 msec of packet delay we have 64 bytes of data, 64 PCM samples, and 26 bytes of overhead. This means that a single call needs 90 kbps instead of 64 kbps, which represents an overhead of 40.625%.)
- it provides for a more flexible approach to the compression, for the big-pack length can be reduced without a dramatic impact on the Ethernet behaviour; this is a key factor.

4 SIMULATOR OVERVIEW

This part describes the simulation model developed in OLTECO and used to analize the integrated communication subsystem under study. We refer to it as MELONE (Model for Evaluation of LOcal NEtworks). It consists of about 3000 SIMULA 67 statements and runs on a IBM 370 system under TSO and on DEC 10 system under TOP10 OS.

MELONE is a hybrid, completely modular and interactive simulator with a very nice and easy-to-use interface through which it is possible to define both system configuration and traffic patterns. It consists of an analytical core and a simulated environment. The core realizes the access method to the channel while the environment simulates with some detail the input pattern of all the stations: terminals, image sources and sinks, file servers, telephones. The interaction with the program involves a configuration phase that is the definition of the number of stations of each class and a traffic definition phase that is the definition for each station of the produced traffic in terms of average information generation rate and average information length. MELONE will use these average values inside distributions proper to the producing stations. The dimensioning of the stations is out of the purpose of the model. MELONE is also equipped with statistics, graphic and debugging facilities.

Now a few words about model core: the core is a single server with random service time. The users are the data link packets. Service time is contention time plus transmission time. The server queue is filled by all the NIMs. If the queue length is greater than one, a collision occurs and a contention period begins. Contention periods depend on the access method parameters and on the queue length. The length Q of the queue grows for packet arrivals as an instantaneous result of the simulated environment; the average length of the contention period Tc is achieved by using the following relation:

$$Tc = \frac{1 - (1-1/Q)^{(Q-1)}}{(1 - 1/Q)^{(Q-1)}} * tau$$

Where tau is the propagation delay. Each packet possesses a length (generated in the simulation part) that depends on the origin of that packet. The packet length and the protocol overhead determine the packet transmission time. If a collision occurs, after the contention period Tc(Q), only one packet of the Q contending packets acquires the channel, the others are randomly enqueued again into the server queue. All the packets that lose the contention, have no memory of the contention and are treated as all new arriving packets. A packet alone in the queue does not contend at all and its service time depends only on its length. If, during a contention period, new packets arrive in the transmission server queue, the contention period is consequently updated.

This analytical core has been substituted by an equivalent simulated core to validate the hybrid model. Results revealed a very good agreement in a wide range of load values and a very quick execution of the hybrid model.

5 EXPERIMENTS DESCRIPTION AND RESULTS

We used MELONE heavily. In this section we will describe the experiments performed and their results.
The sets of proofs are as follows:

- VOICE ENVIRONMENT

The first set is related to a system configuration with only T-NIMs and telephones. Therefore the traffic consists of voice. The experiments are performed by varying the following parameters:
1. SAMPLE RATE. The analog voice signal is digitized using PCM techniques. The PCM sample (8 information bits every 125 usec) are assembled in packets, by sample rate we mean the size of the packets generated by the T-NIM. The packet size varies from 16 msec (64 PCM samples) to 64 msec (512 PCM samples).
2. NUMBER OF TELEPHONES PER T-NIM. It may be 4 or 8.
3. TRANSMISSION ALGORITHM. It may be "pure Ethernet" or MVP.
   The experiments performed using only vocal traffic are reported in part 5.1.

- DATA AND VOICE ENVIRONMENT

The same set of experiments has been repeated for a mixed flow of voice and data environment; the data percentage of the available bandwidth may be 10%, 20%, 30%, 40%.
The results of this set of experiments and the comparative discussion are reported in part 5.2.

5.1 VOICE ENVIRONMENT

In this part the two protocols are compared under the same only vocal traffic varying:
- the number of telephones per T-NIM: 4, 8;
- the sampling rate: voice packet length may be 16, 32, 64.

5.1.1 STANDARD ETHERNET PROTOCOL

The following curves are derived:
1. average transmission delay versus the number of simultaneous active calls: figures 5 and 6;
2. throughput, offered load and real load versus the number of simultaneous active calls. The offered load is the amount of information generated by the user, the real load takes into account also of the overhead due to retransmission caused by collisions. The offered load measures the generated PCM flow at telephone level while the real load is measured at the cable level. Figures 7 and 8.
3. average normalized transmission delay versus the line throughput for 4 and 8 telephones per T-NIM: figure 9.
4. the average delay, the delay for 95% and for 100% of the packets versus the number of simultaneous calls. This means that 95% (100%) of the packets

experienced a delay less than or equal to the plotted value: figure 10.
We recall that such a short packet traffic with constant generation rate is a
very bad work condition for an Ethernet backbone.

5.1.2 DISCUSSION

In this part we refer to the curves in figures 5 to 10. The first remark
is about the delay experimented by each packet transmitted on the subnetwork,
the delay varies with the line load (number of calls), with the packet size and
with the T-NIM configuration.

- THE EFFECT OF THE NUMBER OF TELEPHONES PER T-NIM

In figure 5 and 6 the delay versus the number of callsis shown.

- In the low traffic region, the 4 tel/T-NIM configuration experiences a lower
  delay, in this region the main component of the delay is the internal (to
  the T-NIM) time.
- But when the traffic increases, the second configuration performs better.
- The point at which the delay begins to grow quicker corresponds to a smaller
  number of calls in the 4 tel/T-NIM case: as soon as the traffic increases,
  the number of collisions is higher when the number of contending stations is
bigger.
Therefore the 8 tel/T-NIM configuration is preferred, this conclusion is even
more enforced from the observation of figures 7 and 8, the actual line load
that allows the same throughput to be reached is greater than in the 4
tel/T-NIM solution.

- THE EFFECT OF THE PACKET SIZE

The analysis of the curves in figure 5 and 6 shows that in the low load region
a smaller packet size produces a smaller absolute delay (we mean the real value
and not the normalized delay that implies a completely reversed situation)
because the contention effect is still not relevant. In the heavy load region,
the situation is reversed, for, under the same load value, the contention
number increases quicker in the smaller packet case. This appears even more
clearly from figure 7 and 8: the throughput is higher using large packets
because of the better line utilization.

We again face the problem of tradeoff among packet length (packetization
delay), line utilization, and compression. But, since the maximum allowable
delay is a strong constraint of the voice flow and since a packet size
reduction dramatically reduces the number of calls that the system can hold, it
seems that a solution with a packetization delay of 16 or 24 msec is the more
convenient when echo suppression is present in the gateway (see conclusions).

Figure 9 shows the normalized delay versus the throughput: the trend of
the delay when the throughput is increased. The curve knee indicates the
maximum throughput value reachable for each considered packet size and T-NIM
concentration. The 8 tel/T-NIM case appears clearly more stable than the other.

The conclusion is that in a pure voice environment, the telephone
concentration with T-NIMs is helpful in controlling the transmission delay,
mostly when the traffic is high. From the communication point of view, the
packet length has to be carefully chosen for the opposite trend of delay vs.

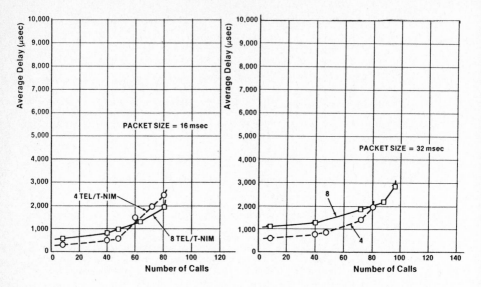

Figure 5. Pure Voice in Ethernet Environment   Figure 6. Pure Voice in Ethernet Environment

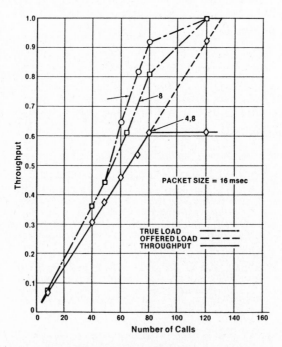

Figure 7. Pure Voice in Ethernet Environment

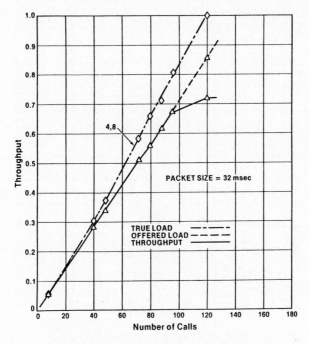

Figure 8. Pure Voice in Ethernet Environment

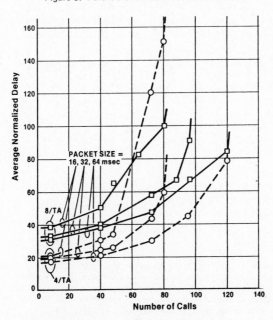

Figure 9. Pure Voice in Ethernet Environment

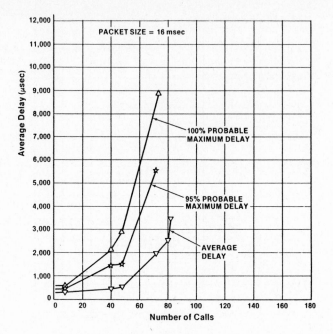

Figure 10. Pure Voice in Ethernet Environment

calls and of the throughput vs. calls. The number of maximum allowable simultaneous calls is in the range of 70 to 100 unidirectional, which means 35 to 50 bidirectional communications.

According to us the best result can be obtained with 16 or 24 msec packetization delay with an 8 tel/T-NIM concentration obtaining 90 contemporary active telephones. This solution takes into account also the voice quality that is not only the transmission parameters, but also the overall conversation round trip delay.

5.1.3 MULTIFRAME VOICE PROTOCOL

The same set of experiments has been performed using MVP. Resulting curves are reported in figures 11 to 16, and their meaning corresponds exactly the meaning of curves in figure 5 to 10.

5.1.4 DISCUSSION

The same traffic pattern of the previous part has been used and varying the same parameters in order to allow a comparison on coherent data. About the telephone concentration on the T-NIM the same remarks of the previous protocol held. Nevertheless, in this case, the difference on the delay due to the concentration of telephone per T-NIM is more evident (figures 11, 12). Now the packet length is equal to the packetization delay multiplied by the number of active telephones connected to the transmitting T-NIM. The resulting packet is long enough to obtain a good line utilization also when the packetization delay is small and it is no longer necessary to have a high concentration degree to achieve a good line throughput (figures 13, 14). The normalized delay curve knee of figure 15 is placed in an acceptable throughput region (greater than 70%). The conclusion is that the smaller big-pack reveals better delay characteristics (below 2 usec with size equal to 16 msec with 120 unidirectional calls). MVP solves most of the problems in a more satisfactory manner.

5.1.5 COMPARISON BETWEEN ETHERNET AND MVP

The results of the experiments performed show MVP performs better than the pure Ethernet. MVP has the curves of the pure Ethernet protocol as lower limit of its performance characteristics. This occurs when all the ongoing connections activate only one telephone per T-NIM. This argument suggests the choice of the 8 tel/T-NIM solution with small packetization delay (8 msec): MVP will still have a big packet size and good line utilization characteristics. Furthermore since every T-NIM has knowledge of the open connections, the introduction of some sort of adaptive algorithm able to generate packets whose size optimize the line performance with respect to the particular load conditions could be useful. We are going to analize the opportunity to introduce such an algorithm. This topic will make the MVP still more interesting.

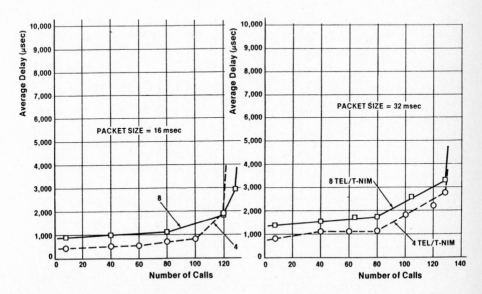

Figure 11. Pure Voice in M.V.P. Environment   Figure 12. Pure Voice in M.V.P. Environment

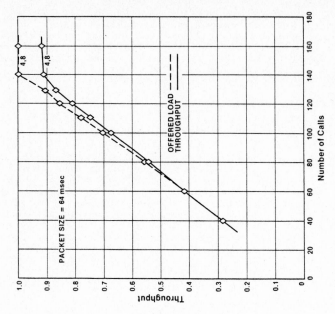

Figure 14. Pure Voice in M.V.P. Environment

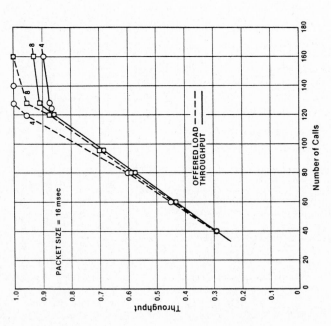

Figure 13. Pure Voice in M.V.P. Environment

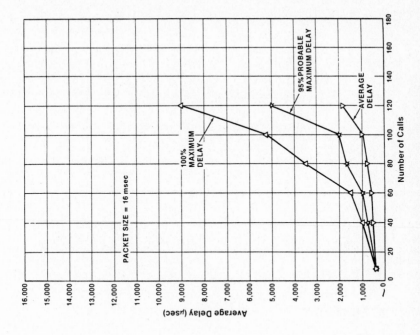

Figure 16. Pure Voice in M.V.P. Environment

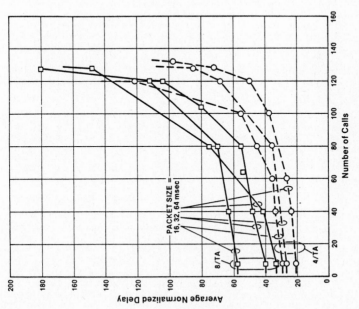

Figure 15. Pure Voice in M.V.P. Environment

5.2 VOICE AND DATA ENVIRONMENT

The experiments described in the previous section have been repeted with mixed voice and data traffic.

5.2.1 PURE ETHERNET PROTOCOL WITH MIXED TRAFFIC

The experiments have been performed with a constant amount of data flow on the line but varying the amount of voice flow. We considered a data flow load of 10%, 20%, 30%, and for each value varying the voice flow load from 30% to 90% of the available bandwidth. We simulate on the network a very frequent trasmission requests: 10 pkt/sec for data and a continuous telephone call for voice so that the percentage of offered load is a constant for all the simulation time. The telephone concentration is 8 tel/T-NIM. The data station number that corresponds to 10%, 20%, 30% load is 40, 110, 150 D-NIMs respectively, while 30%, 60%, 90% voice load correspond to 5, 10, 17 T-NIMs respectively. The interarrival time of data packets is exponentially distributed, data packet length follows a trimodal distribution whose mode values are 64, 512 and 1500 bytes. A packet length will assume with 70% probability the first value, with 20% probability the second and with 10% probability the last one.

5.2.2 COMPARISON BETWEEN PURE ETHERNET AND MVP

When data traffic is present on the line, the advantages of MVP with respect to pure Ethernet protocol are more and more evident. This can be explained very easily: as the load increases, it is more important to make a very efficient use of the bandwidth. The pure Ethernet protocol because of the small size of voice packets, wastes a lot of the available bandwidth due to the high number of collisions and to high protocol overhead. In figure 17, the knee of the Ethernet protocol delay curve is located in a low traffic region. It is also remarkable how the MVP throughput curve is close to the true load curve. As a conclusion:
- MVP allow better delay characteristics (fig. 17, 18)
- MVP allow a greater number of simultaneous calls (fig. 19, 20)
- with MVP the coexistence of data and voice does not create too many problems.
Figures 21, 22   give a summarized view of pure Ethernet and MVP throughput comparison with mixed traffic and varying the packet size.

6 CONCLUSIONS

The results obtained using the model, show clearly that Ethernet can be used to implement medium-small voice communication systems. The number of connectable telephones in a pure voice environment varies from 300 to 700. Indeed, with 700 telephones, the blocking probability, that is the probability that the SPC cannot accept a new incoming call, should be small. In terms of CCS, that is a measure used in telephony, it is possible to handle traffic of about 13 or 5.35 CCS/line for systems with 300 and 700 telephones respectively. The quality of 5.35 CCS/line hires up well with the performances of the most common existent PABX. It is also interesting to note that the size of 60% of installed PABXs in the world is between 150-350 connected telephones, and therefore it seems that the system we have defined can find an interesting market place .

Figure 18. Voice and Data in M.V.P. Environment

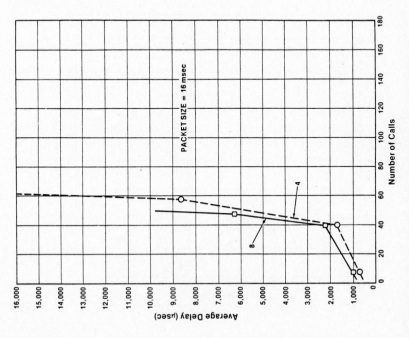

Figure 17. Voice and Data in Ethernet Environment

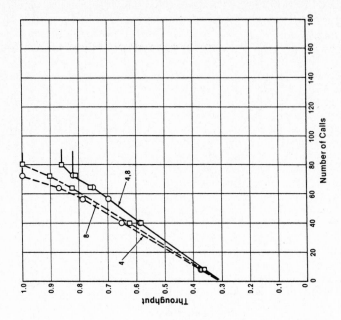

Figure 20. Voice and Data in M.V.P. Environment

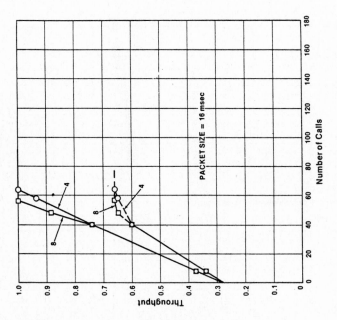

Figure 19. Voice and Data in Ethernet Environment

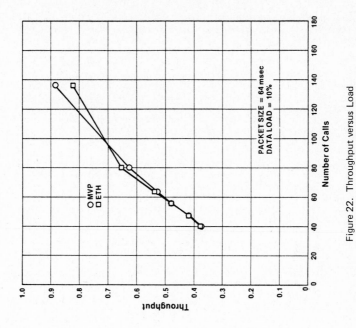

Figure 22. Throughput versus Load

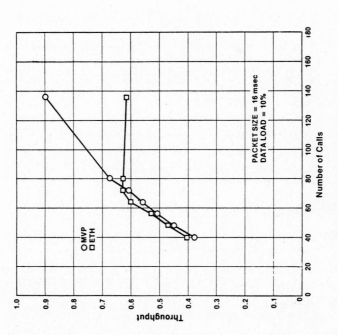

Figure 21. Throughput versus Load

The Ethernet approach to voice transmission is not the easiest way to implement a PABX: good results need more complex voice transmission procedures (MVP and/or adaptive voice packet length procedures). Nevertheless many advantages can be reached using this technique: the distributed approach allow a complex PABX system to be obtained at low complexity and, it seems, competitive in cost with the existing solutions. Moreover, and this is the main advantage, in such a way we are able to achieve a system that offers many services which, using the conventional approach it is difficult, if not impossible, to implement.
Furthermore Ethernet represents one of the most well known and experimented ways to solve the data communication problem in local environment.

In the connection with the PSTN given the delay values, echo suppressors must be used. On the contrary using 4 wire telephones there are no echo problems in the local environment, and the voice quality should be good, despite the delay. In fact, the percentage of lost packets in the conditions shown above, is always zero. For a better judgement of the voice quality we implemented a system prototype in order to study the phenemenon of the effect of the delay on the voice quality and on the techniques usable to implement larger-size systems (adaptive algorithms, compression and so on).

7 REFERENCES

/BRA 67/ P.T. Brady "A Statistical Analysis of on-off Patterns in 16 Conversations" BSTJ Jan. 1967

/BRA 69/ P.T. Brady "A Model for Generating on-off Patterns in Two-Way Conversations" BSTJ Sept. 1969

/BRA 70/ P.T. Brady "Effects of the Transmission Delay on Conversational Behaviour on Echo-free Telephone Circuits" BSTJ Jan. 1971

/COH 79a/ D. Cohen "On Network Protocols for Speech Communication" ISI NOTE 1979

/COH 79b/ D.Cohen "A Network Voice Protocol NVP-11" USC/ISI Dec. 1979

/COH 80/ D. Cohen "On Packet Speech Communication" Proc. Fifth Int. Conf. on Comp. Comm. ICCC'80 ATLANTA Oct. 1980

/DAV 78/ D.W. Davies "A subjective Comparison of Selected Digital Codecs for Speech" BSTJ Nov. 1978

/DIX 80/ "The Ethernet. A Local Area Network Data Link Layer and Phisical Specifications" Sept. 1980

/EML 63/ J.W. Emling, D.Mitchell "The Effects of Time Delay and Echos on Telephone Conversations" BSTJ Nov. 1963

/JAY 80/ N.S. Jayant "Effect of Packet Losses in Waveform-Coded Speech" Proc. Fifth Int. Conf. Conf. on Comp. Comm. ICCC'80 ATLANTA Oct. 1980

/MAR 80/ R. Marcogliese "Valutazione delle Prestazioni di Rete Locale, Metodologie Strumenti, Proposte per CNET" Nota 2 Collana PFI-CNET Oct. 1980

/MEL 78/ D. Melvin "Microcomputer Applications in Telephony" IEEE PROC. Feb. 1978

/MEL 80/ D. Melvin "Trends in the use of LSI/VLSI Technology in the Telephone Industry" COMPCON '80 Feb. 1980

/MET 76/ R.M. Metcalfe, D.R.Boggs "Ethernet: Distributed Packet Switching for Local Networks" CACM vol.19 NO 7 Jul. 1976

/MIN 75/ D.Minoli "Optimal Packet Length for Voice Communication" IEEE Trans. on Comm. Mar. 1975

/OLA 80/ G.C.O'Leary "Local Access Area Facilities for Packet Voice" Proc. Fifth Int. Conf. on Comp. Comm. ICCC ATLANTA Oct. 1980

/OLA 81/ G.C.O'Leary, D.H.Johnson "A Local Access Network for Packetized Digital Voice Communication" IEEE Trans. on Comm. Vol 29 NO 5 May 1981

/RAV 81/ P.C. Ravasio, R.Novarese "Performance Evaluation of an Ethernet-Based Integrated Communication System" Int. Note OLTECO 1981

/RAV 81a/ P.C. Ravasio, J.Pickering "Voice Transmission Protocols for an Ethernet-Based Integrated Communication System" Int. Note OLTECO 1981

/RIE 63/ R.R.Riesz E.T.Klemmer "Subjective Evaluation of Delay and Echo Suppressors in Telephone Communications" BSTJ Nov. 1963

/SHO 79/ J.F.Shock, J.A.Hupp "Performance of an Ethernet Local Network-a Preliminary Report" Proc. loc. Area Comm. Net. Symp. MITRE NBS May 1979

/SHO 80/ J.Shoch "Carrying Voice Traffic Through an Ethernet Local Network a general Overview" Proc. of Loc. Netw. for Comp. Comm. Zurich Aug. 1980

/TOB 79/ F.A.Tobagi, V.B.Hunt "Performance Analysis of Carrier Sense Multiple Access with Collision Detection" Proc. of Loc. Area Comm. Net. Symp. MITRE May 1979

LCN DESIGN

LOCAL COMPUTER NETWORKS
P.C. Ravasio, G. Hopkins and N. Naffah (editors)
North-Holland Publishing Company
© IFIP, 1982

A LOCAL-AREA COMMUNICATION NETWORK
BASED ON A RELIABLE TOKEN-RING SYSTEM

W. Bux, F. Closs, P.A. Janson,
K. Kümmerle, H.R. Müller, and E.H. Rothauser

IBM Zurich Research Laboratory
8803 Rüschlikon
Switzerland

The architecture of a local-area communication network designed and
implemented at the IBM Zurich Research Laboratory is described. A
token-ring subnetwork allows for a low-cost entry point; growth
potential to large networks is provided through interconnecting rings
by bridges and a high-performance store-and-forward node, called
Block Switch. To ensure reliable token-ring operation, we employ the
concept of a monitor function. We also show how, in addition to the
transmission of data frames, a token-ring can provide synchronous
channels, e.g., for voice services. All functions above network
access and the basic transport mechanism are executed on an end-to-end
basis. Thus, Block Switch and bridges can be completely implemented
in hardware, allowing easy obtainment of an aggregate throughput
capacity in the order of 100 Mbps.

INTRODUCTION

This paper describes the major architectural aspects of an experimental local-area
network (LAN) intended to provide the basic communication functions for various
types of devices, such as terminals, work stations, printers, communication controllers, host computers, etc. The LAN is structured in a two-level hierarchy: Token
rings are used as subnetworks; the backbone network employs two different elements,
bridges and the Block Switch, for interconnecting rings.

The smallest configuration consists of a single ring which can support up to about
100 to 200 user stations. This limit is of practical, not architectural nature,
suggested by traffic load, reliability, maintenance, and network-management considerations. In many enterprises, the number of stations to be connected to a LAN
exceeds that limit. Therefore, a solution must be provided to build larger networks
by interconnecting several rings through a backbone network.

Figure 1 shows the structure of the local network suggested. Individual rings
employ a reliable protocol based on the token-access technique [1] - [6]. The
Block Switch [7] of the backbone network performs routing for the inter-ring data
traffic. A third element, called bridge, provides the necessary buffering capacity
for the inter-ring traffic. Considering the high data rate of each ring, 4 Mbps
in our prototype, it is obvious that the Block Switch must be able to support very
high throughput rates, an immediate consequence of this being it will not be able
to execute complex functions, such as link error recovery, address translation, or
adaptive routing. This problem is overcome by performing functions such as data-
link control and path (network) control only within the stations attached, i.e.,
end-to-end. The protocols related to the basic network-access and transport functions are confined to the bottom layers of architecture, Physical and Data-Link
layer. The architecture clearly separates these functions from Data-Link Control
which, in HDLC terminology [8], is primarily understood as the execution of the
"elements of procedure".

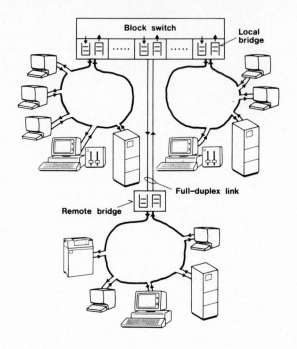

Figure 1
Structure of local network

We shall first describe the ring network, its access protocol and recovery strategies, then the elements of the backbone network, bridges and Block Switch will
be described in detail.

An experimental network consisting of two rings interconnected by a backbone
network is operational at the IBM Zurich Research Laboratory. At present, the
ring data rate is 4 Mb/s, total throughput of the backbone net is about 150 Mb/s.

THE RING SYSTEM

In this section, we first describe the physical configuration of the ring system,
show the data format, and then discuss the token-access protocol. A rationale for
the design described is given in [6]. A further subsection then describes the
concept of a "monitor" function employed to achieve reliable ring operation, and
finally, the synchronous operation of the ring is discussed.

Overview

Figure 2 depicts the major components of a single ring system. Physically, the
ring consists of a set of interconnected distribution panels and lobes radiating
from the panels. The distribution panels can be placed at suitable points in a
building. Wiring from the distribution panels to the stations is star-shaped.
Contained in the distribution panels are by-pass relays used to cut inactive or

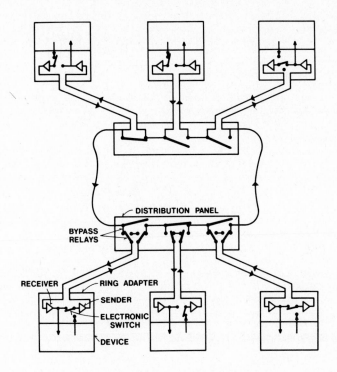

Figure 2
Ring configuration (Copyright © 1981 IEEE)

malfunctioning stations out of the ring. In disconnected state, the lobes are
locally wrapped around, which enables a station to test its adapter before inserting itself into the ring. Details of the wiring strategy, the distribution panels,
and the transmission technique used on the ring can be found in [9] and [10].

Devices are connected to the ring via ring adapters which contain the analog and
digital circuitry necessary to receive and (re-)transmit the electrical signals,
and to execute the ring-access protocols. As pointed out in the Introduction, all
protocols related to network access are confined to the bottom layers of architecture and, hence, are implemented within the ring adapters. In particular, the
mechanisms for access-related error detection and recovery are also implemented
in the adapters. Furthermore, ring adapters are equipped with simple hardware
watchdog circuits which detect failures in either analog or digital circuitry.
This self-diagnostic mechanism will automatically disconnect a malfunctioning
adapter from the ring by closing the bypass relay, see Figure 2.

Ring-Access Method

Advantages of ring systems with respect to transmission technology and efficient
use of the bandwidth are well-known, see, e.g., [10] and [11], however, lack of
reliability is sometimes claimed to be a potential deficiency of rings. A major

goal of our effort was to demonstrate that a token ring can be designed such that
operation becomes highly reliable. A second key-point was to show that, on a
token ring, synchronous channels with guaranteed end-to-end delay and throughput
can be provided in addition to the asynchronous (packet-oriented) data operation.
Real-time and non-real-time voice services represent possible applications of
the synchronous-operation capability.

How the above issues are reflected in the frame format and the access protocol
is discussed in the next two subsections.

Frame Format

Transmission on the ring is in the form of variable-length frames, the structure
of which is shown in Figure 3. A frame is delimited by start- and end-delimiters
(DELs, DELe) and consists of a Transport-Control field (TC), TO- and FROM-link
addresses (AT, AF), the Transport-Information field (TI), and the Frame-Check-
Sequence field (FCS). For ease of description, we subsequently refer to the com-
bination of start delimiter, TC, and the two link addresses as "frame header"
(FH) and to the combination of FCS field and end delimiter as "frame trailer" (FT).
The meaning of the above frame elements is described below.

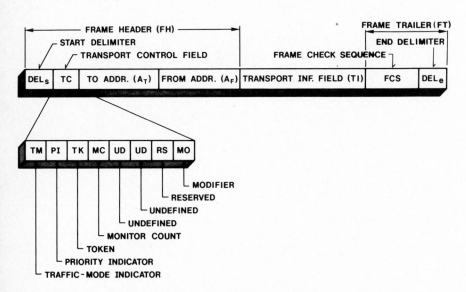

Figure 3
Frame structure (Copyright © 1981 IEEE)

Delimiters

Delimiters consist of four-bit patterns representing violations of the
differential (polarity-insensitive) Manchester code [10] employed on the
ring, followed by two unused bits and two "qualifier bits" which serve
to distinguish between start delimiter, end delimiter, and a "shut-off"
delimiter. (The shut-off signal is used to force any transmitting adapter
into REPEAT mode, see sub-subsection below on Token Errors, Token Super-

vision and Recovery.) Compared to other delimiters, such as the HDLC/SDLC flags, our code-violation pattern has the advantage of a greater immunity against noise in the sense that the probability of delimiters being simulated by transmission errors is significantly smaller.

Transport-Control Field

The Transport-Control field serves the following purposes: access control, multiplexing of asynchronous and synchronous traffic, ring supervision and recovery. It consists of the following eight bits:

1) TRAFFIC-MODE INDICATOR (TM): It serves to distinguish between a frame carrying asynchronous traffic (TM=0) and synchronous traffic, e.g. voice (TM=1).
2) PRIORITY INDICATOR (PI): The PI is needed to guarantee timely access for stations with synchronous traffic.
3) TOKEN (TK): Access to the ring is controlled by the token which can be in either of two states: "free" (TK=0) or "busy" (TK=1).
4) MONITOR COUNT (MC): MC is manipulated by the ring monitor for ring supervision/recovery purposes. For details, see the section below on Reliable Token Operation.
5) UNDEFINED BITS (UD): The meaning of these bits is not defined.
6) RESERVED BIT (RS): Usage of this bit is reserved; it does not carry any information relevant to the ring-access protocol.
7) MODIFIER (MO): It allows to distinguish between normal "user" frames, i.e., the TI contains user data, and "transport control" frames, i.e., the TI contains well-defined control information related to the ring operation.

Link Addresses

The address space is architected based on our notion of a local network consisting of several interconnected rings. To simplify the routing function in the Block Switch, we use structured TO- and FROM-addresses each four bytes long. The first two bytes of the link address denote the ring number (unique in the entire local network), the second two bytes being the station number (unique on one ring).

Transport-Information Field

The Transport-Information field contains higher-level data; it may contain any sequence of bits. In case of HDLC/SDLC, it consists of a control and (possibly) an information field, as defined in these data-link control procedures.

Frame-Check-Sequence Field

The Frame-Check-Sequence field is two bytes long and generated according to the standard HDLC/SDLC generator polynomial of degree 16. The FCS protects the MO bit, the TO- and FROM-addresses, and the TI field.

Link-Access Protocol, Asynchronous Operation

In this subsection, we describe the basic ring-access protocol for asynchronous operation. Token supervision and recovery, also considered as part of the ring protocol is described in the subsection in Reliable Token Operation. The synchronous operation and its interaction with the asynchronous access protocol is then discussed in the subsection on Synchronous Operation.

Access to the ring is controlled by passing a token contained in the TC field around the ring. The token can be in either of two states: busy or free. A busy token is always associated with a full frame according to Figure 3, whereas a free token is contained in a TC field preceded by a start delimiter and followed by idles.

If an adapter has a frame pending for transmission, it turns an arriving free token to busy on the fly, enters TRANSMIT mode, and transmits its frame, see Figure 4. In TRANSMIT mode, an adapter interrupts the ring by means of the electronic switch shown in Figure 2. When the adapter has finished transmission, it generates a free token in the form of a start delimiter followed by a TC field in which all bits – including TK – are set to zero, provided that: i) the adapter has received back the entire FH including both addresses; ii) the FROM-address received equals the station's own address, and iii) the PI bit is still zero. The reaons for imposing these conditions on the generation of a free token are as follows: a) Receipt of a FROM-address different from the station's address, indicates that an error in the access protocol has occurred. Consequently, the transmitting adapter refrains from issuing a free token. (Recovery from this and other access-related errors is described in the following subsection.) b) As will be described in the subsection on Synchronous Operation, the ring is switched into synchronous operation at regular time intervals. To guarantee timely start of the synchronous-access intervals, the monitor is allowed to set the PI bit in

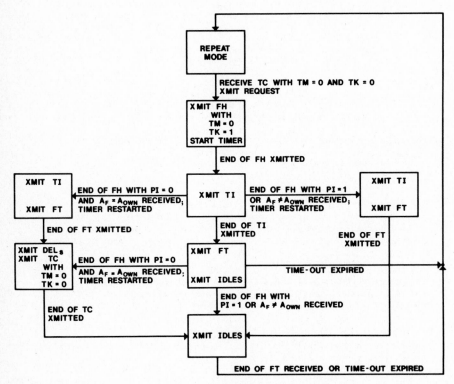

Figure 4
Ring access protocol (Copyright © 1981 IEEE)

any TC field passing through with busy token. This indicates to the transmitting adapter, which receives back the header of its frame, that it must not issue a free token.

Following transmission of the frame (and usually of a free token), the adapter keeps transmitting an idle signal until it receives the next end delimiter which is the end of its own frame provided no access error has occurred. Upon detection of the end delimiter, the adapter enters REPEAT mode, i.e., it "closes" the ring with the electronic switch in Figure 2.

In REPEAT mode, a ring adapter simply retransmits all data on the ring with a short latency, typically one bit time. It also monitors the TO-address fields of the frames passing through. When it detects its own address, it enters RECEIVE mode, i.e., it copies the frame, however, it does not modify the passing frame.

In [6], several strategies for token generation and for switching between transmit and repeat modes have been compared. The above method has been adopted because of its efficiency and because it guarantees robustness of the protocol against errors.

Further details of the protocol related to error detection and recovery are described in the next subsection.

Reliable Token Operation

Reliability of the token mechanism is of utmost importance for the ring protocol. Our approach to achieve reliable operation is to have a monitor function responsible for supervising the proper token operation and performing fast recovery in case of errors. The monitor functions are provided within every ring adapter; on one ring, however, there is only a single monitor active at any time.

As will become clear from the subsequent description, error detection and recovery requires the cooperation of monitor and transmitting adapters. However, our strategy is that normal adapters play a passive role in token recovery in the sense that their reaction to a detected protocol error is to enter REPEAT mode and to refrain from issuing a free token. All active recovery measures are taken by the monitor itself. Supported by insights from protocol validation [12], we are convinced that this assignment of recovery responsibilities yields the most robust access protocol.

Token Errors, Token Supervision and Recovery

Access to the ring is exclusively controlled by the token. Particular supervisory functions are therefore embedded into the protocol to invoke recovery actions when the token is corrupted. We classify the token-related error situations into three different types:

1) LOST-TOKEN SITUATION: During a certain critical time interval, neither a free nor a busy token is transmitted over the ring. This can occur, for example, if a start delimiter is disturbed and also during ring initialization.
2) CIRCULATING BUSY-TOKEN SITUATION: A TC field with busy token continuously circulates around the ring. This may be caused by noise hitting the free-token bit.
3) DUPLICATE-TOKEN SITUATION: Two (or more) stations are transmitting simultaneously because both have received a free token. Such an error situation can occur, e.g., if a free token is generated by noise hitting a busy token.

How the ring recovers from these error situations is subsequently described.

Recovery from Lost-Token Error

One of the basic tasks of the monitor is to constantly check the data
stream passing through for tokens. From the description of the access
protocol in the sub-subsection on Link-Access Protocol, Asynchronous
Operation, it becomes clear that the time interval between subsequent
observations of a free or busy token (or equivalently of a start delimiter)
is upper-bounded by the maximum frame transmission time plus the ring latency.

Therefore, the monitor can detect a lost-token error with the aid of an
appropriately adjusted time-out T1 which the monitor starts whenever it
observes a start delimiter. Upon expiration of the time-out, the monitor
first transmits a number of shut-off delimiters to force any station from
TRANSMIT to REPEAT mode, then clears the ring from possible garbage by
transmitting idles for a time interval longer than the ring latency, and
eventually issues a new free token.

Recovery from Circulating Busy-Token Error

A permanently-circulating busy token can be detected by the monitor with
the aid of the Monitor-Count bit (MC) in the TC field. Any adapter transmitting a frame sets MC to 'zero' in the TC field. When the frame passes
through the monitor, it changes MC to 'one'. In this way, the monitor is
able to detect any TC field with busy token circulating more than once
around the ring by checking the MC bit. Recovery is again performed by the
monitor through transmitting shut-off delimiters, clearing the ring, and
then transmitting a start delimiter followed by a TC field with free token.

Recovery from Duplicate-Token Error

Duplication of a free token can lead to a situation where more than one
station is transmitting simultaneously. Two mechanisms in the access
protocol are provided to recover from this error situation. The first
mechanism is that a transmitting adapter checks the FROM-address field
which it receives back. A second recovery mechanism is needed for those
cases where a transmitting station does not receive back any intact FH
at all. In such a case, the time-out T1 shown in Figure 4 will expire.
As shown in the state diagram of Figure 4, the reaction of an adapter to
either of these situations is to finish the transmission of the current
frame and afterwards to enter REPEAT mode without generating a free token.
Thus, the error is converted into a lost-token situation and recovered
accordingly.

Monitor Failure and Recovery, Ring Initialization

The ring is supervised with one active monitor, however, every ring adapter
contains a complete passive monitor function which can be activated to assume
the role of the active monitor.

As pointed out above, one of the basic tasks of the active monitor is to guarantee
proper circulation of the free token. Therefore, passive monitors can conclude
from the fact that they have not observed a free token for some critical time
interval T2 that the active monitor has failed. Time-out T2 has to be longer than
the maximum frame transmission time multiplied by the total number of stations
attached. It is started/restarted at each passage of a TC field with free token,
irrespective of the value of the traffic-mode indicator. Following expiration
of the T2 timer, passive monitors enter competition mode. In competition mode,

all passive monitors continuously transmit a "monitor-recovery" broadcast message. Upon receipt of a monitor recovery message from another passive monitor which carries a FROM-address greater than its own address, a passive monitor terminates competition mode and enters REPEAT mode. Eventually, the monitor recovery message which carries the greatest FROM-address will succeed in traveling around the ring. When a passive monitor receives its own monitor recovery message, it enters active-monitor mode, transmits shut-off delimiters, clears the ring, and then issues a free token.

The procedure described above cannot only be used for monitor recovery, but also to resolve contention when several adapters with monitor capability simultaneously connect to an inactive ring, i.e., to a ring which does not yet carry any signal.

Synchronous Operation

The token-ring protocol allows priority access to be provided for selected stations. One important application of priority access is for synchronous operation requiring guaranteed bandwidth, e.g., 64 kbps in the case of PCM voice channels. Another application of the synchronous capability is to use it as a vehicle for attaching existing data devices requiring guaranteed bandwidth and delay.

Stations wanting to establish a synchronous connection have to go through a call set-up procedure which involves a central control station. The control station will grant or reject a request for a synchronous connection depending on the number of synchronous connections already established and on the bandwidth required for asynchronous data traffic. The assignment of bandwidth to the two traffic types is completely flexible, as will become clear from the subsequent description.

The protocols for synchronous connection set-up and disconnect have not been defined; the subsequent description focuses on the mechanism by which synchronous full-duplex connections and asynchronous types of transmission are concurrently provided on the same ring. It is assumed that the synchronous connections have already been established and that all stations holding a synchronous connection are designated either as "calling" or as "called" station. This property is defined during connection set-up and is used to avoid ambiguities.

The monitor seizes the circulating token at periodic time intervals and issues a priority token only to be used by synchronous stations. We have to distinguish between two cases:

a) Token free at the start of synchronous operation: the monitor, in this case, sets the Traffic-Mode Indicator (TM) in the TC field passing through to "one" and thus has issued a free priority token.

b) Token busy at the start of synchronous operation: the monitor cannot issue a free priority token immediately since the data frame being currently transmitted should not be preempted. The monitor sets the Priority Indicator (PI) in the next TC field passing through with busy token but leaves the Traffic-Mode Indicator unchanged. This prevents the source of the data frame from issuing a free token as it would normally do. Instead of sending out a free token, the adapter sends idle information until it receives back the end delimiter of its frame, c.f., Figure 4. Upon receiving the end delimiter of the data frame, the monitor issues a free priority token (i.e., a TC field with TM = 1 and TK = 0).

After release of a free priority token, the synchronous operation continues as
follows: The first calling station A downstream from the monitor changes the
token to busy, appends TO-address B and FROM-address A, and puts its
synchronous data into the information field. Station B — like every called
station — monitors for its own address in the FROM-address field. Upon detection
of its own address, it copies the information field and puts its own synchronous
data — destined to A — in the information field of the same frame. As in normal
asynchronous mode, adapter A removes its own frame from the ring, but instead
of discarding the information field, A copies it since it contains synchronous
data from its partner B. Generation of a new priority token follows exactly the
same rules as for asynchronous operation. When all synchronous stations have had
exactly one transmission opportunity, the monitor will receive the free priority
token and remove it from the ring by changing the Traffic-Mode Indicator to zero.
This terminates the synchronous operation.

A certain degree of unfairness among stations with asynchronous traffic is introduced by the above procedure since the strict round-robin schedule of the free
asynchronous token is disturbed by the synchronous operation. As shown in [6],
fairness can be regained in a relatively simple way by injecting the free asynchronous token at the very place where it had been removed before starting the
synchronous operation.

THE BACKBONE NETWORK

Basic Concept

Figure 1 shows the two-level LAN. The key element of the backbone network is a
central switching facility, called Block Switch [7], which switches blocks of
data (frames) at high speeds. Rings are attached to this switching facility via
bridges which can either be local to the switch ("local bridge") or remote to
the switch ("remote bridge"). In the latter case, the bridge is connected with
the switch through a high-speed full-duplex link. This configuration is useful
in situations where rings have to be interconnected over a relatively long distance.

Though not discussed in the present paper, it is conceivable in the frame work of
our network architecture, to have a third hierarchical level in the form of a
Block Switch which interconnects several configurations like the one shown in
Figure 1. This would allow very large local networks to be built.

Some key ideas concerning the architecture and implementation of the backbone
network follow. In contrast to a conventional packet switch, the Block Switch does
not execute functions such as data-link control or path (network) control. As
pointed out in the Introduction, all these functions are only executed between
the two end points of the communication path. Therefore, the Block Switch does
not need any program control to perform its basic functions, and can be completely
implemented in hardware, a fact allowing very high throughput capacities to be
achieved as will be shown.

The primary function of the bridges is to provide an adequate amount of buffer
for inter-ring traffic. An advantage of the concept to separate bridging and
switching elements becomes evident if only a few rings are to be interconnected.
In this case, the switching function of the Block Switch can be replaced by a
fully-meshed network of interconnected bridges which may represent a more
economical solution for up to about four rings.

For installations in which rings have to be interconnected over a relatively long
distance, two solutions are conceivable: i) By inserting active repeaters into the
ring, e.g., in active distribution panels, all rings of an installation can be

physically run to a single central Block Switch such that all bridges are of the local type. ii) Remote bridges are connected to the Block Switch over high-speed point-to-point links. Basically, any kind of full-duplex link may be used for this purpose; the one being currently investigated in our research prototype will be discussed in the subsection on connection of remote bridges.

Subsequently, we first describe the major components of the backbone network, bridges and Block Switch.

<u>Bridges</u>

The basic purpose of bridges is to provide a very simple store-and-forward function without performing any routing: the function of filtering-out the inter-ring traffic from the data stream flowing on a ring is performed by the ring adapter of the bridge; switching the frames to the right target ring is done by the block switch, c.f., the following subsection.

In spite of the very high throughput capacity of the Block Switch, a substantial amount of buffering has to be provided within the bridge to buffer inter-ring frames. Queues in a bridge cannot only build up because of a peak in the inter-ring traffic, but also because the target ring may be heavily utilized at the moment and, hence, ring access from the bridge is delayed. Frames which the bridge cannot accept because of a momentary lack of buffer are discarded without further action; they will be recovered later by end-to-end data-link control. Estimations indicate that, under reasonable traffic-load assumptions, buffers in the order of ten maximum-length frames have to be provided within a bridge to guarantee sufficiently small buffer-overflow probability. We are currently investigating how buffer sizes can be reduced by employing simple flow-control mechanisms at the transport level.

Within one traffic class, i.e., asynchronous or synchronous traffic, organization of the buffers is such that the sequence of frames is preserved. This is achieved by using FIFO buffers, but can also be realized with RAM's. The choice between these two implementation approaches is a question of cost. To guarantee timely forwarding of synchronous frames, i.e., frames carrying synchronous traffic, provision has to be made for synchronous frames to be able to overtake asynchronous frames in the bridges.

<u>Block Switch</u>

The structure of the block switch is shown in Figure 5. The switch is composed of four elements:

1) PORTS for the attachment of input/output buffers.
2) ACCESS-CONTROL unit which arbitrates access to the switching bus among data frames waiting at input ports.
3) LOOK-AHEAD unit which determines whether the target output port for a given data frame is occupied and cannot accept this frame.
4) DATA-TRANSFER unit which controls the data bus and transfers a data frame from its input port to its target output port.

Ports

A port contains all the control functions needed to take a data frame from an input buffer and to place a frame into an output buffer, see Figure 5. A port recognizes a frame waiting in the attached input buffer, and stores the ring part of the frame's TO-address in a specific register. It interacts with access

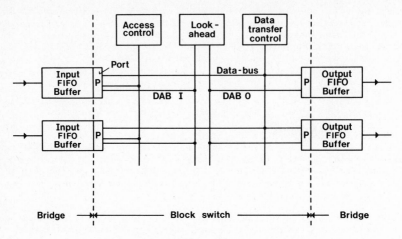

Figure 5
Block Switch structure (After Reference [7])

control and look-ahead unit, and moves the frame from the input buffer onto the
data bus of the switch under control of the data-transfer unit. An output port
recognizes when its output buffer can accept another data frame. It interacts
with the look-ahead unit, and moves frames destined for it into the attached
output buffer under control of the data-transfer unit.

Access-Control Unit

The access-control unit scans the input ports until it finds one with a frame
waiting for transfer. Upon finding a port with a frame waiting, the access-control
unit stops scanning and lets the look-ahead unit take over control.

Look-Ahead Unit

After the access-control unit has found a port with a waiting data frame, the look-
ahead unit requests this port to post the ring part of the TO-address of that
frame onto the Destination-Address-Bus-In (DABI). Based on this address and on a
routing table, the unit determines the number of the output port to which the
frame should be routed, and posts this number onto the Destination-Address-Bus-Out
(DABO). The respective output port has two options. Absence of a response indicates
that it is ready to accept the frame, and the data transfer unit will take over
and move the frame through the switch. At the same time, access control is reactiv-
ated and resumes scanning the next input ports for a waiting frame. If the output
port responds with Not Ready, the look-ahead unit transfers control back to the
access-control unit, and the scan will continue.

Data-Transfer Unit

Once the look-ahead unit has identified a frame as transferable, the data-transfer
unit shifts the frame over the internal data bus as soon as the previous frame
transfer has been finished. The bus is already set up to connect the selected
input port to the designated output port.

Generally, the speed of data transfer through the switch is much higher than the subnetwork transmission rates, because the data bus is short and transfer is parallel. Furthermore, while a frame transfer takes place, access-control and look-ahead units are pipelined to identify the next transferable frame.

Connection of Remote Bridges

Remote bridges are connected to the Block Switch over full-duplex serial links. Buffering requirements are basically the same as in a local bridge, see subsection entitled Bridges.

The speed of data transfer inside the Block Switch is generally an order of magnitude higher than the link transmission rate. For speed conversion, a buffer for one data frame per direction has to be provided for each link at the Block Switch side. These buffers serve as input/output buffers in the switch. Note, that in a local bridge, buffers simultaneously serve as data queues and as input/output buffers for speed conversion.

Data transfer over the link is organized such that each eight-bit data byte is encoded into a 12-bit word. The four bits added, forming a kind of out-band signaling scheme, are used to indicate start and end of frame, priority, and flow-control information. The latter is used to prevent buffer overflow at the Block Switch and the remote bridge: A remote bridge transfers a data frame to the Block Switch only after it has received a Receive-Ready signal from the Block Switch. The out-band signaling scheme allows this control information to be transmitted while data transfer from the switch to the bridge is in progress. Traffic flow in the opposite direction is controlled in an analogous way.

The 12-bit data format and the simplicity of this flow-control mechanism leads to an efficient implementation in hardware which supports the high throughput rate achieved by the Block Switch.

CONCLUSIONS

This paper describes the basic architectural concepts of a local-area network which can grow from a single-ring to a multiple-ring structure where a backbone network with star topology interconnects the rings.

Rings constituting the low-level network employ the token-access technique, the key properties of which are:

- The token operation becomes highly reliable through use of a monitor function. Token errors are rapidly detected and automatically recovered. A failing monitor is replaced without user intervention.

- The ring protocol supports synchronous channels in addition to the asynchronous data operation. Assignment of bandwidth to the two types of traffic is completely flexible.

- The ring protocol has been successfully validated and found error-free.

- The token protocol offers very good performance in terms of throughput and delay over a broad spectrum of speed and distance parameters.

Highlights of the technique suggested for the interconnection of rings are:

- Data-link control and higher-level protocols are end-to-end functions.
  This allows complete implementation of the switch in hardware, and
  a very high throughput capacity to be obtained.

- Bridges and the Block Switch as elements of the backbone network offer
  a high degree of flexibility for configuring a system: i) direct interconnection of rings over bridges in case of a very few subnetworks,
  ii) local bridges in the case where a subnetwork can reach the Block
  Switch direct, and iii) remote switches connected to the Block Switch
  over full-duplex links in case a subnetwork is located too far away
  from the switching facility.

A prototype of the LAN, in which a Block Switch interconnects two rings, is
operational at the IBM Zurich Research Laboratory.

REFERENCES

[1] Farmer, W.D. and Newhall, E.E., An experimental distributed switching system
    to handle bursty computer traffic. Proc. ACM Symposium on Problems in the
    Optimization of Data Communications, Pine Mountain, GA (Oct. 1963) 31-34.
[2] Farber, D.J., Feldman, J., Heinrich, F.R., Hopwood, M.D., Loomis, D.C. and
    Rowe, A., The distributed computer system, Proc. 7th IEEE Computer Society
    International Conference (1973) 31-34.
[3] Penney, B.K. and Baghdadi, A.A., Survey of computer communications loop
    networks: Parts 1 and 2, Computer Communications, Vol. 2 (1979) 165-180
    and 224-241.
[4] Clark, D.D., Pogran, K.T. and Reed, D.P., An introduction to local area
    networks, Proc. IEEE, Vol. 66 (1978) 165-180 and 224-241.
[5] Saltzer, J.H. and Pogran, K.T., A star-shaped ring network with high main-
    tainability, Computer Networks, Vol. 4, No.5, (Oct./Nov. 1980) 239-244.
[6] Bux, W., Closs, F., Janson, P.A., Kümmerle, K. and Müller, H.R., A reliable
    token-ring system for local-area communication, Proc. NTC '81, Piscataway, NJ,
    IEEE (1981).
[7] Rothauser, E.H., Janson, P.A. and Müller, H.R., Meshed-star networks for
    local communication systems, in: West, A. and Janson, P.A. (eds.), Local
    Networks for Computer Communications, (North-Holland, Amsterdam, 1981).
[8] ISO: Data communication - HDLC - Elements of procedures (independent number-
    ing). International Standard ISO 4335.
[9] Meyr, H., Bouten, H., Müller, H.R. and Bapst, U., Manchester coding with
    predistortion: an efficient and simple transmission technique in local
    digital ring networks. Proc. NTC '80, Houston, Texas (Nov. 80) 65.4.1-65.4.7.
[10] Müller, H.R., Keller, H. and Meyr, H., Transmission in a synchronous token
     ring. International Symposium on Local Computer Networks, Florence, Italy
     (19-21 April, 1982).
[11] Bux, W., Local-area subnetworks: a performance comparison. IEEE Trans. Commun.,
     Vol. COM-29 (1981) 1465-1473.
[12] Rudin, H., Validation of a token-ring protocol. International Symposium on
     Local Computer Networks, Florence, Italy (19-21 April, 1982).

LOCAL COMPUTER NETWORKS
P.C. Ravasio, G. Hopkins and N. Naffah (editors)
North-Holland Publishing Company
© IFIP, 1982

TOTALLY DISTRIBUTED, REDUNDANTLY STRUCTURED HARDWARE
AND SOFTWARE LOCAL COMPUTER CONTROL NETWORK

DR. DOREL DAMSKER
NEW TECHNOLOGY DEPARTMENT
GIBBS & HILL, INC.
NEW YORK, N.Y.
U.S.A.

The following presentation of a newly devised local
computer control network is based on the conceptual
design developed for a Solar Cogeneration Industrial
Plant, sponsored by DOE under Contract DE-AC03-81 SF
11533. The control system features a modular local
computer network, whose redundancy can be designed to
meet any availability requirement of a specific application, using the same hardware building blocks.
The intrinsic redundancy applies to the component
level, with an orderly overlapping, as opposed to a
complete system redundancy which is more costly and
less reliable. The control software is hierarchical
and distributed organized with a redundant structure
and topology. The local computer network uses simple
packet switching and routing decision-making techniques, based on a contention method, which presents
the advantage of conveying messages in the order of
their priority. Some details of the concept are presented as they were applied to the Solar Cogeneration
conceptual design.

1.0   INTRODUCTION

Commercially Available Distributed Control Systems

The commercially available distributed control systems are based on
what are now called local computer networks. Such control systems
have developed to a third generation of sophistication.

The first generation has a centralized configuration, mainly a star
configuration, with a master computer-controller at the center of
the structure. The master controls the message traffic using a
polling technique. The remote substations, based either on hardwired logic or on microcomputers, are, in most cases, dedicated only
to data collection functions.

The second generation of control networks, also based on a centralized configuration, are built as a multi-drop structure, with a
common data-communication link, called "data-highway." A centralized arbitration module controls the message traffic.

The first and second generation distributed control systems present
the same weak reliability as all centralized systems. Moreover, the
complexity of data-communication structure adds its forced unavailability and maintenance problems to the disadvantage of the centralized computer control systems. Another disadvantage of these systems consists of the excessive length of their communication paths.[1]

The third generation distributed control systems, only recently
commercially available, feature distributed control over the
message traffic. For that reason, they are called "no-master,
no-slave" networks. Most of these systems exhibit a "ring"
configuration with a "store and forward" mechanism of controlling
message traffic. [2] Other systems are based on a "bus" configuration with a "token passing" or "master for a moment" mechanism of
controlling the message traffic. [3]

The most important disadvantage of existing distributed systems
is their weak reliability.

Implementing redundant distributed systems is more difficult than
implementing redundant centralized systems; even so, the reliability
of centralized systems is not satisfactory. To circumvent this
difficulty, all systems use two redundant communication buses,
in parallel, simultaneously conveying the same message.

Another approach, proposed by the author of this present paper, is
based on a ring configuration with a simple packet switching
technique. [4] But the ring configuration presents a higher unavailability risk than the bus configuration, on which the present
concept is based.

2.0   CONTROL STRATEGY

Almost every industrial or power plant has its own requirements regarding geographical layout, functional tasks, level of acceptable
unavailability, sophistication of control algorithm, etc.

2.1   The Control Structure and the Data Communication Structure

In general, a distributed control system consists of a control
structure and a data-communciation structure.

While control structure components are mainly based on microprocessors, with additional mini-microcomputers and their peripherals,
the data-communication structure components presented here are
based on standard LSI and firmware, conceived according to a newly
devised local computer network.

While data-communication structure can and should be built totally
distributed, the control structure cannot. For any kind of industrial plant, the control structure has a hierarchical (layered)
organizational form where some organized procedures have jurisdic-
tion over others.

The proposed control system is based on the concept that the data-
communication structure is totally distributed. Totally distributed, in our acceptance of these words, means that each intelligent
component has the capabiliity to directly address any other component at any time, without the aid of another intermediate component while the control structure is hierarchically organized.

Both the distributed data-communication structure and hierarchical
control structure are redundant to the extent required by the
specific application.

2.2   The Control Hierarchies

The control structure is organized around the main functional

objectives which are here called "programs". The control structure is composed of two parallel hierarchies (see Figure 1): (a)
a complete programmed (automatic) control, and (b) an interactive
supervising computer-aided control. Each control program, at all
levels, is logically designed, so that if the links with the
superior levels are cut off, the said program will change the control strategy based on the coded stored mode of operation and the
information it continues to receive. This is an extended feature
of the standalone capability of a distributed control. For redundancy purposes, each program will be located in several memory
hardware components as required by the specified degree of redundancy.

Although control strategy is specific to a particular application,
a general outline of the superimposed levels can be organized as
illustrated by Figure 1.

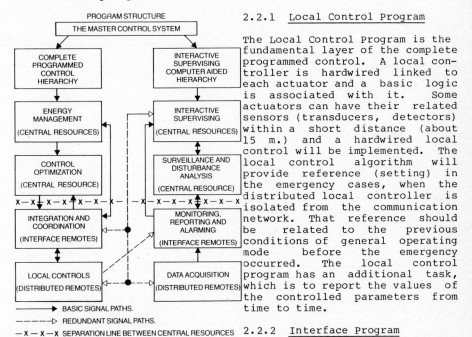

PROGRAM STRUCTURE
THE MASTER CONTROL SYSTEM

COMPLETE PROGRAMMED CONTROL HIERARCHY

INTERACTIVE SUPERVISING COMPUTER AIDED HIERARCHY

ENERGY MANAGEMENT
(CENTRAL RESOURCES)

INTERACTIVE SUPERVISING
(CENTRAL RESOURCES)

CONTROL OPTIMIZATION
(CENTRAL RESOURCE)

SURVEILLANCE AND DISTURBANCE ANALYSIS
(CENTRAL RESOURCE)

INTEGRATION AND COORDINATION
(INTERFACE REMOTES)

MONITORING, REPORTING AND ALARMING
(INTERFACE REMOTES)

LOCAL CONTROLS
(DISTRIBUTED REMOTES)

DATA ACQUISITION
(DISTRIBUTED REMOTES)

→ BASIC SIGNAL PATHS.
---▷ REDUNDANT SIGNAL PATHS.
—x—x—x SEPARATION LINE BETWEEN CENTRAL RESOURCES AND DISTRIBUTED CAPACITIES.

FIGURE 1   Control Structure

2.2.1   Local Control Program

The Local Control Program is the
fundamental layer of the complete
programmed control. A local controller is hardwired linked to
each actuator and a basic logic
is associated with it. Some
actuators can have their related
sensors (transducers, detectors)
within a short distance (about
15 m.) and a hardwired local
control will be implemented. The
local control algorithm will
provide reference (setting) in
the emergency cases, when the
distributed local controller is
isolated from the communication
network. That reference should
be related to the previous
conditions of general operating
mode before the emergency
occurred. The local control
program has an additional task,
which is to report the values of
the controlled parameters from
time to time.

2.2.2   Interface Program

The Interface Program is the next
superimposed level with jurisdic-
tion over a whole segment of process. This program has integrating
and coordinating tasks.

The interface program will include an emergency subroutine which
will perform all tasks according to the operating mode under
isolation condition from superior levels of control.

2.2.3   Optimization Program

The Optimization Program is applied to optimization purposes of
multivariable, multidimensional, nonlinear control systems which
describe certain segments of the process. In order to optimize

such a complex control, algorithm shall be developed and implemented when it is considered beneficial enough.

An overall economic optimization program related to the specific industrial process may be implemented at this level also.

2.2.4 Energy Management Program

The Energy Management Program connected to a Load Management Program will minimize energy consumption and cost.

2.3 Computer Aided Supervisory Hierarchy

The Computer Aided Supervisory Hierarchy is composed of the following programs.

2.3.1 The Data-Acquisition Program

The Data-Acquisition Program should collect data on a local basis from dedicated sensors to this program. According to the concept presented here, the local data acquisition unit covers the same area (segment) of the process as a local control unit does, with both units working together. The scanning cycle is fixed, but the reporting message frequency depends on the operating mode and rate of change, ranging between a minimum and a maximum established cycle.

2.3.2 Monitoring, Reporting, Alarming Program

Monitoring, Reporting, Alarming Program, as its name suggests, analyzes the collected data, filters the acquired information, verifies, reports, validates, memorizes, and alarms the operator when necessary. The monitoring function scrutinizes the data coming from two or three sources, based on a plausibility logic for two sources or a voting logic for three sources, and reports the validated data. The monitoring program provides a routine test of all message sources, keeps an account of their frequency of erroneous messages or missing messages and disables the failing components.

2.3.3 Surveillance, Disturbance Analysis Program

The Surveillance and Disturbance Analysis Program is a centralized computer program which aids the operators with their tasks. Such a program was developed by ERPI for nuclear power plants and will spread, after adaptations, to other kinds of plants. This program provides the operator with a brief report of process status and most significant changes. In a disturbing event, it performs an analysis of causes and suggests the best remedies.

2.3.4 Interactive Supervising Program

The Interactive Supervising Program enables the operator to ask for data from any addressable component and to override any automatic control. In doing so, he is aided by the monitoring, alarming, surveillance, and analysis programs.

3.0 THE LOCAL COMPUTER CONTROL NETWORK

The data-communication structure is based on a redundant local computer network with unique features conceived to ensure different degrees of availability as required for the overall control of an industrial plant. This structure is a variable configuration, depending on the specific application, composed of a multiple use, standard communication node through which other computer component subsystems are interconnected, according to the control hardware system.

3.1   The Communication Interface (Node)

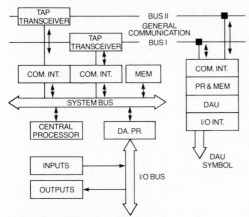

The first building block of this structure (the standard communication interface or node, see Figure 2) consists of an LSI linked to two coaxial buses through passive taps and transceivers. The LSI has its central processor, memory with firmware, input/output ports, DMA logic, and system bus. Unlike current control networks, our redundant network communication interface does not simultaneously send the same packet through both buses to which it is linked, but sends the packet to one bus only. The node uses the contention technique (Carrier Sense Multiple Access/

FIGURE 2   Data Acquisition Unit

Collision Detection - CSMA/CD) of sending-receiving packets through base band modems as opposed to the token-passing techniques used by the said networks. The reason to choose the contention as opposed to passing technique is based on the former's capability to accommodate the message priority policy. The node listens to both buses through which it can receive messages, but will send its regular packet through a dedicated bus. If the message it has to send is of high priority, it can choose any one of the buses which at that moment is in service and free from other signals. This simple packet-switching technique makes the difference between our concept, a conventional local computer network [5] and a long-haul computer network [6]. If a contention occurs on whatever bus, each node will resume the tentative packet sending after a delay commensurate with the priority order of the message. The communication interface is a universal link to the bus for all compatible system components, such as application processors, memories, displays, modems.

3.2   The Data Acquisition Unit

Figure 2 shows an additional external memory and a data-acquisition processor with its I/O bus and ports. With these components added to the standard node, the configuration shown represents a data acquisition unit whose symbol is also illustrated on the same exhibit. Such a unit works according to the program previously described. The packets are regularly sent to the bus which is dedicated to data-acquisition task. The packets are regularly received by the interface units, but they may be received by any other component of the network if the address of the component is made common with the interface address.

3.3   The Local Control Unit

The Local Control Unit has similar configuration to the Data

Acquisition Unit made up of a standard node and a control processor. The two configurations, explained in Sections 3.2 and 3.3,
are identically built, in order to change redundantly the program
between the two units. The control unit regularly sends packets
through the bus dedicated to control messages. The frequency of the
control unit reports depends on its processing power and its control
task.

3.4   The Interface Unit

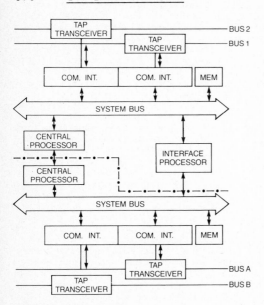

FIGURE 3   Interface Unit

The interface unit is compri-
sed of two regular nodes in a
back-to-back arrangement with
or without an interface processor (Figure 3). Such a
unit can perform several programs and be used for several
network needs depending on
the capacities linked to the
two system buses. From the
illustrated configuration,
one can see that the interface can work linked to either
two, three or four buses.
When linked to four buses,
the interface unit transfers
packets from one network
(buses 1 and 2) to another
network (buses A and B). If
the networks are compatible,
a separate interface processor is not necessary for
packet transfer. A virtual
addressing mode with simple
wrapping techniques can be
used through a hand shaking
interface between the two
central processors. [4]

In another alternative, a dual port memory might be linked to the
two system buses instead of the interface processor, when a large
difference between the bit rates of the two networks should be
mitigated.

The intertie link between the two networks, obtained by the interface described above and illustrated in Figure 3, filters the
message of mutual interest to both networks, while an amplifier-
repeater transfers all messages without selection.

The requirement for power plants of more than one control
(sub)network was presented in Reference [4]. If the two
(sub)networks, which are to be linked, are completely different, the
intertie processor (gateway) should have an adhoc hardware and software.

The interface unit, linked to three buses (bus 1, 2 and A) can receive and send packets to all buses. The third bus (bus A) can be
a dedicated interface bus. Because two equivalent units, such as
a pair of control and data acquisition units, cannot reliably ensure
enough the redundant exchange of tasks between them, the use of an
interface unit as a monitoring unit over a process control segment

is a beneficial novelty of this concept. One interface unit can
monitor a large number of control and data-acquisition unit pairs.
Two, three or four buses can be used for this purpose. The interface regularly receives the reports of all units through the control and data-acquisition buses. The reports, coming from the same
pair of units, are compared based on operating mode implied, expected rate of change and time constants. The received values
are verified and validated. A report is sent to the central
facility (eventually through the third bus: the interface bus).
The non-concordant data are analyzed by the plausibility logic; the
wrong report is invalidated and its source is further controlled.
If the remote continues to send erroneous messages, the interface
stops the faulting remote and alerts the superimposed layers. A
control remote is replaced by its counterpart data-acquisition unit.
A data-acquisition unit does not need a replacement since the
control unit also reports the essential data with a lower frequency. The control algorithm can be located in the memory
of either the data-acquisition unit or anywhere in a nearby component.

A faulted unit can be replaced without discontinuing the system
work. This method permits complete testing of channels from sensors
to the receivers of messages. The messages related to the same control algorithm are directly received by all the parties involved in
the same control function.

The interface unit works as a cross-tie to enhance the reliability
of the system. It offers a supplementary path for message circulation.

3.5   Three Bus Local Control Network Configurations

A three bus configuration might be chosen for two reasons: (a)
the packets are too numerous for two buses, (such a situation may
occur when a central control room is linked to several subnetworks
and supervises a large number of distributed controls); (b) the
availability criteria require a high degree of redundancy (e.g.,
nuclear power plants).

Figure 4 shows some three bus configurations based on the same
modules as previously described in this paper. For the above
Item a, Figure 4 presents a pair of control and data-acquisition
units working on buses 1, 2 and 3. Usually, the control unit will
communicate with bus 1 and the data unit with bus 3. The interface
unit III can monitor this pair of modules. Bus 2 is utilized for
subnetwork intercommunication packets. If one of the buses or one
of the units fails, the system will continue to work on a packet
priority basis. Figure 4 also shows an interconnection between two
three-bus configurations (1, 2, 3 and A, B, C). Depending on the
redundancy required, two or three interface modules will be used.

To meet the requirements of Item b, three times redundancy is illustrated on the lower side of Figure 4. For the same actuator(s),
a group of three control units work in parallel. The output values
potentially imposed on the actuator(s), are checked by a "two out of
three logic." If one of the controller works irregularly, an alarming message is sent through the other two reliable controllers. A
redundancy is provided even for the validity check logic, through
the data-acquisition unit, if such an extra measure is considered
useful. Threesome data acquisition units can also be implemented

if thought necessary to meet a required very high availability.
That was the case with NUREG 0696, issued by the Nuclear Regulatory
Commission (first draft July 1980).

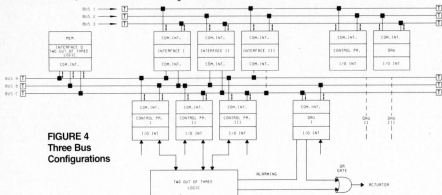

FIGURE 4
Three Bus
Configurations

If necessary, the redundancy can be upgraded to a four bus configuration. Using the same hardware illustrated by Figure 3, the
interface computer can be used for local program purposes, receiving
messages from four buses and sending through one out of four buses.

As previously described, each module of the system is continuously
in service; there is not stand-by component. But the system is conceived so that if any component, hardware or software, fails it will
continue performing further all its objectives. The redundancy is
built in the system at the module level with overlapping tasks and
not as usual at the complete system level. The system features an
intrinsic redundancy.

3.6   Interconnections Between Local Computer Control Networks

In most cases, local computer control networks require interconnections between the networks for information exchange [6,7]. Such requirements for large power plant control and data communication
systems were defined in previous work as described by Reference [4].
Large scale industrial control and data-communications computer networks are increasingly needed for operational and managerial
purposes. The best economical and technical way to implement such
networks is to link local computer control networks between them
through long haul communications channels [1].

We have to define several categories of interconnection between
local networks. There are local networks which are located either
near to or far from one another. There are either tight or loose
connected local networks. Two tight connected local networks have
to exchange most of their running messages between themselves.

Loose connected local networks serve mostly as support for large
long haul packet switching networks. In the case of loose connected
local networks, a small part of the running messages through the
long haul links are addressed to a given local network, the remaining messages have to be conveyed to other local networks. Our
approach of contention control and simple packet switching techniques
resolves the transmission/receiving problems of all such networks
using the same standard communication interface unit as defined
in Section 3.4 and Figure 3.

Tight connection between closely located local control networks is
solved through the interface unit as described in Section 3.5 and
Figure 4.

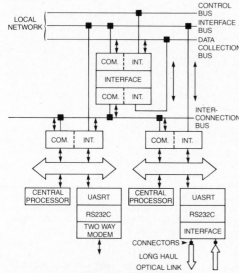

Tight connection between two
remotely located local
networks will use a similar
interface configuration. The
interface configuration will
be linked to our contention
local network through the
standard communication LSI and
with an appropriate interface
to the long haul link. Such a
case is described in Section
5.0 and Figure 5.

A solution for loose connection
between two remotely located
local networks is illustrated
by Figure 5. This solution uses
only standard communication
interface LSIs. A dedicated
new bus was added as support
for long haul links messages.
This bus will free the local
computer control network buses
from the bulk of external
messages. The long haul link
will usually transmit all of

**FIGURE 5   Local Network and Long Haul
Loose Interconnections**

its packets to the interconnection bus. Packets will be transmitted
to the interface (or another bus) only in emergency cases. The
interface unit will extract the messages addressed to the linked
local network and resend the message to other buses if necessary.

Other long haul links will withdraw the packets addressed to them
from the interconnection bus.

Figure 5 illustrates two kinds of long haul links, one over a telephone line and one over a fiber optic duplex link. Through an
appropriate interface, the local computer network can be tied to all
types of long haul links.

The connection of such local computer networks and long haul links
presents the following advantages:

-   Large long haul packet switching networks can be built in a sim-
    pler way using a simple routing decision similar to the approach
    for local networks. For compatible protocols, a wrapping tech-
    nique (1, 4) offers an easy solution to addressing modes.

-   Large long haul packet switching networks, based on local net-
    works, can enjoy shorter links (following the geographical de-
    ployment of the local networks) instead of long dedicated
    line. Such new control networks feature intrinsic redundancy
    and distributed control over the message traffic.

4.0   OPTIC FIBER LINKS FOR COMMUNICATION BUSES

Instead of using coaxial cables, optic fiber links can be also used. Figure 6 illustrates an optical distributed configuration. It shows a closed loop (ring) using Directional Tee Couplers (DTCs) which link the Remote Substation (RSs) through transmitters (TS) and receivers (Rs) to the optical bus. The difference between a coaxial cable configuration and the T coupler configuration consists of the bidirectional way of conveying signals by the coaxial bus as opposed to the unidirectional way in which the DTCs convey the light waves. While the coaxial cable bus cannot be closed and remains an open loop, the optical bus should be closed to accommodate access to the bus for all candidate senders.

To circumvent the reliability weaknesses of T coupler networks, we propose a redundant contention ring (Figure 7). The Transmissive Star Couplers (TSCs) represented on the exhibit are used instead of DTCs. If one of the fibers or one of the couplers fails, the ring remains closed for all other remote substations.

Using Reflective Star Couplers (RSCs) (Figure 8), instead of Transmissive Star Couplers, the configuration loop can work either closed or open. Such a redundant ring may replace two parallel coaxial buses from bandlength and reliability point of view.

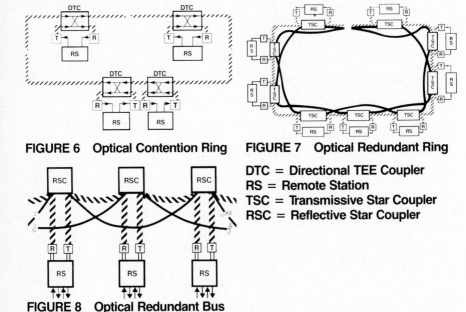

FIGURE 6   Optical Contention Ring   **FIGURE 7   Optical Redundant Ring**

FIGURE 8   Optical Redundant Bus

DTC = Directional TEE Coupler
RS = Remote Station
TSC = Transmissive Star Coupler
RSC = Reflective Star Coupler

5.0   SPECIFIC APPLICATION FOR A SOLAR COGENERATION PLANT

The solar cogeneration plant consists of a solar heliostat field, a receiver on top of a central tower, and five gas turbine sets which send compressed air to the receiver and generate electricity. The exhausted air, compressed and heated, is sent to the industrial plant and thermal energy storage. A description of the control system in the area of the gas-turbine plant, based on the above described concept, follows. (See Figure 9.)

The core of the system configuration is a three general communication coaxial cable arrangement. Each remote station is linked to two buses through a double communication interface and a complete independent way of sending/receiving messages: the contention (CSMA/CD) method.

Each Gas-Turbine Set has a control and a data acquisition unit, independently linked to the buses.

The data acquisition unit will collect all parameter values and their rate of change. Both remotes receive all inputs independently and have same outputs through the OR GATES.

The coordination and integration program (interface program) for all gas turbines is processed by the remote called interface for all units (IFAU). The interface receives the data from all DAUs, performs a coordinating function among the five sets (e.g., guides the droop controllers, in order to balance the electrical loads) and integrates the controls of the gas-turbine plant with the controls in the solar field and the controls in the industrial plant area.

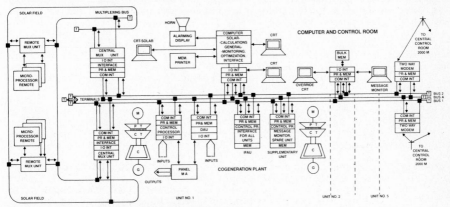

FIGURE 9   Solar Congeneration Plant. Master Control System

Because there are five gas turbine sets, it is worthwhile to have in the cogeneration area of the control system, a supplementary remote unit which is used to monitor the messages, to check if all remotes are sending acknowledged messages, to verify if the messages of Control and DAU remotes are in a plausible agreement, and to ascertain if the commands emitted by interface are followed by control remotes. If a control remote fails the supplementary unit will alarm and report to the superior levels, disable the failing remote, and will supplant this remote by its DAU.

If the interface or supplementary remote fails, their redundant programs are processed by the computer installed in the computer room. The main task of this computer is to coordinate the solar control system and to integrate the control of the solar cogeneration and industrial plant.

The computer and the operators have direct access to all remotes. The configuration accommodates all programs as described in

Section 2.0. Two special gateways interface the Master Control
System with the local control network in the solar field. The local
computer control network in the gas turbine plant is connected with
the local computer control network of the industrial plant through
two telephone lines and two two-way modems.

6.0   CONCLUSION

A new concept of local computer control network is presented. It
features modular structure, with intrinsic and variable degrees of
redundancy, established by the controlled plant requirements,
priority of conveyed messages, and total distribution of hardware
and its control. The process control is hierarchical and distributed at the same time.

A unique type of bus configuration was chosen, as opposed to a ring
configuration, for reliability, expandability, modularity, and
ability to be reconfigured.

A CSMA/CD (Ethernet) [9] system was chosen as opposed to a token
passing access method for the simplicity and message priority
ability. The priority of the message is related to the type of
message (e.g. alarm, control, or bulk data) as opposed to message
priority related to the location of the remote substation as with
the token passing access method.

The above presented system offers enough bandwidth to ensure the
access of messages to the buses by delaying non-essential messages
until a smooth operating mode with less message circulation occurs
and by using at least two buses carrying messages independently from
one another.

The above described system features broad and comprehensive methods
of malfunction detection. A monitoring unit surveys the ability of
each remote station to fully understand and acknowledge messages.
The monitoring unit(s) sends and receives routine testing messages.

The interface unit(s) checks the information collected from two or
three remotes, verifies and validates the right information, which
is used further by the upper levels of software. The control action
is monitored by the surveillance and disturbance program as well as
by the interactive program.

Besides the above mentioned malfunction detection methods, common
practiced error recovery and self-testing methods are used.

References

1.   D. Damsker, "New Hierarchical Controls and Data-Communications
     in an Electric Power System Environment," International Mini-
     Micro-Data-Communications Conference, Geneva, Switzerland,
     June 17-19, 1980, Proceedings, p. 253.

2.   E. Janecek, "Packet-Switching Network Tightens Control System
     Response," Control Engineering, February 1981, p. 80.

3.   Forney Engineering Corp., ECS-1200 System presented by Control
     Engineering, August 1980, p. 46.

4.   D. Damsker, "Universal Power Plant Data Communications Network,"
     International Conference on Computer Technology, ASME, Century
     2, San Francisco, CA, August 11-15, 1980, Proceedings p. 32,

5. J. Estrin, B. Carrico, "Local Network for Distributed Process-
    ing," Electronics, February 10, 1981, p. 149.

6. C. Warner, "Connecting Local Networks to Long Haul Networks,"
    Fifth Conference on Local Computer Networks, Minneapolis,
    Minnesota, Oct. 6-7, 1980, p. 71.

7. D.D. Clark, et al., "An Introduction to Local Area Networks,"
    IEEE, Proceedings, Vol. 66, Number 11, November 1978, p. 1497

8. D. Damsker, "Multiplexing and Networking Through Fiber Optic
    Links," IEEE, Transmission and Distribution Conference, Minne-
    apolis, Minnesota, September 20-25, 81TD 702-0.

9. R. Ryan, et al., "Local Network Architecture Proposed for Work
    Stations," Electronics, August 25, 1981, p. 120.

APPENDIX

The ISO-OSI Reference Model of the Local Control Network

The International Standardization Organization (ISO)-Open Systems
Interconnection (OSI) model is a good abstract representation of
the functional requirements and procedures necessary to achieve
communication in a general sense between any two communicating
devices. The orderly description of the functions which should be
performed at each level of the model ensures the necessary compatibility and the standardization of hardware and software of all
communicating devices built on the same basis as this model.

Figure A presents the ISO-OSI and the IEEE Local Area Network
Standard 802 reference models. The reason for illustrating the two
models is to show that our Local Control Network complies, in
general terms, with these models and qualifies as an "Open Systems
Interconnection." (The term "Open" characterizes the ability of two
stations to intercommunicate easily and freely on a peer-to peer
basis as well as their capability to achieve cooperation for a
common but distributed task.)

The IEEE Local Area Network (LAN), Draft Standard 802 has used a
modified version of the OSI Reference Model. Figure A presents the
IEEE Local Area Network Reference Model, as it has progressed to
date (Oct. 19, 1981). The IEEE 802 Reference Model is concerned
only with the two lowest layers of the OSI model. The Data Link is
mapped into two sublayers, namely the Logical Link Control (LLC) and
Media Access Control (MAC) sublayers. Some functions of the MAC
sublayer extend into the Physical Layer. The IEEE 802 Local Area
Network has a peer-to-peer communications architecture based on a
point-to-point logical link with a single data path medium and
physical channel segment. The higher layers above the Link Level
are not considered by this simple data communications architecture.
The model supports for multiple higher layer application protocols
(A,B,C--) and accommodates only one Physical Service Access Point
(P-SAP).

Figure B portrays our Distributed Redundant Local Control Network
Standard Communication Interface Reference Model.

Typically, only one application protocol (A) coming from the higher layers is serviced. This formal restriction illustrates the more specialized service performed by our control network. But multiple application protocols are also accepted as they can be presented by multi-programs entities.

The Logical Link Control Sublayer should provide a Type 1 (Connectionless) operation, because broadcast and multicast addressing methods shall be used as well as node-to-node addressing capability. Acknowledged and nonacknowledged frame exchange and error recovery procedures should be provided for this latter type of addressing. A nonacknowledged frame is used for broadcast and multicast protocol data units. An exchange identification command (XID) shall also be provided. More logic procedures should be realized by our Data Link Control Sublayer, which are not provided by the IEEE 802 model. One of them is to convey the priority grade of the format which will prevail in the selection of the Physical Service Access Point. Another one is a command which will enable/disable the backing-off procedure and will set the deference time in the Media Access Sublayer.

There are differences between the IEEE 802 and our model concerning the Media Access Control Sublayer. Our Data Terminal Equipment has two different Physical Service Access Points (PSAPs).

The Media Access Control Sublayer shall supply a Physical Service Access Point (PSAP) selection procedure. Regularly, the MAC Data Units are delivered to one preferred PSAP. The second PSAP will be selected in several cases, such as if the first PSAP delivery channel is busy, and the Data Unit has a first priority grade or the access of the first PSAP delivery channel is prohibited by the Data Management Facility. In some circumstances, a command coming from the higher layers will request the transmission of the same data unit to both PSAPs. A 32 bit Cycle Redundancy Check (CRC) is used to generate the Frame Check Sequence (FCS). The media access control is the Carrier Sense Media Access/Collision Detection. The Link Management procedure of the two models have a slight difference consisting of the logic of deference time and backing-off procedure. The logic of deference time is related to: a) the message priority grade; b) the bus(es) allowed for access; and c) the station topological location. The message backing-off is enabled for routine and batch data units during transients and some critical operating modes.

A Data Management (Monitoring) Facility is provided for network planning, operations and maintenance. This facility is functionally separated from the "monitoring program" of the control structure. The Data Management Facility deals with network expansion, malfunction detection, reconfiguration and faults repair demands. It interfaces with the monitoring program of the Application Processes as well as Data Link Sublayers. The Data Management Facility is serviced by a Bridge, Interface Unit (see Figure C).

Referring to Figure B, the physical layer is described by its three components: the Physical Signaling Sublayer, Access Unit Interface, and Physical Media Attachment. No major difference is to be noticed between our Physical Layer and the Physical Layer described by Chapter IV, IEEE LAN 802.

Figure C represents the Reference Model of the Interface Unit, termed also the Bridge, as it was described in Section 3.4 and

Figure 3 of this paper. The Interface Unit consists of two twin Communications Interfaces built in accordance with the Reference Model Figure B. The Interface Unit allows for using three or four physical channels on the same local control network as well as interconnecting a pair of compatible two buses local control (sub)networks. In order to coordinate the operations of the two Data Terminal Equipments and to interface with the higher levels, the Network Layer services should be involved.

According to IEEE LAN 802 Draft Standard, Appendix D, we divide the Network Layer into two Sublayers, namely the Global Network Sublayer and the Communications Service Sublayer. But the internetworking functions assigned to each sublayer of this Network Layer are otherwise defined because our model deals essentially with a Bridge and not with a Gateway as in the IEEE LAN 802 model.

The Global Network Sublayer functions are limited to Data Units switching and distributing functions, such as: directing a Protocol Data Unit coming from higher levels to one, several or all four buses; transferring a Protocol Data Unit, coming from one or two buses, to other one or two buses controlled by the twin Data Terminal Equipments; and implementing reconfiguration orders coming from Data Management Facility.

The Communications Service Sublayer is involved in interconnections with remotely located local control networks. Its functions are defined later in this Appendix.

The remotely located local control networks (Figure D) are interconnected through long haul links. According to our concept, the more advantageous and reliable interconnection method employs Half Bridges and privately owned physical links for internetworking. Gateways are used only for interconnections with incompatible networks and/or where the service of public packet switching facility is unavoidable. Gateway protocol services are performed by higher level application entities.

The Half Bridge (Figure E) consists of a Standard Communications Interface linked onto Mediums 1 and 2 of the local control network, a standard Global Network Sublayer and a second package of Data Link/Physical Layers linked to a long haul link. Usually the half bridge does not need any kind of higher level service above the Global Network Sublayer and does not have an application layer.

The Data Link Layer is a simplified version of the Logical Link Control, because this layer has to perform only point-to-point asynchronous balanced connection link. Within the local network, the Half Bridge has an interconnection only with one (or two in more redundant applications) Full Bridge(s). There is no intermediate address necessary for the packets sent and received through the long haul link except the end-to-end local network and station addresses. For the packets coming from the Full Bridge, the Half Bridge has the address of its interconnected outside local network. The route decision through intermediate local networks is made by the Communications Service Sublayer of the Full Bridge (see Figure C).

Using the above mentioned techniques results in only one Standard Communications Interface and a few protocol procedures to cover the functional requirements of a very broad industrial local control network and its intercommunications.

D. Damsker

Figure A

The ISO-OSI Reference Model

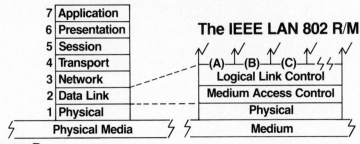

Figure B

DRLCN–Communications Interface

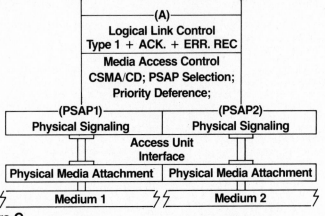

Figure C

DRLCN–Bridge Reference Model

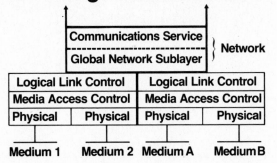

Figure D

DRLCN–Internetworking Scenarios

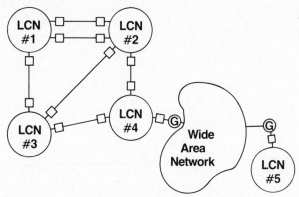

Figure E

DRLCN–Half Bridge Loose Interconnection

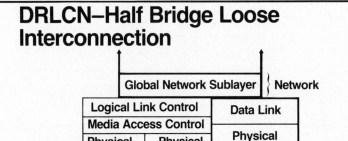

ACKNOWLEDGMENT

We acknowledge the support and encouragement received from the U.S. Department of Energy and Sandia National Laboratories - Livermore in the development of this concept.

LOCAL COMPUTER NETWORKS
P.C. Ravasio, G. Hopkins and N. Naffah (editors)
North-Holland Publishing Company
© IFIP, 1982

HISTORY AND DEVELOPMENT OF THE
EPICS LOCAL COMPUTER NETWORK

Hidetoshi Kawai

Software Technology Center
Information-technology Promotion Agency, Japan
Tokyo, JAPAN

The EPICS centralized channel level heterogeneous local computer network has been used for the last nine years by one hundred users for pattern information research. The major object of research has been a large-scale online synergetic computing facility capable of interacting with individual computer systems designed for specific fields of recognition research: handwritten Chinese characters, pictures, speech, scenes, and natural language. EPICS was developed as a star-configuration computer complex in which a center-host provides users with a TSS environment, and six peripheral-hosts communicate with each other through newly developed hardware, controlled by a program resident in the center-host.

Local networking requires interactive sharing of resources distributed among several hosts. Hetero-netting must eliminate technical problems involving non-connectability and incompatibility among hosts. EPICS high-level protocol processors are nonresident in the center-host, and carry out several kinds of resource services; input/output between processes, data file record transfer, semaphores, message communication between processes, and remote job entry.

This paper reports high-level protocol usage trends for the last nine years, front-end protocol processing by heterogeneous minicomputers, aimed at overcoming conflicts between protocol processing and data processing in the center-host, virtual Japanese document transfer among three heterogeneous computers, and virtual file transfer with downloading, a method suggested by experience with peripheral-hosts and implemented on online personal microcomputers. Our front-end netting experiments showed that the fastest way to heteronetting is not to establish compatibility among a wide range of resources, but to reduce noncompatibility to a specific, thin resource-dependent sublayer of high-level protocol.

1. INTRODUCTION

The Electrotechnical Laboratory Pattern Information Computing System (EPICS) 1) centralized heterogeneous local computer network has been used for the last nine years in the Electro-technical Laboratory of the Japanese government by one hundred users for research on pattern information processing. The Laboratory has been involved in the Pattern Information Processing System (PIPS) 2) project since the preliminary planning stages as part of a national synergetic development program aimed at developing an open online computing facility.

The major system requirements for this computing facility are: 1) continuous utilization of general resources, data files, and recognition processes; 2) utilization of programming environments; and 3) reconfiguration of individual processing systems for specific recognition research fields: handwritten Chinese characters, picture, speech, scenes, and natural language. To overcome confilcts between these fields, EPICS is set up as a heterogeneous star configuration channel level local computer network in which the center-host provides users with general resources, TSS environments, and large scale computer facilities; six peripheral-hosts provide specialized facilities for specific research fields.

The principle advantage of local hetero-netting is the interactive sharing of resources distributed among multiple hosts and maintained by individual authorities. Because of this setup, local hetero-netting must eliminate technical problems such as nonconnectability and incompatibility between hosts.

Results obtained with OCTOPUS 3), a preliminary hetero-netting system, suggest that protocol simplification is essential for local hetero-netting, and recommend a simple communication control protocol. In addition, MERIT 4), a middle-scale heterogeneous local computer network, shows that an intensive administration system capable of tailoring is needed for local hetero-netting.

In EPICS, the input/output channel of the center-host uses a newly developed hardware Computer Communication Controller (CCC), controlled by a module resident in the center-host. The CCC connects the center-host with each peripheral-host, and transfers data at 2 Mbps. EXEC, a nonresident module processes high-level protocols to make the data word structure compatible among hosts. EXEC performs session control, RJE processing management, semaphore control, and remote process control.

Since the standard data transfer rate is 50 kbps in high-level protocol, protocol processors should not be accommodated in the center-host, but in front-end minicomputers. The experimental Telephone Computer Network (T-NET) 5) has provided some front-end protocol processing techniques that indicate a thin sublayer of high-level protocol hierarchy is enough for resource-dependent processing. The experimental Information-technology Promotion Agency Computer System (IPACS) has also provided a thin high-level protocol sublayer of virtual Japanese document transfer by a method of eliminating printed forms control functions.

High-level protocol usage patterns observed in EPICS over the last nine years show that peripheral-hosts will most likely become online personal microcomputers eventually. In fact, a newly developed microcomputer has already been connected to a display terminal, and the PIPS Universal Computing Element command system (PULCOM 6) has been developed to provide online personal computer users with virtual file transfer high-level protocol with downloading. It has been confirmed that file transfer protocol with downloading is highly useful for developing application systems such as optical readers for handwritten Chinese characters, LISP machines, PASCAL machines, BASIC machines, and magnetic bubble data base machines 7) for each online personal computer networking with the center-host.

The following describes findings made over the last nine years on trends in high-level protocol usage, front-end protocol processing by minicomputers using T-NET, virtual Japanese document transfer without printed forms control functions among large-scale computers using IPACS, and virtual file transfer with downloading implemented on an online personal computer using PULCOM. It also proposes a high-level protocol hierarchical structure, developed as a result of experience with EPICS. The hierarchy does not attempt to establish compatibility with a wide range of resources among heterogeneous hosts, but rather reduces noncompatibility to a specific, thin resource-dependent sublayer of high-level protocols.

2. TRENDS IN HIGH-LEVEL PROTOCOLS IN EPICS

EPICS basically consists of a large-scale center-host and six middle-scale peripheral-hosts as shown in Fig. 1. High-level protocols are processed by the EXEC nonresident program module in the center-host, and are supported by a low-level protocol processor, GCOM, which controls the newly developed channel CCC. EXEC processes EPICS commands issued by a user program in either the center- or peripheral-host. EPICS-commands comprise six sequences:

(1) Remote job entry
(2) Reverse remote job entry

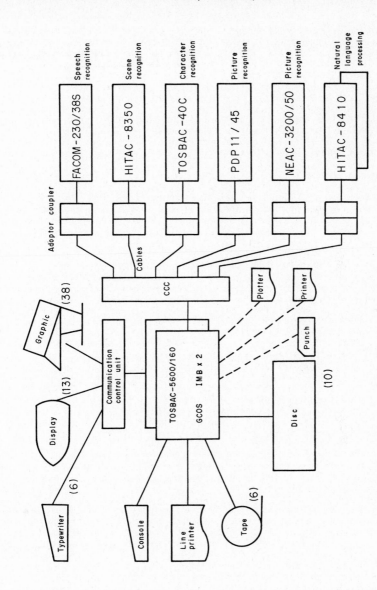

Fig. 1. Configuration of EPICS local computer network

(3) Remote file record input/output
(4) Message sending/receiving to/from remote program
(5) Process interlocking and data storage/reference in a common process group area
(6) Creation/modification/deletion of center-host permanent files.

2.1 Observed Trends

Although EXEC provides these six sequences as macrocommands for user programs, only five high-level protocol sequences were observed, as shown in Table 1. The trends were decreased high-level protocol frequency, decreased remote job entry frequency, and increased data file transfer.

2.2 Reasons for Trends

The reasons for decreased high-level protocol frequency include: (1) user preference for TSS environment despite the lack of CCC support; (2) experiments subdivided into input/process/output stages; and (3) more jobs without high-level protocols.

Table 1. High-level protocl usage trends

	1975	1978
Batch program number/month	5000	1500
Program size (k bytes)/job	104	80
Processing time s/job	30.5	92.8
High-level protocol sequence frequency/month	2000	31
items (%): data file transfer	40	75
reverse remote job	51	15
remote job entry	2	3
program communication	2	2
checking connective integrity	4	5

The reason for decreased remote job entry frequency is that users tend to store information in center-host rather than peripheral-host because of its easy filing and interactive editing services. Therefore, only short utility jobs are still stored in the peripheral-host.

The relative increase in data file transfer reflects the fact that data file transfer among several hosts is executed separately from data processing within a particular host when an experiment is subdivided into several stages. In addition, the kinds of data transferred have increased; not only external binary data but also text data such as program source lists and messages are now transferred. The absolute decrease in data file transfer comes from the fact that large-volume data such as picture data is transferred at a high rate by a low-level protocol, and that small-volume data such as speech data is transferred not through a CCC but through a newly developed intelligent terminal, an online personal computer as described in 5.

2.3 Other Findings

Program communication using semaphores between hosts is currently limited to a demonstration program developed for users to interact with several hosts. Very little program communication between peripheral-hosts has been observed because peripheral-hosts manage resources for their own users rather than for remote users. Therefore, a large-scale demonstration program for interlocking peripheral-hosts was developed for another PIPS 2) system.

Permanent files are maintained separately from temporary user programs, not by high-level protocol, but by the TSS environment. This indicates that the tendency towards strong host dependency is probably not motivated by high-level protocol, but by a host dependent utility. The virtual Japanese document transfer protocol proposed in Chapter 6 does not require any intelligent functions for printed forms control because of strong host dependency. Large chains of programs cannot be executed smoothly in the center-host because EXEC requires loading time and buffer allocating time to process high-level protocols activated by several peripheral-hosts. To avoid conflicts of protocol processing and data processing in the center-host, the front-end protocol processing technique has been suggested and evaluated as described in Chapter 4.

3. USER ENVIRONMENT AND PROTOCOL SEQUENCE RECOMMENDATIONS

In three out of six peripheral-hosts, only two high-level protocol sequences, file transfer and checking connective integrity, proved effective. Each of these three peripheral-hosts, F23, P11, and N23, is installed on the same floor as the user's office.

As shown in Fig. 2 case 2, T40 is installed in a laboratory on a different floor from the user's office, and includes specialized input/output devices for the particular field of research. In early research, the remote job entry protocol sequence was used frequently to input large-volume Chinese character data from magnetic tapes mounted on the T40. In later research, source data was stored in center-host files rather than laboratory files. With that development, the T40 could be regarded as an online personal computer with an optical character reader. Data files were transferred by a low-level protocol activated by a utility as a remote job.

The other two peripheral-hosts, H83 and H84, are installed in a separate computer room, neither in the user's office nor in the laboratory floor. Two high-level protocol sequences, reverse remote job and program communication, proved highly efficient. When reverse remote job protocols are processed, the peripheral-host is regarded as an automonous entity because the user only operates specialized input/output devices and the TS terminal of the center-host from his laboratory.

4. T-NET HIGH-LEVEL PROTOCOL HIERARCHY

The T-NET telephone computer network is an experimental network for developing high-level protocol hierarchy for protocol processes accommodated in front-end heterogeneous minicomputers 8) (see Fig. 3). EPICS-EXEC combines several functions: session control 9), semaphore control, message box control, user process control, three high-level protocol processes which include remote job entry, reverse remote job control, and permanent file maintenance. The resource independent protocol layer is not separated from the resource dependent protocol layer in the EPICS high-level protocol structure.

4.1 High-level Protocol Layers

High-level protocol hierarchy is resource-dependent. The first and highest hierarchical level, called proper protocol, and the host dependent layer, is distinguished from host independent layers. Proper protocol does not exchange messages between hosts, but specifies system environments which give specific meanings to messages specified by other protocol layers. Host independent protocol layers include a transport field, a communication field, and a processing field. The transport field is a low-level protocol and covers the lower four hierarchical

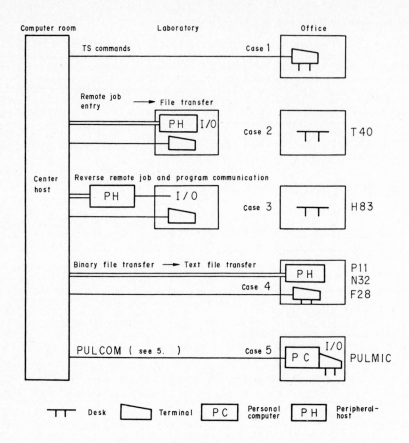

Fig. 2. High-level protocol usage trends and user's environment

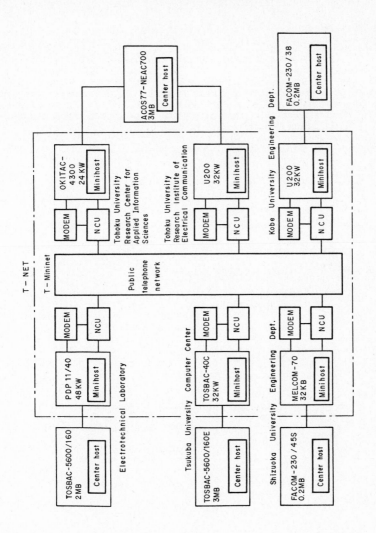

Fig. 3. Configuration of T-NET telephone computer network.

layers 9): physical, link, network, and transport.

Host independent high-level protocol layers are further subdivided into two
layers. One, called resource protocol, is the virtual resource controlling layer,
and the other, called communication protocol, is the communication controlling
layer. The communication protocol is not based on resource intelligence, and
corresponds to the communication field mentioned above. The communication protocol is also further subdivided into four sublayers (Table 2): session selection, virtual terminal, and file transfer. Resource protocols vary with the kind
of resource: mail, remote job, file record, data base, fascimile, resource
administration, or process synchronization. The mail process interprets the mail
protocol which is the resource protocol concerning mail, and so on.

Table 2. High-level protocol hierarchy

Host dependent	Proper protocol	System control & Utilities	
Host independent	Resource protocol (Resource dependent)	File copy	
		Resource control	Mail Japanese document RJE Data base Resource management
	Communication protocol	Virtual terminal & File transfer Selection of protocol process Session protocol	
	Transport protocol	Transport layer Network layer Data link layer Physical layer	

4.2 Relationship between High-level Protocols and Processes

Proper protocol is interpreted by proper processes: the resource process management process, real user process, real file process, transmission media control
process, read resource control processes, and the system management process which
manages all of the above processes. In T-NET, read resource processes and the
real process are only accommodated in the host; other processes are accommodated
in the front-end minicomputer. As shown in Fig. 4, several processes are activated when the system manager activates the system from the operator panel.

The resource process consists of three subprocesses:

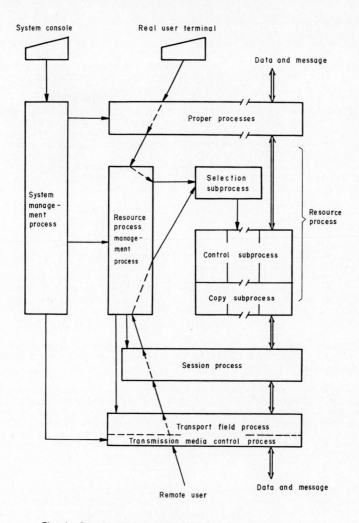

Fig. 4. Relationship between high-level protocol processes

(1) The selection subprocess, unique to each host and common to all resource processes. It interprets the selection protocol syblayer and manages the control subprocess selected by the user.

(2) The control subprocess, resource dependent and used to exchange messages according to virtual terminal protocol, and to control the resource selected by the user.

(3) The copy subprocess unique to each host according to the file transfer protocol and used to perform burst type file transfer among hosts.

The virtual terminal protocol process consists of a selection subprocess and a control subprocess. The latter utilizes information on network virtual terminals specified in the network. The file transfer protocol process consists of a selection subprocess, a control subprocess, and a copy subprocess. The latter is used to copy files among hosts in a virtual file structure.

As an example of a resource process, mail protocol interpretation is explained below.

(1) The mail process consists of a selection subprocess, a mail control subprocess, and a copy subprocess. Only a mail control subprocess is resource dependent and interprets a thin sublayer of high-level protocol. A pair of mail control subprocesses uses a session managed by a pair of session processes, one of which is activated in the user host and the other in the remote host. Its operational specifications are given by the virtual terminal protocol. The session used by the pair of copy subprocesses is specified by the file transfer protocol.

(2) In the initial state, the resource process management process must be active in order to activate the selection subprocess when a local user or a remote user issues a network command to a host.

(3) The selection subprocess establishes a session with the remote selection subprocess, fetches a protocol selection command from the user, notifies the system of the selected control subprocesses used throughout the session, activates the selected control subprocess, and finally deactivates itself. The selection protocol procedure can be omitted if the local control subprocess activates the remote control subprocess, but only if the local resource process management process knows the neames of all the remote control subprocesses.

(4) The mail control subprocess establishes a session with the remote mail control subprocess, fetches a resource control command from the user, notifies the remote mail control subprocess of the resource control command, obtains a response to that command from the remote mail control subprocess, and then displays the response on the user terminal. When the user issues a termination command for the protocol, the command and the response are excahnged again and the session is released.

(5) When the mail control subprocess receives a command to mail a letter, it activates the copy subprocess after the command and response are exchanged. A pair of copy subprocesses transfers the letter in the same way as the file transfer protocol process, according to the file ttransfer sublayer.

As mentioned above, the resource process takes care of remote resources in the network in accordance with the resource protocol dependent on the resource selected by the user. Therefore, a protocol processing system using hetero-netting can be regarded as an interpreting system for network commands based on a pair of resource processes. In T-NET, a resource process in a user host is called a requester process, and in a remote host, a server process. A resource process for

a particular resource is always based on virtual terminal protocol and file transfer protocol. The virtual terminal and virtual file are the main poles of hetero-
netting.

5. PULCOM PROCESS DISTRIBUTION TO ONLINE PERSONAL MICROCOMPUTERS

Usage trends in EPICS peripheral-hosts indicate that users prefer to process private resources in their own hosts personally. Therefore, an online personal
microcomputer equipped with the PULMIC Command System (PULCOM) has been developed.
As a high-level protocol, the file transfer protocol with downloading has proved
practical for developing application systems, because of its programming environments.

5.1 PULCOM Programming Environment

The PULMIC microcomputer is installed in the display terminal and loaded with the
PULCOM command system. It consists of the PIPS Universal Computing Element
(PULCE) 6), 40 16-bit registers, a 32 bit x 16K-word microprogram memory (PM), a
256K-byte main memory (MM), a cartridge magnetic tape, and a timer and communication lines connected to the display terminal and center-host to provide users
with the TSS environment. An online personal microcomputer is used to provide
the user with the following software tools:

(1) File system
(2) Text editor, language system
(3) Loader
(4) Run time subroutines
(5) Debugging aid.

The PULCOM approach is not stand-alone, but online in order to utilize cross
software, especially file systems and language systems, of the center-host.
Application program debugging and running processes can only be distributed from
the center-host to online personal computers. PULCOM is also available to other
users of the center-host in order to utilize PULMIC remotely from a TSS terminal.
A program being executed in the microcomputer can access resources of the center-
host.

The following cross software can be used in the center-host to develop an
application system and to develop PULCOM itself:

(1) Microprogram assembler: general macro-assembler capable of accepting the
instruction definition set for any particular microprogram memory.

(2) Data description assembler: general data-assembler for main memory which
usually stores intermediate language programs, i.e., minicomputer TOSBAC-40C
object programs, etc.

(3) Simulator: PULMIC simulator with absolutely loadable PM image files and
linkable MM image files, both resident in the center host.

5.2 Four Basic PULMIC Connections

PULCOM has four operation modes corresponding to the four basic PULMIC-to-center-
host connection, as shown in Fig. 5. These are described below.

(1) Through mode: PULMIC does not work. The user uses the center-host TSS
from the display terminal.

(2) Stand-alone: The user uses PULMIC from the display terminal. The user
can debug microprograms and intermediate language programs.

H. Kawai

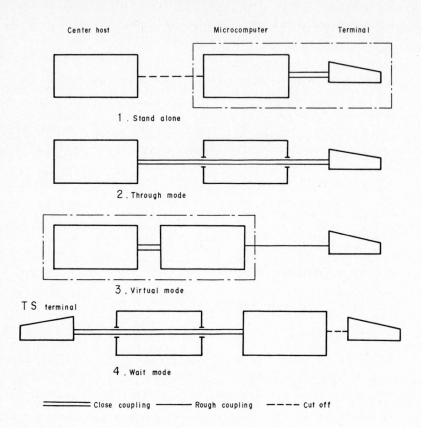

Fig. 5. Four basic connections

(3) Virtual mode: A PM or MM image file from the center-host is transferred to and stored in PM or MM. File transfer high-level protocol includes downloading or memory dumping.

(4) Wait mode: The PULMIC user can watch the processing progress of the PULCOM command issued by another user to the center-host. PULCOM performs back end processing of application systems developed by the PULMIC user.

5.3 PULCOM Command System

PULMIC has two buttons. Pushing the initialization button causes PULMIC to activate the initial program loader, and pushing the interrupt button puts PULCOM into virtual mode.

The PULCOM command set includes mode transition commands for the four modes mentioned above, file transfer command for downloading or dumping, and debugging commands. PULCOM also provides a user microprogram with run time subroutines for notifying microprogram termination to PULMIC, for display terminal input/output, for center-host input/output, for PM read/write, and for executing high-level protocol file transfer with downloading or dumping.

The information structure of a virtual file transferred over a communication line consists of memory addresses and their contents. Both are represented by hexadecimal numbers in ISO code. Therefore, while it is easy to develop a file transfer protocol process, it takes time to transfer a virtual file. In practice, it takes less than two minutes to load a 3K-byte PM image or 5K-byte image over a 9.6 kbps line. For a 77 kbps line, it takes less than one minute to load a 760 kB MM image. However, it takes the LISP machine more than one minute to load a 16 kW LISP interpreter PM image, and a half hour to load a 200 kB LISP application program over a 9.6 kbps line. Therefore, cartridge magnetic tape has been adopted to shorten the load time to six minutes.

As for a magnetic bubble data base machine, a 2M-byte MM image was loaded over a period of a week, a little at a time, over a 1.2 kbps 30 km telephone line. The experiment showed that it was practical to load 16M-bytes of data per week over a 9.6 kbps line to develop a data base.

Therefore, we can say that the PULCOM has proved sufficiently practical for further development.

6. THIN RESOURCE-DEPENDENT SUBLAYER OF HIGH-LEVEL PROTOCOL IN IPACS

The IPACS distributed heterogeneous local-line computer network is aimed at supporting software technological development in the Software Technology Center of the Information-technology Promotion Agency, Japan. The center invites researchers and engineers from four main fields: user, mainframer, software houses, and research institutes; the agency puts advanced software technology into practical use.

As each basic software technology requires its respective computer, integration for practical use should be done on IPACS. IPACS provides users with virtual terminal service and virtual document transfer service. Virtual terminal service is implemented by passing server host TSS commands through a 1.2 kbps communication line using only the 'CR' or 'ETX' string termination characters for transmission control. Logon/logoff to/from a server host are the only two new user host TSS commands provided.

Virtual document transfer service is implemented by file transfer protocol using another exclusive 48 kbps line with data link control, a subset of IBM's Binary Synchronous Communication (BSC). The big problem facing virtual Japanese

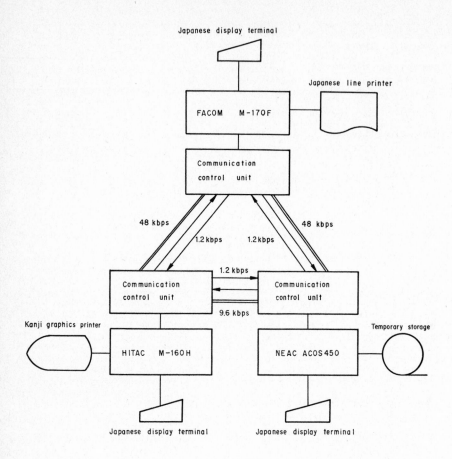

Fig. 6. Configuration of IPACS local-line computer network

document transfer was the incompatibility of printed forms control functions among hosts. A thin resource-dependent protocol sublayer has been obtained by reducing these noncompatible functions to a virtual document consisting of simple strings of Japan Industrial Standard (JIS C6226) codes covering more than six thousand Chinese characters.

Software documents and system data in Japanese can be printed out only by a utility developed on a specific host. Each of three hosts provides users with a way to input/output Japanese documents at their display terminals. Virtual documents in Japanese can be transferred by file transfer protocol, then printed out using virtual terminal protocol to activate the printing utility in a server host.

The virtual Japanese document transfer protocol sublayer in IPACS breaks down the proper processing from a file transfer protocol to a virtual terminal protocol, to thin resource-dependent high-level protocol.

7. CONCLUSION

Nine years of work on the EPICS centralized heterogeneous network suggests that separation of protocol processing from data processing and development of specialized peripheral-hosts are more important than compatibility among many heterogeneous hosts 10).

Following EPICS, three other systems, T-NET, IPACS and PULCOM, have been developed. T-NET has suggested two improvements: moving protocol processing to the front end minicomputer, and developing high-level protocol hierarchy from the standpoint of resource dependence. PULCOM has been implemented on an online personal microcomputer to provide the user with an efficient programming environment through the use of file transfer protocol with downloading. IPACS has shown how a thin resource-dependent high-level protocol can be developed through the example of a virtual Japanese document transfer protocol sublayer which reduces the incompatible printed form control functions.

The quickest way to heterogeneous local computer networking is not to establish compatibility over a wide range of resources among hosts, but to reduce noncompatibility to a specific, thin resource-dependent sublayer of high-level protocol.

References

1) H. Kawai & A. Fujimasa: Use of High Level Protocols in EPICS, Trans. IECE of Japan, Vol.E59, No.6, pp.7-13, June 1976

2) H. Nishino: PIPS PROJECT-BACKGROUND AND OUTLINE -, Proc 4th IJCPR, pp.1152-1161, November 1978

3) J.M. Burk and J.E. Schoover: Computer system maintainability at the Lawrence Livermore Laboratory, Proc. EJCC, pp.263-272, 1972

4) An introduction to the MERIT computer network, INWG-G134, University of Michigan, October 1976

5) H. Kawai et al: Front-end processing of user protocol with public telephone network, Proc. 4th ICCC, pp.663-668, 1978

6) H. Iizuka et al.: Development of a high performance universal computing element - PULCE, AFIPS Proc. NCC, Vol.47, pp.1255-1264, 1978

7) T. Uemura et al: The design and Implementation of a Magnetic-Bubble Database

Machine, Information Processing, IFIP Congress 80, pp.433-438, 1980

8) R.S. Gardell et al: Network Front End Processors: A Viable Approach to Network Interfacing, Trends and Applications 1976: Computer Networks, NBS, IEEE Computer Society, 76 CH 1143-7C, pp.113-120, November 1976

9) Reference Model of Open System Interconnection, ISO/TC97/SC16N227, August, 1979

10) R.F. Sproll & D. Cohen: High-Level Protocols, Proc. IEEE, Vol.66, No.11, pp.1371-1386, November 1978

LOCAL COMPUTER NETWORKS
P.C. Ravasio, G. Hopkins and N. Naffah (editors)
North-Holland Publishing Company
© IFIP, 1982

ADMINISTRATOR CONTENTION
OPTICAL RADIAL NETWORK - ACORN -

T. Kunikyo, T. Ozeki

Toshiba R & D Center
Kawasaki, Japan

Optical passive star networks are characterized by high Bandwidth Length (Bw-L) product, high reliability and reasonably
large station number. This paper presents two optical star
networks with combined packet switching and circuit switching capabilities: ACORN and RACORN. ACORN's packet switching is characterized by simplicity and RACORN's packet
switching is characterized by high Bw-L product. Both networks adopt ordered time-slot assignment controlled by an
administrator which is selected on contention basis from
among the stations. Analysis has shown that both packet
switching mechanisms are applicable to real time systems.

1. INTRODUCTION

LAN (Local Area Network) systems are expected to be prevalent in the near future
in offices or plants. They will connect many resources and will carry many useful data among them. These expectations are brought about by recent LSI technology progress. The price for logic circuits and memories has been dramatically
reduced year by year. On the other hand, the labor cost has been rising. Therefore, it is a natural expectation that, as the first step, there will be many
computers installed in offices or plants in the near future to promote efficiency
and to improve the quality of the work to be done there. The second step is to
connect these resources by LANs to realize automated offices or plants.

General requirements for LAN to realize future offices or plants are as follow:
1) Capability of handling various kinds of data (code, image or speech)
2) High efficiency and wide bandwidth
3) Short response time
4) Capability of connecting a large number of stations
5) Wide service area
6) Low cost and small space requirement
7) Network expandability
8) RAS
   ○ high noise immunity
   ○ immunity from domino effect failure
   ○ failure isolation and on-line recovery
   ○ distributed bus access mechanism
   ○ distributed power source.

An example is the Ethernet[1], which satisfies most of these requirements. High
efficiency, large station number, small station size and low cost can be expected.
Especially, it contains no active element in the common bus and consequently it
is free from domino effect failure. Bus access mechanism is CSMA/CD and is distributed among stations. There is no central station as a single point of failure. However it seems clear that a passive local computer network, requiring
Bw-L products significantly in excess of a few MHz.km, will be a fiber optical

network in some form. Additionally, fiber optical cable merits are light weight, small diameter and electromagnetic noise immunity. Fibernet[2] has been proposed as a fiber optical network. However, it will not suffice for real time applications, so long as it adopts the CSMA/CD protorol.

This paper presents two optical networks named ACORN (Administrator Contention Optical Radial Network) and RACORN (Reservation ACORN). ACORN is characterized by real time applicability, low cost and simplicity. RACORN is characterized by real time applicability, network diameter insensitive response time and high Bw.L products. Both networks have wavelength division multiplex circuit switching capability.

2. THE MODEL

In fiber optical local networks, network toplogy is of major importance. Straightforward substitution of fiber optical components into the Ethernet runs into a problem wherein the access coupler insertion loss must be very low, in order to accommodate a useful number of stations. On the other hand, the passive star configuration has two main advantages. It permits a much larger number of stations to be connected than does a linear system with comparable component losses; and transmission loss between any pair of transmitter and receiver, including those in the same station, is theoretically equal. Consequently, receiver design is easier than that for the linear system. Consequently, the star configuration was adopted.

The next point to consider is the switching mode. The efficiency of a network depends on the relationship between its switching mode and message length distribution. In the present networks, short data bursts are transmitted by packet switching and long data groups or image data groups are transmitted by circuit switching. Both switching mechanisms are implemented by wavelength division multiplex technology on a single fiber cable.

Several wavelengths are assigned to line switching and line switching is controlled by the packet switching network.

The packet switching portion of this network is intended to be appropriate to real time systems. Therefore, slot access mechanism is realized by ordered system. This is accomplished as follows. There is only one active administrator in the network. The rest of the administrators in each of the stations are kept inactive by the slot information, which is generated by the active administrator. When the stations in the network are powered sequentially, the administrator of the first powered station becomes activated and other stations' administrators are inactive. If the power to the active administrator is turned off, another administrator becomes activated by the time out function. Since each administrator is assigned a different time out period, only one administrator becomes activated and the rest of the administrators are kept inactivated as before. The administrator function is slot generation. Two network systems are proposed with different slot access mechanisms in the following.

The first network is characterized by simplicity. The administrator generates the Frame Header (FH) shown in Figure 1 as the basis of data transmission and

FH: Frame Header
SP: Substitution Pulse

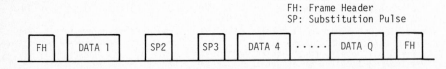

Figure 1
ACORN Frame Structure

reception. Each station is assigned a sequence number to draw in order and a station with a packet ready for transmission counts variable length slots from the FH
and transmits the packet on its slot. Other stations, which do not have a packet
ready for transmission or are not powered, do nothing. The administrator is always searching for such stations. When it finds one by detecting that no data
has been transmitted within a certain period after the end point of the preceeding
packet, it sends out a Substitution Pulse (SP) and the next station takes a turn
in transmitting a packet. ACORN (Administrator Contention Optical Radial Network) is an optical star network, whose configuration is a combination of this
packet switching network and wavelength division multiplex circuit switching
network.

The second network is characterized by high Bandwidth-Length (Bw-L) product. The
frame structure, shown in Figure 2, is divided into two areas, the reservation

RH: Reservation Header
EH: Execution Header

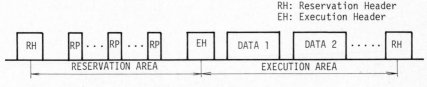

Figure 2
RACORN Frame Structure

area and the execution area. The administrator generates the Reservation Header
(RH) and the Execution Header (EH) as the basis of data transmission and reception. Individual slots in the reservation area are permanently assigned to an
individual station. Any station, which has a packet ready for transmission, sends
out a Reservation Pulse (RP) in its slot to reserve several slots in the execution area. The station watches other stations' RPs and counts up the number of
the slots preceding its assigned slots. After the reservation area, the administrator generates an EH and the station counts the number of slots from EH and
sends out the packets in its reserved slots. Since the frame structure, shown in
Figure 2, should be established at the star-coupler by signals from various stations, and the transmission delay between a station and the star-coupler varies
according to the distance involved, a station must adjust the transmission timing
so that its packet may exactly fit its assigned slot.

RACORN (Reservation ACORN) is an optical star network, whose configuration is a
combination of this packet switching network and a wavelength division multiplex
circuit switching network.

3. ANALYSIS

The performances for the four network systems (ACORN, RACORN, Ethernet and Fibernet) were analyzed and their efficiency and response time are compared. Parameters are packet length, the number of stations, bandwidth and network diameter.
It is assumed that every station has a packet ready for transmission at any time.
Several parameters are introduced, as follows:

    P: packet length including preamble, header and trailer.
    C: clock frequency
    T: turn around time (twice the propagation delay between stations)
    Q: number of stations
    H: frame header length and Reservation Pulse length
    G: guard time length at the end of Reservation Pulse and data

The ARCORN transmission diagram is shown in Figure 3. Frame length F, efficiency

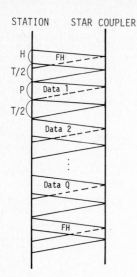

Figure 3
ACORN Transmission Diagram

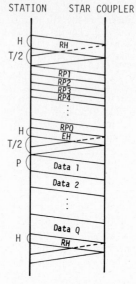

Figure 4
RACORN Transmission Diagram

E, response time R, and effective bandwidth B are expressed as

$$F = H/C + (Q+1)T/2 + QP/C$$

$$E = \frac{QP}{FC}$$

$$R = F + T/2$$

$$B = CE$$

The RACORN transmission diagram is shown in Figure 4. RACORN's F, E, R and B are expressed as

$$F = (2+Q)H/C + T + QP/C + 2QG/C$$

$$E = \frac{QP}{FC}$$

$$R = 2F + T/2$$

$$B = CE$$

Ethernet's or Fibernet's E and B are expressed[1],[2] as

$$E = \frac{P/C}{P/C + WT}$$

$$W = \frac{1-A}{A} , \quad A = (1 - \frac{1}{Q})^{(Q-1)}$$

$$B = CE$$

The ACORN, Ethernet and Fibernet behavior is similar, in that their efficiency is sensitive to clock frequency. As the clock frequency increases, the fixed length packet transmission time decreases. On the other hand, idle time between packets for ACORN and collision handling time for Ethernet/Fibernet are not affected by the clock frequency and are constant.

Figures 5 and 6 display efficiency curves and effective bandwidth curves, respectively. ACORN and Ethernet/Fibernet efficiency drops as clock frequency increases. On the other hand, RACORN efficiency is insensitive to the clock frequency. Because of the efficiency drop, ACORN and Ethernet/Fibernet effective bandwidth shows saturation as the clock frequency increases. On the other hand, RACORN's effective bandwidth increases in proportion to clock frequency.

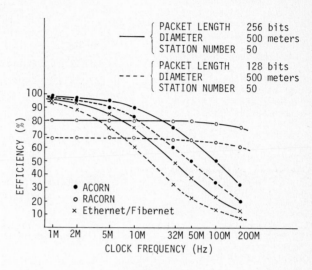

Figure 5
Efficiency - Clock Frequency Tradeoff

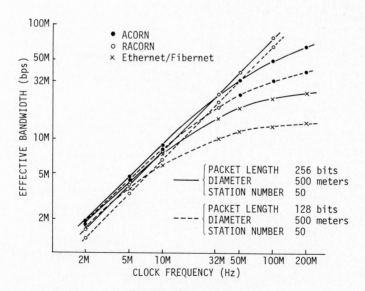

Figure 6
Effective Bandwidth - Frequency Tradeoff

Figure 7 suggests a similar result. At a small network diameter, RACORN's efficiency is lower than that of others. However at a large network diameter, RACORN's efficiency is higher than that of the others because of its insensitivity to network diameter. These three curves show that RACORN's Bw-L is larger than that of the others. Figure 8 simply shows that a long packet is transmitted efficiently, because the percentage of idle time between packets or collision handle time decreases with the increase in packet length.

Figure 9 shows that efficiency is insensitive to the number of stations. Figures 10, 11 and 12 show that response time is short at a high clock frequency, a small station number and a short packet length, respectively.

Figure 13 shows that the ACORN response time increases as network diameter increases, because of the turn around time. On the other hand, RACORN response time is almost constant, even at 10 km network diameter. A 1 ms response time is possible for the following parameter combination: 5 km ∿ 10 km diameter, 256 bit packet length, 32 Mbps clock frequency and 50 stations. This suggests that RACORN is applicable for process control systems.

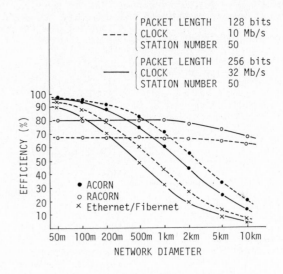

Figure 7
Efficiency - Network Diameter Tradeoff

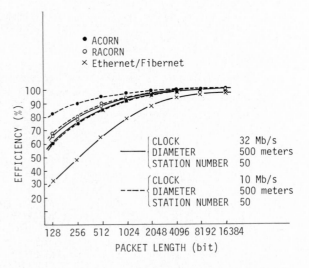

Figure 8
Efficiency - Packet Length Trade off

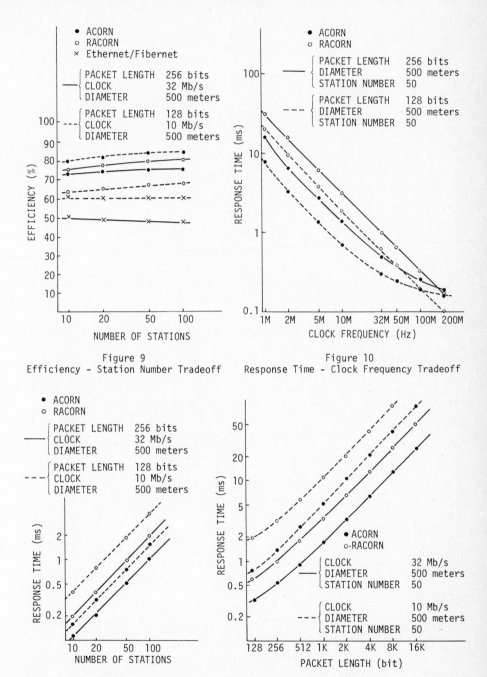

Figure 9
Efficiency - Station Number Tradeoff

Figure 10
Response Time - Clock Frequency Tradeoff

Figure 11
Response Time - Station Number Tradeoff

Figure 12
Response Time - Packet Length Tradeoff

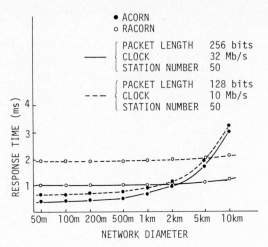

Figure 13
Response Time - Network Diameter Tradeoff

4. CONCLUSION

It seems clear that a passive local computer network requiring high Bw-L products
will require a fiber optics technology. For topology, passive star configuration
has an advantage in allowing a large number of stations. To be used in a real
time application, bus access mechanism should be an ordered system, and the administration function should be distributed among all stations for reliability,
from which only one administrator need be activated at any one time. Based on
these concepts, two optical star networks, ACORN and RACORN have been presented
and their performance analysed in comparison with Ethernet/Fibernet performance.
ACORN's packet switching is characterized by simplicity. RACORN's packet switching is characterized by high Bandwidth-Length product and network diameter insensitive response time. In addition to these packet switching mechanisms, both networks incorporate a wavelength division multiplex circuit switching mechanism.
It is expected that these networks will provide efficient and fast communication
media for offices and plants in the future. Since each network emphasizes different advantages, the decision as to which one to use will be determined by specific
requirements and economics for each application.

5. ACKNOWLEDGEMENTS

This work has been supported by the Agency of Industrial Science and Technology,
Ministry of International Trade and Industry, under Optical Measurement and Control System project.

REFERENCES

(1) R. M. Metcalfe and D. R. Boggs, "Ethernet: Distributed Switching for Local
    Computer Networks," COM ACM 19(7), pp.395 ∿ 404, (July, 1976).

(2) E. G. Rawson and R. M. Metcalfe, "Fibernet: Multimode Optical Fibers for
    Local Computer Networks," IEEE Trans. Commun. COM-26(7), PP.983 ∿ 990 (July,
    1978).

LOCAL COMPUTER NETWORKS
P.C. Ravasio, G. Hopkins and N. Naffah (editors)
North-Holland Publishing Company
© IFIP, 1982

TRANSMISSION IN A SYNCHRONOUS TOKEN RING

H.R. Müller and H. Keller

IBM Zurich Research Laboratory
8803 Rüschlikon
Switzerland

H. Meyr

Technical University RWTH
5100 Aachen
W. Germany

A synchronous token ring is the subnetwork technology chosen
for the experimental local-area network as directed and implemented at the IBM Zurich Research Laboratory. The following
key points are addressed: 1) Wiring concept; 2) code selection
and, 3) ring synchronization by means of phase-lock loops.
Wiring of a single ring is based on a two-level hierarchy with
passive or active distribution panels placed at convenient
locations in a building. Stations are connected to the distribution panels by means of relays (passive panel) or via active
panels via electronic gates in a star-type arrangement.

INTRODUCTION

Local-area networks allow fast and efficient communication between information
systems clustered in a locality [1,2]. The low-cost in-house high-bandwidth technology can be used to provide distributed switching. In this paper, we discuss
transmission and synchronization aspects of a token ring operating at a data rate
of 4 Mbit/s, as we have studied in an experimental system at the IBM Zurich
Research Laboratory.

Synchronous transmission was chosen, since it allows operation at lower signal/
noise ratios than asynchronous start/stop operation, thus allowing for longer
transmission distances. Asynchronous packet-burst operation with preambles was
rejected due to synchronization delay.

Several transmission codes were evaluated. The two-level differential Manchester
code was chosen, since it is simple to implement, provides low jitter, and frame
delimiters can be easily created with code violations.

There are three ways to achieve synchronous transmission. First, no master clock
is provided, the frequency is established by mutual phase-lock loop (PLL) synchronization, and hence stability and synchronization time depend on the ring length
[3]. Second, all stations use their own quartz oscillator to send, and are synchronized to the upstream station with a phase-lock loop. The frequency differences
between stations are compensated by inserting or deleting a bit from a special
header field when buffer overflow or underflow occurs, and by using an elastic
buffer at the receive side. The elastic buffer required at every station to compensate for quartz effects, causes a delay, which degrades performance. Third, the
approach we have chosen uses a master clock and requires only one elastic buffer
at this location. The ring adapter which provides this clock is identical with the
one where the active monitor function is located, i.e., the function guaranteeing
integrity of the token operation as described in the companion paper [4]. When
another adapter has to assume the role of the active monitor, e.g., in case of
monitor failure, then this adaptor will provide the clock.

RING STRUCTURE

In order to achieve long distance and ease of wiring, a two-level wiring structure
was chosen, see Fig. 1. The ring is powered by the active stations. Distribution

RING TOPOLOGY

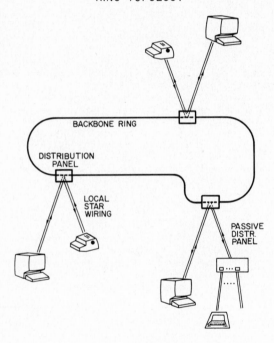

Figure 1
Ring Topology

panels, Fig. 2, will be installed at strategic points of a building, from where
star-type wiring (cable bundling) is foreseen. The section between a terminal and
distribution panel is called a local lobe, which normally consists of two twisted
pairs. The local lobes comprise two sections; station to wall plug and wall plug
to distribution panel. The length of these local lobes can extend to approximately
500 feet. The limitation is given by crosstalk. This approach is similar to the one
described by Saltzer and Progran in [5]. With our approach, the worst-case ring
distance is reduced to the main-ring distance plus twice the maximum distance
between distribution panel and station. With the relatively long station to distri-
bution-panel distance, wiring of a building is facilitated, since the main-ring

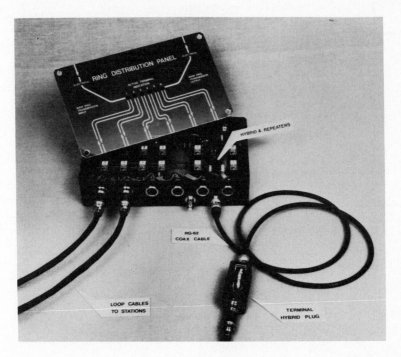

Figure 2
Experimental Distribution Panel

cable between distribution panels does not have to be extended to every office,
thus resulting in a significant distance gain. The energization of the relays in
the distribution panels is accomplished via a phantom circuit and current sources
provided at the station side (Fig. 3). By providing transformer coupling on all
transmission links, good protection of the relays is achieved. Our experiments
with the model described above have shown that relays can be powered reliably
over 1,000 feet over twisted-pair cables.

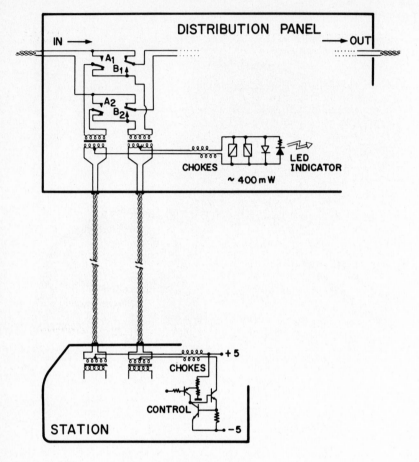

Figure 3
Relay Powering Concept

TRANSMISSION AND CABLE CHARACTERISTICS

Coding

The objective is to find a transmission code which results in a simple transceiver
design. Due to varying cable lengths, a fixed equalizer cannot be used. Complex
equalizers and scramblers are ruled out to reduce cost and synchronization
problems.

Codes with two amplitude levels allow the simplest receiver/transmission circuit
since they do not require adaptation to different attenuations and automatic gain
control, as the decision threshold is insensitive to in-put-level variations.

To get a simple timing recovery circuit at the receiver, codes with high transition density are preferable. In addition, a zero dc component of the code is needed for ac coupling. A further important requirement in a token ring is a small delay per station to achieve high efficiency. This rules out block codes which are word organized.

The above requirements leave us with basically two codes: the Manchester code and the Miller code [6]. The latter was ruled out, because it has a low-frequency component, resulting in additional jitter when ac coupling is used. The Manchester code [7] fulfills all the requirements mentioned. AC coupling also allows the use of different cables with different characteristic impedances in different sections of the ring. The Manchester code is also well suited for optical transmission. The differential Manchester code allows for the interchange of a and b wire in a wire pair without leading to data errors. The transmission efficiency of a Manchester code can be greatly improved at no substantial increase in hardware complexity if predistortion is used [7,8].

Code and predistortion are depicted in Fig. 4. Simulations were made to determine the optimum predistortion parameters. Since the cable attenuation in the MHz region is mainly determined by skin effect, it is proportional to the square root of the frequency [9,10]. Good agreement between simulation and experimental results is obtained when dc attenuation is included.

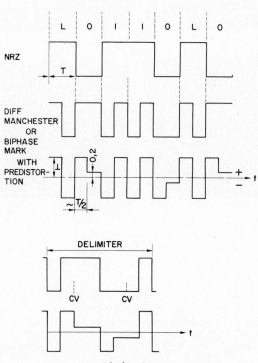

Figure 4
Differential Manchester Code with Predistortion

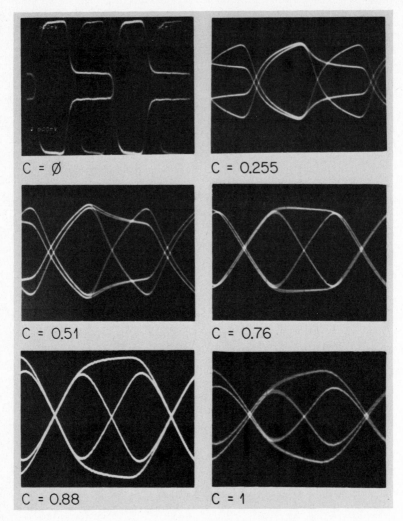

Figure 5
Experimental Eye Patterns for Various Cable Lengths

Parameter: C; C = 1 → 31.5 dB attentuation

Figure 5 shows experimental eye patterns for the Manchester code with pre-distor-
tion as a function of the normalized cable parameter C; C being proportional
to cable length. C = 1 corresponds to 31.5 dB attenuation. Experiments confirmed
that, from a signal-distortion point of view, maximum attenuations up to 30 dB
can be tolerated with code violations as frame delimiters (Fig. 4). A simple
high-pass filter at the receiver allows transmission distance to be increased
even further, corresponding to an attenuation of 35 dB. However, cable crosstalk
will limit us to lower attenuations [11].

Cable Characteristics

The parameters determining the maximum distance are crosstalk and attenuation.
Far-end and near-end crosstalk need to be analyzed [11] to select the proper
cables. Analysis has shown that distances of 4000 feet and more can only be
obtained by using low-capacitance cable [12,13] with maximum attenuations not
exceeding 5 dB/1000 feet at 4 MHz. Since two wire pairs have to be provided per
station, near-end crosstalk occurs on the cable between station and wall plug.
Near-end crosstalk can be minimized by providing an aluminum shield around each
pair, and by combined twisting. This technique has proven to be quite successful
in the T2 carrier system. Lower attenuation is achieved by decreasing the ratio
of conductor material to insulation material. When using cable bundles between
wall plugs and distribution panels, far-end crosstalk has also to be considered
(see Fig. 6).

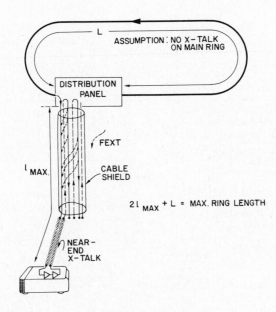

Figure 6
Worst-case Far-end Crosstalk Situation

Transceiver Structure

The basic structure of the transceiver is shown in Fig. 7. It basically consists of four units: sender, receiver with energy detector, bit synchronizer, and control logic. The receiver provides amplification for the incoming signals. The energy detector is needed to indicate loss of energy. Energy outage is indicated if the cable has a short/open, or if a station is inserted or removed. The sender is of the current-source type and is impedance-matched to avoid reflections. The control logic controls the insertion, the local wrap (between station and distribution panel) and the freeze of a PLL during energy outage, as well as synchronization. The insert control and synchronization will be discussed in the following section.

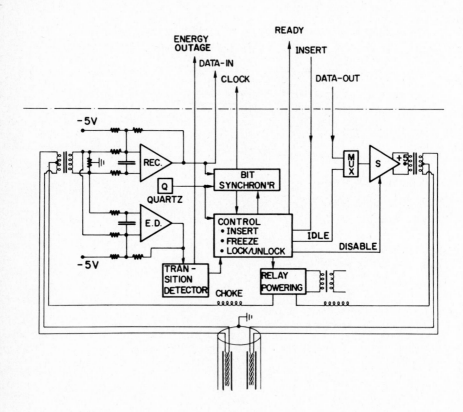

Figure 7
Basic Structure of Ring Transceiver

The sender is shown in Fig. 8. Predistortion of the send signal is achieved by applying the sum or the difference of two current sources I_1 and I_2. The dc component is eliminated by feeding from both sides of a transformer, depending on whether the signal is one or zero. To reduce crosstalk, the risetimes are purposely increased. The receiver is built with high-speed comparators and a low-pass filter at the input. To determine an energy outage properly, a transition-count averager is used. The number of input transitions must reach at least 80% of the guaranteed bit transitions of the Manchester code.

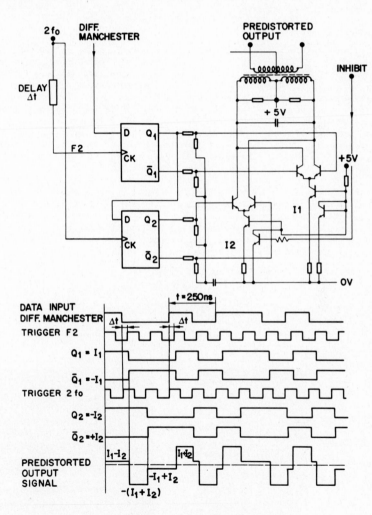

Figure 8
Experimental Sender

A maximum ring distance of 4500 feet is obtained under the following assumptions:
a mean crosstalk attenuation for a single disturber of 72 dB at 4 MHz and a maximum of two significant disturbers; a minimum peak signal to rms-noise ratio of
23 dB to allow 8 dB for receiver imperfections, clock jitter and clock phase
offset; 4 dB for relay and transformer losses; another 2.3 σ of 6 dB for signal
level; receiver tolerance and attenuation variation (temperature). A further
assumption is that the theory outlined in [11] which states the requirement that
99% of all systems meet the specification is met. Longer distance can be achieved
either by shorter local lobes, and/or triax cable between distribution panels,
and/or by optical transmission.

Station Insertion/Removal

The insertion of stations into the ring or their removal causes a temporary loss
of synchronization. To allow fast resynchronization, we adopted a mechanism by
which the phase-locked loops are slaved to a master clock. Before a station can be
inserted into the ring, the local lobe is tested. If successful, the station
insert command from the higher level will be used to initialize insert. To allow
for sufficient relay settling time, the phase-lock loop is disabled for 1 msec.
Measurements showed that relay bouncing does not exceed 0.7 msec. After the
1 msec time interval with the energy detector on, phase synchronization starts,
and is accomplished in less than 50 µsec provided no other resynchronization is
in progress. After 2 msec, the transceiver is set into repeat mode, the sender is
enabled, and the higher level is alerted by a ready signal.

Should acquisition not be achieved within 2 msec, e.g., due to a longer relay
switch time, or some frequency deviation on the receive side due to a resynchronization process upstream, another time interval of maximum 1 msec is granted by
the insert control logic. During the phase acquisition, the frequency acquisition aid is disabled. It is basically only used to bring the VCO close (within
$1^\circ/oo$) to the quartz frequency during power-up of a station.

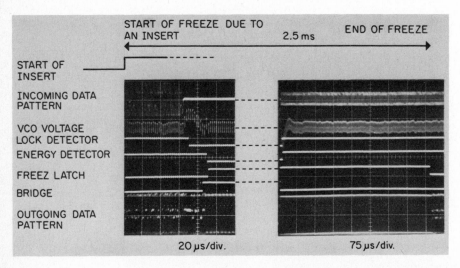

Figure 9
Time Sequence of Freeze Process (After Station Insertion)

The next active station downstream of the inserting station senses the insertion event by an energy outage, and disables its own phase-locked loop. From now on, its frequency acquisition aid is enabled to maintain a stable clock on the downstream section over a long time. The PLL phase detector is disabled during energy outage. During the 2.5 msec freeze time, the station sends an idle pattern downstream to ensure energy and clock integrity. After the freeze period, normal operation is resumed given that energy is detected. The freezing action caused by an energy outage due to an inserting/removing station upstream is illustrated in Fig. 9. Resynchronization cannot be resumed in the freeze mode because relay bouncing can extend to over 1 msec when a station is disconnected from the ring.

Removal of a station demands no sequenced control; the phase-locked loop in the next active station downstream freezes its frequency as described above. To ensure that during short-term data outages (no transitions for at least five bit intervals), the next station downstream is not affected, fill-bits are inserted at the sender.

TIMING RECOVERY CIRCUITS

Principles of Operation and Building Blocks

To obtain the baseband data timing, information is derived from the data waveform itself, utilizing a phase-lock loop (Fig. 10). Every elementary signal of the differential Manchester code has a regular end-bit zero transition and a (random) mid-bit transition, if two consecutive symbols are identical. Since the eye pattern of the Manchester encoded waveform is not symmetrical (see Fig. 5), timing recovery should only use the regular end-bit transition to obtain minimum jitter.

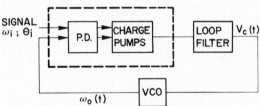

Figure 10
Block Diagram of a Charge Pump PLL

In our design, synchronization and Manchester ambiguity resolution is achieved by code violation in the manner shown in Fig. 4. Closer examination of this procedure reveals that a considerable amount of hardware would be needed to distinguish the mid-bit from the end-bit transitions. Consequently, for ease of implementation it was decided to utilize a phase detector operating on every zero transition.

The phase detector in Fig. 11 is widely used for bit synchronization in disc drives. It can be implemented easily with standard TTL circuits up to 8 MHz. The phase detector generates an error signal only if there is a zero transition in the signal. In addition to the building blocks of a conventional sequential logic phase detector (shown within dashed lines), we find a one-shot (OS) with a pulse width of $T/4$ (T: length of an elementary signal of the Manchester code), an enable flip-flop and a pulse-shaping circuit that produces a pulse at every signal transition. Every such pulse sets the enable flip-flop true ($\stackrel{\wedge}{=}$ High). Assume now the data signal leads the VCO, then, the negative-going edge of the OS sets the latch

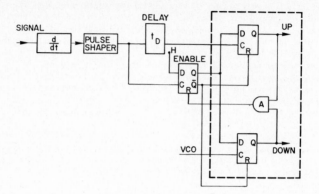

Figure 11
Sequential Logic Phase Detector for Waveforms with Randomly Missing Transitions

Up true after exactly T/4 seconds. The next negative-going VCO transition resets
the enable flip-flop. Conversely, when after a data transition pulse the enable
flip-flop is true and the VCO is leading the data signal, the Down latch is set
true. After T/4 seconds, the OS resets the Down latch. Thus, the stable equilibrium point of the synchronizer is T/4 seconds delayed with respect to the
incoming data transitions; the on-time of either terminal Up or Down is proportional to the phase error defined with respect to this reference point. Note,
that in any case, the synchronizer is active only if a signal transition has
occurred.

The binary phase-detector signals are converted into analog signals by means of
current pumps. The error signal to the loop filter consists of rectangular pulses
with duration proportional to the phase error. Any actuation of the current pump
gives rise to transients in the loop-filter output. In a second-order loop, these
transients can easily be so large as to overload the VCO, thus severely limiting
the applicability of this type of loop. Filters must be added to reduce this so-
called frequency ripple [14]. The loop is then at least of order three. The filter

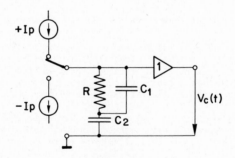

Figure 12
Loop Filter

configuration of Fig. 12 was employed in our design. The filter transfer function of Fig. 12 is an impedance,

$$Z_F(s) = \frac{Vc(s)}{Ip(s)} = \frac{1 + s\tau_2}{sc_2 \cdot [1 + s\tau_2/b]} \tag{1}$$

with

$$\tau_2 = C_1 \, R \cdot [1 + C_2/C_1]$$

$$b = 1 + C_2/C_1 \; .$$

Since the filter has two poles, the phase-lock loop is of order three.

The initial acquisition of frequency is a difficult practical problem since the narrow PLL loop bandwidth required for jitter reduction severely restricts the pull-in range. A method for rapid and reliable frequency acquisition is to add a frequency detector to the traditional phase detector as shown in Fig. 13.

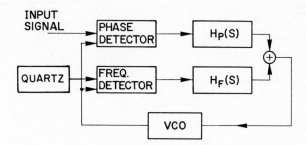

Figure 13
PLL with Phase and Frequency Detector

With a large initial VCO frequency offset, the phase detector has essentially zero dc output, and the frequency detector generates a voltage proportional to the frequency difference between the VCO and input signal driving that difference to zero. The phase detector takes over when the difference is small, completing acquisition. Among the various possible frequency detectors, the rotational phaser frequency detector [15] is particularly well suited for our purposes. Operation of this frequency detector can be briefly outlined as follows: The quartz oscillator provides the 16 and 8 MHz clocks. The latter is divided into four quadrants A, B, C and D as shown in Fig. 14. The frequency detector monitors the rotation of the phaser of the 8 MHz PLL clock with respect to the four quadrants. Let the k-th cycle of the VCO be denoted by a subscript k. The situation $\omega_i > \omega_0$ can be recognized by observation of $C_k \rightarrow B_{k+1}$, in which case the frequency detector generates a positive pulse. Similarly, if $B_k \rightarrow C_{k+1}$ is observed, the frequency detector generates a negative pulse in recognition of $\omega_i < \omega_0$. Note that the rotational phaser frequency detector possesses the very desirable feature that in lock, no error signal is generated since the transition $B_k \rightarrow C_{k+1}$ or vice versa is impossible, provided the phase error is small.

In our ring, every station is basically capable of functioning as a frequency master, i.e., there is a quartz oscillator with frequency ω_0 at every station. Therefore, rather than deriving the frequency-detector signal from the incoming

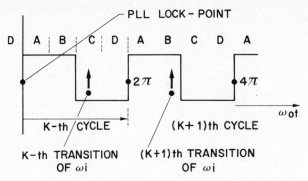

Figure 14
Division of VCO Cycle into Four Quadrants

waveform, the local quartz oscillator is used for this purpose, thus greatly
simplifying the hardware design and fastening synchronization. The local quartz
is also used as insert control sequencer. A block diagram of the complete bit
synchronizer is shown in Fig. 15.

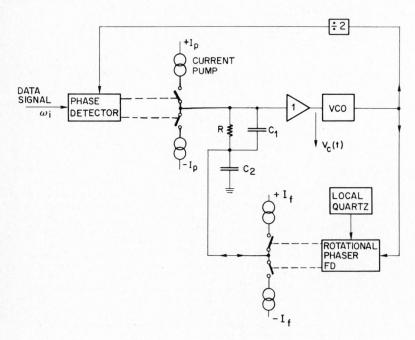

Figure 15
Block Diagram of a PLL with Additional Frequency Detector

Analysis

Charge pumps are used to obtain accurate Pll filter parameters [14]. An exact analysis of the charge pump PLL has to take into account the time-varying nature of the circuit: The dynamic equations of the loop during the on-time of the charge pumps are different from those when the pumps are inactive. If the loop bandwidth is narrow enough with respect to the input frequency, an approximate analysis based on averaged response, time-continuous operation is permissible [14]. There are, however, certain features arising from the discontinuous operation that need attention, even for narrow bandwidth. The primary features are loop stability and in particular, frequency ripple.

We start with an averaged response (over a bit interval), time-continuous operation, and shall later discuss frequency ripple. The average current over a cycle of the input signal is

$$i_d = I_p \cdot \frac{\Theta e}{2\pi} \,. \tag{2}$$

The VCO control voltage is given by

$$V_c(s) = I_d(s) \cdot Z_F(s) = \frac{Ip}{2\pi} \; Z_F(s) \cdot \Theta_e(s) \,, \tag{3}$$

where $I_d(s)$ is the Laplace transform of $i_d(t)$, and similarly for the other symbols. The control law of the VCO is given by

$$\Theta_0(s) = K_0 \, V_c(s) \cdot 1/s \,. \tag{4}$$

The open-loop transfer function of the PLL with the loop-filter transfer function of Eq. (1) equals

$$G_3(s) = \frac{K}{0_2} \; \frac{1}{s^2} \; \frac{1 + s\tau_2}{1 + s\tau_{2/b}} \tag{5}$$

with

$$K = \frac{Ip \, K_0 \, R}{2\pi} \,.$$

The Bode diagram corresponding to Eq. (5) is shown in Fig. 16. The transfer function $G_3(s)$ of the third-order loop has an additional pole located at $s = -b/\tau_2$ compared to a second-order loop. Location of the additional pole must be chosen so that good frequency-ripple suppression as well as little peak gain of the closed-loop transfer functions $H_3(i\omega)$ are achieved. Little peak gain is very important for jitter suppression in a large chain of repeaters [16].

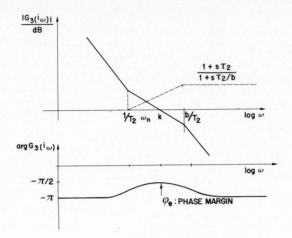

Figure 16
Bode Diagram of the Open Loop Transfer Function $G_3(s)$ of the Third-Order Loop

A look at the Bode diagram reveals that these are two conflicting requirements.
Good frequency-ripple suppression requires a pole location of b/τ_2 at the lowest
possible frequency. On the other hand, we must maintain the phase margin as large
as possible in order to minimize peaking; this dictates a pole far above the
cross-over frequency.

The closed-loop transfer function is found to be

$$H_3(p) = \frac{K\tau_2 \, (1 + p)}{p^3 \, 1/b + p^2 + K\tau_2 \cdot p + K\tau_2} \quad , \qquad (6)$$

where p is the normalized Laplace operator $p = s\tau_2$.

Peak gain as a function of b is plotted for several values of $K \cdot \tau_2 = 4\xi^2$ in
Fig. 17. For large values of $K\tau_2$, we observe a very distinct threshold behavior.
As an example, take $K\tau_2 = 100$. For $b > 200$, the peak gain practically assumes its
value for $b \to \infty$, that is, the same peak gain as the second-order loop with
damping $K\tau_2 = (2\xi)^2$. The important conclusion that can be drawn from Fig. 17 is
that for reasonable values of $b > 200$, the third-order loop shows no degradation
with respect to peaking, when compared to a second-order loop.

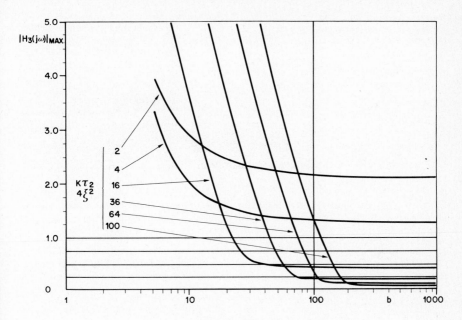

Figure 17
Peak Gain of the Third-Order Loop

The rotational phaser frequency detector was qualitatively introduced in the last section. It can be characterized by the mean value of the pulses of its output, since (Fig. 18) that mean value serves to charge the integrating capacitor in the loop filter. This mean value of the current pulses depends on the phase increment per cycle of the VCO of the rotating phaser with angular frequency $(\omega_i - \omega_0)$,

$$\Delta\varphi = |\omega_i - \omega_0| \; \frac{2\pi}{\omega_0} \tag{7}$$

with $\Delta\varphi$ the absolute value of phase increment per cycle of the VCO. The phase increment $\Delta\varphi$ is the amount of phase the incoming signal advances or retards with respect to the VCO signal if the VCO signal makes a full rotation.

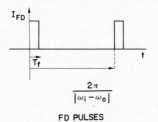

FD PULSES

I_{FD}: Amplitude of the current pulse A

T_f: Width of the current pulse

Figure 18
FD Pulses

If $\Delta\varphi < \pi/2$, then for every rotation of the phaser we observe a transition $B_k \rightarrow C_{k+1}$ or vice versa and the mean value is a linear function of the frequency difference $\Delta\omega = (\omega_i - \omega_0)$,

$$i_f = \underbrace{(I_{FD} \cdot \frac{T_f}{2\pi})}_{K_f} \cdot \Delta\omega \qquad (8)$$

with

T_f: current pulse width

i_f: mean value of current pulses

K_f: frequency detector gain.

For $|\Delta\varphi| > \pi/2$, not every phaser rotation includes a $B_k \rightarrow C_{k+1}$ transition. Assume that at the k-th cycle, the ω_i transition occurs in A_k. Now, since $\Delta\varphi > \pi/2$, there exists the possibility that $A_k \rightarrow C_{k+1}$ is observed, in which case, no pulse is generated. Maximum output of the phase detector is given for

$$\Delta\varphi = \pi/2 = \frac{\Delta\omega}{\omega_0} \cdot 2\pi \quad ,$$

i.e., a frequency difference of $\pm 25\%$.

Using the same reasoning for $|\Delta\varphi| > \pi/2$, we find a periodic frequency characteristic as depicted in Fig. 19.

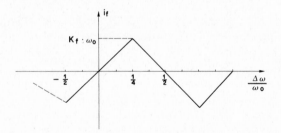

Figure 19
Characteristics of the Rotating Phasor FI

Finally, the dynamic response of the PLL, during frequency acquisition has to be investigated. The frequency detector is active only during the initial frequency-acquisition process and entirely disabled in the following tracking mode. At first sight, disabling the frequency detector seems to be an unnecessary complication since the frequency detector does not generate an error signal in the tracking mode. This indeed is true, if the frequency detector derives its information from the incoming and the VCO signals. If, instead, the frequency detector uses the local quartz as frequency reference, there always exists a frequency difference between the quartz frequency and ω_i, the frequency of the incoming signal. This difference, then, erroneously generates pulses that can be troublesome.

In the linear region of the frequency detector, the VCO input voltage equals

$$V_c(t) = \frac{1}{C_2} K_f \int_0^t \Delta\omega(t')dt' ,$$

(9)

(see Fig. 15).

From this, a first-order differential equation for the frequency difference

$$\frac{d \Delta\omega(t)}{dt} + \frac{K_0 K_f}{C_2} \Delta\omega(t) = 0$$

(10)

is obtained.

An initial error $\Delta\omega(0)$ decays exponentially with time constant

$$T_{acq} = (\frac{K_0 K_f}{C_2})^{-1} = (\frac{K_0}{C_2} \frac{I_{FD} \cdot T_F}{2\pi})^{-1} .$$

(11)

Given K_0 and C_2, the designer can realize a specific loop dynamic by appropriate choice of the current pump I_{FD} and/or the pulse width T_f without altering the in-lock loop dynamics.

The foregoing analysis is based on averaged response, time-continuous operation. As pointed out earlier, there are features, arising from the discontinuous operation, that need attention. These features are loop stability and frequency ripple. The reader interested in detailed analysis is referred to the paper by Gardner on a charge pump PLL [14]. We briefly recapitulate the results of interest in this paper.

Frequency ripple is caused by switching the current pumps on and off. In a second-order charge pump PLL, the loop filter has the transfer function

$$Z_{F2}(s) = R + \frac{1}{sC_2} .$$

(12)

Upon each cycle of the phase detector, the pump current I_p is driven into the filter which responds with an instantaneous voltage jump of $\Delta Vc = I_p R$. At the end of the charging interval, the pump current switches off and a voltage of equal magnitude occurs in the opposite direction. Frequency of the VCO follows the voltage step, so there will be a frequency excursion of

$$\Delta\omega_0 = K_0 I_p R = 2\pi K .$$

In many applications, this frequency ripple cannot be tolerated.

The situation is different for a third-order loop. The extra capacitor C_1 smoothes the discontinuous rectangular jump into a ramp-like, exponential function for each pulse.

Define $\beta = |\Delta\omega_0|_3 / |\Delta\omega_0|_2$ as the ripple-suppression factor with $|\Delta\omega_0|_2 = 2\pi K$. Gardner [14] has shown that β equals approximately

$$\beta = \frac{b-1}{\omega_i \tau_2} |\Theta_e| \qquad \omega_i = \text{input frequency} .$$

(13)

When the loop is tracking near equilibrium, the phase error $|\Theta_e|$ is small, so the frequency-ripple suppression is substantial.

Cascade of Repeaters

In a cascade of PLL timing recovery circuits, (see Fig. 20), as encountered in a ring system, accumulation of the jitter must be considered. The most severe jitter is systematic, i.e., pattern dependent and correlated at all repeaters. The problem of systematic as well as random jitter accumulation has been extensively studied in the literature, e.g., [16-18].

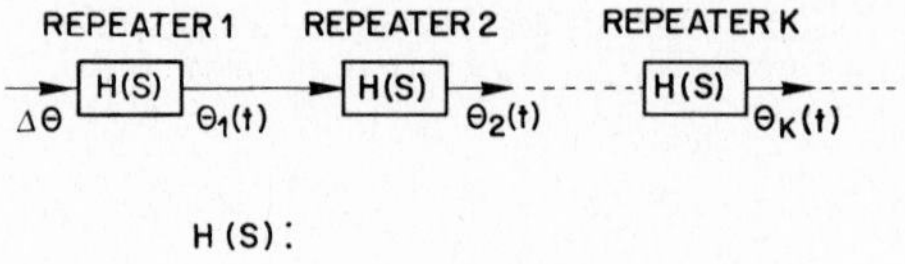

Figure 20
Linear, Deterministic Phase-transient Model for a Repeater Chain

Results for Manchester-encoded data have been reported in [7]. It was found that the limiting factor for transmission from one repeater to the next was cable attenuation and not timing jitter, provided a well-designed PLL with little peaking and a bandwidth of not greater than $0.01 \times 1/T$ is used. Using the normalized power spectral density $N_0/2$ at $\omega = 0$ computed in this paper and the results given in [7], the accumulated jitter for a given number of repeaters, loop damping ξ and loop bandwidth B_L is readily obtained. As an example take

K = 64 repeaters

ξ worst case = 5 (ξ nominal = 6)

$N_0/2 = 4 \cdot 10^{-4}$ ([7], Fig. 12)

from station to station equal cable length $\rightarrow C = 0.25$ and for loop bandwidth/data bandwidth = 0.01 the accumulated systematic jitter ([16], Fig. 3)

$$\sigma^2 = 14.9 \times 10^{-4} \qquad (\xi_{min} = 5)$$

or

$$3\sigma = 0.12 \quad .$$

Operating with every transition, the jitter power (experimental values) increases roughly by 80 resulting in a systematic accumulated jitter of

$$\sigma^2 = 0.12$$

or

$$3\sigma = 1.0 = \left(\frac{\Delta t}{T}\right)_{max} \quad .$$

for 64 stations.

The systematic jitter power is over an order of magnitude higher than the random jitter, hence the latter is neglected in the analysis.

The result shows that with a dribble-down buffer of length 5 (middle = 3), enough elasticity is achieved. The alignment jitter at the last station causes no problem, since it is only two to three times higher than the jitter power after the first station.

Limitation of total accumulated jitter is given by cycle slips. Experiments showed that σ must not exceed 0.2. Jitter reduction can be obtained by decreasing PLL bandwidth.

Besides jitter accumulation, deterministic phase transients in a cascade of repeaters must be studied, too. The phase of a repeater after insertion into the loop is completely arbitrary. Hence, if at $t = 0$, repeater 1 is inserted into the loop, the next repeater downstream sees a phase error of $\Delta\Theta$, where $\Delta\Theta$ is the random phase difference between the two repeaters.

The phase error $\varphi_k(t) \overset{\Delta}{=} \Theta_{k-1}(t) - \Theta_k(t)$ in the Laplace domain is found to be

$$\varphi_k(s) = [H^{k-1}(s) - H^k(s)] \, \Delta\Theta(s) \ . \tag{14}$$

After some algebraic manipulations, for $\varphi_k(t)$ we arrive at the approximate relation, given that $\xi \geq 4$,

$$\frac{\varphi_k(t)}{\Delta\Theta} \overset{\Delta}{=} \begin{cases} 1 - e^{-2\xi\omega_n t} & k = 1 \\ \dfrac{1}{(k-1)!} \, e^{-2\xi\omega_n t} (2\xi\omega_n t)^{k-1} & k - 1 \ . \end{cases} \tag{15}$$

Of particular interest is the maximum of $\varphi_k(t)$ as a function of k, since this value determines the worst case in bit error performance,

$$\frac{(\varphi_k)_{max}}{\Delta\Theta} = \frac{1}{(k-1)!} \, e^{-(k-1)} \cdot (k-1)^{k-1} \ . \tag{16}$$

For large values of k, the above formula can be simplified by using the Stirling formula for X!. Equation (16) results in

$$\frac{(\varphi_k)_{max}}{\Delta\Theta} = \frac{1}{\sqrt{2\pi} \sqrt{k-1}} \ . \tag{17}$$

After $\omega_n t = 7.87$ and $k = 64$, the peak error is already down to 5%, or in other words, the ring is operational again. The results for φ_{kmax} with k as parameter are shown in Fig. 21.

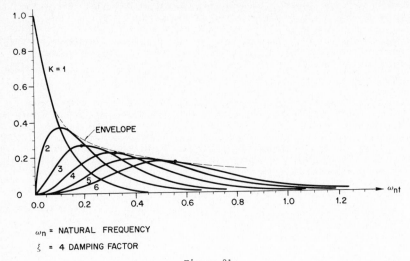

ω_n = NATURAL FREQUENCY

ξ = 4 DAMPING FACTOR

Figure 21

Phase Error $\dfrac{\varphi_k}{\Delta\Theta}$ as a Function of ω_{nt}

CONCLUSION

The experimental ring synchronization system discussed in detail above has been
operational for several months. We have shown that resynchronization after
station insertion/removal is obtained within 2.5 msec including relay switching
time. Absolute worst-case jitter analysis shows that systematic low-frequency
jitter limits the number of stations to 128 if only passive distribution panels
are used. The dynamic insert concept was thoroughly tested and found to be
reliable. The experimental model works with a ring length of 2800 feet, two
distribution panels, and cable attenuation of 10 db/1000 feet at 4 MHz with
considerable near-end crosstalk (two twisted pairs per cable) and local lobes
of 1000 feet, with error rates < 10^{-9}. As an outlook it can be stated: (i) that
the speed of the experimental transmission system is not limited to 4 Mbit/sec,
and (ii) work is in progress which allows the attachment of a station to a
distribution panel with a single-wire pair by using hybrid transformers at both
ends, and a simple preamplifier at the distribution panel which is also remotely
powered by the station.

ACKNOWLEDGEMENT

The authors are indebted to P. Bächtold for his contributions to the design and
measurements of the phase-locked loop hardware.

REFERENCES

[1] Clark, D.D., Progran, K.T. and Reed, D.P., An introduction to local-area networks. Proc. IEEE, Vol. 66 (1978) 1497-1517.

[2] Penney, B.K. and Baghdadj, A.A., Survey of computer communications loop networks: Part I, Computer communications, Vol. 2, No.4 (August 1979).

[3] Wilkes, M.V. and Wheeler, D.J., The Cambridge digital communications ring. Proceedings of the Local-Area Communications Network Symposium, Boston, May 1979.

[4] Bux, W., Closs, F., Janson, P.A., Kümmerle, K., Müller, H.R. and Rothauser, E.H., A local-area communication network based on a reliable token-ring system. This Conference.

[5] Saltzer, J.H. and Progran, K.T., A star-shaped ring network with high maintainability. Computer Networks, Vol. 4, No. 5 (Oct/Nov 1980).

[6] Severt, R.H., Encoding schemes support high-density digital data recording. Computer Design (1980) 181-190.

[7] Meyr, H., Bouten, H., Müller, H.R. and Bapst, U., Manchester coding with predistortion: An efficient and simple transmission technique in local digital ring networks. IEEE National Telecommunication Conference, December 1980.

[8] Wiedmer, A., Means of predistorting digital signals. U.S. Patent 3.980.826, Sept. 1976.

[9] Wigington, R.L. and Nahman, N.S., Transient analysis of coaxial cables considering skin effect. Proc. IRE, Vol. 45 (1957) 166-174.

[10] Braun, F., Steinlin, W. and Ryser, H., Transmission in local digital loop communication. Zurich Seminar on Digital Communication, Zurich (IEEE 78 CH 1325-0, 1978) C2.1-C2.6.

[11] Cravis, H. and Crater, T.V., Engineering of T1 carrier system repeated lines. Bell Syst. Tech. J. (May 1963).

[12] Setzer, D.E., Low capacitance multipair cable for 6.3 megabit per sec transmission system. Proceedings of ICC 72, pp. 19-19/19-23.

[13] Okamoto, K., Nods, H. and Onishi, M., High-frequency crosstalk performance of Z-type shielded cable. Proceedings of ICC 72, pp. 19-13/19-18.

[14] Gardner, F., Charge-pump phase-lock loops. IEEE Trans. Commun., Vol. COM-28, No. 11 (Nov.1980).

[15] Messerschmidt, D.G., Frequency detectors for PLL acquisition in timing and carrier recovery. IEEE Trans. Commun., Vol. COM-27, No. 9 (Sept. 1979).

[16] Shimamura, T. and Eguchi, T., An analysis of jitter accumulation in a chain of PLL timing recovery circuits. IEEE Trans. Commun., Vol. COM-25 (1977) 1027-1032.

[17] Mengali, U. and Pirani, G., Jitter accumulation in PAM systems. IEEE Trans. Commun., Vol. COM-28, No. 8 (Aug. 80) 1172.

[18] Duttweiler, D.L., The jitter performance of phase-locked loops extracting timing from baseband data waveforms. Bell Syst. Tech. J. Vol.55 (1976) 37-88.

LOCAL COMPUTER NETWORKS
P.C. Ravasio, G. Hopkins and N. Naffah (editors)
North-Holland Publishing Company
© IFIP, 1982

COMONET: AN INTRA-BUILDING DATA LINK

Thomas L. Sterling   Ronald D. Williams   James L. Kirtley, Jr.

Massachusetts Institute of Technology
Electric Power Systems Engineering Laboratory
Cambridge, Massachusetts
U.S.A.

COMONET is a local network architecture developed to support
the communication needs of distributed intra-building systems for
control and monitoring applications comprising many ports with
low communications demand. A set of specifications for this
class of data link systems is presented. Two signal paths are
used, one for arbitration and the other for data transfers. Link
arbitration and data transfer control are implemented with
distributed mechanisms. COMONET supports separate systems
simultaneously and operates in environments characterized by high
peak to average queue ratios.

I. Introduction

COMONET (**CO**ntrol and **MO**nitoring **NET**work) [1] is a local network architecture
developed to provide communications support within buildings for distributed
control and monitoring systems, including energy management, fire sensing and
alarms, intruder detection, and remote control. These types of systems may
comprise hundreds or thousands of separate components distributed within the
buildings they service. The average usage of the communications medium is low
because the communications demands of most components in such systems are
extremely low. However, the peak traffic demands can be much greater because of
the indeterminate rate of access request arrivals from the large number of
potential request sources. COMONET incorporates an arbitration mechanism for
resolving multiple link access requests using a separate signal path for control
and a distributed arbitration state data base. Link requests are made by the ports
using short pulses on the control path. The queueing order is stored in the
distributed arbitration state data base and is updated as a function of the
request pulses. Large transient queues can be managed without reduction in message
transfer efficiency using only the access request pulses to establish the queues.

COMONET was devised to provide inexpensive communications for distributed
building-oriented systems, thus extending the benefits of active energy management
systems to small commercial, and possibly residential structures. Fourteen
specifications were derived as essential characteristics of any local network
architecture intended to be used as an intra-building data link providing support
for such systems. These criteria are discussed in Section II of this paper. An
overview of the COMONET architecture is provided in Section III. An important
feature of any network is its technique for arbitration among ports contending for
network access. The arbitration mechanism employed by COMONET is atypical in the
arena of local networks and is discussed in detail in Section IV. The protocol
for data transfers among the network ports is presented in Section V. In Section
VI, methods for dealing with different types of operational pathologies are
outlined. Finally, we describe the position of COMONET in relation to other local
area networks.

II. Specifications for an Intra-building Data Link

The communications needs of control and monitoring systems within buildings are different from those of other distributed systems such as automated offices. The architecture of local networks should reflect the message traffic characteristics of the application. Therefore, the architectures of local networks for building oriented control and monitoring (BOCM) systems will be different from those of other distributed systems.

A dominant characteristic of BOCM systems is that they may comprise thousands of spatially distributed components. The components may be in close proximity to each other or be separated by as much as a kilometer of the communications medium. The components interface through ports, and in many systems, most of the ports will require access to the link infrequently with short messages The essential information content of many messages is only one bit, exclusive of addressing, error detection, and formatting data. There may be many applications of distributed systems within a single building. Each application may be implemented as a completely independant distributed system, or all of the applications may be integrated into one complex distributed system to permit cost reduction for individual applications through the sharing of common communication and processing resources. While there are examples of these approachs, a compromise can yield advantages of both. A common communications medium should be employed by all BOCM systems within a single building while the systems should remain independent at all higher levels of identity.

The average communications requirements of each port in each system are low. However, in a shared data link environment, the aggregate peak communications requirements of the multiple systems can be very high. Certain system functions may demand bounded response times even when many ports are waiting for link access. A mechanism for distinguishing between ports with high and low response time bounds is necessary as part of any priority structure.

The robustness of a network communications facility in this environment is critical. The network would not be viable for control and monitoring applications without an architecture providing automatic recovery from crashes. The recovery procedures must be distributed as is the arbitration mechanisn because there is no link supervisor. While it is desirable that transient failures be avoided, it is essential that total failure of the network be almost impossible. No link can be perfect in this sense, and the individual system components must incorporate fail-soft features to avoid catastrophic failure modes.

Some BOCM systems may be implemented using the power distribution lines as the communication medium. This approach is desirable because minimal installation of additional wiring is required. A disadvantage is the increased cost resulting from the modems required for each port. Also, power lines may not go everywhere that communication is needed. The use of carrier line communications for BOCM systems implies that the data rates will be relatively slow (between 50 and 500 bps). High peak numbers of pending requests can be expected under these operating conditions. The arbitration mechanism must be able to coordinate network usage even with this situation.

From these and other observed characteristics of building oriented distributed control and monitoring systems, a set of fourteen requirements for any communications network intended to serve these systems is summarized here:

1. The physical separation of the distributed elements of a system incorporating a link may range from less than a meter to more than a kilometer with no degradation in quality of service.

2. Multiple, possibly unrelated, systems must be supported concurrently and independently by a single link.

3.   The communications facility must support simultaneous interconnection of large numbers of separate components. Some applications may comprise thousands of elements which are connected by the data link.

4.   The cost of interfacing components to the link must be low to sustain economic viability for many applications.

5.   For long-term reliability the link must be inherently passive, although a few repeaters for very large systems would be acceptable.

6.   All link functions must be distributed among the link interfaces at the ports, with no link supervisor.

7.   There must be no predetermined master/slave relationships among system components at the link level, and therefore

8.   Master/slave relationships should be established and modified dynamically.

9.   The link must permit transfer of pure bit strings among system components without restricting word lengths or parity checks.

10.   Data transfer rates must be determined by the capacity of the medium, rather than fixed by the link protocol.

11.   The link message encoding must be appropriate for both level and modulated transmissions.

12.   Reliability of operation must result from inherent robustness of the network architecture and protocol.

13.   Bus access contention arbitration must avoid message collisions even with many pending access requests.

14.   Within individual priority groups, the order of bus acquisition must be determined by the order of bus access requests.

III. Overview of COMONET Architecture

The communications requirements imposed by control and monitoring systems distributed within buildings differ from those of automated offices or of general purpose instrumentation. [3,4,5,6,7] Local networks currently employed for these latter tasks are less well suited to the demands of the former. The COMONET architecture and protocol were devised to match closely the specifications delineated in the previous section.

COMONET comprises a potentially large set of essentially identical ports interconnected by a multidrop data link. The ports are distinguished by associated unique identification numbers (id) or addresses. All communication among the user level components is conducted through link level ports, as shown in Fig. 1. The COMONET link level ports are represented by squares, the distributed system level components by circles. Each port has a unique id with p ports shown interconnected. The COMONET port id's are not necessarily contiguous. The system component labels are symbolic and represent multiple distributed systems supported by the same COMONET. The labels are of the form: Xm where X is an alphabetic character identifying the separate systems and m is the numeric identifier for a specific component within a given system. Systems **A**, **B**, and **N** are explicitly displayed with system **A** containing **a** components, system **B** containing **b** components, and system **N** containing **n** components. The presence of additional user systems serviced by this COMONET is implied. Each system level component of each distributed system is connected to the system through its respective dedicated port. The choice of id's for the ports of specific system level devices is arbitrary but restricted to be unique and must be correctly referenced by related system components. The interface between each system level device and its respective port consists of a number of signal paths as indicated by the slash through the connecting lines. A description of a possible protocol for this interface is provided in a later section.

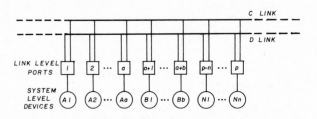

Fig. 1. COMONET Block Diagram

The data link interconnecting the COMONET ports consists of two separate signal paths: the control path and the data path labeled respectively "C" and "D." The D path is employed to transfer system level serial data between ports, addresses of receiving ports, and link level command words to modify the link state. The C path is used to support the distributed arbitration mechanism. The distribution of the arbitration function helps to eliminate the need for a link level central controller; this was one of the requirements specified in the last section. Command words and certain other techniques yet to be discussed fulfill the residual functions ordinarily delegated to a central control unit.

The separation of access contention arbitration from data transfer functions within COMONET is not limited to the segregation of signal paths. These processes are actually performed separately and concurrently. The COMONET arbitration mechanism designates the next port which will acquire the D path after the port using the D path has relinquished it. There is no access contention arbitration period required between D path usages by successive ports. When a port relinquishes the D path by sending a special command word, the successor port has already been designated by the distributed arbitration structure and this next port may proceed immediately.

Each port is at all times in one of three states: monitor, slave, or master. A monitor is any active COMONET port which is neither a master nor a slave. The monitor continuously updates its subset of the distributed COMONET arbitration state from signals received on the C path of the link, and continuously updates its copy of the link state from signals received on the D path. The port as monitor compares all transmitted port addresses on the D path with its own identification number to determine if it is being accessed by a master port.

A port is granted master status by the COMONET arbitration mechanism. There is never more than one master port on a COMONET. A port which is master controls the D path of the data link and is the only port which can modify the state of the link. The master designates other ports as slaves and may free them. The primary restriction for a master is a possible limitation of its tenure which may be imposed by the arbitration mechanism as a function of the number and type of other pending requests for access to the D path.

The slave port is assigned slave status by the current master port of the COMONET. A slave port may return to monitor status either by being explicitly freed by the current master or by the master port relinquishing its control of the D path and thereby terminating its master status. When a port first becomes master there are no slave ports. The master port selects a slave port by placing its address on the D path preceded by another special command word. Slaves receive and send data only under the direction of the master port. Slave ports cannot affect the state of the D path.

The three possible states of a COMONET port are shown in Fig. 2 with the sources of the state modification commands. The diagram shows that a monitor can become either a slave or a master but the master and slave ports can only directly become monitors. A monitor port becomes a slave by command from the master (**M**). A monitor port becomes the master by command from the arbitration mechanism (**A**). A slave is freed by its master under ordinary conditions. The master returns to a monitor status by its own action under normal conditions. Under extraordinary circumstances, pathologies may occur in COMONET behavior. Crash recovery procedures have been incorporated to assure robust performance. The information in the square brackets of the state transition labels identify sources of state modification commands during crash recovery. For example, the failure of a master to relinquish the COMONET within its allotted time results in the arbitrator, **A**, forcing the return of the master and its slaves to monitor status. A second example concerns the situation of two ports attempting to send data simultaneously. The detection of this condition will cause all ports to return to monitor status.

<u>Sources of Status Modification</u>

A $\equiv$ arbitration mechanism
M $\equiv$ master
S $\equiv$ slave
[ ] $\equiv$ crash recovery

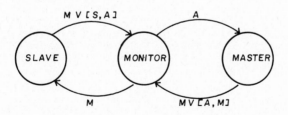

Fig. 2 COMONET Port Status

Both virtual and structural COMONET architectures are apparent from the preceeding discussion of port states. The structural architecture is static, defining the physical interconnection, addressing, and protocols of the ports. The virtual architecture is dynamic, prescribing the relationships among the ports at any time. There are three normal classes of virtual architecture illustrated in Figs. 3, 4, and 5. It is possible for COMONET to have neither a master nor a slave, as shown in Fig. 3.   This can occur during the brief interval between the relinquishing of the D path by a master port and the acquisition of the D path by the next pending port.   This situation will also occur when no port needs to transfer data.   A master port can exist on the COMONET without any slaves as shown in Fig. 4, but no system level data can be transferred in this mode.   This condition will exist immediately after a port has acquired master status or after a master port has freed its slave port(s).   Fig. 5 shows the relationship among ports during the normal mode of operation.   One port, **M**, is the master and a second port, **S**, is the slave while the remaining **p** - 2 ports are monitors.   Data can be transferred between ports **M** and **S** under the supervision of port **M**. Switching between these virtual architecture classes is conducted in a distributed manner with each port altering its status according to Fig. 2.

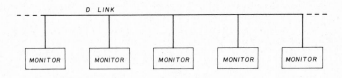

Fig. 3 COMONET without Master

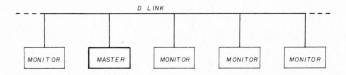

Fig. 4   COMONET with Master but no Slave

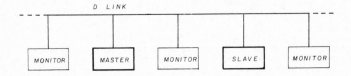

Fig. 5   COMONET with Master and Slave

IV. COMONET Arbitration

An important part of any network architecture is the method used to resolve contentions among multiple ports for access to the medium. Examples of the mechanisms either currently employed or proposed for this purpose are the collision systems and the token systems.[4] The potentially large number of ports served by COMONET may generate very long queues of pending service requests. An additional factor contributing to the possibility of long queues is low bandwidth communication media which may be used in some installations (such as those employing power line carrier). Low bandwidth circuits will still exceed the average throughput requirements of most applications, but the peak activity may be orders of magnitude greater than the capacity. The demand for network reliability dictates the need for efficient handling of a substantial backlog of requests, even if such a condition rarely occurs. Another factor affecting arbitration is the need that certain applications have for bounded real time response for certain ports. These applications require a multilevel priority structure offering some ports preferred access in the event of long queues. For these reasons, COMONET incorporates an arbitration mechanism not currently employed by other networks.

To examine briefly an idealized model of the arbitration problem, assume a Poisson distribution for the arrival of link access requests from the ports. If the average arrival rate is r for a sufficiently small time interval t, then the probability of a link access request during this interval is rt and the probability that no request will occur is $1 - rt$. The assumption of Poisson arrivals dictates that, for t sufficiently small, the probability of more than one access request arriving in one interval is zero. As a second idealization, assume that a control path (C path) having infinite bandwidth is available, and as a final idealization assume that the distance between ports is zero. The event of each access request is indicated by the requesting port transmitting a zero width, finite energy signal on the C path to all other ports. In this idealized model, it is guaranteed that there can be no collisions among bus access request signals. The arbitration mechanism used in COMONET is an approximation of this idealization.

The arbitration state of a network may be defined as the minimum information which reflects the history of bus access requests and bus acquisitions by the network ports such that the order of succeeding acquisitions can proceed unambiguously. There are many ways to represent, distribute, and use the information that is the arbitration state of a network. COMONET represents the arbitration state in a form easily used by the ports. The germane arbitration state information for a 'first-come/first-served' strategy is the ordered queue of ports having requests pending. No central controller is provided to retain the state information and to allocate bus access to the ports. Therefore, the ports themselves must perform these functions.

The total arbitration state of a network must be maintained within the aggregate of network ports, but it is not necessary for each port to have access to the full state description. Each port must retain only the subset of the network arbitration state relevant for that port. Such data as the identities of all of the ports with pending link service requests are extraneous to the needs of any individual port.

Distribution of the network arbitration state among the COMONET ports is illustrated by the following model. Each port maintains two arbitration state variables, BCNT and QCNT. BCNT represents the total number of pending bus access requests including the one currently being serviced. The value of BCNT is the same for all ports, so this variable is redundant rather than distributed. The QCNT state variable resident in each port retains a value equal to the number of pending service requests ahead of that port. QCNT is different for each port actively seeking servicing. The value of QCNT for those ports not attempting to gain master status is irrelevant. According to the previously stated definition

of the network arbitration state, only the QCNT's and knowledge of the designated
master port are necessary to prescribe completely the arbitration state. BCNT
represents no unique information, but exists to achieve the goal of minimum
communication. The application of BCNT allows the arbitration mechanism to
function with only: 1) C path signals, 2) indication from the D path when the
ports relinquish their master status (EOF), and 3) the system level requests for
service imposed at the interfaces to the ports. The value of BCNT is used to
initialize QCNT when the associated port requests service.

     The operation of this arbitration strategy is shown in Fig. 6. The value of
BCNT is incremented upon receipt of the BAR (bus access request) impulse on the
C path. The value of BCNT is decremented upon receipt of an EOF signal on the
D path from the master port relinquishing command of the D path. The value of
QCNT for a specific port is set to the value of BCNT when that port receives a bus
request from its associated system level component. The port applies an impulse
to the C path at the same time. Every port having a pending link access request
decrements the value of its QCNT upon receipt of an EOF signal from the D path. A
port havng a pending service request becomes master when its QCNT becomes equal to
zero. This process eliminates contention among waiting ports when the D path
becomes available.

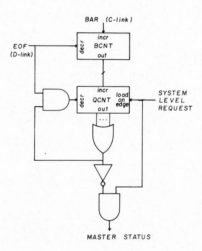

Fig. 6   Ideal COMONET Arbitration

     An approximation of this ideal arbitration mechanism is implemented using
finite width pulses on the C path instead of the zero width impulses of the
previous ideal example. A minimum pulse width, **w**, can be defined for a finite
bandwidth communication medium with a given signal-to-noise ratio and a maximum
permissable error rate. BAR pulses of width **w** are applied to the C path to signal
requests by pending ports. The nonzero pulsewidth introduces the possibility of
overlapping BAR signals. An activity detect and defer mechanism is used to limit
the performance degradation resulting from multiple BAR collisions. Each port
monitors the C path to determine if a BAR signal from another port is currently
being applied. If not, the port may assert a BAR signal. If a BAR signal is
present when the port receives an access request from its system level component,
the port refrains from asserting its BAR signal at that time. Instead, it waits
for a unique time interval after the sensed C path BAR signal has finished before

attempting to send a BAR. The use of the unique time interval delay guarantees that multiple ports attempting concurrent requests will not repeat the requests simultaneously. Certain pathological cases may still permit two or more ports to assert BAR signals simultaneously resulting in collisions of messages on the D path. Recovery procedures for this anomalous behavior are described in Sec. VI.

The COMONET arbitration technique is a modified version of the arbitration state which has been described. The need for a priority structure was specified in Sec. II, and the current definition of COMONET includes two priority levels in addition to the BAR level. These two priorities are referred to as INT and URG for **INT**errupt request and **URG**ent request, respectively. The URG requests take precedence over INT and BAR requests, and INT requests are serviced before BAR requests. Only very special ports, such as load shedding systems or safety related apparatus, are expected to exploit the URG level.

The indication of the event of a port requesting access is not sufficient with the addition of more priority levels. The priority of the request must also be communicated. The present COMONET distinguishes among the three types of requests by pulsewidth encoding of the signal applied to the C path. The BAR signal is as previously described. The INT signal, marking the event of an interrupt priority level link access request, is a single pulse on the C path of width 2**w**. An URG signal sent by ports making urgent priority level requests is a 4**w** wide C path pulse. Other coding schemes are possible, but this selection uses the narrowest pulses to optimize the use of C path capacity.

The arbitration state must be augmented to support the two additional priority levels. Two parameters, ICNT and UCNT, are provided to maintain records of the number of INT and URG pending requests, respectively. The total number of pending requests is then equal to the sum of the values of BCNT, ICNT, and UCNT. Copies of ICNT and UCNT are contained in each port, in addition to the copy of BCNT. These three parameters are updated in a manner similar to that of a single priority level. Additional information is required to describe this augmented arbitration state; the priority of each request must also be appropriately distributed among the ports.

The augmented arbitration makes necessary the inclusion of additional information in each port's view of the distributed mechanism. It is sufficient for each port to know the priority level of its own pending request and the priority level of the current master port. The first is normally available from the associated system level device. The second is more difficult to acquire, but it is available without resorting to the transmission of extra information on either the C or D paths, by using the procedure illustrated in Fig. 7. Four states are shown with each related to a different priority state of the current master port. MB, MI, and MU states are associated with the BAR, INT, and URG priority levels, respectively. The fourth state, MN, is active when there are no pending requests. The values of the BCNT, ICNT, and UCNT arbitration parameters are categorized into three groups: 0, 1, and > for parameter values of zero, one, and greater than one, respectively. Included is a set of three elements (**uib**) used to delineate the state of the BCNT, ICNT, and UCNT parameters where **u**, **i**, and **b** may be 0, 1, or >. It is assumed that this finite state machine is synchronous and that state transitions occur only at the time of a clock signal. The end variable, **E**, is one clock cycle long and is active when the current master relinquishes the D path. The (**uib**) set is applied to the values of UCNT, ICNT, and BCNT before any decrementation from the **E** signal. A change of state occurs only with an active **E** signal.

The BCNT, ICNT, and UCNT parameters are respectively decremented upon receipt of an **E** signal when MB, MI, or MU is in the active state. No parameter is decremented when MN is active. QCNT is decremented during an **E** signal only if the port has a pending request of the same type as that of the current master port. QCNT will be initialized with the value of one of the other three parameters depending upon the priority of the request made. As in the more simple model, a pending port becomes master when the value of its QCNT becomes zero.

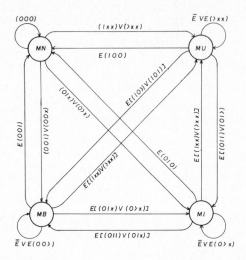

Fig. 7   COMONET Link State Diagram : Current Master Priority Type

The complete arbitration mechanism structure incorporating the three levels of immediacy is illustrated in Fig. 8. In addition to the arbitration state variable registers, the primary functions are shown. Included are the input discriminator, the output encoder, the timeout and release unit, and the null synchronizer. The input discriminator monitors the C path and measures the widths of incoming control signals, S_i, and updates the values of the state variable registers when BAR, INT, and URG signals are detected. The output encoder sends the C path signals from the port when requesting link servicing and initializes the QCNT state register. The timeout and release unit imposes maximum link usage intervals for each immediacy type and contributes to crash recovery in the event of missing master ports. The null synchronizer initializes the port state variable registers when the port is first activated or when state errors are detected.

Ports are expected to be attached to and removed from a given COMONET throughout its use. The question of parameter value initialization arises with this system as it does with any redundant data base. There are a number of potential solutions to this problem, and the current definition of COMONET uses a relatively simple approach. The technique requires that a port operate in a standby mode when it is first connected to the link. The port waits for the C path to enter a null state so that its zero parameter values will be correct as the port begins regular service. When a port is first connected to the link, it is not in synchronization with the arbitration state, and it cannot recognize a null state in the normal way shown in Fig. 8. However, if there are pending requests, the time between the relinquishing of the D path by a current master (indicated by an E signal) and the acquisition of the link by the next master (indicated by any new signal on the D path) is finite and bounded. The null state is detected by a new port when no new signals immediately follow an E signal. Disadvantages of this method include: 1) the possibly substantial time before a heavily loaded link achieves the null state, thus preventing the new port from operating during this period, and 2) some possible pathologies which must be guarded against as discussed in Sec. VI.

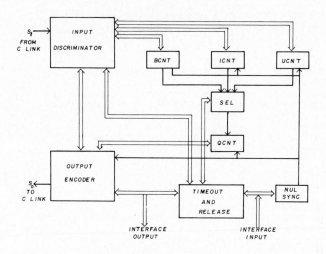

Fig. 8 Block Diagram of COMONET Arbitration Unit

V. Link State and Data Transfer Protocol

The D path is used for data transfers between the master and slaves. There is only one master port when the D path is active. The status of master is granted to a port by the arbitration process which does not use the D path except to carry the E signal when the master relinquishes the link. Arbitration is therefore not an issue when describing the D path.

Signals on the D path are assumed to be either active, **A**, or neutral, **N**. This does not presume any particular form of encoding, and both level and frequency coding techniques are possible. The simultaneous imposition of **A** and **N** signals on the path is interpreted as an **A** signal alone. An **A** signal is considered to be dominant and can override an **N** signal.

There are two classes of data transferred on the D path: link level data and system level data. System level data are bit strings supplied by the system level devices which, with one exception, are passed through the transmitting port along the D path to the receiving port and finally to the destination system level device. System level data have variable lengths and, again with one exception, have no meaning at the link level. The one exception is the transfer of port addresses. A master port designates a monitor port as slave by sending the address of the destination port which is provided by the master's associated system level device but interpreted by the new slave's link level port.

All bit strings are encoded using Manchester code to provide self timing and to facilitate detection of anomalous D path message collisions. A logical "1" is encoded as an **N** to **A** signal transition while a logical "0" is represented by an **A** to **N** transition. Every message begins with a three bit header and is concluded with a special termination (EOT) signal. Assuming the bit width to be 2**p**, the header is preceded by an **N** value signal at least 3**p** long. The start bit of the header is an asynchronous **N** to **A** transition. The second bit of the header is the synchronization bit which is an **A** to **N** transition 2**p** after the start bit. There is no transition between the first and second bits, and the timing for the message is fixed by these first two bits. The third header bit is the class bit, and it determines whether the remaining message is link level or system level. An **A** to **N** transition has been arbitrarily assigned to system level bit strings and conversely, **N** to **A** transitions indicate link level messages. The EOT signal is one of two non-Manchester encoded signals used on the COMONET D path. An EOT is a 3**p** length **N** signal, and it breaks the self timing bit string. The overhead for each message is only 10**p** so that even short messages can be sent efficiently.

The link state of COMONET defines the mode of interaction between the master port and slaves, and is not related to the arbitration state. The link state is normally determined by the master port. The state is set through the use of command words which are the only permissable link level messages. A command word is sent by the master and assimilated by all COMONET ports. The link state is another redundant COMONET parameter with each port retaining a copy.

There are four primary link states with corresponding command words. Two states determine the direction of system level data transfers with respect to the master port. The MSD (master sends data) state permits system level messages to be sent by the master port to the slave port. All ports not designated as slaves ignore system level messages while in the MSD state. The MSD state is entered when the master port sends the MSD command word. The SSD (slave sends data) state permits system level messages to be sent by the slave port to the master port. All other ports ignore messages sent in the SSD state. An SSD command word is generated by the master on the D path to put COMONET in the SSD state. The third primary state is the SID (slave identification number) state which is used to designate monitor ports as slaves. All slave ports are freed to become monitor ports when the SID state is entered. Each system level message sent by the master while in the SID state is interpreted as the identification number of a new slave port. All monitor ports receive messages in the SID state and compare these messages to their own unique identification numbers. Each port having a valid comparison becomes a slave port. An SID command word from the master is required to enter the SID state. The last primary state is the NUL state and is entered when the EOF (end of function) command word is broadcast by the master port. The EOF command is used by master ports to relinquish the link.

The command word is a fixed length bit string providing a limited number of link level messages. Command words should be selected to provide error detection and correction. The current version of COMONET uses a seven bit command word providing eight distinct messages with double bit error detection and single bit error correction. Every link port contains sufficient hardware to decode the seven bit command words to the three bits of relevant information.

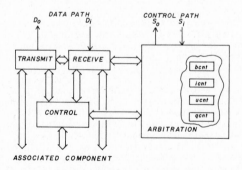

Fig. 9   Block Diagram of COMONET Port

A block diagram of a complete COMONET port implementation is provided in Fig. 9. It consists of four functional units: the arbitration unit, the transmit unit, the receive unit, and the control unit. There are three interfaces to the outside world. At the top of the diagram, the arbitration unit connects to the control path where the S_o and S_i signals are tied together. The output to the D path is provided by the transmit unit of the port while the signals on the D path are monitored by the receive unit. The D_o and D_i signal lines are connected together at the D path. The third interface is to the system level component associated with the COMONET port. The control unit supervises the operation of the other units in accord with the commands from the system level interface. Data is transferred to and from the system component directly to the transmit and receive units.

VI. Crash Recovery

The presentation to this point has involved the normal operation of COMONET. Unfortunately, circumstances can lead to degraded performance which, without correction, could degenerate to total system failure. Conditions capable of crashing the system include 1) undetected collisions among C path signals, 2) C path and D path data transfer errors, and 3) improper link usage by a port. These problems are addressed by the COMONET structure to limit the effect of any erroneous operation so that the system will recover. This degree of robustness is considered essential for any system lacking a central controller, and this need is especially great for a system intended to support several independent distributed applications.

The undetected collision of two or more request signals on the C path will result in the two or more ports attempting to become master of the D path at the same time. This will cause message collsions on the D path. COMONET includes provisions for ports to monitor the D path as they transmit on it. This monitoring process makes allowances for noise spikes and line loading effects, but the detection of an **A** signal on the D path when the port is transmitting an **N** signal will cause the port to cease operations. The other port will detect only the dominant **A** signal and continue to use the link. It is possible, due to timing considerations, for both ports to terminate their master status. Since no EOF will be generated, the D path will not return to the NUL state, and the system will crash without remedial measures. A timeout mechanism is incorporated for this condition to allow all ports to return to the NUL state, permitting system recovery.

The second D path signal which is not Machester encoded is the mumble (MBL) signal. MBL is a 3p (or longer) **A** value signal. This signal is powerful because it can interrupt and dominate any other signal. The MBL signal is used to recover from two kinds of failures relating to slaves; both of which occur in the SSD state. A transmitting slave which detects a D path collision asserts a MBL signal. As the slave port completes its MBL signal, it ceases all transmission, relinquishes slave status, and returns to a monitor status. The master port, sensing the train of MBL's, signals its associated system level device which must then redesignate the slave port and proceed according to some prespecified system level contingency plan. The alternate failure mode results from a slave failing to respond in the SSD state. If no response is received from a slave within some timeout interval after the link is placed in the SSD state, the master asserts an MBL which causes any active slave to return to monitor status. Again, the master port signals its associated system level device of an error.

It is possible for a port to lose arbitration state synchronization and fail to acquire the D path when it should become master. A timeout cycle is initiated by every port after each EOF. If the cycle is completed without the link leaving the NUL state, each port generates its own internal TOF signal which performs the same function as an EOF signal. The missing master is simply skipped. The logical OR of the EOF and TOF signals is another interval signal **E** as used in section IV.

The tenure of a link master can be limited as a function of pending requests and of the priority request type of the master to assure throughput in a multiple system environment. Two process times are identified. T_B is the length of time any BAR priority level master port may use the link if there are other pending requests. A BAR priority master port may retain the link indefinitely if there are no pending requests. T_I is the length of time any INT or URG priority level master port may maintain link control. T_I is much shorter than T_B. A system level device which fails to relinquish the link within the allotted time has its use of the link automatically terminated by the port generating an EOF command word. The port then imposes a relatively long penalty timeout period, T_P, upon the device. This function is not included as a punitive measure for recalcitrant system designers. It is intended to provide some protection for the link when the link access request line from a system level device is inadvertently jammed by a systems level hardware failure.

The design goal for COMONET crash recovery is to make the medium foolproof but not "cruelproof." No claim is made that these procedures protect the network from intentional tampering. The aim has been to institute a wide array of automatic recovery procedures to provide a high degree of reliability against potentially fatal conditions.

VII. Conclusions

COMONET should not be considered as a competitor for existing local area networks. This network is intended to work in a different environment where available bandwidth may be severely limited. It satisfies the basic needs of building oriented distributed control and monitoring systems. Strong crash recovery procedures provide high reliability. The arbitration mechanism produces efficient usage with particularly good performance expected at peak access request density. The generality of virtual system organizations supported by COMONET and the lack of restrictions on system level data formats makes COMONET a flexible environment in which many applications can be implemented satisfactorily. The capability of single installations to support multiple distributed systems simultaneously can result in high economic efficiency.

Acknowledgements

The authors wish to acknowledge the contributions of R. Dorman, J. Jackson, B. Larsen, W. Morgan, A. Sobel, and J. Troisi. T.L. Sterling wants to express his appreciation to the Fannie and John Hertz Foundation for financial assistance provided through a graduate fellowship.

REFERENCES

1.   Sterling, T.L., Williams, R.D., Kirtley, J.L., "Control and Monitoring System Communications for Effective Energy Use", IEEE Transactions on Power Apparatus and Systems, Vol. PAS-100, No. 11, November 1981, pp. 4407-4412.

2.   H.V. Bertine, "Physical Level Protocols," IEEE Transactons on Communication, Vol. COM-28, No. 4, April 1980, pp. 433-444.

3.   R.M. Metcalfe and D.R. Boggs, "Ethernet: Distributed Packet Switching for Local Computer Networks," Communications of the ACM, Vol. 19, No. 7, July 1976, pp. 395-404.

4.   D.D. Clark, K.T. Pogran, and D.P. Reed, "An Introduction to Local Area Networks," Proceedings of the IEEE, Vol. 66, No. 11, November 1978, pp. 1497-1517.

5.   P.E. Green Jr. "An Introduction to Network Architectures and Protocols," IEEE Transactions on Communication, Vol. COM-28, No. 4, April 1980, pp. 413-424.

6.   F.A. Tobagi, "Multiaccess Protocols in Packet Communication Systems," IEEE Transactions on Communication, Vol. COM-28, No. 4, April 1980, pp. 468-488.

7.   "IEEE Standard Digital Interface for Programmable Instrumentation", IEEE STD 488-1975.

8.   V.C. Hamacher, G.S. Shedler; "Performance of a Collision-free Local Bus Network Having Distributed Control," Proceedings of the 7th Annual Symposium on Computer Architecture, May, 1980.

LCN APPLICATIONS

LOCAL COMPUTER NETWORKS
P.C. Ravasio, G. Hopkins and N. Naffah (editors)
North-Holland Publishing Company
© IFIP, 1982

LOCAL AREA NETWORKS
TECHNICAL ISSUES - USER SERVICES - SOCIAL IMPACT

Willy Jensen

University of Tromsø
Norway

There is an overwhelming interest in local - or
private - networks. Time has come to advise a
shift in this interest from the lower layers of
basic technology to architectural issues and
user service capabilities. The architectural
relationship to the OSI model is of particular
importance when discussing internetworking
issues. The construction of distributed interworking application systems offering user services
to personal workstations represents many technical
and analytical challenges: application layer
protocol design, human computer interaction
facilities, technical and organizational integration
of services.

1. INTRODUCTION

To make predictive statements of the future is of course always very
difficult. Considering a time scale of - say ten years - we do have
some knowledge of many aspects of the development trends of
information technology. We are for example able to indicate which
hardware products will be commercially available during most of this
period, simply because the bulk of this equipment is already operating
as prototypes in the computer and telecommunication laboratories
around the world. The degree of uncertainty increases substantially
when we try to foresee the evolution of user services offered by
means of the various technical components.

The situation becomes even more doubtful when it comes to our ability
to predict the social impact of extensive use of various information
services. There will be comprehensive changes in organizational
structures, in working life infrastructure and most probably in rather
basic relationships between individuals and their environment. The
nature of these consequences is still subject to heavy discussions,
and there seems to be a consensus that the consequences will depend
on the way of introduction and the policy for and regulations of the
use of computer based information and communication services.

A very typical feature of the present situation as far as local area
network development is concerned is that by far the most heavy efforts
are concentrated on the basic technology. People concentrate on media,
media access procedures, media bandwidth, signal attenuation, etc.,
and only very little analysis and research is made into how we can
minimize the negative social consequences.

When discussing local area networks and their possible patterns of development, we should notice:

- the "technology" of local area networks has developed partly independently of that of "long-haul" networks. To some extent, the situation is similar to that of the mid sixties when very enthusiastic "networkers" started the packet switching era. Another point of resemblance is the hardware oriented forces of development. Too little attention seems to be paid to the really challenging issues: improved user services through interworking distributed applications and, in particular, the possibilities for individualization of services and service access primitives.

- the lack of consistent architectural models for local area networks reflects their premature state of evolution. One reason is that the most well known local network prototypes were designed before the important ideas of OSI modelling were published. A second reason is the misconception that local area networks could not be described in an "OSI-way". A third reason could be that R & D groups on local area networks possess some resistant attitudes towards broadly accepted models which could turn out to be vehicles for standardization destroying the private nature of local nets.

- a typical characteristic, of the recent accelerated development of high speed local networks (media) is caused by other fast developing technical components: microprocessors, graphical presentation devices, storage units. Again, this is rather equivalent to, for instance, the relationship between the minicomputers and the long-haul packet switched networks 10 years ago.

- the first high performance local network cables and cable interface units are commercially available. These pieces of hardware are still very expensive, at least in Europe. An increasing number of local network products will appear in the marketplace. Some of them will also offer services and protocols for distributed systems management and distributed applications.

- the standardization efforts within ISO, IEEE and other international bodies have already had significant influence on the further development of local networks. The general improvement of computer and communication technologies, combined with the impact from the standardization work will ensure even better utilization of the existing Physical and Data Link Layer services.

2.   TECHNICAL DEVELOPMENT

2.1 Basic technology and methodology

Basic technology in the context of local area networks seems to be:

Transmission media

- cable based systems including baseband coax cables, broadband coax or CATV will be subject to improvement. Various waveguides will be commercially used.

- fiber optics is expected to be the leading medium for local data transmission during the eighties (more than 50% of total installed value).

- infrared diffuse transmission, in particular for inroom use is a very interesting alternative for some applications.

- most of the existing cable (or network) interface units (NIUs) are still far too expensive. Improved technology (e.g. VLSI) will hopefully contribute to price reduction.

Computer and storage technology

The microprocessor development will continue. In parallel to this development, the other end of the computer spectrum will be supplied with huge processors (probably tightly coupled multi-processors).

More powerful network stations may be able to bring the effective bandwidth (i.e. for applications communication) closer to the raw bandwidth of the medium.

Equipment for storage of information represented in computer readable form will follow the same trend: increasing capacity and decreasing price and physical volume.

Registration and presentation equipment

There is a growing awareness of the importance of developing high quality tools for human-computer interaction. This includes technical devices for presentation of information in form of graphics, picture and voice/sound as well as "soft" procedures for computer assisted human control of the registration, processing, storage, spread and presentation. Rastergraphical high-resolution displays, voice synthesizers and laser printers are among the (more or less) existing devices for high quality presentation.

Methods for systems design

As the technology grows in complexity and the user's demands for service quality, reliability and availability increase, the systems design process becomes more difficult. We still have very inadequate methods in this area, but I believe that the ideas of interconnected open systems - each dedicated to provide a selection of services - constructed within the framework of ISO OSI will prove to be a significant contribution, see Figure 1.

Methods for systems implementation

There is no revolution expected for programming languages in the near future. However, very conscious use of portable software combined with progress in the international standardization efforts could ease the very difficult, time consuming and expensive system implementation phases. VLSI techniques and microprogramming are also valuable implementation tools. Modularity will, however, require very clear and strictly defined interfaces.

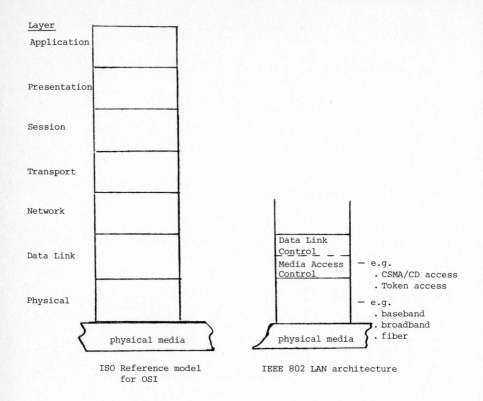

Figure 1
Open Systems Interconnection Models

The IEEE standardisation of Local Area Network architecture,
protocols and services takes place within the framework of
the ISO Ref. model for OSI and will include:

- a refinement of Data Link Layer

- alternative entities at Data Link as well as at the
  Physical Layer

- optional standards for the layer interfaces. These are
  expected to be more detailed than an ISO layer service
  specification.

2.2   Compatibility, standardization, internetworking

The basic technology provides us with very flexible and powerful
components for construction of tools for information services. The
various components must be refined and adapted to various applications.
And this leads to what I will consider as the most promising feature
of the current trend of technological development:

If the growing number of specialized resource components of each category of basic technology can be selected and <u>combined</u> in appropriate ways, we will be able to construct computer assisted information services which are individually adaptable still preserving their integrity with other services.

So, in our efforts to construct computer assisted services for information processing, storing and spread, we are faced with problems of:

- <u>combination</u>, i.e. given the nature and desired quality of the economical and technical constraints, choose the optimal selection of technological components.

- <u>integration</u>, i.e. considering present and future user needs, decide on the appropriate degree of medium and/or service integration (e.g. local network/PABX, CATV).

- <u>individualization</u>, i.e. to attempt a joint effort with the user(s) in constructing a computerized workstation giving easy access to the appropriate services and resources (humane interface dialogue, appropriate presentation devices, etc.).

- <u>organizational and social consequences</u>, i.e. analyzing the possible non-technical consequences of extensive use of computerized services, and thereby be able to adjust the technical solutions, the process of introduction and the non-technical associated measures so that the social and organizational consequences are optimized according to some objectives.

The solutions will in most cases lead to needs for interworking open computer systems. The technical way of providing interconnection will very often be some kind of high-performance private (and local) data network.

This interconnection of (specialized) open systems comprising heterogeneous equipment requires standardized interfaces and communication protocols. Moreover, there will normally arise needs for connections and communications to systems/resources/individuals external to the private network. Therefore, the requirement of compatibility through use of standards will be extended to national - or even an international - scale.

The OSI Reference model (2), describes a common conceptual and architectural framework for all work on network interconnection. The Transport Layer is intended to form a universal common service interface upwards, and there is an explicit requirement that the Transport Protocol(s) shall have end-to-end significance. The prevailing interpretation of this is that interconnection of networks should take place at Network Layer (or lower). The sublayer concept could be used to introduce internet (i.e. gateway-to-gateway) protocols at Network Layer, see Figure 2 and (2).

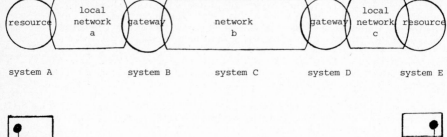

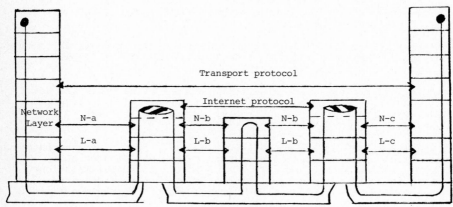

Figure 2
Internetworking at Network Layer

Several interconnecting mechanisms may be used in series.
Sub-layering at Network Layer may be used to distinguish
between "native" protocols and internet protocols.

N-a: Network Layer protocol of network a
L-a: Data Link Layer protocol of network a

Internetworking will always involve use of a node common to the
actual networks:

i.   bridge construction applies when (almost) identical networks
       must be interconnected because of the existing range
       restrictions for most locally used transmission media.

ii.   simple gateway construction applies when networks of compatible
       architecture are to be interconnected. The capsulating/
       decapsulating techniques described for PUP "media translators",
       (6) would normally be adequate.

iii.   complex gateway construction is necessary to join networks of
       different architecture. Generally, this interconnection
       problem may be impossible.

The architectural aspects of the general problem of networks interconnection are probably not yet completely understood. On one hand,
we may apply the OSI Reference Model concept of tandem subnetworks
restricting the relaying functions to Network Layer or lower. On the
other hand, we may consider the different networks as communicating
systems in separate planes in some architectural space. In particular
this view could prove to be fruitful when local (private) networks are
interconnected by means of (a) trunk network(s). This latter more
general approach to internetworking will probably not lead to any
practical simplifications as far as implementation is concerned.
It could, however, in some situations be a slightly more convenient
way to a conceptual understanding, e.g. by allowing network superposition. Figure 3 is an attempt to describe the idea (which is
similar to the method of developing intra-Application Layer -
architectures "orthogonal" to the OSA, cfr. (3).

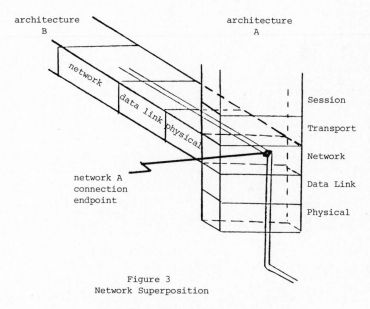

Figure 3
Network Superposition

The figure indicates an example where the physical
connections of one network are considered as
mapped onto the network connections of the other.

One may consider the functional structure B as a
Transport entity of A (but in another plane).

This approach is probably in conflict with current
ISO thinking, but could possibly contribute to the
discussions on network interconnection.

3. USER SERVICES

3.1 The style of open working

The user services of modern information technology should provide
powerful and flexible facilities assisting in processing and storing
as well as dissemination of information.

The services offering such facilities must be adapted to the various
applications and user communities. Realization through use of
dedicated and interconnected open systems also allows for possible
stepwise expansion which has clear economical advantages. Among
these dedicated resource systems - often called servers - are:

- archive servers - central and distributed - constructed from file
  server(s).

- presentation servers like high quality print servers (central) and
  advanced colour displays with graphical capabilities (distributed).

- number crunching computers (central).

- document processing resources, i.e. systems offering (special)
  services for production, editing, modification of documents
  containing textual, graphical and pictorial information (central/
  distributed).

- communication assisting systems like mail servers, name servers,
  etc. (central/distributed).

- other application oriented servers offering for instance special
  facilities for program development, computer aided design and
  construction, computer aided instruction, etc. (central).

- OSI management and system oriented servers, e.g. terminal servers
  (concentrators), network servers (gateways), dedicated servers for
  maintenance and resource surveillance, security, accounting, etc.

Now, the flexible use of common shared computer based information
services combined with access to powerful communication tools
facilitates cooperation. An open organisation could in fact be mapped
onto interconnected open computer systems which are interworking
according to patterns reflecting the organisational structure.

The rationale for local, private, networks providing the interconnection mechanism is as follows:

- Economy   Use of private circuits not subject to PTT regulations
  and tariffs reduce costs (in spite of development, installation
  and maintenance expenses).

- Flexibility and Control   Private networks could be operated,
  extended and developed without interfering action from the PTTs.
  This results in substantial degree of freedom, e.g. in the way
  new technology is applied.

- Performance   The possibility to utilise advanced technology
  enables the construction of very fast and reliable networks,
  probably also with inherent intelligence adding value to the
  Transport services.

- Group communication   Most of the communication paths and information exchange volume are found within an organisation. Using local
networks as vehicles for such communication reflects the high
priority compared to external - or remote - communication (similar
to PABXs and local post).

3.2   Services involving high performance multicasting networks

The most striking common features of modern local area networks are
their high-speed (raw bandwidth > 1 Mbps) and the limitations in
physical extension. Another interesting feature associated with many
local nets is their use of multiple-endpoint physical connections,
i.e. multicasting.

We know that the availability of excessive medium bandwidth and
broadcasting may simplify medium access methods and related protocols.
These features also represent exciting tools for substantial
improvement of various classes of user services:

- presentation services offered through advanced graphics equipment
requires large processing capabilities as well as transfer capacity
to transfer data and control information between users and
resources.

- archiving services, realised by centralised storage resources and/
or by distributed data archives, will depend on having Mbps
bandwidth available.

- distributed management services will certainly lean on fast and
reliable local bulk data transfer services which as well may be
utilised to exchange programs - in absolute or relocatable code -
between appropriate nodes. Such features will be applied for
system start and restart, program loading from software banks
(compare "telesoftware"), security copying and for other
maintenance and operations purposes.

- transaction oriented multicasting services are directly utilised
in group-communication, e.g. circulars, polls, conferencing.
Automatic multicast query is expected to be an important basic
feature of many distributed applications (name and address look up,
parallel search for identified data items, etc.).

The low level characteristics of local networks encourage use of
connectionless transport services, e.g. datagram service at Network
Layer. The Network Layer implementations may also be affected by
new switching techniques like packet switching "on the fly" which
might not require temporary storage. Thus, we may expect a development where the environment for user services will be changed as well
as that for the more basic services. This again is expected to have
impact on e.g. cost/performance ratios for local open working.

3.3   Personal interconnected workstations

Computer based information services will be offered through workstations with local processing and storage capabilities and access
to common resources through local as well as remote network(s).
A workstation could be individually adapted in the sense that the set
of local services selected for a particular workstation is subject
to its user's personal needs and tastes. It is also possible to
adapt the appropriate user interface, i.e. the form and syntax of the
man-computer interface procedures, to personal capabilities and tastes.

Figure 4 roughly indicates an architecture well suited as a framework
for design and implementation of job-oriented or even profession-
oriented computer services. We can already observe the first
premature systems for assistance in various office functions. The
access to document preparation services, archives, information banks,
printing and communication facilities make these systems valuable for
consultants and various officials. The hard problems associated with
office automation is how to formalise the human experience, attitudes,
"emotional know-how" and informal communication.

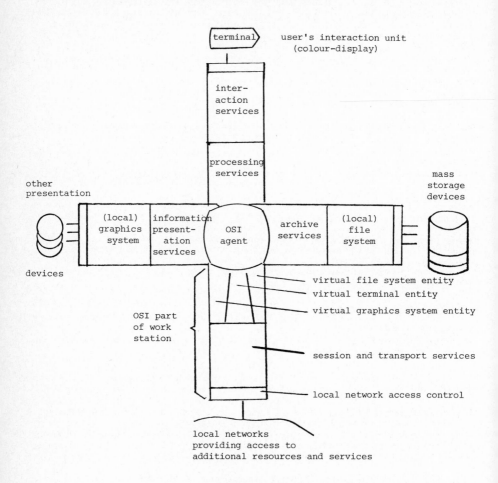

Figure 4
Personal Workstation Architecture

A typical workstation will have a private, i.e. a
closed part. An operating system part will act as
an agent for those applications that become open
by communicating through the services and protocols
of the OSI part.

Examples of typical classes of profession-oriented systems are:

- various systems for dealing with applications and enquiries require document production services, access to background information like previous and similar cases, access to laws and regulations and efficient mechanisms to procure expert opinions and comments from involved parties (teleconferencing).

- teaching assisting systems should provide high-quality services for communication, database access and document production including graphics.

- booking and store keeping systems as well as banking and medical advisory systems are examples of database and communication oriented systems where reliability and security is mandatory.

- engineering assisting systems should contain advanced graphical capabilities and they could also be directly linked to production planning and process control systems.

The new technology for presentation services is a necessary prerequisite for construction of convenient and powerful mechanisms for interactions between human users and computer services. The design of appropriate user interfaces for operation of very complex and comprehensive computer services by a wide variety of user groups is indeed challenging.

Some principles for human - computer interactions via graphical display units are guiding the present early phases of development of office automation systems. These include requirements of the visual appearance of the documents being processed, of the services for parallel multiple document treatment through use of multiple display-windows, of the options for selection of parameters for individual adaptation (e.g. impaired hearing or eyesight) and of the presentation of appropriate menus of user commands to reduce the use of handbooks.

3.4   Service integration and future trends

Fragmentation, distribution and individualisation are buzzwords characterising the development of computer based services and equipment. Another complementary trend is that of integration.

We may consider several modes of integration depending on the angle of view applied:

- Transmission services integration   CATV based systems supporting voice, video and data simultaneously through the use of FDM techniques are in use, see (5). Another approach is the integration of voice and data networks in digital PABX systems. 64 or 80 kbps transmission services will be offered for ISDN.

- Network integration   Interconnection of different networks - in particular interconnection of local networks with long-haul networks as the intermediary medium - is a necessary prerequisite for full scale communication services.

- User services integration   We find of course many degrees of this kind of integration, for instance:

. access to all services needed in a certain profession from one
  and the same workstation, see 3.3.

. integration of working life information services with home and
  leisure time services. This means that one can access the
  "private" databanks, the neighbourhood bulletin boards and tele-
  meetings from the same kind of (portable) device as used in ones
  working station.

. complete integration of various information and computing services
  in an advanced environment of presentation services and equipment.
  We include services applicable to voice/sound, film/video, text
  and data. Information in mixed formats could be retrieved and
  published with very few technical limitations (legislation should
  protect human rights, national security, etc.).

The nature and design of protocols associated with distributed and
interworking application entities are major research topics in the
years to come. These problems should be considered in the context
of the whole infrastructure of the ISO OSI Application Layer. The
Application Layer protocols - including those for distributed
resource management - may turn out to be very complicated, e.g. in
the case where the distributed nature of the applications is invisible
to the users ("tightly coupled applications").

The development of Presentation Layer protocols dealing with very
different data presentation modes (voice, video, data) is closely
linked to the corresponding applications.

4. SOCIAL ASPECTS

4.1 Consequences

We have already approached some of the consequences of the
communicative and integrated user services development. The rather
clear distinction for most people between working life and leisure
time could change substantially. As this happens, very basic cultural
characteristics will become unstable.

We have also briefly pointed out the very promising prospects for
many groups of disabled persons. Electronic communication services
could offer important contributions to improvements of the working
and social conditions of many disabled persons.

Comprehensive use of information technology has always had substantial
impact on important parts of working life and thereby on society.
Examples of early machinery are the various devices for printing,
typewriting, document copying, telephone, telex, etc. With the
development of computer technology, this impact will penetrate all
parts and aspects of working life.

The very fast technological development has, however, influenced for
example the office sector much less than expected a few years ago.
Some of the most interesting reasons for this are:

- Computer technology was based on a centralised organisational
  structure. Coordinated decentralisation requires very powerful
  communication services which were not available. Centralisation
  is normally met with human resistance.

- Office work is often a mixture of highly specialised functions and very broad informal know-how created through experience and informal (social) communications. This kind of knowledge is very difficult to computerise.

- The early services offered have been inadequate with respect to cost benefit, reliability and quality.

The local area networks with personal "intelligent" workstations providing powerful services from (interworking) shared resources seem to be the framework for solving the problems listed above. Within this technical and architectural context, it will be possible to:

- map a local network realisation onto a decentralised organisation (or vice versa). Powerful communication services will be at hand.

- utilise the personal workstation to build in some of the informal experience based know-how and, at the same time, have access to powerful general or special information service providers.

- install cost beneficial computer services through a stepwise process by adding resources and services to a set of interconnected open systems as fast as the needs arise and the economy permits.

Among the expected consequences of a computerised working life are:

- improved efficiency.

- improved quality of service in that more time will be available for the difficult tasks and for personal contact.

- changed physical working conditions including redundancy.

- professional (and national) vulnerability.

- changed psychological working environment including:

  . feeling of isolation because human assistance is replaced by computer assistance (change in social network).

  . alienation relative to human responsibility. The operator feels that the computer directs his/her work too much. Still, he/she has to face responsibility towards (complaining) customers/clients.

  . forced change in human working style required by the computer systems.

- changes in organisation structures and patterns of influence. On one hand, we can expect increased democracy and decentralisation as a result of improved communication services. Local networks should therefore give increased individual group identification, solidarity and active engagement. Notice that we are considering two-way communication services facilitating publication as well as reception.

  On the other hand, centralisation of activity and influence may be achieved if a single group (e.g. of experts) gain control over the use of the very powerful services.

  Now, the final result depends upon the organisation itself, its leadership and control structures.

4.2 Regulating measures

The technology itself has no social consequences. We should discuss
the use of technology, the aims for such use and the way the services
are introduced. The introduction of powerful, comprehensive and
perhaps complex computer services should include a set of regulating
measures of economical, sociological, juridical, political and
technical nature. It is no longer possible or desirable to reject
computer based services. The accompanying measures should aim at
avoiding/reducing the obvious negative consequences, thus optimising
the benefits at the individual, the organisational and the
national level.

As mentioned above, introduction of computer services is often closely
related to conflicting interests of economical or political nature.
Regulations, agreements, long range planning, education programs
and other actions have been implemented in some countries to prevent
conflicts, protect weak groups and prepare the facing of what is
considered as a new society.

Among the more specific measures which I believe will be needed are:

- legislation on Worker Protection and Working Environment.

- legislation protecting information about individuals.

- agreements between Trade Unions and Employers' Federations
  ensuring the workers of a reasonable opportunity to participate
  in system specifications, training projects and that relevant
  information is made available in appropriate form. The general
  agreement should also include procedural matters on the rights and
  duties of data shop stewards, on how conflicts should be resolved,
  etc.

- political programs and long term plans for how to utilise computer
  technology to the benefit of society. These must include industrial
  development as well as actions to improve education and research.
  Organisational and administrative measures may also be appropriate
  (political/technical advisory boards, security surveillance bodies,
  decentralisation, etc.).

- education and research is by far the most important measure to
  achieve positive results from large scale introduction of computer
  services. Society cannot be expected to accept technology without
  being familiar with it. Comprehensive education and research
  programs on the consequences of extensive use of technology are
  absolutely necessary to avoid many misconceptions and unnecessary
  side effects of computer services and their use. To analyse the
  relationships between technological development and social
  development, a substantial knowledge of technology is necessary.
  Defensive attitudes should be obsolete. Teleinformational services,
  including the local ones, will be extremely powerful tools for
  achievement of our political, social, economical and individual
  aims, whatever they may be.

However, we do need a better understanding of the effects of computer
and communication services penetrating society to be able to exert
appropriate control mechanisms.

REFERENCES

1. Jensen, W., Local Area Networks: Taxonomy and Architectures Related to ISO OSI (University of Tromsø, May 1981).

2. Data Processing - Open Systems Interconnection. Basic Reference Model (ISO DP 7498, December 1980).

3. Backman, C., Distributed Systems: Requirements and architectural considerations (Int. Symp. on Distributed Data Bases, Paris, March 1980).

4. The GILT standard. A standard for OCBMS Interconnection in the GILT environment. (GILT Working Paper, September 1981)

5. Hopkins, G., Multimode Communications on the MITRENET Computer Networks, Vol. 4, No. 5, 1980.

6. Metcalfe, R.M. and Boggs, D.R., Ethernet: Distributed Packet Switching for local Computer Networks (CACM, Vol. 19, No. 7, 1976).

LOCAL COMPUTER NETWORKS
P.C. Ravasio, G. Hopkins and N. Naffah (editors)
North-Holland Publishing Company
© IFIP, 1982

FURTHER DEVELOPMENTS ON THE CAMBRIDGE RING NETWORK
AT THE UNIVERSITY OF KENT

Stephen E. Binns, Ian N. Dallas and Edward B. Spratt

Computing Laboratory
University of Kent
Canterbury, Kent
England

INTRODUCTION

This paper gives an overview of the work carried out on the Cambridge Ring Local Area Network by the Computing Laboratory at the University of Kent, concentrating on the period from Xmas 1979 to June 1981. Future plans are also discussed. It is in part based on the material in [20]. A general introduction to the subject of Local Area Networks is given in [05], and an extensive bibliography is given in [16]. The reader who is unfamiliar with Cambridge Rings will find a brief description in Appendix 1. More detailed accounts are given in [10] and [22]. Appendix 2 contains information on Ring Protocols. References [12] and [15] contain information on Local Area Network issues in the context of UK Universities and US Universities respectively.

THE FIRST PHASE

Work on the Kent Ring, covering the period from the inception of the project in mid 1978 to the establishment of an working system eighteen months later and the first few months of full operational use is described in [19]. This covers the reasons for installing a Local Area Network at Kent and the choice of a Cambridge Ring, construction of the ring devices and how the ring was put into service. Other sections cover reliability and maintenance, protocols, software and software tools.

DESCRIPTION OF THE CURRENT RING

A diagram showing the state of the Kent ring in July 1981 is given in Figure 1. For comparative purposes the original ring, as it was in January 1980 is given in Figure 2, it was at this time that the ring was first used on a fully operational basis.

The main user services are provided by two mainframe computers acting as hosts or time sharing servers. One is an ICL2960 running under the EMAS Operating System ([21] and [18]), and this system is interfaced to the ring by a DEC (TM) PDP11/34 Front End Processor (DEC is a trademark of the Digital Equipment Corporation) which is itself attached to a General Peripheral Controller (or GPC) on the 2960. In view of the critical nature of this connection there is a duplicate ring connection for the 2960 (including a second GPC). The other host is a DEC VAX 11/780 running under Unix(TM) (A trademark of the Bell Telephone Laboratories). Users access these systems from consoles attached to Terminal Concentrator Processors (or more shortly TCP´s) on the ring; at the present time these devices are largely based upon DEC PDP11 equipment. The consoles themselves are situated in various buildings across the campus, being mostly connected to the terminal concentrators by direct lines.

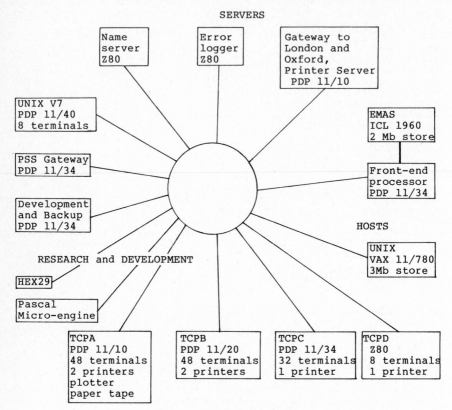

Figure 1
Ring Configuration July 1981

There are also several peripherals on the terminal concentrators which may be used on a shared basis either by the hosts or terminal users, these include a graph plotter, a paper tape reader and punch, line printers and character printers. For instance the VAX can only access line printers and a plotter via the ring. A PDP11/40 running Unix is also attached, but this is not yet a host in the current context, in that it is not accessible from consoles on any of the terminal concentrators. We return to this point in a later section.

A Remote Processing Server using leased PTT lines enables work to be sent from the 2960 to be processed at the University of London Computer Centre, the ICL2980 at Oxford and the CDC7600´s at the University of Manchester Regional Computer Centre. Returning output is sent to the ICL2960 filestore or a dedicated line printer which is under operator control in the main computer room.

Another PDP11/34 on the ring is used for several purposes. Firstly as a backup for the ICL2960 Front End Processor, secondly for remote terminal emulation (System tuning on the 2960 and VAX) and thirdly for software development. The remaining PDP11/34 is being used to develop software for a PSS/Ring Gateway. There are three Zilog Z80 micro systems in use. As a Nameserver , an Error Logger and a Development system. The remaining nodes on the ring are a Hex29 system and a Pascal Microengine(TM) (A trademark of Western Digital). These are being used on research projects based on the ring, more information on these activities is given in a later section. A separate engineering ring is used for testing and commissioning new hardware and in particular for work connected with extending the main ring. Also it is a backup source of tested components for the main service ring.

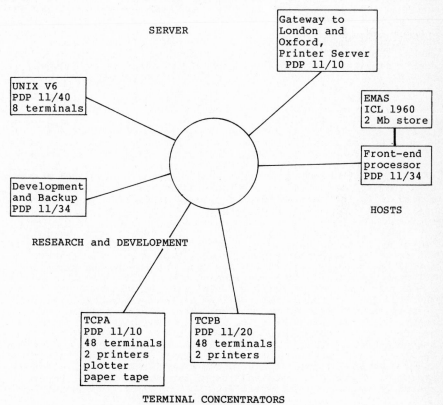

Figure 2
Ring Configuration January 1980

RELIABILITY AND MAINTENANCE

Overall we have been very pleased with the reliability of the ring in our environment. It has proved to be more reliable than any of the major devices which are connected to it. One illustration of our confidence is that an Error Logger was only put into service some 9 months after first utilising the ring in a fully operational role.

Detailed records have been kept by the operations staff since February 1981. Over the period 2nd Feb to 22nd November 1981, a total of 16 breaks was recorded. All but one of these breaks was less than 10 minutes in duration. The majority were due to engineering work being carried out on the ring or associated equipment.

There was a larger number of automatic resets of the ring caused by the monitor station. These were however transparent to the users as any transmission errors were corrected by high level protocol software.

This resulted in a total downtime of some 5 hours over 39 weeks. The largest single downtime (three and a half hours) occurred when a repeater power supply in one of the monitors overheated, and this has been the longest break we have yet experienced.

Our experience with hard ring errors has been that they arise in two different ways. Firstly when new devices are put on the ring and fail soon afterwards, and secondly faults which develop a considerable time after a device is put into service. In the latter case most of the faults have been traced to some early printed circuit boards which used pins rather than plated through holes, and these boards will be phased out as circumstances permit. The first type of fault indicates that our testing procedures should be tightened up, and this is being considered. It is clear that the availability of tested devices from specialist suppliers would markedly reduce this type of fault.

Soft ring errors may be said to occur when hardware is partially functioning, in that it is possible for the consequential faults to be corrected by the software protocols . The latter have proved to be very resilient under such conditions. In many cases it has been possible to continue running the ring in service mode until a suitable time can be found for replacing a faulty device. This is usually done between 9am and 10am during System Development time. Clearly there are bound to be times when it is necessary to carry out hardware and software tests which involve most (or possibly all) of the connected devices. However the ring itself is normally available during these times. During the 39 week period mentioned earlier there were 33 controlled breaks involving the ring with a total downtime of some 26 hours. The time taken in total, for both types of break is only considered acceptable in the context of a system where a large amount of development work is being carried out.

Pinpointing the exact location of a ring error has occasionally posed problems, partly since the information available on the monitor and the error logger is not always precise. The availability of the LSI components being developed by Cambridge would be helpful in this regard, since in this case faulty repeaters would also dispatch error packets rather than just the work stations as with our current ring.

LOCAL AND WIDE AREA PROTOCOLS AND A PSS GATEWAY

This section assumes that the reader has some familiarity with the more frequently used protocols on Cambridge Ring Local Area Networks (LAN´s) and Wide Area Networks (WAN´s) such as may be found in reference [04].

The protocols in use on the Kent Ring are largely based on the Basic Block and Byte Stream Protocols as defined by Cambridge and in use on their Ring. For brevity in what follows we will refer to them as BBP and BSP respectively. Detailed descriptions of BBP and BSP orientated towards the implementor are given in [08] and [11]. As is customary with modern protocols, the ones in use on the Ring are layered, with BBP at the lowest level.

At the present time the protocols used at Kent above the BSP level are the Interactive Terminal Protocol (or ITP) and the Remote Job Entry protocol (or RJE)[01]. These were originally developed by the Edinburgh Regional Computer Centre (ERCC) for use on the RCONET Network which links the Universities of Edinburgh, Strathclyde and Glasgow. It is essential in our environment to have a connection between the Ring and Wide Area Networks (or WAN´s) such as the British Telecom Packet Switching Service (or more shortly PSS). The accepted name for a system which connects two dissimilar networks, is a "Gateway" and such a system is under development at Kent. This makes it necessary to determine the relationship between the LAN protocols on the ring and the WAN protocols on PSS. Happily it is the case that BSP is almost at the level of the Transport Service, which is one of the approved PSS standards. (In fact at level 4 of the proposed ISO Reference Model for Open System Interconnection[26]). Work carried out by one of the authors (Dallas[07]) has shewn that it is feasible to define a realisation of the Transport Service for the ring which it is natural to refer to as the "Transport Service Byte Stream Protocol" or TSBSP. We have decided to move to this protocol on our ring since it will make it relatively straightforward to use the higher level protocols defined for PSS, such as the Network Independent File Transfer Protocol [23] and the Job Transfer and Manipulation Protocol [25] both between individual systems on the ring, and between these systems and remote computers over PSS. The Gateway forms the link between the Ring and PSS, and it will operate at the Transport Level (see Figure 3).

It is envisaged that users on ring terminals will have access to PSS via the Gateway using the TS29 terminal protocol[26], defined for PSS (this is an enhanced version of the CCITT Triple X protocol). Initially this is likely to be via a specialised terminal concentrator , but in the longer term it is envisaged that there will be a protocol convertor server which will allow consoles on any of the terminal concentrators to be used.

The Kent PSS Gateway hardware is based on a DEC11/34 computer running under RSX11M, with a DEC supplied X25 package, which is due to be delivered for field trial in Aug 1981. One important function this system will have to perform is that of controlling access to PSS and charging for usage. This project is scheduled for completion in the third quarter of 1982.

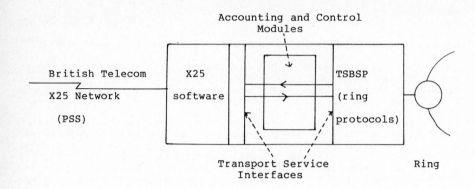

Figure 3
PSS   GATEWAY

As an interim measure it is planned in the third quarter of 1981, to evaluate some alternative Gateway software which has been developed at the Edinburgh Regional Computer Centre (or ERCC). This will allow users at Kent to have terminal access to other sites using PSS. Using the CCITT Triple X protocols, this software includes a protocol convertor from ITP to Triple X (and vice versa).

Before concluding this section it should be remarked that we have been impressed with the performance of the BBP and BSP protocols defined by Cambridge. They have worked well in our environment, which is interestingly rather different from that at Cambridge.

TERMINAL CONCENTRATORS

As previously stated the terminal concentrators currently in service at Kent are based upon DEC PDP11 hardware. However one of these systems is 10 years old and needs replacing, whilst another handles 48 terminals plus some peripherals and it is considered that it would be prudent to lessen our dependence on it. Additionally we have a requirement to extend the number of these devices and put them into departments sited outside the building which houses the Computing Laboratory. Thus there is a case for a reasonably low cost device that can handle some 8-16 consoles and optionally a printer, to replace some of our existing terminal concentrators and allow expansion in small increments at modest cost.

We have developed a Zilog Z80 Microcomputer system to fulfil this role. A prototype is working and printed circuit boards have been designed. Line speeds will be autobaud selected and will run up to 9.6K baud. The ring will be used for loading and fault diagnosis. Our intention is to construct a small number of systems inhouse for proving purposes and then to seek arrangements whereby they can be manufactured and marketed. The protocol used on our terminal concentrators is basically ITP [01], which has already been referred to in the previous section. It was originally devised for teletype like terminals. The terminal concentrator software, which was developed for use on RCONET (section 5), was adapted for ring use and enhanced to provide a line editing facility. This is particularly useful in the context of the EM common editor, which is available on EMAS and UNIX, since it appears to the user as part of this software. This approach was originally adopted since there was no raw (i.e. single character) mode to support such editing in the host processor, so it was decided to move this to the TCP, and send edited lines to the host as though they had just been typed in. The TCP software has recently been developed to allow a raw mode type of facility. Although the common editor is referred to as EM at Kent, it is in fact a subset of the original EM editor, which was developed at Queen Mary College, (QMC), London for UNIX.

The design of the software for the micro terminal concentrators is partly based upon that for the original PDP11 devices. The kernel is written in Z80 Assembler with the base level processes in BCPL [13], using a compiler for this language which has been developed at Cambridge. The aim being to write as far as possible in a high level language. Up to the end of May 1981, the micro based terminal concentrator has taken about a man year of effort, split equally between hardware and software. It is perhaps worth remarking that during the final stages of developing the software it was tuned using an analyzer which was designed and built in the laboratory. It is planned to develop this device so that it can be used with other micros e.g. the Motorola 68000. The availability of this terminal concentrator will undoubtedly meet a short term need, but in the longer term it is likely that users will require more sophisticated editing facilities, this will probably involve processing power in the terminals and more powerful terminal concentrators. In the Kent context it is considered important to avoid putting any more loading onto the hosts by adopting such an approach. Since rings may not always go to each building or department on our campus, it is envisaged that some of these terminal concentrators will be linked to the nearest point on the ring by RS422 serial lines using a specialised ring station, and one is being developed based upon a Z80 micro. This will be a single board system and it is anticipated that it will find many other uses, e.g. a nameserver, an error logger, a time of day server and for a simple front end for PDP11 systems. We also refer to this last point in section 9.

A SAMPLE RING TERMINAL SESSION

This section contains a demonstration session using a ring terminal. It shows logging on (and off) the hosts, use of the EM common editor including the use of the open command. Copying files between the hosts and archiving files on the 2960. Comments for the reader start with two slashes, these are of course not part of the actual terminal session.

```
<press space bar repeatedly>        //Adjust TCP to terminal speed
TCPD Host:unix
login:ebs
password:
<Message of Day>
You have mail
$ mail                    .        //Use Unix mail facility
From root Thu Mar 12 17:39:51 1981
Message from spooler:lanpaper8 printed
?d                                  //Delete message
```

```
See reception a. s. a. p -MW
? q                                     //? is mail prompt, exit with q
$ em
>a
this is a demonstration                 //Data Entry
message to shew use of em,
this line has a baad erryr or sew in iitt
.                                       //Dot (period) is terminator
>w message                              //write to named file
3
>q
$ cpemas -m message                     //Send file to EMAS and mail me
                                        //when done
$ stop

<logoff unix message>



<press space bar repeatedly>
TCPD Host:emas
USER:cur099
PASS:
Logged on
SS 2. 02b
17/03/81    12.29.19    Users=36    Fsys=3    Latest ALERT=16/03/81

Command:files
 ARLST       DATAEX2        **EBSRING     *ELV1#1#SCE
 EX1BDET     *LANDRAFT      *MESSAGE
//Files with one *  are cherished, ie saved onto magnetic tape after
//2 weeks of not being used, non asterisked files are cleared after
//2 weeks non use, the files marked with ** , are to be archived.

Command:archive(message)

Command:em(message)
Editor
3
>1, $p
this is a demonstration
message to shew use of em,
this line has a baad erryr or sew in iitt
>o                                      //Use open command in editor
                                        //note this
                                        //command is always available
\
this line has a baad erryr or sew in iitt
this line has a bad error or so in it
                                        //Use control chars to edit
                                        //the offending line, giving
                                        //the correct form
>wq   newmessage                        //write file and quit
3

Command:list(newmessage, .lpcl)        //List file on a local printer

Command:cpunix(newmessage, newmessage)
                                        //Send edited file back to
                                        //Unix
```

```
Command:stop
17/03/81    12.33.09    CPU=3.08 Secs  CT=10 Mins   PT=969   Ch=65 Units
Logoff
```

EXTENDING THE RING

      One of the projects being carried out in the Laboratory relates
to ways and means of extending the Ring LAN over the Kent Campus.
The reasons for wishing to do this are twofold. Firstly to provide
high   speed links between central and departmental facilities
including both intercomputer links and terminal connections, and
secondly to lessen our dependence upon leased PTT lines which are
becoming increasingly expensive. It is a local requirement that the
first phase of the extension will link the Computing Laboratory with
the Digital Systems Laboratory in the Electronics Building (see
Figure 4). This will at the same time cover one of the largest
distances which it is necessary to allow for in our context. Later
phases will include connections to other parts of the campus.

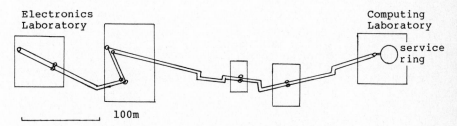

Figure 4
The First Phase of the Distribution Ring

      Originally we thought in terms of stretching the existing ring
by exuding petals from it which went through the relevant buildings,
together with a means of nipping them off in case of an excessive
number of errors or a total ring break on one of the individual
petals. This would have been done in a manner which retained the
integrity of a core ring. A similar aproach will be found in [14].
However more detailed consideration showed that this would imply
modifications to the monitor and being able to take care of ring
traffic in a sanitary way when the nipping takes place. For these
and other reasons this approach will not be followed.

      Our plans for the ring extension now involve the use of a
Bridge. This term denotes a device which provides a high speed
connection between two Local Area Networks of the same type.
Initially two rings will be used. A distribution ring which will
extend over the site connected by a bridge to the existing service
ring. This will ensure the integrity of the latter in the event of
problems on the distribution ring. Since it is not considered
practical to run the distribution ring to every building on the
site, we plan to link in such places using serial spurs, running at
speeds of up to 1 megabit/sec (See Figure 5).

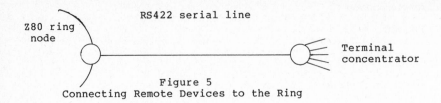

Figure 5
Connecting Remote Devices to the Ring

Appropriate cabling is being laid over the next few months (Jun-Sep), both in existing and new ducting, with the intention of having a linkup to the Electronics Building by Oct 1981. The use of new cabling has proved necessary since an attempt to use some existing twisted pair cables has not yet proved wholly satisfactory, for it may have meant running the ring at less than full speed with marginal reliability. However we are pursuing this work to a definite conclusion.

An experimental bridge has been constructed, based on a simple Z80 system. The bridge is transparent to existing ring software, performing the destination address mapping using the existing basic block protocol. This follows the approach used at Cambridge, where a high performance bridge has been developed.

Whatever means is to be used for extending the ring, it will be necessary to allow for the connection of departmental equipment which is not directly under our control. It is envisaged that anything in this category will normally be interfaced directly, or via a serial spur (see Figure 5) to the main distribution ring.

ADDING HOSTS (TIME SHARING SERVERS)

There are currently two hosts functioning as time sharing servers on the Ring. An ICL2960 running EMAS and a DEC VAX11/780 running Unix(TM). Interfacing hosts is not necessarily a simple or straightforward exercise. For example it was relevant in our context that the only modifications to the EMAS software were in the DEC PDP11/34 Front End Processor to attach it to the Ring, with no changes in the 2960 itself. A discussion on this point is given in [18], the salient point being that when EMAS was reimplemented on the ICL2900 range the designers envisaged that these systems would run in an environment where access over a network would be the normal mode of working. It is of course not bound to be the case that the same design choice would be made with other systems.

The other host is the Unix DEC VAX 11/780, here the initial Ring connection used a standard DEC PDP11 program interrupt interface on its Unibus adaptor. This has now been superseded by an interface based on a DEC KMC11 which allows more efficient data transfers using DMA techniques. Here it was important to have a good implementation language (viz ´C´), good systems hooks, the availability of the system source code and effective system generation facilities.

A PDP11/40 running UNIX is also interfaced to the Ring. However because of restrictions on the size of the operating system kernel on this machine the current connection method only permits a single non multiplexed BSP stream, operating in half duplex mode. This uses the standard BSP protocol, which has already been referred to in a previous section, but with the addition of a header line to direct the file to the correct part of the relevant filestore. This allows the transfer of files between the 11/40 and the VAX, though it should be noted that the files are sent and not requested. Work is now in hand to implement a system permitting multiplexed BSP streams (see [06]) using a Z80 system on the ring as a loosely coupled front end processor for the 11/40. This appears to be a possible way of accessing the 11/40 from any ring terminal.

An ONYX Z8000 microcomputer system has been purchased for evaluation purposes, and this may be put onto the ring at a later date, probably using an RS422 serial interface to a Z80 front end processor.

The next host to go onto the ring will be a VAX 11/750 running Unix for the University Administration. It will then be able to access certain peripherals e.g. line printers, via the ring. Initially this computer will be used for payroll and budgetary work, but in the longer term it will take over the present administrative workload which runs on the 2960. Other services which this system could provide might be a Mail Server and a simple Appointment Server. Clearly it will be important to allow only authorised access to some of the stored information on this system. One other possible application is to replace a link to the University Central Council for Admissions (UCCA) Computer at Cheltenham, which currently uses a Univac RJE protocol. This would of course imply that UCCA moves to PSS protocols.

RESEARCH WORK

Here we outline some of the research projects which are based on the ring.

1. Compiler Servers.

This project involves the development of special purpose systems, which are optimised for one particular task, namely compiling programs. This is currently being done in terms of UCSD Pascal, but future work may involve other languages. The hardware which is being used consists of two Pascal Microengines and a PDP11/34 computer. The current status of the work (see also [17]) is that the basic communications software has been written for the microengines and they may be used as multi-servers [17]. They are able to access ring services (e.g. listing files on the printer server and sending or receiving files from other ring devices). Although it is planned to use the microengines as compiler servers this has not yet proved possible due to the unavailability of the relevant source codes. However it has proved possible to set up a PDP11/34 as such a server and source code can be submitted to it from any machine on the ring with a suitable "byte stream driver", (e.g. the VAX 11/780) and receive back listing and code files. This has the potential to lift a considerable load from the mainframes. It is envisaged that at a later stage in the project use will be made of a Unix based fileserver, which is also under development.

2. A Microprogrammable Server.

This work is based upon a Digital Microsystems Hex29 system which has been modified in the Laboratory to have a microprogrammable control memory. This system is interfaced to the ring and is accessible as a server from other ring devices, and in particular the Pascal microengine used as a work station (see [02]). Software is currently being designed and implemented to both (a) develop high level software tools for microprogramming and (b) to use this machine as a testbed for implementing high level languages using microcode. At the present time a large subset of Pascal has been implemented in this way.

3. A Dedicated Typesetting and Text Processing Server

The production of high quality documents by computer techniques demands specialised hardware and software. The project aims to concentrate these facilities into a dedicated ring server, thus providing the specialised environment necesary to encourage the development of better and more "user-friendly" systems, The server should also provide a high quality document preparation service to a wide user community at moderate cost.

FUTURE PLANS

The following Ring Developments are under consideration

1. A Booking Server which would control access to the ports on the main hosts for defined purposes e.g. a timetabled class or to guarantee that at least one port was available for a specific department. One advantage of this approach is that the consequential administrative load will not be on the hosts themselves.

2. Additional time sharing servers (hosts) e.g. a VAX running VMS. This however would be dependent on the availability of sufficient software support.

3. A Spooler Server to provide editing and filing facilities for users who process their work off-site. Such a facility will enable these functions to be moved off the 2960, and consequently ease the loading on this system. This system might also provide text processing facilities of a simple nature.

4. The selection of a 16 bit micro to act as a long term replacement for the Z80. At the time of writing this report the choice appears to lie between a Zilog Z8000 and a Motorola 68000.

5. A Fileserver [03], possibly on a distributed basis.

CONCLUSIONS

The Kent Ring project has now been underway for about 30 months. Substantial progress has been made which has led to a fully operational ring-based Local Area Network. The project has demonstrated that a Cambridge Ring is able to meet two important objectives; firstly to set up a reliable resilient service and secondly that it provides one means of dealing with an evolving situation in a consistent and flexible manner. It is clear that the experience gained in interfacing the ICL2960 and the DEC 11/780 to the ring will be of great value in the context of attaching further time sharing servers. In particular it should be a straightforward matter to draw up an operational requirement in the context of interfacing a standard manufacturers operating system. We are using the Ring as a research vehicle and anticipate further projects in this area.

ACKNOWLEDGEMENTS

1. To our colleagues who have collaborated together on the Ring project:

        Mr. D. J. Caul
        Dr. R. P. A. Collinson
        Mr. A. L. Ibbetson
        Mr. M. N. A. Lee
        Mr. P. W. Riley
        Mr. T. E. Schutt (1 April 80 to 15 March 81)
        Mr. G. E. W. Tripp
        Mr. G. S. Watson

In particular we wish to thank these persons for clarifying several points which arose during the preparation of this report.

2   To the University of Cambridge Computing Laboratory and in particular Professor M. V. Wilkes (up to July 1980), Professor D. J. Wheeler, Dr A. Hopper, Dr R. M. Needham and Mr M. Johnson, for their advice and willing assistance during the Kent (Cambridge Ring) project.

3. To the Joint Network Team of the Computer Board and the Science Research Council for a grant (1) towards funding Ring developments over the period 1 August 79 to 31 July 80, (2) a capital grant for an ICL2960 General Peripheral Controller, to serve as a backup connection to the Ring and (3) A grant to support maintenance and a further development programme on the Kent ring over the period from Aug 1980 to July 1982.

3. To the Science Research Council for funding the purchase of the Pascal Microengines(TM) and the loan of a Terak Computer under the auspices of the Distributed Computing Programme.

REFERENCES

The following list of references includes some items which may not be very well known outside the UK. Particularly the so-called "Rainbow" series on Wide Area Network Protocols (ie the Red, Green, Blue and Yellow Books).

[01] Barry, P. T. , "RCONET Protocol Specifications", June 1977, Edinburgh Regional Computing Centre.

[02] Bird, R. P. , "A Dynamically Microprogrammable Machine as a Variable Function Resource in a Local Area Network", (Paper given at ICS 81, International Computing Symposium on Systems Architecture, London, 1981).

[03] Birrell, A. D. and Needham, R. M. , "A Universal File Server", IEEE Transactions on Software Engineering , Vol SE-6, No 5, Sept 1980.

[04] Charles, B. J. , "An Introduction to Current Networking Standards", Joint Network Team, Oct 1980.

[05] Clark, D. D. , Pogran, K. T. and Reed, D. P. , "An Introduction to Local Area Networks", Proc IEEE, 66 , 11, Nov 1978.

[06] Collinson. R. P. A. , "Rings and small Unices-Some Thoughts", University of Kent Computing Laboratory, 1981.

[07] Dallas, I. N. "Transport Service Byte Stream Protocol", Proc IBM/IFIP International Workshop on Local Area Networks, Zurich, 1980. (see [28]).

[08] Dallas, I. N. "An Implementation Guide for BBP", University of Kent Computing Laboratory, 1981.

[09] Dallas, I. N. "Protocols used on the ring-A Simple Guide", University of Kent, 1981.

[10] Hopper, A. "The Cambridge Ring - a Local Network" in Advanced Techniques for Microprocessor Systems, ed. F. K. Hanna, Peter Peregrinus Ltd. 1980.

[11] Johnson, M. A. "Ring Byte Stream Protocol Specification", Systems Research Group Paper, University of Cambridge Computing Laboratory, April 1980.

[12] Larmouth, J. , "Local Area Networks-A presentation of requirements and capabilities", University of Salford, April 1980.

[13] Richards, M. and Whitby-Strevens, C. , "BCPL-The Language and it´s compiler", Cambridge University Press, 1979.

[14] Saltzer, J. H. and Pogran, K. T. , "A star shaped network with high maintainability", Computer Networks 4, p239-244, 1980

[15] Saltzer, J. H. , Reed, D. P. and Clark, D. D. , "Source Routing for Campus-Wide Internet Transport", Proc IBM/IFIP International Workshop on Local Area Networks, Zurich, Aug 1980, (see [28]).

[16] Schoch, J. F. , "An Annotated Bibliography on Local Area Networks", IFIP WG6. .4 Working Paper 79-1 and Xerox Parc Technical Report SSL-79-5, Xerox, Palo Alto Research Centre, October 1979.

[17] Schutt, T. E. , and Welch, P. H. , "Applying Microcomputers in a Local Area Network", Proc Online Conference on Local Networks and Distributed Office Systems, p491-501, London, May 1981.

[18] Shelness, N. H. , Rees, D. J. , Stephens, P. D. and Yarwood, J. K. , "An Experiment in Doing it Again, But Very Well This Time", Internal Report CSR-18-77, University of Edinburgh Department of Computer Science, 1977.

[19] Spratt, E. B. , "Operational Experiences with a Cambridge Ring Local Area Network in a University Environment", Proc IBM/IFIP International Workshop on Local Area Networks, Zurich, Aug 1980 (see [28]). Available as a University of Kent Computing Laboratory Report.

[20] Spratt, E. B. , "Developments of the Cambridge Ring at the University of Kent", Proc Online Conference on Local Networks and Distributed Office Systems, p503-518, London, May 1981. [21] Whitfield, H. and Wight, A. S. , "The Edinburgh Multi-Access System", Computer Journal, Vol. 18, No. 2, 1975.

[22] Wilkes, M. V. and Wheeler, D. J. , "The Cambridge Digital Communication Ring", Local Area Communication Networks Symposium, Mitre Corp. and National Bureau of Standards, Boston, May 1979.

[23] Wilkes, M. V. and Needham, R. M. , "The Cambridge Model Distributed System", ACM Operating Systems Review, Vol. 14, No. 1, January 1980.

The next four references are available from the Data Communication Protocol Unit, The National Physical Laboratory, Teddington, Middlesex, UK.

[24] A Network Independent File Transport Protocol (The Blue Book), prepared by the High Level Protocol Group, and revised by the FTP Implementors Group, February 1981.

[25] A Network Independent Job Transfer and Manipulation Protocol (The Red Book), prepared by the JTP Working Party of the Data Communication Protocols Unit DCPU/JTMP(80) 1.

[26] A Network Independent Transport Service (The Yellow Book) prepared by Study Group 3 of the British Post Office PSS User Forum, SG3/CP(80) 1980-2-16.

[27] Character Terminal Protocols on PSS (The Green Book). A recommendation on the use of X3, X28 and X29 prepared by Study Group 3 of the British Telecom PSS User Forum. Revision 1, February 1981.

[28] Local Networks for Computer Communications (Proceedings of IFIP Working Group 6.4 International Workshop on Local Area Networks, organised by IBM, Zurich, Switzerland 27-29 August), edited by West, A. and Janson, P. , North Holland 1981.

Copies of references [02], [06], [07], [08], [09], [17], [19] and [20] may be obtained from

> The Documentation Officer
> Computing Laboratory
> Cornwallis Building
> University of Kent
> Canterbury
> Kent, CT2 7NF.

APPENDIX 1   THE CAMBRIDGE RING

This Appendix gives a short description of the Cambridge Ring
Local Area Network. Apart from a few minor corrections it is
identical to the Appendix in [18]. It follows closely the treatment
given in Hopper (1980). The reader who requires more information
should also consult Wilkes and Wheeler (1979). A general
introduction to the subject of Local Area Networks is given in
Clark, Pogran and Reed (1978).

A Cambridge ring consists of a set of nodes which are joined
serially in the form of an endless loop. These nodes are of two
types. Firstly, repeaters which are used to regenerate the digital
signals which transmit information round the ring. Secondly a node
may be used to connect a device (typically a computer) to the
network, in which case it consists of a repeater plus a station.
Individual devices are connected to these stations by means of
access boxes, which are specific to the relevant device. The figures
below show a 3 station ring (Figure A1.1) and a node (Figure A1.2).

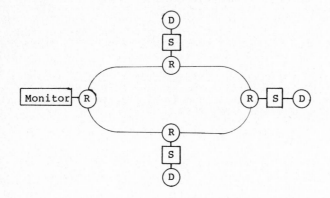

Figure A1.1
A Ring with 3 Stations

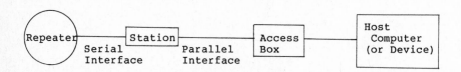

Figure A1.2
Station/Repeater Ring Node with Access Box Connecting
to a Host Computer (or other Device)

Information is sent between stations in minipackets (or ring
packets). The format for one of these "packets" is given in Figure
A1.3.

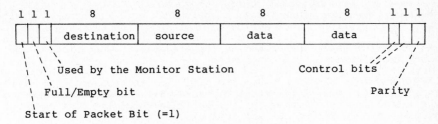

Figure A1.3
Minipacket Format for Cambridge Ring

The Cambridge ring works on the "empty slot principle", which operates as follows. When the Ring is initialised a specialised work station called the monitor station sets up a framing structure on the ring so that at least one minipacket is in flight round it, the exact number of such packets being dependent upon the length of the ring and the number of nodes (e.g. at Kent there is, currently, one such minipacket). There are gap digits in the form of zeros which precede the minipacket(s). The monitor station is also used for monitoring the ring, clearing lost packets and accumulating error statistics.

When a station has a packet ready for transmission in its shift register it waits until the next slot (i.e. the next empty packet on the ring). It then reads the full/empty bit and writes a one at the output. If the full/empty bit was a zero it transmits the packet if, however, the full/empty bit was a one, the slot is already taken and this procedure is repeated for the next packet, and thus minimizes the delay at each node.

The transmitted minipacket then goes round the ring to its destination where the control bits are set on the fly to indicate busy, rejected, ignored or accepted. In the latter case the data is copied into the destination station. The minipacket now returns to the source where the full/empty bit is set to zero; thus emptying the slot, but the current content of the minipacket is also compared with the original content, thus providing a consistency check. The Cambridge design has a built-in anti-hogging feature, so that a station which has just transmitted a packet cannot immediately send another packet. (Hogging occurs when one station takes most or all of the of the available bandwidth).

Thus minipackets which are to be transferred are delayed at the originating station until an empty slot is found but transmission then goes at the full speed of the ring. Since it is possible for the ring to get clogged with packets returning marked busy, when devices with varying speed characteristics are interconnected using the ring, there is a feature in the hardware which delays the re-transmission of minipackets which are returned to the sender marked as busy.

The ring is built using TTL technology and operates at 10MHz with a maximum distance of about 100 metres between repeaters. The signals are transmitted along twisted pairs, such as are used for the full duplex operation of teletypes. Transformers are used throughout for common mode rejection and isolation. The repeaters

are powered from the ring since they have to operate reliably
whether they are connected to a station or not. The number of bits
delay at a station is a fraction of a bit and there is a minimum
ring delay of about 5 microseconds. LSI versions of the repeater and
station have been designed at Cambridge using Uncommitted Logic
Array techniques, on Ferranti chips.

Facilities are provided to aid in maintenance and error
recovery. If one of the start of packet bits is incorrectly set or
the full/empty bit becomes full, this is detected and then corrected
by the monitor station. If the full bit becomes (incorrectly) set to
zero then the minipacket might be ignored at the destination but
will be detected by the source, whilst the transmitter will detect
if the monitor station bit becomes corrupted in such a way that the
slot is marked empty. In general errors are detected by the source
or monitor station within one ring delay.

The parity bit at the end of the minipacket is used for
localising transient faults and ring breaks. This works as follows
Each station continually computes the parity of every passing packet
and empty slot, and then writes it into the parity bit. If this does
not match the old parity bit then a fault has occurred and since the
correct parity is inserted at each station the fault must have
occurred since the last active station. In other words the ring is
continuously being monitored for errors and any fault detected is
located to the nearest active down-stream station. The error
information is then transmitted to the monitor station by inserting
a special minipacket into the next vacant slot. A variant on this
approach is used to detect ring breaks, since the repeaters are
designed so that a continuous stream of zeros are emitted when there
is no data at the input, and this causes a fault packet to be sent
to the monitor.

A typical configuration for a small ring with seven stations is
shown in Figure A1.4.

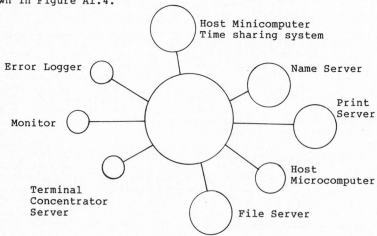

Figure A1.4
An Example Six Station Ring

This could be used as follows:

(a)   Consoles on the terminal concentrator processor could   access
the   host minicomputer which runs a small time-sharing system
or alternatively the microcomputer on a serial (or one   at   a
time) basis.

(b)   The   minicomputer   and the microcomputer both access the file
server which provides common filestore facilities.

(c)   The printer server provides printing facilities   which   could
be accessed by the other ring devices.

The   term   "server"   denotes that the device "serves" users (or
perhaps devices) on the ring, or more   generally   on   a   Local   Area
Network. Two   of   the   servers   shown   in Figure Al. 4 exist on the
Cambridge Ring and are based upon Z80 micros ; these are   the   Error
Logger Server and the Name Server.

The Error Logger Server, which immediately precedes the monitor
station,   normally   has   a   hard   copy   output device and is used to
record error messages produced by the system from the other stations
on the ring (including the monitor). It is   also   possible   to   send
textual   messages   to the error logger server under program control.
Thus a hard copy record of events on the ring is produced,   this   is
especially   useful for the detection of intermittent faults and will
be examined on a regular basis by maintenance staff.

The   Name   Server   contains   a   lookup   table,   typically   in
programmable   read   only   memory,   consisting   of   the names of ring
devices, (i.e. a service, a process or a computer   anywhere   in   the
system)   in   character   string   format   and their ring addresses when
presented with a name. It is also capable of performing the converse
translation. This device enables reconfiguration of the ring devices
to be carried out in a transparent fashion as far as   other   devices
on the ring are concerned.

The   Fileserver   acts   as   a   common   disc   filestore   for ring
devices, typically to enhance disc capacity on hosts, or possibly to
provide such facilities for host devices which do not have discs   of
their own.

References

[1]   Clark, D. D. , Pogran, K. T. and Reed, D. P. , "An Introduction
to Local Area Networks", Proc IEEE, 66 , 11, Nov 1978.

[2] Hopper, A. "The Cambridge Ring - a Local   Network"   in   Advanced
Techniques   for   Microprocessor   Systems,   ed.   F.   K.   Hanna, Peter
Peregrinus Ltd. 1980.

[3] Wilkes, M. V. and   Wheeler,   D.   J.   ,   "The   Cambridge   Digital
Communication   Ring",   Local   Area Communication Networks Symposium,
Mitre Corp. and National Bureau of Standards, Boston, May 1979.

APPENDIX 2   SIMPLE GUIDE TO RING PROTOCOLS

TERMINOLOGY

Throughout this appendix, the following terminology is used:

MINI-PACKET is the 38 bit structure sent around the ring.

OCTET is a grouping of 8 bits.

BLOCK is a group of 1 or more octets.

INTRODUCTION

The protocols used on the Cambridge Ring are analogous to an onion skin. You peel off one skin, (i.e. the header and trailer of one protocol), and you are left with a new skin, or protocol underneath.

This can be represented diagramatically, as shown below:

```
----------------------------------------------------------------------
 |      *|      *|                              |             *|   Basic Blo
 | HEADER| ROUTE |           DATA               |    CHECKSUM  |   Protocol
----------------------------------------------------------------------

         |                              |
  _____|                         _____|
 |                                |
 |                                |


    -----------------------------------------------------------------
    |     *|     *|                                              |   Byte
    | RDY/ |      |                                              |
    | NOTRDY/| DATA/ |           DATA                            |   Stream
    | RESET/ | NODATA |                                          |
    | CLOSE |      |                                             |   Protocol
    -----------------------------------------------------------------

             |               |
      _____|          _____|
     |                 |


       ----------------------------------------------------------------
       | RJE or ITP  |                                          |   RCONET IT
       |   HEADER    |              DATA                        |   RJE Proto
       ----------------------------------------------------------------

               |              |
        _____|         _____|
       |                |


          -------------------------------------------------------------
          |    DATA RECEIVED FROM A TERMINAL OR CARD READER, SAY   |
          -------------------------------------------------------------
```

* These are made up of 2 octets.

PROTOCOLS AND THEIR USES

Currently, the following protocols are in use on the ring:

BBP - Basic Block Protocol (a Cambridge protocol).
BSP - Byte Stream Protocol (a Cambridge protocol).
SSP - Single Shot Protocol (a Cambridge protocol).
ITP - Interactive Terminal Protocol (an RCONET protocol).
RJE - Remote Job Entry Protocol (an RCONET protocol).

If a mini-packet is transmitted from one station on the ring to another, without using any protocols, then

a) it can get lost.
b) it can get corrupted, without the receiver knowing.
c) it has to compete at the receiving station with other mini-packets from other transmitters to that station.

Point b) may be overcome if each octet of data in the mini-packet consists of say 7 bits and a parity bit, or the 2 octets of data are considered as 15 bits and a parity bit. However, neither of these schemes allow the transmission of data where all 8 or 16 bits are significant.

If BBP is introduced, then a block of octets can be transmitted from one station to another without competition from other transmitters to that station. This is because on seeing a header, the receiving station locks on to the transmitter by setting its source select register.

Despite this, mini-packets can still get lost, and corrupted.

Since there is a checksum at the end of a BBP block, mini-packet loss and corruption usually will be detected. (The checksum calculated by the receiver will not be the same as that sent by the transmitter). On detecting such a condition, the whole block will be thrown away.

BBP also has a route mini-packet of 12 bits, (4 of the 16 bits of data are unused). This means that blocks can be transmitted to many ($\sim$ 4000) different users/processes on the same station. Each is identified by a station and port number, where port number is what appears in the route mini-packet.

So, BBP will transmit blocks from one station to another, with no guarantee of what should happen if an error occurs, and the receiver throws the block away, and with no rules as to what should happen if say, the receiver runs out of buffer space.

Hence, another layer of protocol is required. Amongst other things, this layer will take care of these conditions. BSP is such a protocol.

Although at the same level, SSP does not take care of the problems to the same extent as BSP. SSP is a simple protocol for simple uses, e.g. making requests to the name-server and down-line loading. A variation on SSP is used to make a connection between two ports on different stations - an OPEN request.

BSP, therfore is quite a sophisticated beast, and is used once an OPEN request has been issued and accepted.

By a system of sequence numbers, timeouts and control commands, BSP can ensure that any data which is transmitted from one station to another, eventually will always arrive at the destination station, error free and in the correct sequence, (i.e. the blocks will be in the correct order). Lack of buffer space is taken care of by commands which indicate whether buffer space is available for the next transfer. Within the command repetoire of BSP are commands to get a link between 2 stations into a pre-defined state if something goes disastrously wrong, or a machine attached to a station crashes.

The layer of protocol above BSP is the applications protocol layer. Such protocols are ITP, RJE or NIFTP (Network Independent File Transfer Protocol) etc. These protocols by inference are applications dependent, and their description will not be covered here.

THE FUTURE

Who knows what the future holds? What is certain is that BBP, SSP and BSP are here to stay. Many of the applications level protocols will need to be replaced by the equivalent network independent standard protocols, e.g. NIFTP, TS29, JTMP and VTP.

BSP, (with a little help from BBP and the initial connection protocol (OPEN)), currently forms the basis of a transport service. It will be extended, so that it forms THE Transport Service, as defined by the "Yellow Book".

Note, the Transport Service provides to the applications level, a set of network independent primitives or commands. The applications level communicates with the Transport Service via these primitives, and the Transport Service maps these primitives on to the underlying protocols. This means that the applications level knows nothing of the underlying communications medium, and in the future, communications subnets may be replaced by subnets employing different communications techniques, (even carrier pigeons!), without modifications being required to the applications level, (and above).

LCN DISTRIBUTED OPERATING SYSTEM

LOCAL COMPUTER NETWORKS
P.C. Ravasio, G. Hopkins and N. Naffah (editors)
North-Holland Publishing Company
© IFIP, 1982

THE CHORUS DISTRIBUTED OPERATING SYSTEM :
DESIGN AND IMPLEMENTATION

Marc GUILLEMONT

Institut National de Recherche en Informatique et en Automatique
BP 105
78153 Le Chesnay Cedex
FRANCE

CHORUS is an architecture for distributed systems. It
includes a method for designing a distributed application,
a structure for its execution and the (operating) system
to support this execution.
One important characteristic of CHORUS is that the major
part of the system is built with the same architecture as
applications. In particular, the exchange of messages,
which is the fundamental communication/synchronization
mechanism, has been extended to the most basic functions
of the system.

1. - INTRODUCTION

CHORUS ([BAN 80],[ZIM 81]) is an architecture for distributed systems. It has
been designed for a wide variety of machines and networks and for a large class
of applications : process control, mail systems, office automation, telecommunications, etc ... It includes a basic methodology for designing distributed applications, a structure for executing them and the (operating) system supporting
this execution.

A prototype implementation is currently under development on micro-processors
Intel 8086 connected through Danube, an Ethernet-like local network. System and
actors are written is Pascal.

This paper focuses on the architecture of the (operating) system : balance of
functions between kernel and system actors, communication between kernel and
system actors, implementation of I/Os and interrupts, interface of the system.
It first presents (section 2) an overview of the CHORUS architecture. A second
part (section 3) presents the internal structure of a current implementation of
the system, including implementation of interrupts, I/Os, error handling and
protection. A third part (section 4) presents the various levels of interface of
the system.

2. - OVERVIEW OF CHORUS

In CHORUS, a distributed system is a set of interconnected sites (computers). On
each site, active entities are called actors ; an actor is, in a first approximation, equivalent to the usual concept of sequential process. An actor may
create or destroy other (local or distant) actors ; it may communicate with other
(local or distant) actors by exchanging messages through ports. An actor can
manipulate local objects.

On each site, the (operating) system provides (in cooperation with systems on
other sites) services to application actors. The system supports and controls the

execution of actors.
The (operating) system includes a kernel present on each site and system actors
which can be distributed.

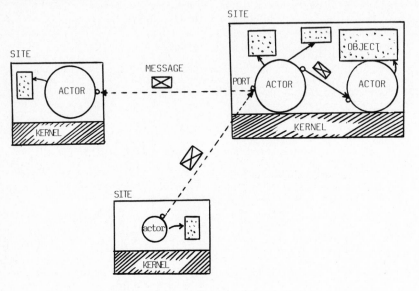

Figure 2.1. : Run-time architecture of the CHORUS system

2.1. - Execution of an actor

An actor is the local and sequential unit of execution.
Local : an actor is entirely (code an data) on one site.
Sequential : an actor processes, sequentially, the messages it receives. The
processing of a message constitutes a processing-step. Each message triggers the
execution of a processing-step and only the reception of a message may trigger
the execution of a processing-step. An actor may execute only one processing-step
at a time : within an actor, there is no interweaving of processing-steps.

A processing-step is designated by its entry-point in the actor. A switch procedure determines, for each message, which entry-point is to be entered to process
the message. This switch procedure may be dynamically parameterized by the actor.

The sequence of processing-steps depends of course on the messages received by
the actor on its ports and is ultimately determined by a selection procedure ;
this procedure permits to decide, at the end of each processing-step of the
actor, which message is to be processed next. This selection procedure may be
dynamically parameterized by the actor.

The switch and selection procedures are executed by the local kernel.

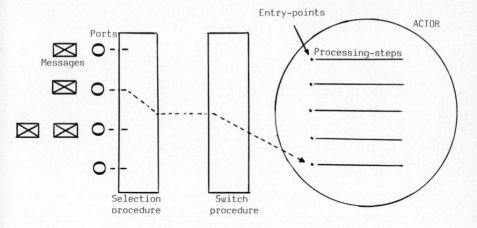

<u>Figure 2.2.</u> : Execution of an actor

As a processing-step may be triggered only by the reception of a message, an actor could be blocked, waiting for a message which would never comes (for instance if the sender of the message has failed). In order to avoid these deadlocks, an actor may enable a time-out on a port ; the effect of enabling such a time-out is :

- if some message arrives onto the port before the end of the time-out, the time-out is disabled,
- if no message has arrived onto the port at the end of the time-out, the system generates a diagnosis message which is sent onto the port ; this message, as any message, will trigger a processing-step in the actor.

The time-out on a port may be disabled by any message received onto the port or by only a subset of these messages ; in the second case, the time-out is enabled for a couple (P',P), which means that only messages sent through P' onto P may disable this time-out. Several time-outs of the second type may be enabled simultaneously on the same port P.

2.2. - <u>Creation and destruction of actors</u>

An actor is built from a <u>model of actor</u> (see section 2.5.).

An actor may create another actor, locally or on a distant site ; the creation of actor is a service offered by the system. The main parameters for a creation are :

- the name of a model of actor
- the name of a site where the actor is to be created,
- an initial message for the newly created actor.

Several actors may be created from the same model of actor.

The actor is created with an "umbilical" port on which it receives its initial message ; this message triggers a first processing-step in the actor, the <u>"initial-step"</u>.

An actor may require its own termination ; it may also, under some conditions, require the destruction of other actors.

Creation and destruction of actors are controlled by actor-creation and actor-destruction control procedures (see section 2.8.).

2.3. - Communication

An actor may communicate with other actors (and with itself) by sending messages through ports.

Actors consume and produce messages and ports allow them to receive and send messages (the same port may be used both for sending and receiving messages). In order to communicate, at least two ports are necessary : one to send the message and one (or more) to receive it ; messages are sent and delivered with the indication of names of both source and destination ports. Using ports to send as well as to receive messages provides an homogeneous designation for both sender and receiver of the message. For instance, in request-reply communications (which are the most frequent), each actor may send its reply to the sending port of the request message it received.

The system provides a communication service which is site independent : the sending actor needs only to indicate the name of the destination port of the message ; the system will find the site where this port resides and will transport the message onto that site. This basic communication facility is a point-to-point datagramm facility : no error control, no flow control, no diagnosis. More reliable communication mechanisms (e.g. "virtual circuits") are built on top of this basic service. No hypothesis has been made about the underlying communication medium ; however, this will impact the performance of communication facilities : for instance, broadcasting is more efficient with a broadcast network but is nevertheless feasible with a meshed network.

Communications may be controlled by control procedures : one send control procedure executed at the sending port and one receive control procedure executed at the receiving port. A send control procedure can check, for instance, that an actor sends only messages corresponding to known formats, while a receive control procedure can check, for instance, that an actor does not receive messages that it would not be able to process.

In order for a port to be used by an actor, two steps are necessary : creation and opening.
Just as actors, ports are created from models of port. An actor may create or destroy local or distant ports. A created port has a name and one send and one receive control procedure.
In order to use a port (either to receive or to send messages), an actor must open it ; the open operation is like to "link" the port to the actor. When the actor does not need the port any longer, it closes it (i.e. it "unlinks" it). A port may be opened by only one actor at a time, but several actors may open and close successively the same port.
Messages sent onto a port which is not opened (i.e. which is not "linked" to any actor) are lost.

The distinction between creation and opening of a port is intended to facilitate reconfiguration, i.e. to change distribution of actors behind ports without any change for external actors : a port keeps its identity through successive openings ans closures ; the above mechanism allows several actors to realize successively the same function (for instance to balance load or in case of failure) keeping the same interface for the actors which use that function.

Example of failure : actor A performs some function F behind port Pf ; actor B is in charge of looking after actor A ; B is able to perform function F (or some equivalent function) and B knows the name of the port Pf of A. Actor A fails ; the system automatically closes ports of A, among which Pf ; B detects the failure and B opens port Pf. For external actors, Pf is still the port which offers the function F in spite of a short interruption of service.

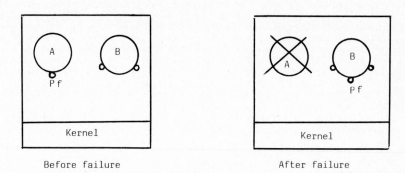

      Before failure   After failure

Figure 2.3. : Dynamic reconfiguration after a failure

Creation and destruction of a port are controlled by port-creation and port-destruction control procedures. The opening of a port is controlled by an open control procedure. The closure of a port is not controlled as an actor may always close the ports it has opened (except its "umbilical" port).

2.4. - Access to objects

Objects are passive entities, i.e. they can only be manipulated by actors.

An object is local, i.e. entirely on one site. An actor may create or destroy objects ; an object is created from a model of object. An actor may manipulate an object under two conditions :

- it must be on the same site as the object,
- it must have a link to the object.

Establishment of a link between an actor and an object is a system service. When an actor has a link to an object, it may access the object without any system control. Several actors may manipulate simultaneously the same object. When an actor does not need an object any more, it requests the destruction of its link to the object.

Creation, destruction of an object and establishment of a link are controlled by object-creation, object-destruction and link control procedures.

2.5. - Construction of an actor

Programming actors is done in several steps :

(1) a distributed application is described as a set of treatments (triggered by messages) grouped into modules. A module will be the smallest entity from the point of view of distribution, i.e. treatments in one module will be always in

the same actor and therefore on the same site ; in particular, there is no parallelism between treatments of the same module (on the other hand, two actors issued
from the same model may execute in parallel similar treatments). Communication
between treatments in a module may be through shared data ; communication between
modules is achieved through messages exchange.

(2) modules are grouped in models of actor. Criteria for grouping are essentially
criteria of distribution, protection and performance : modules in the same model
of actor will be, at run-time, in the same actor and a fortiori on the same site.
Communications between modules in an actor could be, in some cases, expedited by
replacing automatically the sending of a message between two modules of the actor
by a procedure call. Control procedures associated with the actor (creation and
destruction) are included in the model of actor.

(3) actors are created from models of actor on a site where they are executed.

2.6. - Construction of a port

A port is described by a model of port ; this model contains the control procedures associated with the port : creation, destruction, opening, send and receive
control procedures.

If a port on site S1 is to be opened by an actor on site S2, the port must be
first transfered from site S1 to site S2.

2.7. - Construction of an object

An object is described by a model of object ; this model contains control procedures associated with the object : creation, destruction and link.

2.8. - Controls

As outlined in sections 2.2., 2.3. and 2.4. the CHORUS system applies controls on
some actions by actors :
        _ creation and destruction of actors,
        - creation, destruction an opening of ports,
        - transmission and reception of messages,
        - creation, destruction and link to objects.

Controls are described by procedures ; these procedures are included in models of
actor, port and object ; in models of actor, these procedures are distinct from
the modules which describe processing of messages received by the actor.

Control procedures are executed by the system on each site. They are executed at
"points of visibility", i.e. when the actor requires some service.

As controls are described independently of processing, this gives some advantages :

        - controls may be adapted to each application,
        - controls may be modified without any other modification in the actors,
        - controls may be changed from a debugging phase to a runtime phase.

3. - SYSTEM IMPLEMENTATION

This section outlines the organization of a current test implementation of the
CHORUS system. It details the distribution of services between the kernel and

system actors and exposes their inter-relations.

3.1. - The kernel and system actor

The system consists of a kernel (which peforms a minimum set of services) and system actors (which perform all other services).

More precisely, the kernel only supports execution of local actors, i.e. :

- selection of the next message to be processed (according to the selection procedure) by one of the local actors,
- switching to the corresponding entry-point (according to the switch procedure),
- management of time-outs on local ports,
- local transport of messages,
- partial management of interrupts (see section 3.2.),
- partial realization of I/Os (see section 3.3.).

All other system services are performed by system actors, in particular :

- creation and destruction of actors,
- creation, destruction, opening and closing of ports,
- distant communication,
- creation and destruction of objects,
- management of links to objects,
- memory management,
- management of names,
- file management,
- etc ...

3.1.1. - Relation kernel/system actors

In order to perform its services, the kernel needs informations like names of local actors and ports, associations between ports and actors, etc ... Updates of these informations are decided by system actors.

However, the kernel and system actors do not share any memory. The kernel handles tables like :

- the list of local actors ; for each actor : the name of its model, its name, its status, its context of execution, reference of its ports, parameters for selection and switch procedure, etc ...

- the list of local opened ports ; for each port : its name, its context of execution, the reference of the actor which has opened it, the queue of messages received, the time-outs (if any), etc ...

- the list of local objects ; for each object : its name, its context of execution.

When a system actor performs a system service, this service may lead to an update of informations in the tables of the kernel ; for instance, if an actor opens a port P, the kernel must get informations about this port. The system actor does not access directly the table of local ports, but it transmits to the kernel a request "parameters of a newly opened port" and the kernel updates its table.

Therefore, system actors do not need to know the structure of the kernel tables. System actors are in charge of controlling that updates are consistent ; the kernel is in charge of controlling that its tables remain consistent.

This clear separation between the kernel and system actors has several advantages :

- the kernel interface is the list of messages it can receive ; this interface is
  therefore clearly specified.

- the kernel may change, its tables too, without any change in actor systems.

- System actors are as independent as possible from the machines : they may be
  more easily transported. (Independance cannot be complete for the Memory Management Actor, for instance).

Transmission of information between system actors and the kernel is performed
exactly in the same way as any actor transmits to the kernel a request for a time
out, for instance (see section 4.1.).

3.1.2. - Distribution of system actors

Indeed, the usual interface between application actors and system actors is uniform : request for the service in a message, reply in another message. As the
message communication is site independent, system actors need not be all present
on each site ; the only constraint is that system actor which transmit information
to the kernel must be local for each site.

On each site, the minimum system consists of a kernel and a set of system actors :

- an actor manager,
- a port manager,
- an object manager on sites which have objects,
- a transport station,
- a files manager on sites which have secondary memory.
  Other system actors may be remote.

3.2. - Interrupts

Interrupts do not activate actors directly : this would contradict the model of
execution of an actor where only a message may trigger a processing-step. The
interrupt mechanisms are seen by actors as ports which send one message (called
interrupt-message) for each interrupt ; i.e., the events which arise as interrupts
in the machine (control of a physical process, I/O, etc ...) are represented by
messages.

More precisely, the implementation of interrupts is described below :

A system actor I opens one port Pi for each interrupt i ; the port Pi represents
the interrupt mechanism i.

When an actor A needs to receive interrupt-messages corresponding to interrupts i,
it sends a request-message to Pi ; this message contains the name of a port Pa
of A on which actor A wants to receive the interrupt-messages. The actor I receives
this message and controls the validity of the request :

- if the control is negative, the request is rejected and I sends a diagnosis
  message to A ;

- if the control is positive, I transmits to the kernel the triplet (i, Pi, Pa).

When interrupt i arises, the kernel receives it and generates an interrupt-message
whose sending port is Pi ans whose destination port is Pa : actor A receives on

port Pa (from Pi) one message for each interrupt i. This message will trigger a processing-step, exactly as any other message.

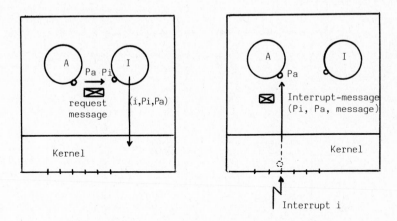

Figure 3.1. : Implementation of interrupts

According to the implementation, preemption may be authorized or not. In the positive case, when the kernel has transformed an interrupt in a message onto port Pa, the current execution of actor is suspended and the processing-step associated with the interrupt-message is started. Preemption allows faster response time for interrupts. This mechanism must respect two conditions :

1/ the suspended actor must not be the actor which processes the interrupt-message : there cannot be preemption or parallelism between two processing-steps of the same actor,

2/ if the processing-steps have priorities (through the associated ports), they must be respected.

3.3. - Inputs/Outputs

All application actors request I/O from system actors which offer a high level interface ; for instance, a File Server actor (which is a system actor) offers operations like : open a file, read a logical record, write a logical record, delete a file, etc ... Communication with a (system) actor is achieved through messages exchange.

For system actors in charge of handling I/Os, the physical devices are seen as ports ; the request for an I/O is a message sent to this port ; the end of I/O is a message sent from this port.

For instance, a physical device D is represented by a port Pd. A system actor S requests an elementary I/O on D by sending a message form its port Ps to Pd ; this message contains the requested parameters for the I/O (read or write, adress of a buffer, number of bytes, etc ...). The kernel recognizes Pd as representing the physical device D and it performs the elementary I/O operation ; the end of I/O is signalled by an interrupt, transformed (by the kernel) into a message (see section 3.2.) from Pd to Ps.

For system actors, the available I/O operations are the operations of the machine itself : forinstance, I/O of one character on an asynchronous line, I/O of 128 bytes on a floppy disk, etc ...

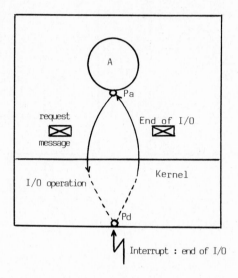

Figure 3.2. : Implementation of I/Os

This organization of I/Os will allow easier implementation of CHORUS on multi-processor machines where I/Os are achieved by specialized processors.

3.4. - Error handling

Many errors may arise during execution of an actor :

- error in a service request (incorrect parameter, unauthorized request, ...),
- error in behaviour (sending an incorrect message, ...),
- error in execution (division by zero, adressing out of memory, ...).

These errors may be handled or not by the actor ; in the negative case, the actor will be usually destroyed and a diagnosis message is produced to signal this destruction.

In the positive case, i.e. if the actor wants to handle some errors, they must be reported to it. These errors are detected by system actors, by the kernel or by the machine ; in the first two cases, the system actor or the kernel may send a diagnosis message onto a port specified by the actor which produced the error ; in the last case, the kernel handles the error and transforms it into a message. In all cases, the actor receives the error report as a message. The port which receives the diagnosis message is not necessarily a port of the actor which produced the error ; for instance, an actor A may watch over an actor B and receive all diagnosis messages associated with B's errors.

In order to handle errors, an actor may open specialized ports associated with ad-hoc processing-steps. According to the CHORUS model, there cannot be interweaving between processing-steps within an actor : if a processing-step P1 produces an error, the processing-step P2 which handles the diagnosis message cannot be executed before the end of P1.

3.5. - Controls

Controls are performed by the system on supporting execution of local actors. Section 2 pointed out which are the standard controls and when they are executed.

Controls are described by control procedures included in models of actor, port or object.

Parameters are transmitted to the control procedure as a message (again !) and result of the control is returned to the kernel in the same way. Execution of a control procedure is like execution of a processing-step.

In models of port and object, the only treatments are the control procedures ; those treatments are structured like control procedures in a model of actor.

3.6. - System actors

This section presents, as an example, one system service : the creation of actor. This service is performed by the "actor manager" (AM) system actor.

The hypothesis in the example (for the sake of simplicity) is that the creation is requested locally and that the model of actor is locally available.

The creation is requested by a message sent onto a port of the AM actor ; this message contains :

- the name of the model of actor,
- the name of the model of the umbilical port,
- possibly passwords (for control purpose),
- the initial message (embedded in the creation message),
- the name of a port on which the creation reply message is to be sent.

The reception of this message starts a sequence of processing-steps which is summarized below :

1/ AM sends a message to the "file manager" (FM) system actor in order to request to read (in the file which contains the model of actor) the record containing the indication of the amount of memory necessary for the execution of the actor.

2/ FM sends to AM a reply message with the record which contains that parameter.

3/ AM sends a "memory request" message to the "memory manager" (MM) system actor.

4/ MM determines some place in memory where the new actor will be loaded. If no room is available, the memory request is rejected and MM sends to AM a negative reply message. If room is available, MM sends to AM a reply message including the adress for the new actor.

5/ AM sends a message to the "program loader" (PL) system actor in order to request the load of the new actor from the model of actor (which is supposed to be in a file).

6/ PL loads the actor directly in memory with the help of FM ; possibly, it intializes the code if there is some adress translation to be performed. PL sends to AM a reply message "end of loading".

7/ AM sends a message to the "name manager" (NM) system actor in order to ask a
   name for the new actor.

8/ NM sends to AM a reply message with a unique global name.

9/ AM sends a message to the "port manager" (PM) system actor in order to
   request the creation and opening of the "umbilical" port for the new actor.

10/ PM creates and opens a new port. PM sends to AM a reply message with the name
    of the new port.

11/ AM transmits to the kernel informations about the new actor : its name, the
    name of its port, its context of execution, etc ... AM requests the kernel to
    check the validity of creation of the new actor. AM sends onto the "umbilical
    port" the initial message and a "positive reply message" onto the appropriate
    port of the requesting actor.

Some remarks about this description :

1/ the specific role of the kernel is very reduced : it acquires information
   (existence and name of the actor, existence of a port, etc ...) without any
   treatment.

2/ the whole creation is a complex operation but it involves several actors and
   the job of each one is rather simple ; the design of the system in actors helps
   in gaining modularity and simplicity.

3/ Several creations may be performed in parallel, so long as AM keeps a memory of
   current creations.

4. - LEVELS OF VISIBILITY

This section describes several levels of visibility of the CHORUS system ; first,
it presents the most elementary level ; then it presents some techniques which
allow to offer to application programmers a higher level visibility of the system.

4.1. - Elementary access to the kernel

The kernel is the lowest level of the architecture. The interface of the kernel
consists in only one primitive, namely RETURN ; this primitive means "end of the
current processing-step" and it has as parameter a set of messages. For the sake
of homogeneity, communication with the kernel is seen from actors as exchange of
messages : among the messages of the RETURN

- some give parameters for the selection for the next processing-step,
- some give parameters for the switch for the next processing-step,
- some give parameters for the time-outs to be enabled,
- others are to be sent on ports of actors.

The distinction between a message intended for the kernel and a message intended
for an actor is in the name of the destination port ; the actor may even not be
aware of that distinction.

When an actor is started, it receives the message which triggers the processing-
step ; during the whole execution of the processing-step, the actor may access
only this message and its local data. The actor modifies local data and constitutes
messages. When the processing-step is ended, the actor RETURNs to the kernel transmitting all its messages. The actor will gain back control only to execute the

next processing-step with a new message.

When the kernel is called with RETURN, it performs the following actions :

- it processes messages for selection, switch and time-outs ; (an actor must
  define, at the end of each processing-step, all parameters for the next selection of a message ; on the other hand, parameters for the switch remain valid
  from one processing-step to the other until they are modified).

- it applies to other messages (i.e. messages for actors) the send control procedures associated with sending ports ; if the control is negative, the message
  is destroyed and the kernel (optionnaly) generates a diagnosis message for the
  sending actor.

- messages are associated with local ports ; if the destination port of the
  message is not local, the kernel associates the message with a surrogate (local)
  port which is a port of the Transport Station actor.

- it applies to each local message the receive control procedure associated with
  the receiving port ; if the control is negative, the message is destroyed and
  the kernel (optionnaly) generates a diagnosis message for the sending actor.

- it determines which message is the next message to be processed by an actor and
  it starts the associated processing-step.

For system actors, the interface with the kernel is a bit different, as they may
transmit to the kernel other messages than parameters for selection, switch or
timeouts (see section 3.1.) ; in other words, system actors may transmit, in the
RETURN, messages which contain informations like "parameters for a new opened port",
etc ... these messages are processed by the kernel in the same way as messages for
selection, switch or time-out.

4.2. - Elementary access to system actors

Communication between an actor A and a system actor S is acheived through messages
exchange : the request of the service is a message sent from a port Pa of A to
a port Ps of S ; in the most frequent cases, the reply of the service is a message
sent from Ps to Pa. The request message triggers a processing-step in S which, in
turn, may trigger n other processing-steps (possibly in other actors), and so on.

As seen in this section and in the previous one, request and reply of any system
service are messages ; this has a great advantage : the decomposition between
kernel and system actors presented in section 3.1. gives a minimum kernel and
numerous system actors ; for performance reasons, it may appear necessary to
include in the kernel system services performed, at the moment, by system actors
or to integrate in one system actor several services performed, at the moment, by
several system acytors ; this modification may be introduced without any modification in application actors which use these services : the interface or the
access protocol remains unchanged. For instance, if two system actors S and T
perform respectively services "s" and "t", they open respectively ports Ps and Pt ;
if actor s performs both services "s" and "t", it opens both ports Ps and Pt : the
service "t" is always represented by the port Pt.

4.3. - Programming interface for the kernel access

Section 4.1. presented the elementary level of visibility of the kernel, in full
details. Programming an actor does not require necessarily to be aware of all these
details. Several levels of programming interface may be built :

1/ A first level consists of a set of procedures, included automatically in the

model of actor ; there is one procedure for each service of the kernel. Request
for a service is programmed by calling the corresponding procedure and transmitting significant parameters for the service. Each procedure constitutes a
message and inserts it in a queue internal to the actor ; standard parameters
(like the code of the service, the format of the message) are managed by the
procedure and are not seen by the programmer. All messages in the queue are
transmitted to the kernel at the RETURN.

2/ A second level of interface consists of another set of procedures (included in
the model of actor) which modify the semantic of the service of the kernel. For
instance, the RETURN must contain all parameters for the next execution of the
selection procedure (see section 4.1.). A procedure can be built which maintains
(in the actor) a memory of the current state of these parameters : its interface
is the modification of a parameter which keeps its value until the next modification. The global state of all parameters is transmitted to the kernel at
each RETURN.

4.4. - <u>Illustrating example : a stack sever</u>

This section presents a short example to illustrate the elementary structure of an
actor.

The SM actor (Stack Manager) manages one stack for other actors ; it has two ports :

- P_PUSH receives messages containing the elements to be pushed on the stack ;
  the push operation has no reply message (see below).

- P_POP receives messages which request to pop an element from the stack ; the
  pop operation generates a reply message with the popped element.

The push operation is performed by a processing-step designated by the entry-point
E_PUSH ; the pop operation is performed by a processing-step designated by the
entry-point E_POP.

The constraints of consistency of the stack are, as usual :

- two operations must not be performed simultaneously on the stack, i.e. the
  operations must be serialized.

- when the stack is empty, no element can be popped ; when the stack is full, no
  element can be pushed.

The first constraint is naturally offered by the CHORUS architecture, as an actor
may process only one processing-step at a time (see section 2.1.). The second
constraint is acheived by a judicious use of the selection procedure as presented
below :

      In this example, the parameters of the selection procedure is a list of
ports of the actor : any message received on a port of the list may be selected
for the next processing-step ; any message received on a port out of the list may
not be selected ; in other words, ports out of the list are "masked" for the next
processing-step. The selection service is represented by the internal procedure
"SELECT".

The parameter of the switch procedure is a list of couples (port $\longrightarrow$ entry-point) ;
a message received on "port" triggers the processing-step designated by "entry-
point". The switch service is represented by the internal procedure "SWITCH".

The inital-step designated by E_INIT and the two processing-steps designated respectively by E-PUSH and E-POP can be described as follows :

```
E-INIT :      ENTRY-POINT ; ( initial step )
              .....            ( create and open P-PUSH and P-POP )
              SWITCH (P-PUSH ⟶ E-PUSH) ;
              SWITCH (P-POP ⟶ E-POP) ;
              RETURN ;

E-PUSH :      ENTRY-POINT ; ( push operation )
              push the element on the stack ;
              IF the stack is not full THEN SELECT (P-PUSH) ;
              SELECT (P-POP) ;
              RETURN ;

E-POP :       ENTRY_POINT ; ( pop operation )
              pop the element from the stack ;
              IF the stack is not empty THEN SELECT (P_POP) ;
              SELECT (P_PUSH) ;
              RETURN (reply message with the element) ;
```

In the processing-step E_PUSH, when the stack is full, the port P_PUSH is not selected : no push request message may be selected for the next processing-step of the actor ; the next processed message will therefore be necessarily a message received onto P_POP (i.e. a pop request message) : the next operation performed on the stack is a pop operation. So, the PUSH operation does not need a reply message : the push messages are processed only when the stack is not full.

This argument may apply as well for the POP operation which does not need neither a diagnosis message.

In addition, if some flow control is applied on messages between users and the SM actor, this SM actor performs synchronization between the users of the stack.

4.5. - Programming interface for the access to system actors

Among all communication protocols between processes, the "procedure call" is widely used. Within a processing-step, an actor may use it in order to request operations realized by the actor itself ; this mode of communication is extended to request services realized by other actors.

In order to acheive this, the kernel offers a new primitive, EP_CALL (for External Procedure CALL), with only two messages as parameters, namely :

- a (request) message sent from the port P of the actor onto the port S of some other actor,

- a message for enabling a time-out on port P.

The effect of this primitive is the following :

1/ the kernel sends the first message and enables the time-out ;

2/ the kernel performs an automatic selection which guarantees that the next processed message can be only one of the two following :

    - a (reply) message sent from S onto P,
    - the (diagnosis) message sent by the kernel onto P if the time-out ends before the reception of the (reply) message.

3/ the reception of any of these two messages will resume the execution of the
   actor exactly in the context it leaved at the execution of the EP_CALL, i.e. at
   the next instruction.

Other messages already prepared by the actor in its processing-step are not sent.
There will be no interference neither with the selection and switch parameters
for the next processing-step.

So, the EP_CALL of a service is seen exactly as a procedure call of that service.
Using this new primitive, procedures may be built in the model of actor which
present any service request as a real procedure call. Such a procedure is built
on the following scheme :

        Procedure SERVICE (parameters of the service) ;
        Constitution of the (request) message M ;
        EP_CALL (M, t) ;
        Analysis of the (reply) message ;
        END ;

and the request of the service is coded as :

        SERVICE (request parameters, reply parameters) ;

5. - CONCLUSION

Implementation of the CHORUS system is built on an intensive use of the message
exchange : every communication, between actors, between an actor and the kernel,
between an actor and the I/O processors is an exchange of messages ; conversely,
any treatment is triggered by a message.

This allows to define an interface simple and implementation-idependent. It also
allows to have only two primitives for the kernel access, which simplifies the
kernel.

The interface of the system may reflect all these exchanges of messages. Requests
of system services may also be programmed as procedure calls.

ACKNOWLEDGEMENTS

It is a pleasure to thank all friends of the CHORUS project who helped me for this
paper : J.S. Banino, A. Caristan, G. Morisset and H. Zimmermann.

BIBLIOGRAPHIE

[BAN 80]   J.S. Banino, A. Caristan, M. Guillemont, G. Morisset, H. Zimmermann
            CHORUS : an architecture for distributed systems
            Rapport INRIA 42, (Novembre 1980), pp. 68.

[BAS 77]   F. Baskett, J.H. Howard, J.T. Montague
            Task Communication in Demos
            6th ACM Symposium on Operating Systems Principles, (November 1977),
            pp. 23, 31.

[BOE 78]   W.E. Boebert, W.R. Franta, E.D. Jensen, R.Y. Kain
            Kernel primitives of the HXDP executive
            IEEE 78, (March 79), pp. 595, 600.

[GAU 80]   C. Gaudé, C. Kaiser, J. Langet, S. Palassin
            Distributed processing as a key to reliable and evolving software
            for real time applications
            IFIP Congress, Tokyo, Melbourne, (October 1980)

[JON 79]   A.K. Jones, K. Schwans,
            Task forces : distributed software for solving problems of subs-
            tantial size
            4th International Conference on Software Engineering, IEEE, (1979)

[JON 80]   A.K. Jones, E.F. Gehringer
            The CM* Multiprocessor Project : A research Review
            Carnegie-Mellon University Report, (July 1980), pp. 214.

[LIS 79]   B. Liskov
            Primitives for Distributed Computing
            7th ACM Symposium on Operating Systems Principles, Pacific Grove,
            California, (December 1979), pp. 33, 42.

[OUS 80]   J.K. Ousterhout, D.A. Scelza, P.S. Sindhu
            MEDUSA : an experiment in distributed operating system structure
            Communications of the ACM, vol 23, 2, (February 1980), pp. 92,
            105.

[WAR 80]   S.A. Ward
            TRIX : a network-oriented operating system
            Compcon 80, San Francisco, California, (February 1980), pp. 344,
            349

[ZIM 81]   H. Zimmermann, J.S. Banino, A. Caristan, M. Guillemont, G. Morisset
            Basic concepts for the support of distributed systems : the CHORUS
            approach
            2nd International Conference on Distributed Computing Systems,
            Versailles, (April 1981), pp. 60, 66.

LOCAL COMPUTER NETWORKS
P.C. Ravasio, G. Hopkins and N. Naffah (editors)
North-Holland Publishing Company
© IFIP, 1982

DESIGN OF A NETWORK OPERATING SYSTEM FOR

THE DISTRIBUTED DOUBLE-LOOP COMPUTER NETWORK (DDLCN) *

Ming T. Liu, Duen-Ping Tsay+, and Richard C. Lian

Dept. of Computer and Information Science
The Ohio State University
Columbus, Ohio 43210, USA

ABSTRACT

This paper presents the framework and model of a network operating system (NOS) for use in distributed systems in general and for use in the Distributed Double-Loop Computer Network (DDLCN) in particular. An integrated approach is taken to design the NOS model and protocol structure. It is based on the object model and a novel "task" concept, using message passing as an underlying semantic structure. A layered protocol is provided for the distributed system kernel to support NOS. This approach provides a flexible organization in which system-transparent resource sharing and distributed computing can evolve in a modular fashion.

In this paper, the protocol structure is first presented. The NOS model as well as the notion of "task" is next described. A two-level process interaction model is then discussed. An integrated naming/protection scheme based upon the capability and small access domain is detailed. Finally, the synchronization template and message passing are proposed to resolve distributed synchronization problems.

------- ----------- ---------------- ---------------- ------------ --- -- ----
* Research reported herein was supported in part by NSF grants MCS-77-23496 and MCS-79-07767 and in part by AF contract F33615-81-C-3201.
+ Present address: Wang Laboratories, Inc., On Industrial *Ave., Lowell, MA 01851, USA.

I. INTRODUCTION

A distributed system can be considered as a special case of a computer network, i.e , one with a high degree of cohesiveness, transparency, and autonomy. To integrate the physical and logical resources of a distributed system into a functioning whole, the concept of a high-level network operating system (NOS) must be implemented [ENS78]. The bulk of a NOS has to deal with such problems as naming, protection, synchronization, heterogeneity, resource sharing, and interprocess communication at the network level [ENS78, FLE80, STA79].

In this paper a robust NOS called MIKE [TSA81] is proposed to provide system-transparent operation for network users and to maintain cooperative autonomy among local computer systems. MIKE which stands for Multicomputer Integrator KErnel, is designed for use in distributed systems in general and for use in the Distributed Double-Loop Computer Network (DDLCN) [LIU79, LIU81] in particular. Following this introduction, Section 2 provides some background and Section 3 describes the protocol structure. Section 4 details the model structure of MIKE, its novel "task" concept, and related issues partaining to task communication, naming, protection, synchronization, exception handling, and accounting. Finally Section 5 summarizes the important features of MIKE.

II. BACKGROUND

2.1 DDLCN

Conceived of as a means of investigating fundamental problems in distributed processing and local networking, the Distributed Double-Loop Computer Network (DDLCN) [LIU79, LIU81, WOL79] is designed as a fault-tolerant distributed system that interconnects midi, mini and micro computers using a double-loop structure in a local environment. Research on DDLCN has covered topics on interface design, communication protocols, distributed operating systems, distributed database systems, and distributed programming systems. A seven-node prototype of DDLCN, interconnecting six PDP-11/23 microcomputers and one DECsystem-20 computer system, has been implemented under a grant from NSF to the Department of Computer and Information Science, The Ohio State University (see Figure 1).

The communication subsystem of DDLCN consists of a double-loop communication network that uses twisted-wire pairs (called communication links) to interconnect individual nodes through hardware devices called the Loop Interface Units (LIUs). The loop channel access protocol described by Reames and Liu [REA75] is incorporated into the design of DDLCN. Message transmission is accomplished through the use of a shift-register insertion technique performed by the loop interface, whereby the loop may carry multiple variable-length messages at one time. This type of protocol allows the simultaneous and direct transmission of variable-length messages onto the loop by more than one interface without the use of any centralized control. Details of the design and operation of DDLCN can be found in [LIU79, LIU81, TSA79, TSA80a, TSA80b, WOL79].

The interprocess communication protocols of DDLCN provide different degrees of reliability for the exchange of multi-destination messages. These protocols are called N-process communication protocols and are intended for use by cooperating processes of distributed algorithms [PAR79]. A new concurrency control mechanism [CHO81] for a distributed loop data base system (DLDBS) has

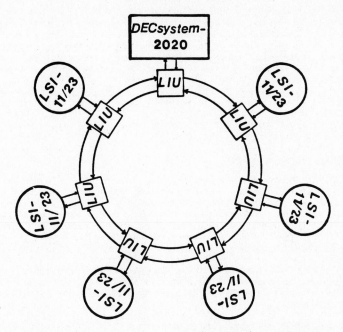

LSI—11/23:

128 K Bytes MOS RAM
Dual Floppy Disk
VT - 100 Terminal

LIU (LOOP INTERFACE UNIT):

16-bit bit-sliced microprogrammable
microprocessors (AM 2900 based)

DECsystem—2020:

512 K Words MOS RAM
2 Disk Drives
Magnetic Tape Drives
I/O Devices & Terminals

Figure 1.

Prototype of DDLCN

been developed for DDLCN, which has several nice features: use of distributed
control without global locking, deadlock-free, simple to implement, good
performance, and robust with respect to failure of both communication links and
hosts. A new language concept, called Communicating Distributed Processes (CDP)
[LIC81] has also been developed for DDLCN, which uses communication/distribution
abstraction to provide a great deal of expressive power for distributed
programming systems.

This paper is concerned with the design and implementation of a network
operating system for DDLCN, called MIKE [TSA81], which provides
system-transparent operation for network users and maintains cooperative
autonomy among local computer systems.

2.2 Network Operating System

DDLCN is a collection of autonomous and heterogeneous computers networked
together [REA75, WOL79]. All of these individual computer systems are
independent and capable of solving their own problems most of the time.
However, since each computer system has only limited resources at its disposal,
it occasionally needs to use resources of other computers in the network. Such
a particular environment is chosen for our research because it is typical of
many found today in industrial, commercial, and university settings.

In order to provide users with a high degree of cohesiveness, transparency
and autonomy, a separate system-wide control software called the network
operating system (NOS) has to be designed to coordinate the operations of local
computer systems.

2.3 Related Works

Recently, several network operating systems have been proposed and
implemented for a number of distributed systems. They include Roscoe for the
Arachne system [SOL79], MicroOS for MicroNet [WIT80], Trix for MuNet [WAR80],
StarOS for Cm* [JON79], and Medusa for Cm* [OUS80].

Operating systems for distributed systems can be designed in two radically
different ways [CLA80, PEE80, TAN81, WAT80]. One way is to superimpose a
network operating system (NOS) on top of a collection of local host operating
systems. The other approach is to throw away the existing operating systems and
to start all over again with a single homogeneous distributed operating system
(DOS).

In order to minimize the modification of existing operating systems, we use
the first approach to design the network operating system for DDLCN (called
MIKE). That is, MIKE is designed to reside on top of existing operating
systems. However, it is worth mentioning here that the concepts of this paper
are so general that they can be applied to the other approach.

2.4 Design Objectives of MIKE

The primary design goals of MIKE are fourfold:

1. To provide system-transparent operation to the users such that they do
   not need to know the different naming and other access mechanisms,
   including its distributed or non-distributed nature, required by the
   network, each node, and each service.

2. To maintain cooperative autonomy among local computer systems such that the local resource management can be retained.

3. To provide a reliable and robust system operation in spite of component node failures.

4. To provide an extensible and configurable environment such that resource sharing and distributed computing can evolve in a modular fashion.

To incorporate the functionalities and features mentioned above into the design of MIKE, we can see clearly that ad hoc arrangements will not be adequate; some systematic design methodology has to be used to effectively realize these goals. In search of a better designed and more reliable operating system, we adopt an integrated approach to the design of NOS for DDLCN. Advanced operating system design concepts have been applied consistently throughout the NOS framework to generate reliable and robust system software Moreover, the NOS model and protocol structure have also been integrated to provide an extensible and configurable NOS for DDLCN [KAH81, WUL81].

III. PROTOCOL STRUCTURE

MIKE is designed as a meta-system due to the need of exploiting existing software investment wherever possible. The approach taken in designing MIKE is to minimize the modification of existing operating systems while allowing them to be embraced by the model as consistently as possible.

MIKE is designed as a NOS kernel to be superimposed on top of a collection of local host operating systems, so that each host can run its own local operating system. MIKE consists of a set of replicated kernels each residing in the Loop Interface Unit (LIU) of DDLCN. This arrangement makes the system more independent of the hardware and software of local hosts and allows the incorporation of special hardware to support the modern design methodology Each LIU is a separate processor independent of the local host computer attached [TSA79]. That is, each node of the DDLCN is a pair of processors: the LIU and its local host.

3.1 The Hierarchical Framework Of MIKE

The framework of MIKE is hierarchically structured. The most distinguishable characteristic of the MIKE framework is its explicit and enforced modular structure. This enables us to describe the system at three different levels of abstraction. Relevant processes are then segregated in each level to shield the implementation details from other layers. The MIKE hierarchy, described from the bottom up, consists of three layers (see Figure 2):

1. the inter-process communication (IPC) layer,
2. the system support layer, and
3. the virtual machine layer.

3 2 IPC Layer

The IPC layer supports the transport of uninterpreted messages of arbitrary length with possibly multiple destinations in DDLCN. It provides reliable mechanisms to guarantee the delivery of messages. Three types of

Virtual   * Higher-Level Application-Oriented Services

Machine   * Basic NOS Services

Layer

ZZZZZZZZZZZZZZZZZZZZZZZZZZZZZZZZZZZZZZZZZZZZZZZZZZZZZZZZZZZ

System   Abstraction Sublayer   Interaction Sublayer

Support   * Task Templates   * Guaranteed Session Protocol

Layer   * Basic Operations   * Reliable Session Protocol

                                   * Unreliable Session Protocol

ZZZZZZZZZZZZZZZZZZZZZZZZZZZZZZZZZZZZZZZZZZZZZZZZZZZZZZZZZZZ

IPC   * Guaranteed Multi-Destination Protocol

Layer   * Reliable Multi-Destination Protocol

           * Unreliable Multi-Destination Protocol

Figure 2.

Protocol Hierarchy

multi-destination protocols are supported, each providing a different degree of reliability.

3.2.1 Unreliable Multi-Destination Protocol

This type of multi-destination protocol implements a facility by which a guardian (1) at the system support layer can send a message to multiple remote guardians. Damaged messages are discarded; however, no attempt is made to acknowledge messages. Therefore, the sending site does not know whether the message has been correctly delivered or not. The objective of this type of protocol is to provide a minimum-overhead facility that can be used either by some guardians in the system support layer that can take care of the unreliable situations or by more reliable multi-destination protocols which we will discuss next.

3.2.2 Reliable Multi-Destination Protocol

This type of protocol demands a positive acknowledgment from the receiving ends. Thus the sending guardian will be notified whether the message has been successfully delivered or not. The reliable multi-destination protocol accomplishes its function by requesting the unreliable multi-destination protocol to send the message. Furthermore, it will ask the latter to retransmit the message if any of the destination nodes has not acknowledged the message. However this retransmission will be requested only for a certain number of times or the monitoring job will be executed within a certain time bound and then quit. So this reliable multi-destination protocol can be considered as a "best effort to deliver" protocol [PAR78].

3.2.3 Guaranteed Multi-Destination Protocol

This type of protocol guarantees to the sending guardian that its multi-destination message will eventually arrive at every destination even some are not unreachable at that moment. This guaranteed multi-destination protocol will request the reliable multi-destination protocol to send the message and resubmit the request until the message is safely arrived at every destination.

The multi-destination protocols per se and their interactions within the IPC layer can be modelled by using the object model and its associated task notion to be described in Section 4. The more powerful and reliable mechanism, which is similar to an "extended type", accomplishes its job by requesting the guardian of the primitive mechanism to perform a series of more basic operations. The implementation of the IPC layer can then be decomposed into smaller and more manageable tasks.

3.3 System Support Layer

The system support layer provides two distinct kinds of services for the virtual machine layer. The first of these two support service groupings (called abstraction sublayer) is oriented toward system reliability and extensibility. The second of these groupings (called interaction sublayer) is oriented toward network communication.

---

(1) In MIKE a guardian is a special kind of process that is associated with a task and safeguards the integrity of the objects in its task's address domain. See Section 4.2 for detail.

The major functions of the abstraction sublayer are to provide templates for the construction of user-defined service/type tasks and to provide primitive system utilities whereby guardians in the virtual machine layer can build more sophisticated or higher-level application-oriented tasks. The rationale for providing these templates at this layer is based on the need to safeguard the integrity of the protection model, to allow MIKE to evolve in a modular fashion, and to stick to the principle of policy/mechanism separation.

The interaction sublayer deals with the interaction of message senders and message recipients. In MIKE it is a rare case that the interaction among remote guardians only involves with simple transactions, in which a guardian sends a message, waits for a reply, and then forgets about it. The most common inter-node activities are initiated by the remote system resource sharing, in which a series of interactions is needed to accomplish the access. A connection will therefore be established among cooperating guardians residing in different nodes of DDLCN to reduce communication overhead and to provide coherent interactions; we call this connection a session. The multi-destination protocols in the IPC layer are concerned with the transport of a unit of message. Therefore, a message is either delivered or not delivered to a destination. For the session protocols in the system support layer, the emphasis is placed on the interrelation and coherence of multiple messages which are exchanged to accomplish some work in the virtual machine layer.

3.4 Virtual Machine Layer

The virtual machine layer provides a virtual machine where the distributed and heterogeneous nature on which MIKE is based are all masked out, and user processes interact without the awareness of the network architecture.

A complete set of standard and basic network-oriented services for system-transparent resource sharing, such as Virtual User service task, Virtual Resource service task and FILE type task, should be defined in the virtual machine layer [TSA81]. Other tasks, such as distributed database service task [CHO81], can also be provided depending on the application environment on hand.

IV. NETWORK OPERATING SYSTEM MODEL

4.1 The Object Model

A novel "task" concept has been developed in [TSA81], which enables the object model to embrace both MIKE and the local operating system regardless of the latter's internal organization. By using the object model, MIKE consists of a set of entities. Entities are typed, and type definitions are represented inside the computer system by type managers [JON78, LIN76]. The type manager forms a protected subsystem for entities of its type, and safeguards their integrity by ensuring that the manipulation of these entities is allowed only through the well-defined operators. New types are definable and the protection system can be extended to handle these newly defined types.

Typed entities can be further divided into two distinct kinds: active (called process) and passive (called object). Processes can be further classified into two categories: transient, and cyclic. A process is said to be transient if it will terminate after the function execution is completed. A special kind of process called guardian [TSA81] is said to be cyclic because it is pre-initialized to execute a particular function, and once being initialized, it will exist "forever". Non-process entities which we call objects are passive, i.e., they do not originate any activity.

4.2 Tasks

By using the object model to structure MIKE, the entity universe is further divided into mutually exclusive sets. Each of these sets is called a task [TSA81]. A task consists of one or more processes and possibly some objects. Entities within a task form the address domain of that task (see Figure 3). All the constituent entities, both processes and objects, must reside in the same physical node. A given task can assume the role of either a resource provider or a resource user or both at different times. Processes can refer directly to the objects in the address domain of its task, but can only operate indirectly to "non-private" objects (i.e., objects in other tasks) by sending messages to the appropriate "guardian" of those objects.

4.2.1 Guardians

One of the processes in a task is called the guardian, which safeguards the integrity of the objects in its task's address domain. In MIKE, a guardian is a special kind of process. Each distinct task is associated with one and only one guardian. A guardian contains, among other things, the following specifications for its task:

1.   the state descriptors of objects in the address space,

2.   the local management policies

At the task creation time, the guardian is the only entity in its task. During the time MIKE is operational, the guardian will spawn processes either to perform some functions or as the results of service requests initiated by processes from other tasks. Guardians are cyclic processes, that is, once being created, they will exist "forever". The word "cyclic" means that the population of guardians is more static than that of transient processes. Guardians, after satisfy the requests from other tasks, will block themselves awaiting the arrival of further service requests. Therefore, the loci of control or processing activities of a guardian are cyclic and give us an illusion that guardians exist "forever".

One of the important functions guardians perform is to enforce local policies, including naming, protection, synchronization, exceptions handling, and accounting, which will be exemplified later in Sections 4.4 to 4.8, respectively. The guardian construct allows us to model different degrees of autonomy according to the local management policy which can be changed dynamically. This also allows the cooperative autonomy to be realized in MIKE in a more organized manner and in a more refined granularity.

4.2.2 Task Classification

In MIKE tasks are classified into three categories. Tasks in each category are formed from the same kind of binding force.

4.2.2.1 Type Tasks

The first kind of binding force is that component entities of a task collectively realize one of the data types existing in the system (e.g., FILE). Tasks in this category are referred to as type tasks. An extended task can be dynamically created based upon the existing type tasks. In MIKE the type is

DECsystem-20

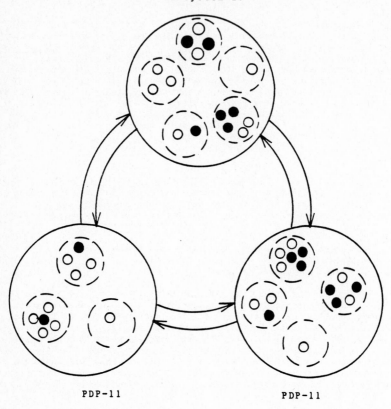

PDP-11   PDP-11

◌ : Task

◯ : Process

⬤ : Data Object

Figure 3.

An Overview of a Three-Node DDLCN

encapsulated. The guardian of a type task is its type manager. A type manager, as described above, is used to enforce the integrity of the objects of its associated type. Figure 4 illustrates three snapshots of the address domain of a type task called FILE (which implements type FILE definition) during its lifetime.

As illustrated in Figure 4a, when a type task is just created, it only contains the guardian and nothing else. Figure 4b illustrates the situation in which no request is received by the guardian at that moment to manipulate the objects (F1 and F2) it guards. Therefore, in addition to the guardian, type task FILE contains objects of type FILE created before by the requests of other tasks.

In Figure 4c, there are a guardian, two processes and two objects in the address space of type task FILE and the objects are all type FILE. The processes, which are created by the requests of other tasks to operate the FILE objects, are spawned by the guardian. They are activated to perform operations (which can be the same or different operations) either on different objects or on the same object.

4.2.2.2 Service Tasks

The second kind of binding force is that component entities of a task are working together harmoniously to provide a network-oriented service, which we will call a service task. The guardian of a service task is responsible for initiating appropriate actions according to service requests it receives. An example of this category is called the Virtual Resource service task. Its function is to provide a local "virtual" resource which is requested by the user residing in the same physical node, but the resource is not locally available. There is another service task called the Virtual User service task, which is a direct counterpart of the Virtual Resource service task, will generate a "virtual" user to use a particular resource which is available locally but needed by users at a remote node. The virtual user will use the resource on behalf of its remote "real" user counterpart. The Virtual Resource and Virtual User service tasks create an illusion such that either all the distributed network resources are available locally or all the resources access are made by the local users. The contribution of these two service tasks to system-transparent resource access is exemplified in [TSA81].

4.2.2.3 Operating System Tasks

The last and also a very important binding force is that the local operating system and its user processes form a task. This is a unique and "super" task, which we call an operating system task or OS task for short. Each node in DDLCN has one and only one OS task. The OS task resides physically in the local computer system. In addition to user processes, it contains the local operating system, which is the guardian. To end users, this OS task is their universe and they communicate only with the guardian of its OS task.

The local operating system safeguards the integrity of the resources it controls. In MIKE each OS task is allowed to have its own "personality", which depends on the original design philosophy of its guardian. Since we stated at the outset that each task is an autonomous and protected subsystem, it can run its own resource management policy independently of other tasks but in a cooperative manner. Furthermore, an OS task is treated by the rest of the system just as another task which acts as a resource provider/user.

Type Task FILE

(a)

(b)

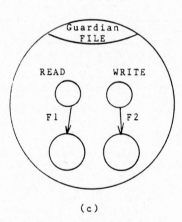

(c)

Figure 4.

A FILE Task

The merits of this logical grouping, i.e "task" concept, are twofold. First, it provides us with a higher level structuring tool to analyze and control the components interaction in a hierarchical way. As outlined in Section 3 1, MIKE consists of three layers: the IPC layer, the system support layer, and the virtual machine layer. An OS task can only reside in the virtual machine layer. Various type tasks and service tasks can exist in any of the three layers as needed. Second, each task forms a unit of protected subsystem and acts as an (optional) autonomous unit. Therefore, each individual task has the capability to manage its resources independently of other tasks and the management policy can be changed dynamically to reflect its interest. The integrity of this subsystem is the responsibility of its guardian. Figure 5 shows a profile of MIKE in terms of the "task" concept.

4.3 Process Interaction Model

As mentioned before, DDLCN consists of a collection of autonomous and heterogeneous nodes. Most of the existing local operating systems, e.g., TOPS-20 Monitor of DECsystem-20, use a mixture of message exchange and procedure invocation for their process interaction. It will not be natural to mandate that the system be communicated by message exchange only, since abnormality can be found in the OS task. Therefore, we adopt a two-level process interaction model for MIKE which dictates that the inter-task communication is through message exchange and the intra-task communication is through either procedure invocation or message exchange.

4.3.1 Intra Task Communication

The lower level of process interaction model applies within the task boundary only. Processes executed within a task are communicated through either procedure invocation or message exchange. All the components of a task are confined in the same physical node; therefore, it is most efficient and semantically sound to model the intra-task activities in this way.

4.3.2 Inter-Task Communication

Logically, MIKE consists of a collection of tasks, each of which acts as an autonomous resource provider/user and is scattered over DDLCN. Since MIKE is designed to be extensible and configurable, new tasks can be added and old tasks can be deleted dynamically. Based on this assumption, all communication among tasks is entirely message based.

The guardian serves as a communication gateway to its subordinate processes when they wish to establish a communication channel with an outside entity. The guardian will send request messages and receive reply messages on behalf of its subordinate processes. The requested guardian will act as an agent and dispatch processes to perform the requested operation on its guarded objects in a well-defined manner and/or send additional messages to other tasks to aid it in carrying out the original request.

The sending and receiving of messages is controlled by a service task called the Messenger. Message communication in each layer of the protocol structure is serviced by a dedicated Messenger as depicted in Figure 6. Messages sent by guardians are always trapped by the Messenger at that layer. The Messenger is actually an interface between two adjacent layers of the protocol structure. One of its important functions is to maintain a set of mailboxes, one for each guardian residing in that layer, and communicating with the Messengers in the layer below and above it. Messages destined for a

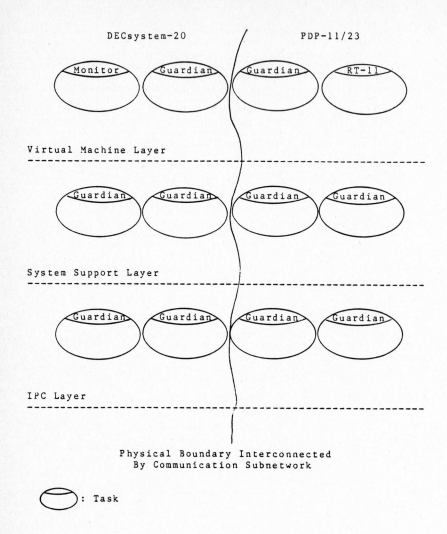

Figure 5.

MIKE Profile Based on Task Concept

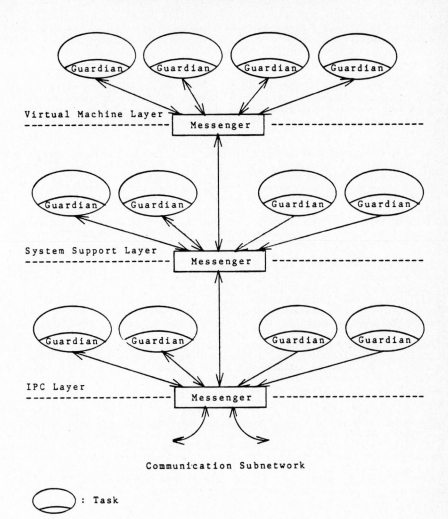

Communication Subnetwork

⬯ : Task

Figure 6.

Inter-Guardian Communication

particular guardian will be queued at the corresponding mailbox by the Messenger at that layer.

4.4 Naming

The naming system of MIKE is designed to provide system transparency and local autonomy, to support the extended tasks and multiple copies of resources, and to facilitate the protection scheme, taking performance into consideration whenever possible. To meet these requirements, MIKE adopts a two-level naming scheme.

As mentioned previously "task" in MIKE is a logical concept for entity grouping. Although we usually refer to a specific task by its name, it actually is the name of its associated guardian. Only the guardians' names are network wide known and all message exchanges are initiated by and terminated on guardians. Processes' names, except those of guardians, are known only to the guardians of their respective tasks. This two-level naming scheme hides the resources "behind their guardians" such that the resource access is regulated by its guardian according to the local resource management policy. It also reduces a lot of unnecessary process interactions and message passings.

The high-level naming is human-oriented and is intended to provide users with transparency. The low-level one is machine-oriented and is intended to cooperate with and to facilitate the protection scheme. The mapping from high-level to low-level is manipulated by the namer located at each node and by the guardians of the respective tasks. The namer, which is a special service task like the messenger in the NOS kernel, maps a human-oriented entity name into a machine-oriented task ticket (capability). The guardian checks the task ticket presented by the requester, maps the submitted entity name into an entity ticket (capability), and grants it to the requester. Relocation of entities is possible. When an object is moved, it is necessary to update the appropriate context in the namers and related guardians for the required mapping. The mappings are shown in Figure 7.

The naming mechanism mentioned above uses the concept of capability-based addressing [FAB74] to provide transparency for users and to enforce protection on resource access. Because the same type task can be allowed to exist in different nodes, multiple copies of resources can exist, if necessary, and can be supported by this mechanism. To support an extended task, the naming problem can be cooperatively resolved by the namer and the guardians of the extended type task and its constituent tasks, but additional interactions between the extended task and its constituent tasks are necessary.

4.5 Protection

Protection is an important issue in a resource-sharing environment. It becomes even more important in a computer network or distributed computing system due to the exposure of communication channels and ease of wiretapping. The major topics in this area include the authentication scheme and protection of resources. Basically authentication mechanisms rely on secrecy (e.g., password) and unforgeability (e.g., magnetically striped plastic card) [SAL75]. In MIKE the authentication scheme, which verifies a user's claimed identity, is not an issue because each local operating system resolves this problem locally.

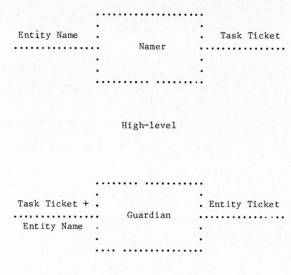

Fig. 7 The two-level naming mechanism

The protection problem which we concentrate on is the access control of resources, i.e., the protection mechanism enforced on a task. To avoid the penalty of time-consuming maintenance and search of access control lists, both naming and protection in MIKE are handled based on the capability concept. The protection mechanism in MIKE is intended to prevent data theft [DON80], to resolve mutual suspicion problem [SCH72], to easily manage revocation and confinement, to provide communication security on an unprotected communication subnetwork, and to cooperatively work with the naming mechanism.

Based upon these requirements, we propose a protection mechanism which combines the approaches of typed memory [GEH79], capability, and enciphering. It forces a system-wide view of access control. Every access to objects in MIKE must be checked for authority. A process's capability list (C-list), which delineates its access domain, provides a closed environment [DEN76] with the least privilege. Within a task, processes' access domains are mutually isolated. The invocation of a procedure within a process causes a domain switching. This small protected domain, which restricts processes' capability to an immediate domain at that instance, significantly contributes to error confinement and resolves the mutual suspicion problem. The frequent domain switching is unavoidable. To alleviate the overhead involved, firmware support on protection and message mechanisms is required.

　　Addressability to entities is supported by tickets. There are two kinds of tickets in MIKE: task and entity. A task ticket contains a requested task's address, an encrypted requester's address, and other information. This ticket is built by the namer and granted to the requester upon the invocation of the procedure where its type task (or object type) and the corresponding capability in C-list are explicitly declared. Similarly, an entity ticket, which contains a requested task's (the guardian's) address, an encrypted requested entity's address, an encrypted requester's address, an encrypted access rights, and other information, is built and granted by the guardian of the respective task upon request.

```
......................................................
.                 .             .                    .
. Address .  Encrypted  .       Other                .
. .   of    . Requester's .                           .
.   Task    .  Address   .     Information            .
.                 .             .                    .
......................         ........................
```

(a) Task Ticket's Format

```
..................................................................
.         .          .             .           .               .
. Address .Encrypted. Encrypted  . Encrypted .   Other       .
.    of    . Entity's. Requester's .  Access   .               .
.   Task   . Address .   Address   .   Rights  . Information.
.         .          .             .           .               .
..................................................................
```

(b) Entity Ticket's Format

Fig. 8 Ticket's Formats in MIKE

　　Since enciphering is not necessary for every task, the guardian of each task can decide this based upon its requirement and situation. The trade-off is mainly based upon performance and the degree of security. This decision is specified in the creation template of the type task at its creation.

To prevent data from being stolen, residual control [DEN76, TSA81] is proposed to completely isolate the access domain and to prevent information from being disclosed either unintentionally or maliciously.

To validate the access, the guardian simply decrypts the ticket verifies the requested object's address and the access rights, and compares the requester's address with the address accompanying the message embedded by the communication facility. Figure 8 shows the formats for both task and entity tickets.

Under this scheme, the prevention of data theft and wiretapping of communication channel is feasible. The revocation and control of the capability and confinement problem can be easily resolved. It tightly couples with naming to form an integrated naming/protection mechanism.

4.6 Synchronization

One of our main concerns in NOS design is to control resource access so as to maintain resource consistency and to arrange an access sequence. Although there are many synchronization mechanisms available for solving this problem, most of them are not applicable to a distributed computing environment due to their requirement of sharing a common memory. Recently, some progress has been made; notable among them can be found in [HOA74, HAN75, CUN80] which adopt abstract data types, in [HAB75, RAM80, LEI81] which use (high-level) non-procedural specifications, and in [JAM77, ATK77, HOA78, CUN80] which take advantage of message passing. These approaches are intended to increase its reliability, flexibility, and applicability, respectively.

In MIKE our desirable goals for the synchronization mechanism are to provide adequate efficiency and fault-tolerant capability in distributed computing environments, to have adequate expressive power, and to provide modularity and verifiability.

To meet these goals the synchronization mechanism we propose is based upon the following concepts:

Distributed Resource Sharing
= Abstract Data Type
+ Distributed Synchronization

Distributed Synchronization
= Message Passing
+ Synchronization Template

Abstract data types can be easily implemented using the concept of type task. A resource and its predefined operators constitute a protected resource environment and users cannot directly manipulate resources. The guardian will dispatch processes to access resources on their behalf.

The synchronization template is a non-procedural specification of resource and priority constraints. It comprises synchronization variables, conditions, operations, and priority. The synchronization variables are used as bases for the construction of synchronization queues. All the synchronization conditions, operations, and priority are specified based upon these variables. The synchronization conditions, which are in the form of boolean expressions in terms of synchronization and the resource status, assure the consistency and integrity of resources. The synchronization operations are used to update state variables as the status changes. The synchronization priority can be specified on a static or dynamic basis. Its main purpose is to increase resource utilization, to avoid starvation, or to fit user's special requirements. This synchronization mechanism has adequate power to express various synchronization problems and is easy to verify.

The non-procedural synchronization template is part of the creation template when a type task or an entity is created. The creation template for a type task contains predefined operators, a synchronization template, and protection options for enciphering and is treated as a default template for the task. A user can only specify his own synchronization template at the creation of his entity if it is necessary.

Incoming requests for resource accesses are in the form of variable-length messages and are queued by the Messenger according to their destination tasks. The underlying IPC communication protocols described in Section 3.2 guarantee our message mechanism being fault-tolerant. The guardian is a message-driven process; any incoming messages will be immediately decrypted and verified by the guardian and stored in appropriate synchronization queues. These requests will be honored based upon the synchronization constraints specified in the template.

This distributed synchronization mechanism maps a remote synchronization problem into a local synchronization problem, enforces resource protection, provides attributes for distributed applications, and is suitable for distributed computing environments.

4.7 Exception Handling

The general errors within a task, which includes type, naming, protection, and synchronization, will be handled by the guardian. This inclusion is very natural due to the concept of "task".

4.8 Accounting

To take advantage of the concept of the type task, the function of usage recording is also embedded in the guardian to facilitate the measurement and accounting of resource utilization. The recording of resource usage will be peformed by the guardians upon completion of every access request.

V. SUMMARY

In this paper we have presented the NOS model of MIKE for DDLCN. The MIKE structure is based consistently on the object model. A novel "task" concept is used to further group resource entities. Each task is an autonomous unit and its constituents coexist in the same physical node. The inter-task communication is done by message passing and is regulated by the associated guardians; therefore, only guardians' names are known network-wide. The two-level naming scheme can provide users with system transparency and can be used with the protection scheme for error confinement The synchronization template associated with the underlying protocols and message mechanism can resolve the distributed synchronization problems.

The aforementioned features can be used to make MIKE a very reliable and reasonably efficient NOS for DDLCN. It can provide system-transparent resource sharing for the users while allowing individual guardians to guard their respective resources and to respond to requests as they see fit. Furthermore, the users can retain the original local operating system with which they are familiar, and see DDLCN as a single integrated computer system controlled by their local operating systems. Thus, it seems that the design of MIKE is successful in accomplishing its original goals set in Section 2.4.

ACKNOWLEDGEMENTS

The authors wish to express their appreciations to Dr. John R. Lehmann of the National Science Foundation and to Bernard H. Groomes of the Air Force Flight Dynamics Laboratory for their constant encouragement and support.

REFERENCES

[ATK77]   Atkinson, R., "Synchronization in Actor Systems," 4th SIGPLAN-SIGACT Symp. on Princ. of Prog. Lang., pp. 267-280, January 1977.

[CHO81]   Chou, C. P., "Design of the Distributed Loop Data Base System (DLDBS)," Ph.D. Dissertation, Department of Computer and Information Science The Ohio State University, Columbus Ohio, June 1981.

[CLA80]   Clark, D. D. and Svobodova, L., "Design of Distributed Systems Supporting Local Autonomy," Proceedings of COMPCON'80 Spring, pp. 438-444, February 1980.

[CUN80]   Cunha, P. R. F., Lucena, C J. Maibaum, T. S. E., "A Methodology for Message Oriented Programming," Proceedings of the 6th GI Conference on Programming Languages and Program Development Darmstadt, March 1980.

[DEN66]   Dennis, J. B. and Van Horn, E C., "Programming Semantics for Multiprogrammed Computations," Communications ACM Vol. 9, No. 3, pp. 143-155, March 1966.

[DEN76]   Denning, P. J , "Fault Tolerant Operating Systems," ACM Computing Surveys, Vol. 8, No. 4, pp. 361-486, December 1976.

[DON80]   Donnelley, J. E. and Fletcher, J. G., "Resource Access Control in a Network Operating System," Proceedings of ACM Pacific'80 Conference November 1980.

[ENS78]   Enslow, P. H , "What is a 'Distributed' Data Processing System ?" IEEE Computer, Vol. 11, No. 1, pp. 13-21, January 1978.

[FAB74]   Fabry, R. S., "Capability-Based Addressing," Communications ACM, Vol. 17, No. 7, pp. 403-412, July 1974.

[FLE80]   Fletcher, J. G. and Watson, R. W., "Service Support in a Network Operating System," Proceedings of COMPCON'80 Spring, pp. 415-424, February 1980.

[GEH79]   Gehringer, E. F., "Functionality and Performance in Capability-based
           Operating Systems," Ph.D. Dissertation, Purdue University, May 1979.

[GRA72]   Graham, G. S. and Denning, P. J., "Protection - Principles and
           Practice," AFIPS Conference Proceedings, Spring Joint Computer
           Conference, pp. 417-429, 1972.

[HAB75]   Habermann, A. N , "Path Expression," Department of Computer Science,
           Carnegie-Mellon University, Pittsburgh, Pennsylvania, June 1975.

[HAN75]   Hansen, B., "The Programming Language Concurrent Pascal," IEEE Trans.
           on Software Engineering, Vol. SE-1, No. 2, June 1975.

[HOA74]   Hoare, C. A. R., "Monitors: An Operating System Structuring
           Concept," Communications ACM, Vol. 17, No. 10, pp. 549-557, October
           1974.

[HOA78]   Hoare, C. A. R., "Communicating Sequential Process," Communications
           ACM, pp. 666-677, August 1978.

[JAM77]   Jammel, A. J., and Stiegler, H. G., "Managers versus Monitors,"
           Proceedings of the IFIP, pp. 827-830, 1977.

[JON78]   Jones, A. K., "The Object Model: A Conceptual Tool for Structuring
           Software," in Lecture Notes in Computer Science, Vol. 60, (Bayer, R.,
           Graham, R. H., and Seegmuller, G., editors), pp. 8-18,
           Springer-Verlag, Berlin, 1978.

[JON79]   Jones, A. K., et al., "StarOS, A Multiprocessor Operating System for
           the Support of Task Forces," Proceedings of 7th Symposium on Operating
           Systems Principles, pp. 117-127, December 1979.

[KAH81]   Kahn, K. C. and Pollack F., "An Extensible Operating System for the
           Intel 432," Proceedings of COMPCON'81 Spring, pp. 398-404, February
           1981.

[LEI81]   Leinbaugh, D. W., "High Level Specification and Implementation of
           Resource Sharing," Computer and Information Science Research Center,
           The Ohio State University, Columbus, Ohio, February 1981.

[LIC81]   Li, C. M., "Communicating Distributed Processes: A Programming
           Language Concept for Distributed Systems," Ph.D. Dissertation, The
           Ohio State University, Columbus, Ohio, March 1981.

[LIN76]   Linden, T. A., "Operating Systems Structures to Support Security and
           Reliable Software," ACM Computing Surveys, Vol. 8, No. 4, pp.
           409-445, December 1976.

[LIU79]   Liu, M. T., et al., "System Design of the Distributed Double-Loop
           Computer Network (DDLCN)," Proceedings of First International
           Conference on Distributed Computing Systems, pp. 95 105, October
           1979.

[LIU81]   Liu, M. T., et al., "Design of the Distributed Double-Loop Computer
           Network (DDLCN)," Journal of Digital Systems, Vol. 5, No. 1/2, pp.
           3-37, Spring/Summer 1981.

[OUS80] Ousterhout, J. K et al., "Medusa: An Experiment in Distributed Operating System Structure," <u>Communications</u> <u>ACM</u>, Vol. 23, No. 2, pp. 92-105, February 1980.

[PAR78] Pardo, R., Liu, M. T., and Babic, G. A., "An N-Process Communication Protocol for Distributed Processing," <u>Proceedings</u> <u>Symposium</u> <u>on</u> <u>Computer</u> <u>Network</u> <u>Protocols</u>, pp. D7.1-10, February 1978.

[PAR79] Pardo, R., "Interprocess Communication and Synchronization for Distributed Systems," Ph.D. Dissertation, Department of Computer and Information Science The Ohio State University, Columbus, Ohio, August 1979.

[PEE80] Peebles, R. and Dopirak, T., "ADAPT: A Guest System," <u>Proceedings</u> <u>of</u> <u>COMPCON'80</u> <u>Spring</u>, pp. 445-454, February 1980.

[RAM80] Ramamritham, K. and Keller, R. M., "Specification and Synchronizers," <u>Proceedings</u> <u>1980</u> <u>International</u> <u>Conference</u> <u>on</u> <u>Parallel</u> <u>Processing</u>, pp. 311-321, August 1980.

[REA75] Reames, C. C. and Liu, M. T., "A Loop Network for Simultaneous Transmission of Variable-Length Messages," <u>Proceedings</u> <u>of</u> <u>Second</u> <u>Annual</u> <u>Symposium</u> <u>on</u> <u>Computer</u> <u>Architecture</u>, pp. 7-12, January 1975. (Also reprinted in <u>Distributed</u> <u>Processing</u>, Liebowitz, B. H. and Carson, J. H., editors, IEEE Catalog EH 0127-1, pp. 3.31-3.36, September 1977.)

[SAL75] Saltzer, J. H. and Schroeder M D., "The Protection of Information in Computer Systems," <u>Proceedings</u> <u>of</u> <u>IEEE</u>, pp. 1278-1308, September 1975.

[SCH72] Schroeder, M., "Cooperation of Mutually Suspicious Subsystems in A Computer Utility," Ph.D. Thesis, Massachusetts Institute of Technology, MAC TR-104, September 1972.

[SOL79] Solomon, M. H. and Finkel, R. A., "The Roscoe Distributed Operating system," <u>Proceedings</u> <u>of</u> <u>7th</u> <u>Symposium</u> <u>on</u> <u>Operating</u> <u>Systems</u> <u>Principles</u>, pp. 108-114, December 1979.

[STA79] Stankovic, J. A. and Van Dam, A., "Research Directions in (Cooperative) Distributed Processing," in <u>Research</u> <u>Directions</u> <u>in</u> <u>Software</u> <u>Technology</u> (Wegner, P., editor), pp. 611-638, The MIT Press, Cambridge, Mass., 1979.

[TAN81] Tanenbaum, A. S., <u>Computer</u> <u>Networks</u>, Prentice-Hall, Englewood Cliffs, N. J., 1981.

[TSA79] Tsay, D. P. and Liu, M. T., "Interface Design for the Distributed Double-Loop Computer Network (DDLCN)," <u>Proceedings</u> <u>of</u> <u>1979</u> <u>National</u> <u>Telecommunication</u> <u>Conference</u>, pp. 31.4.1-6, December 1979.

[TSA80a] Tsay, D. P. and Liu, M. T., "Design of a Reconfigurable Front-End Processor for Computer Networks," <u>Proceedings</u> <u>of</u> <u>1980</u> <u>International</u> <u>Symposium</u> <u>on</u> <u>Fault-Tolerant</u> <u>Computing</u>, pp. 369-371, October 1980.

[TSA80b] Tsay, D. P. and Liu, M. T., "Design of a Robust Network Front-End for the Distributed Double-Loop Computer Network (DDLCN)," <u>Proceedings</u>

of Distributed Data Acquisition, Computing, and Control Symposium, pp. 141-155, December 1980.

[TSA81] Tsay, D. P., "MIKE: A Network Operating System for Distributed Double-Loop Computer Network," Ph.D. Dissertation, Department of Computer and Information Science, The Ohio State University, Columbus, Ohio, June 1981.

[WAR80] Ward, S. A., "TRIX: A Network-Oriented Operating System," Proceedings of COMPCON'80 Spring, pp. 344-349, February 1980.

[WAT80] Watson, R. W. and Fletcher, J. G , "An Architecture for Support of Network Operating System Services," Computer Networks, Vol. 4, No. 1, pp. 33-49, February 1980.

[WIT80] Wittie, L. D and Van Tilborg, A. M., "MICROS, A Distributed Operating System for MICRONET, A Reconfigurable Network Computers," IEEE Transactions on Computers, Vol. C-29, No. 12, pp. 1133-1144, December 1980.

[WOL79] Wolf, J. J., Liu, M. T., Weide, B. W., and Tsay, D. P., "Design of a Distributed Fault-tolerant Loop Network," Proceedings of 1979 International Symposium on Fault-Tolerant Computing, pp. 17-24, June 1979.

[WUL81] Wulf, W. A., Levin, R., and Harbison, S. P., Hydra/C.mmp: An Experimental Computer System, McGraw-Hill, New York, 1981.

LOCAL COMPUTER NETWORKS
P.C. Ravasio, G. Hopkins and N. Naffah (editors)
North-Holland Publishing Company
© IFIP, 1982

MOVING A SERVICE FROM A LONG-HAUL TO A LOCAL NETWORK

P. BUCCIARELLI, G. ENRICO

OLTECO - Olivetti Telecomunication S.p.A. - Ivrea (Italy)

ABSTRACT

This paper describes the problems we faced in designing a network utility independent from the degree of dispersion of the interconnected hosts.

As an example of this approach we consider a particular application : a "Distributed File System" that has been designed with criteria of modularity in order to fit the requirement of different distributed architectures.

The utility has been already implemented on a geographic network. We point out the problems that arise when moving the utility to our local network and finally we focus on the need for a standard compatible approach to communication service for both local and geographical networks.

1. INTRODUCTION

Working in computer network manufacture we faced the problem of designing application services (we also call them "utility" or "facility") for both long-haul and local networks.

Even if the user environment of the two families of networks is, generally, quite different, some basic applications can be defined for both of them. (This approach is acceptable if the services supplied by the utility are well suited for both local and long-haul system user environment.) An example of such a common utility is a Network File System to extend the User access from one host file store to the other interconnected ones. Therefore we considered the possibility of designing this kind of facility independently of the fact that it will be implemented on a local or longhaul network.

The main problem we faced was the difference in the available communication facilities of the two systems. The applications on our geographic network are supported (for the communication needs) by a standard (11) transport service.

The ones already implemented on our local network are supported by a transport service without connections.

Such a difference affects strongly the internal functionality of the applications that in the latter case must take care (or can take advantage) of the "peculiarity" of the connection-less communication service. On the other hand, it reflects the difference in media and technology of data.

transmission across longhaul and local areas. A way to reconcile this
difference is to define interconnection rules that include both the
possibilities in order to allow the application to choose the most convenient communication service independently of the supporting system
topology. Efforts towards this solution seem to be encouraged by several
arguments.

The first argument is the urgent need for standards in local network
  interconnection and, on the other hand, the advanced state of definition
of standard interconnection models and protocols in long-haul ones that
constitute a reference point in telecommunication. The second argument is
the strong need of internetworking between local and long-haul networks.

Finally, the possibility of choosing the communication support according to
the requirement of the application (and not to the type of network!) is a
step toward a desirable unified (network independent) approach to
distributed application programming.

This paper describes the problems we faced in designing a network utility
independent from the degree of dispersion of the interconnected hosts.

As an example of this approach, we consider a particular application, a
"Distributed File System" that has been designed with criteria of
modularity in order to fit the requirements of different distributed
architectures.

The utility has been already implemented on a geographic network.   We
point out the problems that arise when moving the utility to our local
network and finally we focus out the need for a standard compatible
approach to communication service for both local and geographic networks.

2.   AN EXAMPLE : THE DISTRIBUTED FILE SYSTEM (DFS)

The aim of the DFS is to extend the user access from a single file store
to all the interconnected hosts' file stores without either duplicating or
centralising any data base.

The DFS allows the User to operate on remote files both in their entirety
  (create, delete, transfer) as well as on their parts (record read/write)
in a way independent from the specific file store organization of hosts.

The DFS is in course of implementation on a long-haul network (LHN) of
small size machines for a banking application (3) and we plan to implement
it also on our Local Network (LNS) (7). The criteria followed in designing
the application make this objective not too difficult to reach.

On the other hand, the possibility to re-utilize on the LNS (at least) the
functional specifications of the DFS, is very attractive. That is due to
the cost of designing and, mostly the cost of validation and performance
evaluation of a new protocol.

Moving the specifications from the LHN to the LNS entails facing some
problems. The main problem is not really due to the application but derives
from the different available communication services provided by the
Networks.

Other problems are more peculiar to this kind of application and their
importance depends on the difference between the user environments of the
two distributed systems, (e.g. giving the User visibility of file location
might be a valid choice, depending on the User environment) both in LHN
and in LNS.

In this section we will describe briefly the architecture of the DFS, the assumptions that made its implementation on the LHN easy and the problems that arise in implementing it on the LNS.

2.1 Services

The Distributed File System (DFS) supplies the User with the following classes of services:

- record access: the User can operate on a record and on its attributes(e.g. : read/write/change record)
- file management: the User can read and modify the attributes of a file as a whole (e.g. open file, read/change file attributes, create file, delete file)
- file transfer: that allows the Users to move an entire file and its attributes across the network between dissimilar file systems.

All the above services inlcude a subservice of Access Control and Accounting.

2.2 Architecture and General Features

Fig.1 describes the architecture of DFS. It shows which are the main components, the interaction between them and the interaction with local environment (file system, user, operating system, lower communicating layer.)

The DFS consists of three types of functional modules. They are:

- The CONTROLLER that interfaces the User and activates the right Protocol Machine according to the User request.
- The MAPPER PROCESS that interfaces the local file system and performs the mapping between the local file structures and a network standardised file format ("virtual file") and vice versa.
- An arbitrary number of PROTOCOL MACHINES. We defined two Protocols, one for File Transfer (FTP) and one for file access and management (DAP).

Any number of instances of identical Protocol Machines can be activated to process simultaneously several User requests.

The maximum number of instances is dinamically limited by the Operating System according to the busy condition of the system.

2.3 Modularity

An important characteristic of the DFS is its modularity. The strict functional subdivision in design and implementation allows

- to extend easily the DFS services by adding other Protocol Machines.
- to change (only) the Protocol Machine process to fit future standards or other interconnection architecture where, for example, a Session layer or a Data Presentation layer is available.
- to choose between two possibilities in installing the DFS:

1) if the Controller process is not loaded on the host, this host
    can be accessed by remote systems but local Users cannot issue
    any request to DFS. (This is the functionality that is necessary
    for a host that works as a Network "server".)

2) if all the component processes are loaded, local User can access
    remote file and local files can be accessed by remote users. (See
    fig.1a, 1b.)

-   to face size limitations adjusting the configuration and number of
protocol machines to suit the limitation of the system.

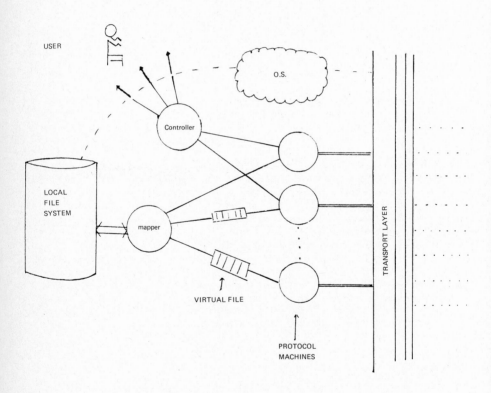

FIGURE 1   The architecture of the DFS

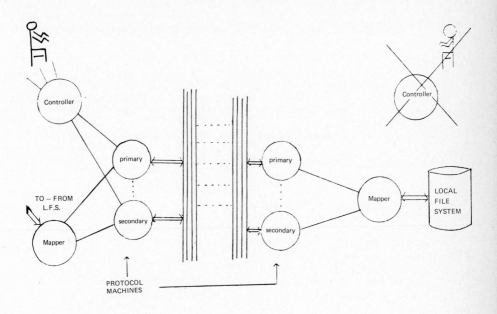

FIGURE 1a and 1b   DFS with reduced functionality (1a) and with full functionality

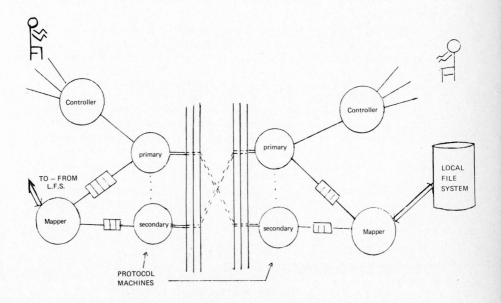

2.4 Adaptability

Another aspect that can be mentioned is ease with which the protocols used can be adapted as standard emerge and evolve. At the moment, no international standard file Transfer Data Access protocols exist even if the standardisation activity in this area is very intensive and some results are fairly stable. Due to our deadline we could not wait for a standard protocol to be produced. Nevertheless, the current standardisation trends have been followed to make easy the adoption of a future standard protocol.

(The adoption of the concept of a "virtual file" to reconcile differences in file store implementation, the organisation of error recovery and resume capability, reflect current standard trends (2).)

2.5 Assumption about the environment

In this chapter we explain some important hypothesis that were considered when the DFS was designed for LHN and the influence they had in its design. The lack of some of these hypothesis constitutes the core of the problem we have to solve in implementing the DFS in the Local net. The environment was such that there was:

a)   The availability of a connection-oriented Transport service.

This must guarantee communication service without either loss or duplication or out of order arrival of any message. The consequence of this hypothesis is that the DFS is quite unaware of communication problems if not explicitly signaled.

b)   The existance of a local interprocess communication system on each host. This allows us to distribute (in design and implementation) the whole functionality among a set of cooperating processes with the advantages described in 2.2.

c)   The heterogeneity of the interconnected hosts. This fact forces all operations and protocols to refer to network standardized file model to guarantee the graceful expansion of the whole distributed system.

d)   Autonomy of each host without the possibility to support an intensive interaction. The consequence of this hypothesis is that in accessing the Distributed File System, the User musts specify the location of the remote file he wants to access. We believe that in a distributed loosely connected environment, the User should retain control over the actual location of data he/she wants to access. Furthermore, the generation of file name is the responsability of the User that must be aware of syntax requirement of each file system he/she wants to access.

Finally the responsibility for updating multiple copies of a modified file (if they exist) on different interconnected file systems, is a User concern.

2.6 The File Transfer Facility on the LHN

The services and functions of the File Transfer Facility (FTF) are described here briefly. A detailed description can be found in (2).

2.6.1   FTF Services
The File Transfer Facility supplies the user with the following services:

- COPY service. This allows the user to copy a (source) file into another (sink) file; one or both files can be remote or local. The effect of the "copy" on the sink file can be:
  REPLACE
  APPEND
  CREATE
- STATUS service. This allows the user to ask for information about the status of the transfer.
- ABORT service. This allows the user to cancel a transfer in progress.

These services include a great set of subservices (e.g.: system access, file access, file management, error handling, recovery etc.)
All the services are achieved by the cooperation of the composing processes:
the Controller, the Mapper, the FTP (File Transfer Protocol) Machine.
An important subservice is Error Recovery. In the File Transfer application, it is particularly critical due to the large amount of carried data. The aim of Recovery mechanism is to <u>allow an interrupted transfer to be continued without retransmission of already transferred data.</u>

2.6.2   FTF Behaviour
In 2.2 we have described the role of each composing process. We will show here how they cooperate.
When the User issues a transfer request, the Controller activates an FTP process (primary). This establishes an internal link with the Mapper process and, a full duplex association with the remote FTP process (secondary) based on a transport connection. A transport connection cannot be re-used for several associations.(Note that the Controller at remote site is not aware of the transfer operation.) A link (and a protocol) between Controllers has been defined to perform "three party transfer" and "Multi file transfer".

On the same association the two FTP machines exchange protocol messages (in both directions) and data (in one direction).
A FTP machine is able to handle only one data transfer at a time. More than one file can be transferred sequentially on one association given that the decision to keep or close it is a Controller concern. (The Controller keeps the association open in case of multi file transfer requests.)
Simultaneous file transfer operations can be performed by activating several instances of the FTP Machine.

In such case, the Mapper process will serve all of them with a round-robin policy.
The FTP machine is a process which consists of four phases:

1)   Association Establishment: this phase is entered only once in the life of the association and consists in a transport connection activation request.

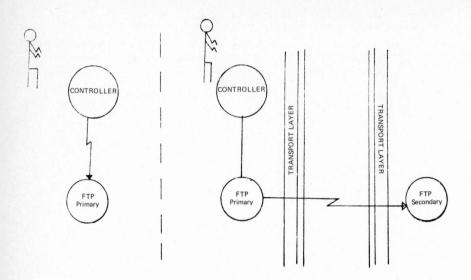

FIGURE 2   Local and remote connection establishing

2)   Initialisation: this phase includes parameter negotiation and check
     of access rights and is entered once before each file transfer.

3)   Data transfer: in this phase the "virtual file" is transferred
     together with control information (checkpoints).

4)   Termination: this phase is entered to close the association and the
     transport connection.

2.7 Transaction Services in the LHN
This set of services includes both file management and record access
operation.
There are some important differences between this class of service and the
previous one.
The first difference is that the most common use is interactive, therefore
a rapid response is required. Furthermore, the traffic generated by these
services on the network has a "burst" rather than a "stream" nature, which
is typical of the transfer service. Some services (e.g. "delete") do not
cause any consistent amount of data to be transferred.
On the other hand, our network supplies a connection-oriented Transport
service. In order to supply consistent and responsive interactive service,
we would like to avoid opening and closing the logical channel with the
remote file system when the User request occurs but we would like to find
it already open.
In our network configuration, it would be impossible because we have about
1500 interconnected hosts. So we fixed a maximum number of links, each

corresponding to an interconnected file system. One process (implementing the Data Access Protocol (DAP)) is dedicated to one link (analogous to FTP process). When a user request occurs, if it concerns a file system that has been already interconnected, the request is enqueued to the corresponding DAP process. Otherwise a new DAP is activated to create a new link, or the least recently used link is replaced (see fig. 3).

On each link data and command flow in both directions; several user requests are multiplexed on the same logical channel; at the end of each transaction, the two entities exchange the right to initiate a new transaction. The protocol provides also the possibility to acquire such a right within transactions.

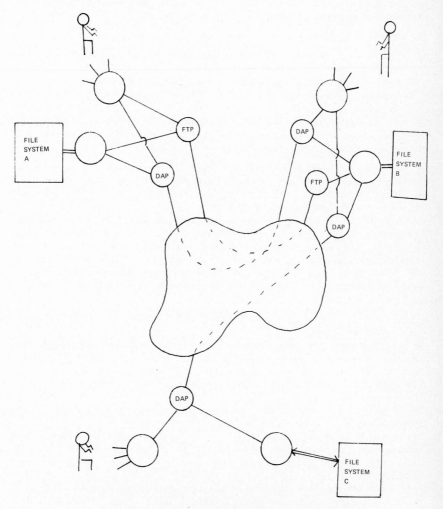

FIGURE 3   The file systems A and C are not interconnected.
The file system B is interconnected with A and C

3. SPECIAL CONSIDERATIONS ON SOLONE, THE OLIVETTI LOCAL NETWORK

3.1 Our Local Network architecture

In the Olivetti Local network environment the kind of scenarios we can
have, the services and features to guarantee are numerous and they can be
different from those normally found in LHN.

In long-haul networks the main goal is to transfer data from one autonomous
node to another and considerable effort is needed to make the transfer over
the slow, error prone links as reliable as possible.

In local networks we have to consider at least three variables: the kind
of information we want to transfer (not only data!), the scope of the LNS
and the technological aspects that are manifestly different from the ones
existing in geographical areas.

The SOLONE architecture defines three classes of Local Network Systems:

1)   LNS as a collection of heterogeneous interconnected systems completely
     autonomous and loosely interacting.
2)   LNS with more homogeneous systems, still autonomous but more
     interacting and with the possibility of Hosts acting as network
     servers.
3)   Functionally distributed systems based on LN technology with a low
     degree of autonomy among nodes and a very high cooperation and
     specialization.

In the three outlined scenarios, the level of cooperation and autonomy of
the interconnected systems is quite different. Namely there is a high
degree of autonomy in the first case while there is a high level of
cooperation with low autonomy in the third case.

We think of LN in perspective as a transport mechanism which permits the
integration of four types of traffic: data, word, voice and image. For each
of these, the same parameters (like throughput, end to end delay,
reliability, availability, distribution of control ....) can be different.

The SOLONE architecture is designed in order to use the same communication
subsystem to build up systems belonging to all the three defined classes.

3.2 Implemented Features

We have implemented a local Network that is now working. For it we have
adopted a protocol architecture according to the ISO OSI model (after
some discussion, because we know that this model is oriented to data
management and conditioned by some problems arising in Geographic Network
environment).

The physical and data link layers are implemented according to the
Ethernet specs (version 1.0 from Xerox, DEC, INTEL).

The network layer is very thin: we have a broadcast channel for
transmission and each node is connected to all the others directly (so
there are not switching and routing functions inside the local subnetwork).

But a Network sub layer is defined for Interconnection purposes.

At the transport layer we have at present three kinds of communication
services: datagram, datagram with acknowledgement and byte stream.

The first is completely connection-less, he second and third use only an implicit unidirectional connection limited to a single transport message. Both (the second and the third) are able to guarantee no loss or duplication of a packet. The difference between them is that one is limited to the transfer of a message that can be incapsulated in an Ethernet packet, the other can transport a message of any length using sequencing and fragmentation.

3.3 Experimental results

The hardware and software project of SOLONE included the development of an application to allow resouce sharing among a number of homogeneous interconnected hosts. This application (currently in the market) allowed us to experiment the relationship between availability of resources-(hardware in particular),communication capability and application requirements.

A pure datagram service does not guarantee the delivery of a message, it only assumes that the probability of loss is very low. We observed that, under certain conditions, this probability remains low only if redundant resources are available. To provide the conditions that support the datagram philosophy, more hardware and more sophisticated memory management are needed.

Since there is no flow control and the controller interfacing the 10 Mbit/sec channel has to pick up all the packets arriving for the host, in a very asynchronous and burstly mode, the risk is that some packets will be lost not for error on the physical connection but for memory unavailability.

This effect is greatly increased by the range of different rates at which the hosts use the information and the existence of some asymmetric functions on the network, supplied by servers.

4.   MOVING THE DFS FROM THE LONG-HAUL TO LOCAL NETWORK

Our current interest is to build on the LNS a network file system to allow the sharing of files. Our idea to use on the LNS the DFS described in Chapter 2 is encouraged by the fact that currently we are particularly interested in LNS of class 1 and 2 (see 3.1). Furthermore we expect in the near future to interconnect our LNS with the LHN solving the problem of internetworking at the lowest possible level. If we implement the same DFS protocols both on the LNS and on the LHN we solve the internetworking problem in a gateway at the Transport Layer. On the other hand,if we have a different DFS on the LNS and LHN we have to elevate gateway problems to the application layer.

Presenting the Distributed File System in Chapter 2 we listed some peculiar aspects of the supporting system and the user environment. Such aspects are the only ones we discussed when passing from the long-haul network to the local one.

They were:
a)   availability of local IPC system
b)   heterogeneity of the interconnected systems
c)   autonomy of each host
d)   connection-oriented transport service

We now consider the existence and importance of these aspects in the LNS.

4.1 Local IPC
The availability of a local IPC is more an aspect of host than of network
environment, and arises only when implementing the service. The lack of a
local IPC makes the implementation of the DFS very difficult. On our LNS
the hosts have their local IPC.
Another aspect of implementation that is related to Operating System
feature is the possibility of activating several processes sharing the same
code. The design of the DFS assumes this capability in order to allow each
host to handle simultaneous operation from/to several file stores.
The hosts of the (current) experimental LNS do not provide the capability
of activating several processes on the same program. This limitation
implies that multiple file transfers cannot occur simultaneously to/from
one host, but this does not affect the possibility of supplying
simultaneous transactional services (record access and file management)
because of the peculiarity of transport service.

4.2 Heterogeneity of hosts
The problem of heterogeneity is relevant also in Local Networks because
it is desirable to interconnect multivendor products. Furthermore a
peculiar aspect of this problem in LNS (scale problem) is the difference
in size and functionality of interconnected hosts.
Such a difference can be very marked due to the fact that a wide range of
users can share the same communication subsystem (e.g. intelligent
terminals, word processing machines, EDP systems).
Considering the DFS, all the functions included in the service to
reconcile differences in file structures remain valid when moving the
application to the local network.

4.3 Autonomy of hosts
The aspects of autonomy of each node and the degree of interaction among
them, cause an LNS to be inserted in one of the classes we proposed in 3.1.
We have already examined in 2 the consequences (from the point of view of
the Service supplied by the DFS) of assuming a high degree of autonomy.
  If we consider LNS of class 1, such consequences are acceptable.
They are quite unacceptable for LNS of class 3. If we consider the LNS
of class 2, the assumption of the transparency of data locality for the
User should be discussed. In our opinion, to give the User the task
of specifying the residence of a file when he/she accesses it, is
acceptable only if we emphasize the perspectives of internetworking.
If the internetworking is not the firsts goal, we estimate better to
priviledge the aspects of program portability and service robustness (due
to system reconfiguration) by hiding from the User the physical locality
of data.

Therefore, to move the DFS to an LNS of class 2 we have to add to the DFS
design some functionality of "file searching". This can be obtained more
easily in LN environment than in a geographic one because the communication
subsystem of our LN supplies to the applications broadcast and multicast
addressing capabilities through datagram service.

4.4 Connection Oriented transport service

To discuss this point we have to consider the traffic generated by the two types of services supplied by the DFS ("transfer" and "transactions") and the commmunication capabilities supplied by our LNS.

The file transfer function of the DFS is very well supported by a connection oriented transport service. The same transport service lowers the efficiency of the file access and management functions of the DFS. In fact a connection oriented transport service does not seem to be suitable for supporting a multidirectional "burst" traffic; the solution adopted in 2.7 is the only reasonable one we found but it does not encourage an interactive use of remote resource via long-haul network.

On the other hand, SCLONE supplies connectionless oriented communication services ("pure" datagram, datagram with "ack"). Such kinds of services support efficiently the communication requirements of the file access and management facility but it is not suitable to support the file transfer.

Therefore, it is possible to move the transactional functions of the DFS to the LNS, gaining in performance, while, the file transfer functionality must be improved in order to cover all the aspects concerning the reliability of data transmission.

An alternative solution we are evalutating is to increase the capability of the LNS transport layer to supply also a connection oriented transport service that follows the ECMA-72 class 4 standard.

The solution that uses the connectionless transport for transactional functions and the connection oriented one for transfer functions is the most desirable. It implies the DFS to be changed only in Data Access protocol.

We have considered several problems which arise when moving the application from long-haul to local network. Among these, the communication problem is the only one which cannot be solved without either changing the application functionality or increasing the existing communication services.

5. CONCLUDING REMARKS

We have analized the specifications of a sufficently common network service, a DFS, particularly in the aspect of communication services : it requires a connection oriented service for file transfer and connection-less service for data access.

Our aim was to design it in a way independent from the distributed architecture on which it will be implemented (local or long haul network).   It seems possible, under certain hipotesis, if we have on each architecture both the services. In such a way the DFS can be designed by choosing the most suitable communication service according to its requirements independently from the network on which it will be implemented.

The availability of both communication services in LAN is feasible: adding connection facilities at the transport level is realistic and this bridges half the gap toward LHN.

On the contrary, in long haul networks it is very difficult to provide both communication modes because we want to use a standard transport layer and standards do not provide connection-less services for LHN.

In mowing the DFS specifications from LHN to LAN we have two aims in mind:

> 1) considering the problem of portability,reutilize a well defined design and supply the same application service in LAN and LHN
> 2) extending the DFS to a global network resulting from the interconnection of the LAN and LHN.

5.1 PORTABILITY

The aim of portability of DFS can be reached with different solutions and costs according to several scenarios which can be outlined as follows:

CASE A
Transport protocols in LAN and LHN are different and offer different services. In moving an application we have two possibilities:

> i) the application takes care of the different transport services in its protocol and functions.This solution is not acceptable for us because it implies re-designing of the application.

> ii) a transport sublayer is added either in LAN or in LHN or in both with enhancement of some functionalities to guarantee the same services.

CASE B

Transport layer with different protocols but offering the same services.
The portability of the application service specs can be achieved without requiring changes neither in the protocol of the

application nor in the transport layer. It can be solved with a local adapting of interfaces.

CASE C

Transport layers with identical protocols.

We have a complete transportability of the application specs. Only a local adapting of the primitives to access the transport service may be necessary.
For the time being, this case is not realistic because there is no agreement in the area of network services for LHN and LAN.

5.2 INTERCONNECTION

In all the three cases A, B and C we can have the transportability of the DFS on LAN but more problems arise when interconnecting the local with the long haul network and utilizing the DFS in such an extended environment.

We cannot accept the first (i) solution presented in the case A because we don't want ro solve the interconnection problem by elevating the gateway up to the application layer.

All the other solutions presented in the cases A, B and C allow the interconnection at transport layer (C also at network layer).

5.3 CHOISING A SOLUTION

Two solutions seem effective, in our view. A brief term one is the solution proposed in the case A (ii): adding a sublayer in the transport to obtain the needed services.

Such a solution allows the application and their protocols to be designed independently from the supporting communication system and solve the network interconnecting problem at the transport layer. It is not a really general solution but it seems the most easy to be applied in our specific case.

A second more general solution is the one proposed in the case B. It consists in defining LAN and LHN transport protocols which can be different but must be able to offer identical services.

It takes in consideration the differences and fairly stable condictions which already exist in LAN and LHN at transport layer.

On the other hand, the standardization activities in this area are very intensive and widely encouraged. Therefore we think that some efforts should be done to define for lan and LHN standard transport protocols which are able to support both connection oriented and connection less communication services.

References

1)   European Computer Manufacturers Association
     "Virtual File Protocol - VIII draft"
     November 1981

2)   M. Bozzetti
     A General overview of the Olivetti Network File System
     IFIP proceedings 1980

3)   M. Bozzetti and others
     ONE/V2 : An Approach to Geographically Distributed Systems
     IFIP proceedings 1980

4)   G. Casaglia
     "Una rete di minicalcolatori e terminali per applicazioni
     bancarie"
     Sistemi e Automazione N° 212 Feb. 1981

5)   P. Bucciarelli
     "A Distributed File System for a Network of small size
     machines"
     To be published in:
     Proceedings of 15th Hawaii International Conference on
     System Sciences Jan. 1982

6)   ISO: "Reference Model of Open System Interconnection"
     Draft Proposal 7498 ISO (TC 97) SC 16n. 537 rev 1980

7)   OLTECO LNS GROUP
     "Solone - System Olivetti Local Nertwork"
     Internal report June 1980

8)   G. Enrico
     "Local Network Design and Implementation in OLIVETTI"
     Workshop at INRIA 6-7 April 1981

9)   National Bureau of Standards
     "Specification of the Transport Protocol"
     Report N° ICST/HLNP-81-1

10) V.B. Hunt, P.C. Ravasio
     Olivetti Local Network System Protocol Architecture
     in proceedings of IFIP working group 6.4
     Zurich, Switzerland, 27-29 August, 1980

11) European Computer Manufacturers Association
     "Standard ECMA-72 Transport Protocol" Jan 1981

LCN GATEWAYS

LOCAL COMPUTER NETWORKS
P.C. Ravasio, G. Hopkins and N. Naffah (editors)
North-Holland Publishing Company
© IFIP, 1982

A HIGH PERFORMANCE GATEWAY FOR THE LOCAL
CONNECTION OF CAMBRIDGE RINGS

Ian M. Leslie

Computer Laboratory, University of Cambridge
Cambridge, U. K.

When connecting together networks which have
radically different characteristics,
problems centre around addressing, routing
and protocol issues. These problems are
somewhat reduced when linking homogeneous
networks together. However, in order to
preserve the local area network properties
of, for example, a multiple ring system, the
gateway designer is faced with stringent
performance requirements. A strategy for
interconnecting Cambridge Rings in the same
local environment by high performance
gateways will be presented. High bandwidth
and low delays through gateways are achieved
in this scheme. The strategy also preserves
the local network protocols used on the ring
at Cambridge, so that communication through
a gateway is as simple as communication over
a single ring.

INTRODUCTION

It is evident that as a local network grows, there are advantages in
splitting it into subnetworks. These advantages lie in reliability
and performance. Reliability is enhanced because a physical failure
can be confined to one subnetwork. Performance will be improved for
traffic which does not travel between subnetworks, both in available
system bandwidth and network delay. In the case of a slotted ring,
point to point bandwidth would also be increased, since this is
related directly to the ring delay. Disadvantages lie in the
expense of a gateway or bridge required to connect subnetworks, and
in the imposition of an internetwork protocol which machines must
observe in order to communicate through gateways. Another
disadvantage may be that while applications residing wholly on one
subnetwork may be better off, applications which make use of many
subnetworks may be adversely affected by any bandwidth restrictions
or long delays through a gateway.

The goal of the work described here is to overcome some of these
disadvantages; that is to keep the local network flavour intact in
a multiple subnetwork environment. The subnetworks used are
Cambridge Rings [1]. Full advantage is taken of homogeneity; this
is not an exercise in the general interconnection of networks. An
example of an internet which connects different types of networks is
the PUP internet [2]. PUP's (PARC Universal Packets) are
encapsulated with in the packets of other networks, which include
ETHERNET's, the ARPANET and packet radio networks. Performance
measurements in one area of application, remote procedure calls,
show this encapsulation to be costly [3]. Significant performance
improvements were obtained by avoiding the use of PUP's for
communication within a single ETHERNET. For the work described
here, it was felt desirable to extend local network behaviour to a
larger network rather than to force large network behaviour on
local network hosts. The results are high bandwidth, low delay
gateways, which have a minimal impact on the protocols used
presently on the ring at the Cambridge Computer Laboratory.

Since the gateway design presented here relies on the lower level
protocols used on the ring at Cambridge, these are presented
briefly. This will be followed by an overview of the gateway
strategy. Attention will then be given to the gateway hardware, the
details of gateway operation and network management issues. Finally
the current status and a look at some of the problems caused by
using gateways are discussed.

BACKGROUND

The Cambridge Ring works on the empty slot principle. A slot or
minipacket is a collection of bits with format as shown in figure 1.
A constant number of slots circulate continuously around the ring.
Stations wishing to transmit wait for an empty slot to arrive, mark
it full, and fill in the address and data fields. The minipacket
continues around the ring to the destination which marks the
response bits and normally accepts the data. The minipacket then
returns to the sender where the response bits may be read.

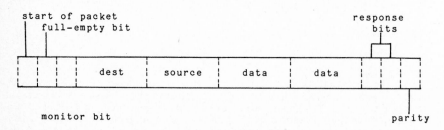

Figure 1.   Ring Slot Format

At Cambridge very nearly all communication is done in basic blocks,
which are made up of the data parts of several minipackets.

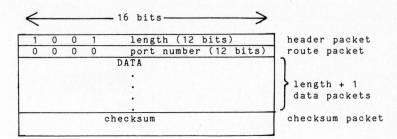

Figure 2. Basic Block Format

A complete description of the basic block protocol can be found in
an appendix of [4]. The format of a basic block is shown in
figure 2. The port number contained in a basic block is used as an
address within the destination machine. It would, for example, be
the means by which a machine would determine the process for which a
basic block was destined.

Above the basic block protocol are two network protocols, the Single
Shot Protocol (SSP) [5] and the Byte Stream Protocol (BSP) [4].

The single shot protocol is stateless and is used where the amount
of data to be supplied and returned can be contained in a single
basic block. Thus no special flow control need be implemented and
the protocol also defines no error control; in the absence of a
reply to a request, the sender must try again. A requester sends
out an SSP request (SSPREQ) block and waits for an SSP reply
(SSPRPLY) block to come back. The formats of the SSPREQ and SSPRPLY
blocks are shown in figure 3. (The formats shown would be
encapsulated inside a basic block; the length fields, route packets
and checksums are not shown.) SSP transactions are used, for
example, in name lookups (see below) and finding out the date and
time.

              SSPREQ   SSPRPLY

   pkt 0: high byte: 6C hex   pkt 0: high byte: 65 hex
          low byte: zero   low byte: zero
       1: port number for   1: zero
          reply   2: return code - zero iff
       2: function code   operation was successful
    3 on: parameters and   3 on: returned parameters and
          data of request   data

          Figure 3. Single Shot Protocol Formats

```
            OPEN                              OPENACK

    pkt 0: high byte: 6A hex         pkt 0: high byte: 65 hex
           low byte: flags                  low byte: flags
         1: port number for                1: port number for
            reply                             connection
         2: function code                   2: return code - zero iff
         3: number of BSP                      successful
            parameters, N                   3: number of BSP
4 to N+3: BSP parameters                       parameters, N
    N+4 on: further parameters       4 to N+3: BSP parameters
                                       N+4 on: further parameters
```

Figure 4. OPEN - OPENACK Formats

The byte stream protocol is a lightweight error correcting and flow
control protocol which is used either when large amounts of data are
to be transferred, or when the risk of losing or repeating
information cannot be accepted. For the purpose of discussing the
gateway design presented here, the only concern is the way in which
a byte stream is set up - the so called "initial connection" in
appendix B of [Johnson 80]. The OPEN - OPENACK exchange looks very
much like an SSP exchange, the difference being primarily in the
port number returned by the OPENACK block, as shown in figure 4. In
an SSP exchange, the reply port number sent in the SSPREQ block
might be considered to be invalid after a reply is received, since
the single shot protocol is stateless. However, in the
OPEN - OPENACK exchange, the connection and reply ports are used
until the stream is closed.

The port numbers to which an SSPREQ or OPEN block are sent are
obtained from a name lookup service, or nameserver. The
nameserver's is the only address which may be written into programs.
To find any other service, the name of the service is given to the
nameserver in a name lookup request. The nameserver will reply with
a station number, port number and function code. This public port
address may then be cached by a machine.

DESIGN OVERVIEW

Perhaps the most fundamental property of a gateway is the level in
the protocol hierarchy at which the gateway operates. At the lowest
level, the gateway would operate on globally addressed minipackets,
routing them to their final destinations. There would be a problem,
however, in preserving the low level responses associated with
minipackets since the gateway, rather than the final destination,
would be marking the response bits. Another problem is committing
global addresses into ring hardware. For example, it was thought
that a global address on the network would consist of a ring number
and a station number. However, with Project Universe[1], global
addresses will now include a site number.

At the next layer up, gateways could route globally addressed basic
blocks. The low level responses are used to transmit basic blocks,
but need not be preserved for higher level protocols. Above this
level one could imagine the gateway being involved in more complex

protocols as in a transport service gateway.

The method used here is a slight variation on the basic block approach. Rather than having global addresses in each basic block, lightweight virtual circuits are used to route basic blocks to their destinations. Thus instead of translating a global address to a next hop using static tables, the gateway dynamically associates a next hop with each active gateway port number. A series of these associations forms a virtual circuit. The aim has been to make operation on the network indistinguishable from the original operation on the single ring, so far as a client machine^2 is concerned.

A gateway routes basic blocks by performing a mapping from the port on which it receives a basic block to a next station and port number. Global addresses are not used by machines on the network other than gateways and nameservers (see below). Although the port number mappings stored in a gateway could be considered to be virtual circuits, unlike most virtual circuits, no attempt is made by gateways to enhance the probability of a basic block arriving at its destination. Error correction and flow control are handled by the end machines, as they are on a single ring.

Much of the problem of designing a gateway is thus concerned with the setting up of these port mappings or routes. There are two different types of routes: routes to ports which are dynamically allocated by client machines and routes to ports which are always active. The former are the reply and connection ports of SSP and BSP, while the latter are the public ports mentioned above. Routes to public ports can be set up statically on the gateway, in which case the name server would return a gateway port for any request naming a service on a different ring. Alternatively, routes to public ports could be set up by the nameserver as name lookup requests were received. For the purpose of setting up routes, gateways and nameservers will have to deal with global addresses.

GATEWAY HARDWARE

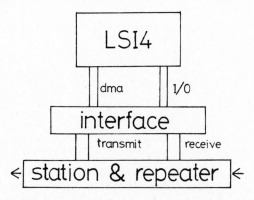

Figure 5. Standard Connection of LSI4 to Ring

The gateway obtains high performance (both high bandwidth and low
delay) by using two high speed DMA interfaces. These are normally
used to connect Computer Automation LSI4 computers to the ring. The
interfaces have programmed logic (a Signetics 8X300
microinterpreter) which has been modified for the gateway.
Controlling these interfaces is an LSI4/10 computer which provides
control, routing information and storage buffers.

The normal connection between a ring and an LSI4 using the DMA
interface is shown in figure 5. Note that the ring station is fully
duplex. Figure 6 shows the configuration of a gateway. The
interfaces cross-couple the rings so that the receiver and
transmitter of each direction of traffic are in the same interface.
Thus in some cases there is no need for traffic to enter the central
machine; the interface could transmit on one ring a minipacket
which it has just received on the other.

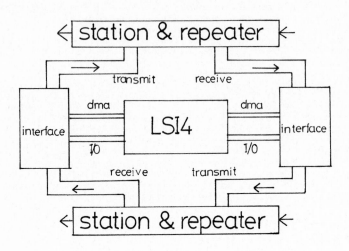

Figure 6. Gateway Configuration

The policy implemented in the interfaces is as follows. Each
interface has two processes, one for reception and one for
transmission. If minipackets cannot be transmitted as soon as they
are received, the central machine's memory is used to buffer basic
blocks or parts of basic blocks. On the other hand, the transmitter
can be in the same block as the receiver, and indeed may be waiting
for the next ring packet to arrive. However, there is no concurrent
reception of basic blocks; the receiver locks on to one station
until a complete basic block has arrived. Similarly, the
transmitter will not transmit several basic blocks at the same time.
This policy allows a potentially small delay (on the order of a ring
packet) through the gateway. However, since the gateway is locked
on to one source for the duration of a basic block, a slow
transmitter, or a slow receiver on the transmission side, can tie up
the gateway for an unacceptable length of time. (Other sources
sending to the gateway will see the response bits of their
minipackets marked unselected during this period.)

An interface interrupts the central machine once for every basic block received. The interrupt may come after the port number or when the whole block has been received, depending upon the status of the port that the block was received on. The status indicates whether or not the gateway has any work to do other than routing the block. If the central machine is interrupted after the port number is received, it performs the routing transformation and marks the block for transmission. A result of the routing operation is that the port number in the basic block is altered. This will change the checksum, so that it too must be altered.

The central machine does get in the way of traffic, if only to the extent that it performs a route mapping. The central control of the gateway is implemented in BCPL [6] and uses a TRIPOS [7] operating system which provides efficient task switching. Even so, early performance testing with a fast source and a sink receiver showed that the bulk of delay was in the central machine rather than the interface.

VIRTUAL CIRCUIT OPERATION

The dynamic port number mappings in a gateway are set up as side effects of the transmission of SSPREQ, OPEN and OPENACK blocks through gateways. Routes are always set up in reverse by mapping ports allocated by the gateway to reply ports in these blocks. (These reply ports will be altered by the gateway before the block is transmitted.) As an example, the setting up of a byte stream in a two ring system is considered below. An SSP exchange can be thought of as a degenerate case of this. It is assumed that static routes to public ports exist on the gateway.

A client, C, on ring X wishes to open a byte stream to a service on ring Y. The public port for this service is port number si on machine S. C send a name lookup request to its local nameserver. The nameserver replies to C and tells it that the service is on the gateway port Gs. Port Gs on the gateway is statically mapped to the public port for the service:
                    Xmap: Gs ----> S, si (static)

C sends off an OPEN block to the gateway with reply port cr. The gateway realizes that this block is destined to an initial interaction port and so allocates a return port on the gateway for S to respond on:
                    Ymap: G1 ----> C, cr (reply expected)
The gateway then overwrites the reply port cr in the open block with G1, adjusts the checksum and sends the block on to port si on S.

S will reply to C on port G1. The gateway realizes that this port was expecting a reply, and so as well as performing the mapping from this port to the original reply port on C, allocates a forward port from C to S which maps to the connection port, sc, supplied by S:
                    Xmap: G2 ----> S, sc (normal)
The gateway overwrites the connection port in the OPENACK block and sends it back to C as well as modifying the status of the reply port:
                    Ymap: G1 ----> C, cr (normal)
Thereafter, only the port mappings are performed; no further allocations are made. Allocated ports are deallocated through timeout rather by explicit closing. When a client transmits to a

gateway on a port which has timed out, he will see an unselected
response for minipackets in the middle of the basic block.

In the SSP case, the SSPREQ block causes a reverse path to be set
up. When the SSPRPLY comes back, the reverse path can be destroyed
and no forward path need be set up.

Extensions to the mechanisms for multiple rings are obvious - static
routes to public ports would be set up through a series of gateways,
and the dynamic set up of reverse routes would work exactly as
above.

ROUTE SET UP TO PUBLIC PORTS

As mentioned above, there is no need for static routes to be set up
to every service from every ring. Routes can be set up by the name
server when a name for which no route exists is looked up. To
overcome the overhead associated with this set up, routes to public
ports can be timed out slowly.

When a name lookup is made for a name referring to a service on
another ring, the nameserver, if it believes the route to exist,
simply passes back the relevant gateway port to the client. If it
does not believe that the route exists, it will make a request to a
gateway (the first one on the route which it determines from the
global address) to set up a route to a particular global address.
The gateway will respond to the nameserver with a port number which
will be passed back to the client. In order to keep the
nameservers' view of routes as accurate as possible, gateways inform
nameservers (and other gateways) when they time out a route to a
public port or when they receive traffic on an invalid port.

Gateways offer two services to nameservers. These are the setting
up of routes and the tracing of routes. The tracing of routes is
used by nameservers to provide a reverse name lookup facility (the
transformation of an address to a machine name).

GATEWAY PERFORMANCE

At the time of writing, the gateway is configured with a single
interface connected to a single ring. Since in the gateway topology
a single interface connects two rings in one direction, the test
configuration provides both a means of developing the gateway - for
example the interface code will remain the same - and a vehicle for
producing realistic test results.

A table of applications and the effects of the gateway upon their
performance is shown in figure 7. Some results are quoted purely as
application data bandwidth, while for the SSP transactions the
results are given as transactions per second. The reasons for the
larger effect of the gateway on the single shot transactions are
that these are small blocks (about 20 bytes) making the gateway
overhead per block a substantial fraction of the block transmission
time, and that the gateway is allocating return paths for each
request made. This is then a test of the performance of the central
machine, currently an LSI4/10. On the other hand sinking the 2
Kbyte blocks requires only a routing transformation to be made every
2 Kbytes, so the sink test is really a test of interface

performance. Other transactions on the network are slow (due to end machine software) and are dominated by blocks other than SPPREQ's and OPEN's so that the gateway has no effect on their throughput, as for example in the large ten block writes to the file server.

APPLICATION	END MACHINES	THROUGHPUT OF APPLICATION DATA	
		direct	through gateway
sinking 2Kbyte blocks	CAP, sink	455 Kb/s	280 Kb/s
name lookup	LSI4/10, Z80	44 trans/s	29 trans/s
(single shot)	LSI4/30, Z80	95 trans/s	48 trans/s
	Z80, Z80	200 trans/s	60 trans/s
fileserver write	PDP11/45, LSI4/30		
1 x 2 Kbyte blocks		54 Kb/s	48 Kb/s
10 x 2 Kbyte blocks		105 Kb/s	105 Kb/s
	Z80, LSI4/30		
1 x 2 Kbyte blocks		100 Kb/s	80 Kb/s
10 x 2 Kbyte blocks		175 Kb/s	175 Kb/s
takefile (byte stream)	CAP, LSI4/30	8 Kb/s	8 Kb/s
workload, swapping to fileserver	CAP, LSI4/30	7 min 12 sec	7 min 34 sec

Figure 7. Gateway Effects on Application Performance

Another test which has been made uses CAP and the fileserver. The CAP computer, which runs a small time sharing system supporting up to four users, swaps segments over the ring to the fileserver; CAP has no local discs [8]. Tests have been run with CAP swapping through the gateway to the fileserver. While a slowdown was experienced under heavy loading, the slowdown was not intolerable. The load referred to in figure 7 was a concurrent Algol 68 compile, BCPL compile and 8X300 assembly. The elapsed time for the fastest of these, the Algol 68 compile, is shown.

PROTOCOL PROBLEMS

Some things which can be done on a single ring are not possible through a gateway. The most notable of these are transmitting ring packets (ie. not using basic blocks), passing ring station addresses and passing port numbers in arbitrary places. Each of these has caused a problem which has had to be resolved.

Recently, experimentation in digital telephony over the ring has caused a simple telephone system to be implemented [9]. The system transmits in single ring packets, so in order to transmit through a gateway, a blocking/unblocking service must be provided on each ring.

The passing of a ring station address was used to replug byte
streams so that if machine A had a byte streams open to B and to C,
it could simply plug B into C and drop out of the conversation.
Formerly an experimental byte stream protocol operation, this replug
facility is being placed at a higher protocol level.

The passing of port numbers in arbitrary places caused a problem for
the gateway in dealing with the fileserver protocol [10, 11]. One
fileserver operation, namely read, caused two port numbers to be
dynamically set up at the client rather than one. (The two port
approach was used to allow data to be transferred without flow
control while still allowing an end positive or negative
acknowledgement.) This is being overcome by introducing the notion
of a subport and establishing a convention for fileserver data and
control subports. This has lead to a largely compatible
modification of the basic block protocol. The route field packet
now has the format:

0 0	subport (2 bits)	port number (12 bits)

CONCLUSIONS

Although still in testing stages, the gateway has proven to be
simple and efficient. The fact that tests have been possible using
present clients, changing only the names they use to gateway test
names, for example FILESERV to GTWY-FILESERV, indicates that the
addition of a gateway will have a minimal effect on machines on the
network.

Much of the simplicity of the gateway has been a result of joining
rings at a low level in the protocol hierarchy, resulting in only a
small amount of state information being kept for each connection.
It will be interesting to see how far this approach will be carried
through in Project Universe where a number of ring collections are
to be joined by a satellite link. The gateways described here are
to be modified slightly to become Universe network bridges, but the
principles of operation will remain the same. This will test the
proposition that one can have connections over a large area and high
performance over a local area without resorting to different modes
of operation.

REFERENCES

[1] Wilkes, M.V. and Wheeler, D.J.,
"The Cambridge Digital Communication Ring", Local Area Communication
Networks Symposium, Mitre Corp. and N.B.S., Boston, May 1979.

[2] Boggs, D., Shoch, J., Taft, E., and Metcalfe, R.,
"Pup: An Internetwork Architecture", CSL-79-10, XEROX PARC,
July 1979.

[3] Nelson, B.J.,
"Remote Procedure Call", PhD Thesis, CMU-CS-81-119, Carnegie Mellon
University, Department of Computer Science, 1981.

[4] Johnson, M.A.,
"Ring byte stream protocol specification", System Research Group,
University of Cambridge Computer Laboratory, April 1980.

[5] Ody, N.J.,
"A protocol for 'single shot' ring transactions", Systems Research
Group, University of Cambridge Computer Laboratory, April 1979.

[6] Richards, M.,
"BCPL: A Tool for Compiler Writing and System Programming", ee,
Vol 35, 1969.

[7] Richards, M., Aylward, A.P., Bond, P., Evans, R.D. and Knight,
B.J.,
"TRIPOS - A Portable Operating System for Mini-Computers", Software
Practice and Experience, Vol 9, No 7, July 1979.

[8] Dellar, C.N.R.,
"Removing Backing Store Administration from the CAP Operating
System"   Operating Systems Review, Vol 14, No 4, October 1980.

[9] Leslie, I.M., Banerjee, R. and Love, S.J.,
"Organization of Voice Communication on the Cambridge Ring", Local
Area Network and Distributed Office Systems, Online Conferences,
London, May 1980.

[10] Dion, J.,
"The Cambridge File Server", Operating Systems Review, Vol 14,
No 4, October 1980.

[11] Dion, J.,
"File Server External Specification", Systems Research Group,
University of Cambridge Computer Laboratory, 1980.

---

[1] a research project linking three universities and three research
establishments in the U.K. through a satellite

[2] Here a client machine refers to any machine other than nameservers
and gateways.

LOCAL COMPUTER NETWORKS
P.C. Ravasio, G. Hopkins and N. Naffah (editors)
North-Holland Publishing Company
© IFIP, 1982

DANUBE LOCAL NETWORK INTERCONNECTIONS
VIA TRANSPAC PUBLIC NETWORK

J.P. Ansart, S. Bloch, T. Seghaier,
M. Martin, C. Mercier Laurent

Projets RHIN et KAYAK
Agence de l'Informatique
Tour Fiat, 1 place de la Coupole
PARIS LA DEFENSE - FRANCE

ABSTRACT:

This article deals with problems concerning the connection
of local area networks across public data networks using
gateways; in particular when the gateway allows the local
area network to be seen from outside as an open system.

In this article, it is shown how a gateway providing a relay
at the transport level (Danube local Network transport
station towards Rhin transport station), wich allows a Danube
network equiped site to be interconnected with any open
systems which is available on the French Transpac public data
network.

INTRODUCTION

From the first appearance of local networks and the applications
that suround them - (eg office automation, signaling systems, etc),
people have become more and more interested, in connecting such
networks to the public networks, and more generally interconnecting
open systems across them. Such interconnection of systems raises
numerous problems, particularly due to the diversity of:
- the protocols used by the hosts to communicate between each other.
- the network types not always offering the same services.

"Homogeneous interconnection" is the term used when networks that
are to be interconnected, are of the same type and so are able to
use the same protocols (standard or non-standard).

The interconnection is said heterogeneous when interconnected networks are not of the same type, the interconnection is said to be a
"heterogeneous interconnection".

INTERCONNECTION PRINCIPLES AND POSSIBLE INTERCONNECTIONS
CONFIGURATIONS.

Interconnection principles:

Within the framework of the seven layered reference model for open
systems interconnection developed by ISO, the problem of interconnection of two systems needs mainly the precise definition of the
level of service at which the interconnection will be performed.

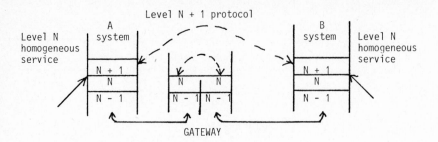

Fig. 1 : Level N interconnection

The next most important thing to be considered within the layered
ISO architectured framework is to determine which physical entities
of the local network will appear to the outside world as a standardized open system.
- whether the system is the whole site (including the local
  network).
- Wether the system are the individual stations of the site (all
  connection via the local network)

INTERCONNECTION POSSIBILITIES OF THE LOCAL AREA NETWORK DANUBE
THROUGH TRANSPAC.

<u>Interconnection</u> at <u>level 3</u> (network service level):

With this type of interconnection, the Gateway provides a network
service relay. It is thus possible to consider each station of the
network as an open system.

The following diagrams illustrate both kinds of network services,
connectionless (datagram) and connection oriented (virtual circuit).

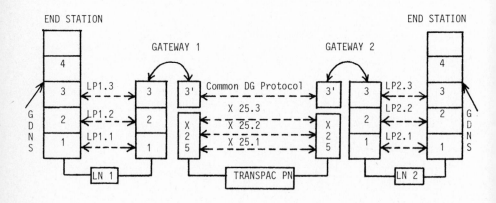

GDNS : Global Datagram Network Service

Fig. 2 : Level 3 interconnection providing a global datagram service

Note :

In this article we consider primarily here the cases in which both local area networks are of the same type (i.e both are connectionless or both are connection oriented).

In fig. 2, the service offered by the Transpac network (X25) is accessed through the entities (3') which handle a protocol common to the gateways. The level 3 provides a global service between the two end stations. Thus, the datagram service is simulated over the Transpac network. This common 3'-protocol can be reduced to a minimum (3 = 3'), when interconnecting homogeneous networks (since in this case LP2 = LP1), but is of important when interconnecting heterogeneous networks. The 3' entity adds functions enabling Transpac VC's to be used efficiently.

In fig. 3 below, the 2nd case of level 3 interconnection offering a global "virtual circuits" service is shown.

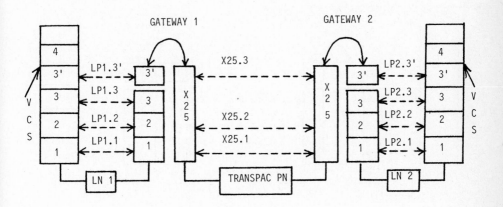

VCS : Virtual Circuit Service

Fig. 3 : Level 3 interconnection offering a global virtual circuits service.

LP1.3' and LP2.3' permits VC's to be built on top of the local network services.

Level 3 interconnection provides a relay at the GATEWAY. It is of connection type allowing for the setting up of virtual circuits between terminal devices. A multiplexing function at GATEWAY level could be interesting in this case in order to optimise TRANSPAC V.C. use. (see figure below)

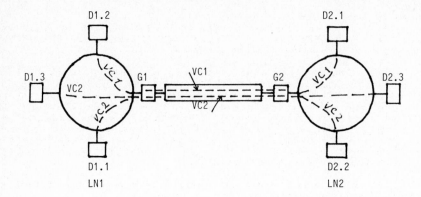

LN1   LN2

In this case, the fig. 3 will be modified as below.

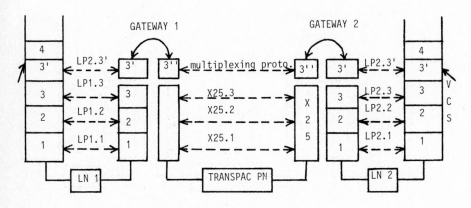

VCS : Virtuel Circuit Service

Fig 3bis : level 3 interconnection offering a global virtual circuit
service with multiplexing protocol on V.C.

Interconnection above level 3

Interconnection at a level higher than level 3 is particularly
interesting when interconnecting local networks which use non-standardized protocols, via PDN's. Such local network protocols may be
homogeneous or heterogeneous.

Globally the local network can be seen as an open system thanks to
the gateways. In this case, the gateway provides an N-level protocol conversion and a N-level service relay. A N-level conversion
assumes a service equivalence at the Nth level between the 2 systems. The level of protocol conversion that needs to be performed in
a gateway depends on the level at which standard protocols are used
by the end systems.

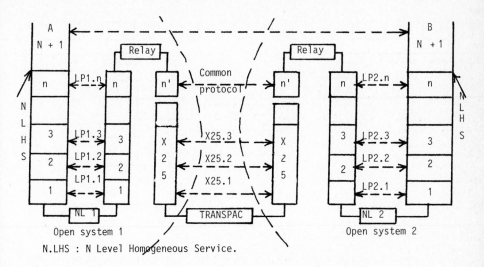

Fig. 4 : 2 local networks interconnection above level 3.

It should be noted in cases where a gateway performs protocol conversion higher than level 3, that it performs some of the functions normally presumed to be part of the end system. e.g. transport end-to-end control is performed by the gateway. Systems which do not use standard protocols above level 3 cannot be termed open systems, however they may be rendered open in this way by the gateway.

General characteristics of Danube Network:

Danube network is built around a coaxial cable on which microprogrammed communicators are tapped. The cable being a broadcast medium, the access is made in - carrier sense Multiple Access (C.S.M.A.). Chiefly, the network offers datagram services. The transport protocol (level 4),adapted to the intended service, provides the upper level :

- a connection service with error and flow control ;

- a broadcast service, "the lettergram".

DANUBE - TRANSPAC INTERCONNECTION (2 implementations).

Interconnection between homogeneous sites from the transport standpoint.

Concerning the KAYAK project, the team lead by C. MERCIER LAURENT and M. MARTIN has implemented a gateway (called a DANUBE port) which enables DANUBE hosts to be reached over Transpac and to be made available to users on a Danube network, as well as for interconnecting Danube networks over the Transpac PDN. This gateway has been implemented providing a global datagram service to the users of the local networks.

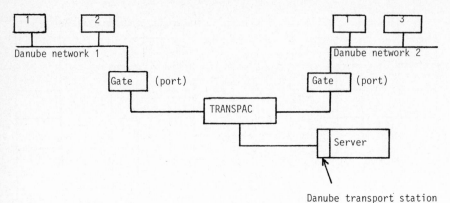

Figure 5 .

The two Danube Gateways working together over Transpac provide the following services:

- V.C. Establishement.

- Segmentation, packet assembly and disassembly of Danube "letters" into packets, on each V.C.

- Possibility of multiplexing Danube connections onto a single V.C.

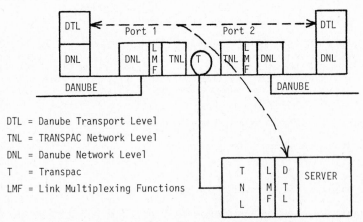

DTL = Danube Transport Level
TNL = TRANSPAC Network Level
DNL = Danube Network Level
T   = Transpac
LMF = Link Multiplexing Functions

Figure 6 : General configuration of the Danube acces port.

To enable access to a server, a DANUBE transport layer over the network (X 25) layer is needed.

Heterogeneous networks interconnection.

Due to the actual variety of networks, heterogeneous networks interconnection is the most frequent problem. These interconnections are
possible using conversion methods, if service equivalence can be
found at a given level in the architecture of the 2 systems. If the
equivalence is not complete, the interconnection is still possible
with a degraded service.

Figure 7 shows this type of conversion.

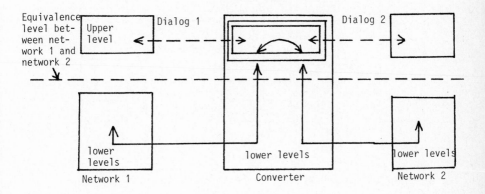

Figure 7

International standardization efforts (Open System Interconnection)
encompassing the global architecture of both local and public networks, will ease the interconnections. Through more precise definition of the different service options in each layer, the architecture permits easier location of the equivalence level between 2
systems.

If a system is not ruled by accepted standards, it is still interesting to conceive a gateway enabling it to present itself to the
ouside world as an "open system".

The main objective of RHIN project is to promote the use of standardized open system protocols and therefore it has developped a gateway allowing a KAYAK office automation site to present itself to
external servers as a standardized open system through Transpac.
The transport protocol between 2 Danube stations is a non standardized (fonctionally equivalent to a "class 4" transport protocol as
discussed in ISO) protocol. For connecting 2 Danube sites or 1
Danube, and any Transpac server with the required standardized
communication software, we have chosen to convert the Danube transport protocol into a class 2 protocol complying with the ECMA
standard.

Therefore, the gateway provides transport service level relay
as can be seen in the following diagram (Interconnection at
level N = 4).

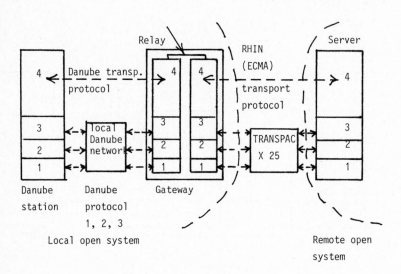

Fig. 8 : Conversion gateway providing a Danube network as "an
open system".

The main software modules for version 1 of the gateway are :
(see figure 9).

- Danube transport station and its network adpter ;
- Danube - Rhin conversion module ;
- Rhin transport station;
- X 25 connection software to Transpac.

A next version of gateway will allow a terminal concentration
fonction to use the transport station Rhin of the gateway
each connected in through asynchronous lines.

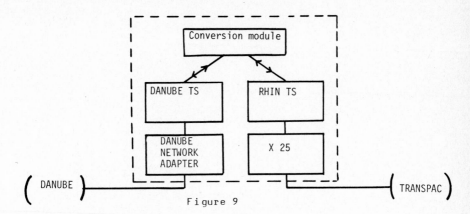

Figure 9

General interconnection tool concept :

Because of multiple software configuration possibilities in order to make possible for one network to communicate with a bulk of other systems, it is interesting to design a gateway made of a set of basic software modules. We are studying an operating system offering the means to configure from elementary interconnection functions, a complex interconnection function (providing "a gateway") which may be immediately operational.

REFERENCES :

J.P. ANSART : Projet RHIN : Objectifs et programmes,ORG 7504.
Projet RHIN/Agence de l'informatique,
Tour Fiat
Cedex 16 92084 PARIS La Défense.

N.NAFFAH,
V. QUINT   : Protocole de transport pour réseaux locaux.

Projet RHIN : Service et Protocole de Transport

REL 2.514.1 : Juillet 1980 - Projet KAYAK - INRIA, Domaine de
Voluceau, Rocquencourt : Description fonction-
nelle du réseau expérimental (DANUBE)

ISO/DP 7498 :Data processing - Open Systems Interconnection
Basic Reference Model: ECMA Transport
Protocol, standard

JL GRANGE,C. HUITEMA, H. ZIMMERMANN :
Utilisation informatique des satellites de télécommu-
nication : Identification des problèmes posés et élé-
ments de solutions.
GEN 3500 Projet NADIR INRIA, Domaine deVoluceau.
Rocquencourt/France.

W.L.ELDEN   : Gateways for interconnecting Local Area and Long Haul
Networks.
Composition systems division.
Harris corporation.
Melbourne, Florida - U.S.A.

LOCAL COMPUTER NETWORKS
P.C. Ravasio, G. Hopkins and N. Naffah (editors)
North-Holland Publishing Company
© IFIP, 1982

NETWORK INTERCONNECTION

André A.S. DANTHINE

Université de Liège
Liège, Belgium

Using an extended OSI model, an attempt is made to unify the
representation of public long-haul and private local networks.
Local Networks with separate address domains are very likely
to be met in broad site networks and an internet sublayer
appears to be the most natural way to achieve the interconnection. Such an internet sublayer will be also necessary for
building corporate networks by the interconnection of broad
site networks. Such an interconnection may use X.25, leased
lines or satellite channels depending upon the requirement in
data rate. The X.25 access will also be mandatory for accessing
special services and Teletex protocol is an interesting public
service to exchange information between non-compatible corporate
networks.

INTRODUCTION

It is widely accepted now that a local network provides a communication structure
between components of a system which are distributed on an area where the
distances are of the order of 1 or 2 Km. As most of the equipments connected to
the local network will have local processing capabilities, they will request
communication less often but the volume associated with each request may be
important. In order to avoid unacceptable delay a local network has another
characteristic : it is a high-bandwidth communication system. One to 10 megabits/sec
is the range of data rate most frequently considered.

In a very big building or in a multibuilding site it may not be feasible to use
a unique local network. Such a broad site network which may cover distance of
10 to 20 Km may be implemented by interconnecting several local networks.

A corporate network may request the interconnection of several broad site networks
using public data networks or public facilities.

Last but not least, equipment attached to a corporate network may have to access
services accessible only through public data networks or may have to communicate
with other corporate networks.

These examples show the importance of the interconnection of networks. This
problem will be addressed here in the framework of the OSI model which with
suitable extensions provides an element of unification badly needed.

NAMES, ADDRESSES AND ROUTES

In Shoch (1978) the importance of a clear definition for the concepts of "name",
"address" and "route" has been stressed. A clear understanding of these three
concepts is essential for the rest of this paper.

A *name* is a symbol identifying some resource or set of resources. The symbol is usually a human-readable string which allows the identification of processes, places, people, machines or functions. "ECHO" may be the name of a well-defined process, "DAVID" is the name of a people, "DEC 20" the name of a machine and "ARCHIVE" the name of a function.

In practice any object which has a name is usually represented by some sort of process which can act on its behalf. One may have several processes for the same name in various contexts. In the context of a machine connected to a communication net, "DEC 20" will be represented by an interface process. In the context of a machine providing time sharing service "DEC 20" will be represented by a process called a logging server. Moreover the names need not to be meaningfull to all users and need not to be drawn from a uniform name space.

An *address* is the data structure which defines any addressable object in a given domain. The format of this data structure can be recognized by all elements in the domain and therefore addresses must be meaningfull throughout the domain.

Address must be drawn from some uniform address space. Such an address space may be "flat" i.e. spans over the entry domain or may be based on a hierarchy.

A well-known example of a hierarchical address system is given by the telephone. Another example is the X.121 address format (Figure 5).

In a flat address space it is not possible to derive from the address any information about the location. US Social Security number is the usual reference for an example of a flat address.

Without a mapping of names into addresses the system would be useless as the name indicates WHAT we seek and the address indicates WHERE it is. However this mapping may take different forms
- a fixed mapping will permanently tie a resource to an address. This introduces constraints. For instance it will not be possible to move a resource to another place if the address space is of the hierarchical type.
- a dynamic mapping will associate an address to a name only when needed. It means that the address associated with a given name may change over time and that a given address may be successively used by resources having different names.

To help the user it is necessary to provide some mechanism to do the mapping of names into addresses. Moreover it is usual and essential to have "well-known addresses". This concept has been introduced in ARPANET. A process server, at a well-known address, was made available in all server-hosts to start the ARPANET Initial Connection Protocol (ICP) (McQuillan & Walden (1977)).

The mapping of names into addresses may be done with the help of a "name server", which plays the function of a directory. A "well-known address" must, of course, be associated to such a name server.

The dynamic nature of the mapping may raise some organizational problems. If, from the name server, an address is obtained how long may this address be used ? It seems reasonable to classify addresses in three categories
- well-known addresses : they are already defined. Such an address and associated resource (name) must have a very long lifetime to allow them to be known by almost all potential users.
- stable addresses : they will be provided by the name server and may be kept and used for a reasonable time. A user will be able to build a limited directory the same way he keeps a small subset of the telephone directory.
- dynamic addresses : they will be provided by the name server or any other server such as the IPC and will last only for a short period of time (for instance during a session).

An address is uniquely defined in a given domain, but a name may be mapped into several addresses. Such situation may arise if a resource (name) is connected to two different networks (domains) or is connected to the same network in two locations. Selection of one of the two addresses must be based on additional information.

From the mapping process, the name of the seeked resource has been mapped into an address. The last thing one needs to reach this address is the *route* to be followed.

In a local network built around a single packet switching node, every destination address is connected to the access node and the network will have only to put the received packet from one incoming line into the outgoing line corresponding to the destination address. No routing has to be done but only a straightforward switching. Here the network address domain and the domain of the addresses directly reachable by the access node are identical and no routing is necessary.

This is not anymore true in a multinode PSN (Packet Switching Network). When the destination address is not in the reachability domain of the access node (source node), a routing action must take place.

This routing action may take place at the source or be done in an incremental manner i.e. hop-by-hop.

In source routing, the source specifies all the intermediate routing decisions and includes this information along with the data being sent. The nodes do not have to maintain routing tables but only to follow the routing instructions (Saltzer & al. (1980)).

In hop-by-hop routing the source specifies only the destination address and the routing decisions are taken by every switching node including of course the access node.

Another interesting variation is the access routing i.e. that all routing decisions are taken by the access node and all intermediate nodes have to follow routing instructions appended to the data being sent. The difference between source routing and access routing is clear. In the first case the route is specified by the user of network. In the second case the network is responsible of the route choice and does it at the access point.

In a datagram network, hop-by-hop routing is the natural choice. In TRANSPAC access routing has been adopted. DATAPAC virtual circuits are built on top of a datagram network and no fixed route has to be followed.

Besides the place where the routing decision is taken an important characteristic is the base for such decision. Routing is based on tables and the time and the way these tables are updated may widely vary.

Fixed routing is the most static solution. The tables are set for very long period based on estimated traffic and no provision for adaptive action is provided. For realability reason an alternate route is very often provided.

Adaptive routing (or dynamic routing) is the opposite solution. The tables are periodically updated to reflect changes in the environment. This update may be done in three different ways (Schwartz & Stern (1980))
- by a central authority collecting all traffic informations and sending back updated tables
- by each switching node in an isolated manner based for instance on hot potatoes or on backward learning
- by each switching node in a distributed manner where each node periodically exchanges routing information with each of its neighbours.

THE OSI MODEL

In the ISO document (ISO (1980)) on the Basic Reference Model of the Open Systems
Interconnection it is cleary stated that the services provided by each layer are
connection-oriented. It is only by extending the actual document that it is
possible to present OSI-like model of a datagram network and of a local network.
The interest of a unique approach for connection and connection-less communication
justifies this extension.

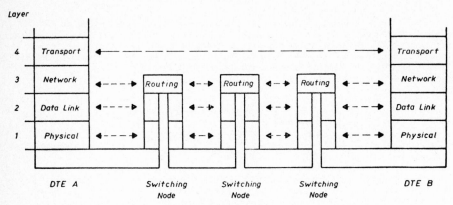

Figure 1
OSI model of a multinode datagram PSN

The OSI model of a multinode datagram PSN is represented in Figure 1. In each
packet switching node the routing is on top of the data link layer. The routing
may be considered as belonging to a lower sublayer of level 3. A more compact
form is given in Figure 2 where the multiple switching node are not any more
apparent.

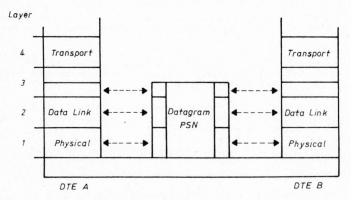

Figure 2
More compact form of the OSI model of Figure 1

For an X.25 PSN the model represented in Figure 3 looks very much the same. Here
no information is available regarding the internal protocol of the network which
may or may not involve an internal datagram network.

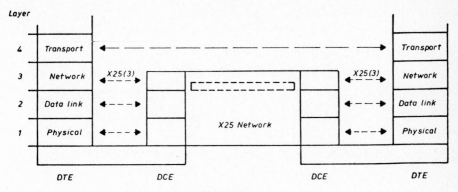

Figure 3
OSI model of an X.25 PSN

In Figure 3, the X.25 (3) protocol appears as belonging to a sublayer of level 3. It is of course clear that beside the routing we have with X.25 (3) the mechanisms for establishing, maintaining and terminating connections.

HIERARCHICAL ADDRESS SPACE AND ROUTING

The two possible structures which may be adopted for the address space will have to be discussed further.

A flat address space first requires that allocation of addresses be done in such way to insure the uniqueness over the whole domain. If the system allocating the address is unique a great care must be taken in order to insure its robustness. If a flat address space is used there is no structure in the address which might aid the routing process. This routing must handle all addresses in full. However for every pair destination-source it is possible to optimize the route.

A hierarchical address space offers two advantages. First by partitioning the address space, it is possible to have several autonomous address allocators. Each has the freedom to create and assign new address within its portion of the hierarchy. A new area may be added without any interference with the already assigned address and a local domain may change its addresses without any interference with the rest of the domain. Of course is a resource is moved from one local domain to another local domain a change of address is mandatory. For instance if an address subdomain is attached to each access node, a change of access node will imply a change of address. Notice that a host connected to two access nodes will get two addresses each by a different authority.

The second advantage of the hierarchical address space lies in the routing process. Assume that the address is based on the following structure

<address>=<network><node><host>

Figure 4 represents such a structure. If the data packet has to be sent from <II4B> to <II2A> the routing process will first check the network address and, as it is the same as its one's, looks into the node field and finds out the route to reach node 2. In a distributed routing scheme the packet will be sent first to node 3 or 1 depending upon the table information. In the next node, the routing process will be repeated and the packet reaches node 2 where the rest of the address field i.e. the host field is examined to find out the destination.

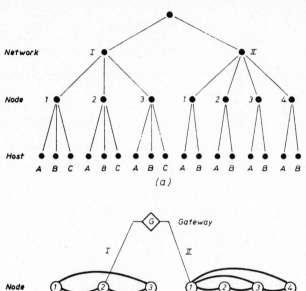

Figure 4
Address structure (a) and topology (b)

If the data packet has to be sent from <IIAB> to <I1A> the routing process
must first recognize that the packet is addressed to another network which may
be reached through a gateway attached to node 1 which may be reached from node 4
in one hop. The gateway will in turn look into the network field and send the
packet to node 2 of the network I where it will be routed to its final destination
as any other packet reaching node 2.

The gateway of Figure 4 may be considered as an internal gateway. Its existence
may be unknown by any host attached to any of the two networks. This is due to
the fact that the global address is recognized by all elements in the domain.
If the two networks are merged in a unique one, the gateway becomes a node of
the global network.

INTERCONNECTION OF X.25 NETWORKS

In recommendation X.121, CCITT has decided to use for public computer networks
a hierarchical numbering scheme similar to the one uses in telephony (Figure 5).
Any addressable entity will be identified by a decimal number built on three fields
- country code (3 decimal digits)
- network code (1 decimal digit)
- national data number (10 decimal digits).

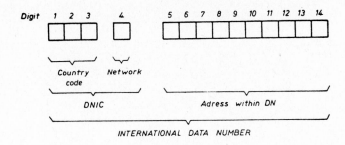

Figure 5
X.121 address format

For country expected to have many public networks engaged in international traffic, multiple country codes have been allocated. Canada has been allocated 302 through 307, USA 310 through 329. With the ten possible network codes it means that this recommendation allows the United States to have 200 networks engaged in international traffic. Small countries have of course only one country code which allows for 10 networks.

The four digits number (country code + network code) is "the data network identification code" (DNIC). For instance DNIC of DATAPAC is 3020 and DNIC of INFOSWITCH 3029.

The ten last digits will be assigned independently by each network. A flat address space or a hierarchical address space may be used. Let us point out that the USA and Canada telephone network is also based on a 10 digits numbering scheme.

If the same data terminal or host is connected to two public networks the same "name" i.e. the same object will have two addresses. The selection of one of these two addresses induce a kind of source routing as the destination network depends upon the selected address. If the source address belongs to one of the two networks, the selection of the destination address is simple. If the source address belongs to a third public network, additional information such as cost and performances will be needed to select the destination address to be used.

With the recommendation X.25, each public network is offering a standard network access interface. This standard network access interface X.25 is valid for national and international traffic due to the fact that the address field in X.25 Call Request are just large enough to accept international data number based on X.121. This means that public address domain is unique. As each national X.25 network is assumed to have its own intranet protocols the simple solution of Figure 4 is not feasible.

The interconnection of X.25 public network is solved by recommendation X.75 related to intergateway exchange. Here the gateway consists of two half-gateways (Figure 6). This fits nicely with the PTT habits of clear responsability sharing.

This interaction takes place through two STE (signaling terminal equipment) which are equivalent to an internal gateway.

Between two DTE attached to two X.25 networks the virtual circuit will be realised by the concatenation of two virtual circuits one in each network (Figure 6). Flow control is propagated through all the sections of the chained protocols.
Revision of X.25 had reduced the risk of uncompatibility and introduced end-to-end significance to acknowledgments. It is not clear what will be the situation for international traffic.

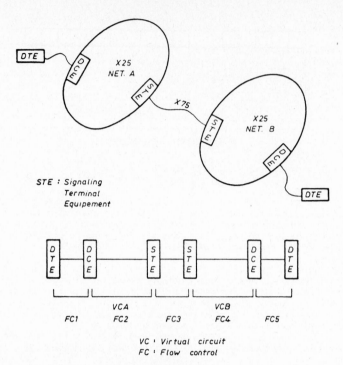

STE : Signaling
        Terminal
        Equipement

VC : Virtual circuit
FC : Flow control

Figure 6
Interconnection of X.25 networks

The OSI model of X.25/X.75 networks is represented in the Figure 7.

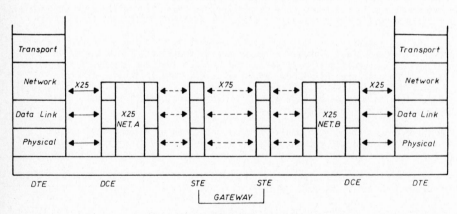

Figure 7
OSI model of X.25/X.75 networks

The model of Figure 7 is a detailled model of interconnected X.25 networks. From the DTE point of view the Figure 3 is still valid.

Another interesting issue is related to the interconnection of private X.25 nets to public X.25 nets. In the local area it is possible to install a private X.25 net. This is not a wide band local net but as X.25 nodes are now off-the-shelf equipments, this solution may look appealing. Most manufacturers of EDP equipment support already X.25. This allow easy interconnection if low bandwidth is acceptable. When we look at Figure 6, it is difficult to see a difference if X.25 NET A is a public net or a private net. It is however very unlikely, at least in Europe, that PTT will offer X.75 connections to private companies. However such an offering seems to be possible in the North American scene. Such an approach raises a few technical issues but none appears to be insurmontable. For instance extended addressing may be partially solved using the user data field of call request. A detailed discussion about X.25/X.75 will be found in Cerf & Kirstein (1978).

THE OSI MODEL OF A LOCAL NETWORK

As already indicated the OSI model is connection-oriented. In particular the data link layer concept has been deeply influenced by the HDLC protocol.

Local networks using bus or ring topology appear different. The transmission medium allows the access node to reach in one transmission any, some or all other nodes. This is achieved by the capability of each node to scrutinize the address field of any packet on the media. With a simple local net, the routing concept seems unnecessary and the network layer of the ISO model may be replaced by an empty layer as allowed by the proposed standard.

Here, as in a single node PSN, every destination address is in the direct reachability domain of the access node. The direct reachability domain of the access node and the address domain of a single local network are identical.

It is therefore tempting to limit the OSI model of LAN (local area network) to the first two layers. This is the proposal of the IEEE 802 Committee in its draft Local Network Standard. This committee proposed a sublayering on level 1 and 2 in order to better fit the characteristics of local network. The Figure 8 reproduces a model where the Data Link Layer is split into a Logical Link Control (LLC) and a Medium Access Control (MAC).

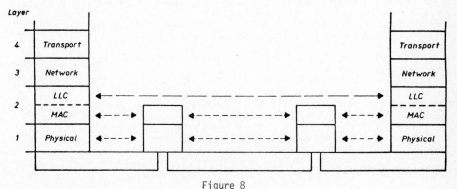

Figure 8
OSI-like model for a LAN

MAC : Medium Access Control   LLC : Logical Link Control

In Figure 8 the MAC sublayer appears to belong the layer 2 of the OSI model.
In IEEE 802 (1981), the MAC is partially in layer 2 and partially in layer 1
but the rationale for such a proposal is not clearly stated.

The introduction of a MAC allows to separate the framing and the synchronization
from the LLC. The Logical Link Control may become more independant of the specific
network topology, of the technology used for the transmission medium and of its
access method. Data rates are also kept at the level of the MAC.

In Figure 4 the two PSN are connected through an internal gateway as a node.
Both PSN belong to the same address domain built on a hierarchy. Two LAN may
behave the same way if they are using a unique address domain and if the gateway
is able to "filter" packet from one LAN to the other. This filter function is of
course different of the repeater function found in each node of a ring LAN or of
the repeater function used to connect two buses in CSMA/CD (Dix (1980)). The
gateway is in fact doing the same kind of routing than the gateway of Figure 4
The OSI-like model of such a situation is given in Figure 9.

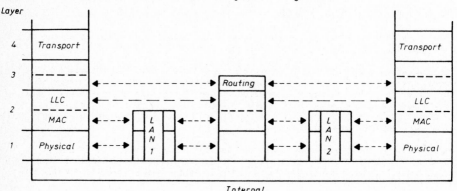

Figure 9
Interconnection of two LAN by an internal gateway

For the user attached to the LAN 1 there is no difference between the situation
of Figure 9 and the one of Figure 8 as in both cases he has access to a global
address domain. That the global address domain is split into two LAN interconnected
by an internal gateway is of no concern for him. Therefore there is an interest
to have a unique OSI model for the situations of Figure 8 and 9. This may be
achieved by always having the lowest sublayer of layer 3 in the OSI model of
even a single LAN. The Figure 10 is the most general model.

It is possible to replace the central part of Figure 10 by the detailled situation
of Figure 8 or by the situation of Figure 9.

The model of a PSN, of a X.25 network or of a LAN appears therefore very much the
same even if the mechanism involved and the service offered are far from being
equivalent.

LAN service is very often related to a datagram service. This is true but it is
important to stress that the technology involved in LAN will provide a high
quality datagram service. Change of sequence may be very unlikely if not impossible and the probability of packet loss may be very low.

X.25 network may be considered as offering a connection oriented service but the
connection mechanism may also be considered as a way of providing a high quality

channel for datagram service.

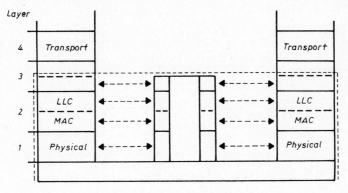

Figure 10
General OSI model of a LAN

INTERNET SUBLAYER

If one has to interconnect networks with different packet formats and internal protocols it is possible to define an internetwork sublayer. Such an internetwork layer will offer a common level of service to transport layer and have its own format. The address domain of each network will have to belong to the address domain of the internetwork sublayer.

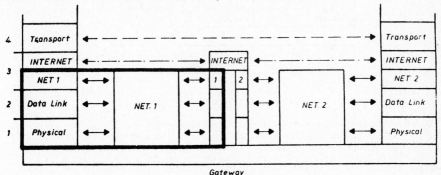

Gateway
Figure 11
OSI model with internet sublayer

The Figure 11 cleary indicates that internet protocol is implemented in hosts and in gateways. As pointed out in Cerf & Kirstein (1978) "the fundamental role of the gateway is to terminate the internal protocols of each network to which it is attached while, at the same time, providing a common ground accross which data from one network can pass into another". The termination of the internal protocols of the net 1 in Figure 11 is put into evidence by the reinforced rectangle. By definition the address domain of the internet is the union of all address domains of the individual networks. The address structure of the internet header

<address>=<network><node><host>

will allow to select an element of the address domain of the next network. Such an address will be either the address of the next gateway or the address of the final destination. With this address the internet layer will be able to construct

a packet for the next network. It will "encapsulate" the internet packet in the
data field of this packet.

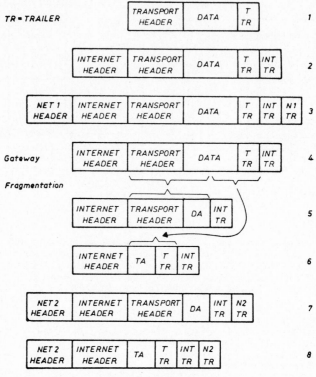

Figure 12
Encapsulation and fragmentation

This encapsulation mechanism is shown at the Figure 12. In (1) is the packet
at the transport level. From the request of service coming from this transport
level, the internet layer build an internet packet (2) and request the service
of NET 1. From the parameter associated with the request, a NET 1 packet is
prepared (3). It has the internet packet in its data field. Through NET 1 the
packet reaches the gateway and is delivered to the internet sublayer (Figure 11)
in the format indicated in (4). The analysis of the internet header will allow
the repetition of the process i.e. finding the next net, the address in this net
and requesting the service of the net layer.

All networks will not have the same maximum size of packet. Fragmentation must
take place somewhere and the internet layer appears to be most adequate. If done
at this level the function may be completely removed from the transport level.
Figure 12 shows the preparation from packet (4), of two internet packets (5)
and (6) which will be carried out by NET 2. Packets in NET 2 are shown in (7) and
(8).

Fragmentation and reassembly may be done in different places. To do the fragmentation at the source host will require a perfect knowledge of the route and of
the characteristics of all nets on the route. If a particular net on the route
requires a fragmentation, the reassembly may be done when one leaves that net,

at the output gateway or at the final destination. The former is the ETHERNET
choice (Boggs (1980)), the latter the ARPA choice (Darpa (1980)). A detailed
discussion about this issues may be found in Shoch (1979).

As early as 1974, the need for a protocol able to work in a multinetwork
environment was cleary identified (Cerf & Kahn (1974)). The ARPA effort in this
area ended up in a new TCP and in an Internet protocol (Darpa (1980) and (Postel
& al.(1981)).This internet sublayer offers a datagram service and its main
functions are routing and fragmentation/reassembly. No recovery, no flow control
but a few additional mechanisms such as optional source routing, return route,
error report (Postel (1980)).

In Europe the network scene has been dominated by X.25. In a couple of years
such a service will be available in every European country and one may expect
X.25 interconnection of public networks not to lay to much behind. A few people
are ready to push X.25 into the local area net but it remains to prove that a
benefit will come from the added complexity. The performance of a datagram
service appears already rather outstanding and for networks developped from the
LAN concept as starting point it is very unlikely to see the connection oriented
approach being adopted in layer 3 of the OSI.

BROAD SITE NETWORK

A LAN is a network which works at data rate between 1 and 10 Mbits/sec and which
spreads over a distance of the order of 1 or 2 Km and the classical example is
a network in a building. However if the building is very big it may not be
possible to cover the projected needs with only ONE net. In such a big building
it may be necessary to have a cluster of LAN's, interconnected in a hierarchical
or a mesh topology. If all the LAN's are based on the same technology and if one
has a unique address space, the gateways will be internal.

However in a multi-building site it may not be possible to apply the same idea.
For instance if one has a single LAN in every building, it may not be feasible
to interconnect them by another LAN of the same technology.

In many cases, the distance involved will be incompatible with the technology.
For a university built on a campus, one Ethernet by building will probably be
feasible but the interconnection of buildings may involve distance almost one
order of magnitude of what this technology allows. Of course nothing prevents
the use of another technology for the interconnecting net.

This situation which will be the normal one on a campus will also be common
on industrial premices. Most large factories have their building spread over
wide area and the BROAD SITE NETWORK will be of interest also outside academic
circles.

It seems therefore that one must be prepared to have more than a unique technology
involved in the subnets constituting a broad site (or campus) network. Saltzer &
al. (1980) mention several properties for what they call a campus environment and
may be more generally called a BROAD SITE NETWORK.
- It has a geographical extent beyond a simple building but within a single
  political and administrative boundary that permits transmission media to be
  installed without resort to a common carrier. This property is the most
  essential one, as the cost for communicating over privately installed equipment
  based on low-cost high bandwidth technology may be more than an order of
  magnitude lower than using common carrier facilities.
- Within this geographical area, a large number of data sources or data sinks will
  require interconnection. Such a data source or sink may be a large frame
  computer, a mini or a terminal as it is mostly today but it may be also a work
  station or a personal computer or a badge reader. In industrial premices a wide

range of equipment will also require interconnection such as computer controlled
machine tools. Every station in factory will soon or later be connected to get
information and to put reports on work done. Today the number of DSS (Data
Source and Sink) requiring interconnection may be in the range of a few hundreds,
but with the advent of desktop computers one may be faced with several thousands
before long and certainly before the end of the next decade. A forecast for the
University of Liege gives the following figures
- 3000 terminals, desktop computers or workstations
- 300 stations for data acquisition in laboratories
- 15 to 30 medium size computers for shared servers
- 1 large computer centre built on a cluster of mainframes.
- Administratively there exist forces both for commonality and for diversity of
  network attachement strategies. The primary force for diversity is that the
  choice of a computer or of DSS's typically pre-determines the technology
  of the network to which it must be attached, because off-the-shelf network
  hardware for that station may be available in only one technology. Furthermore
  some applications may have special requirements for some connection (i.e.
  high bandwidth for channel attachement) that can be met only with a particular
  network supplier's equipment. HYPERCHANNEL is a good example of such a situation.
- The worldwide academic, commercial and regulatory community is very far to have
  reached anything ressembling a consensus on how networks should be organized,
  how protocols should be layered or how functions should be divided. Arguments
  range over issues ranging from obscur matters of taste, through fundamental
  technical disagreements about which requirements should have priority in design,
  to alternative opinions of the direction that communication technology is
  moving. Many different and competing standards have been proposed. It is
  possible to find a good technical case against each one. One must anticipate
  that these trends will be reflected in the broad site environment in the form
  of a diversity of protocols and standards.

Moreover even a standard does not mean compatibility of end-products. In IEEE 802
(1981) it is cleary stated that "While the object of the Local Network Standard
is to provide compatibility, devices built to this standard may not be directly
interoperable. This seeming contradiction arises because the Standard provides
a number of options such that particular local networks can be tailored to
particular applications".

HIERARCHICAL OR MESH TOPOLOGY IN A BROAD SITE NETWORK (BSN)

Starting with a set of LAN located in various buildings of a broad site it is
possible to build a BSN in two different ways. First, every time a host wants
to be connected to two LAN it is possible to have it acting as a gateway between
them. This approach which will endsup in a mesh topology may be in contradiction
with the robustness property of the system. Moreover the gateway traffic and the
host traffic have to share the available access bandwidth And this available
access bandwidth is already a fraction of the row data rate of a LAN. This
approach offers however a property of natural growth for the BSN.

A BSN may also be based on a hierarchical topology. Each LAN is connected through
a gateway to a backbone network (Figure 13). Here, it is very likely to have a
central authority responsible of the backbone net including the gateways. The
backbone network will spread over distances of 10 to 20 Km and is very likely to
be based on a broadband technology.

The choice of the mesh or the tree approach has wide consequence. The use of host
as gateway requires that the gateway must remain very simple. In particular,
routing must be as simple as possible. Moreover the distributed responsability
will contribute to a non uniform performance level for all the gateways. In such
an environment, source routing is a very sound approach (Saltzer (1980))
especially if the route is provided by the name server.

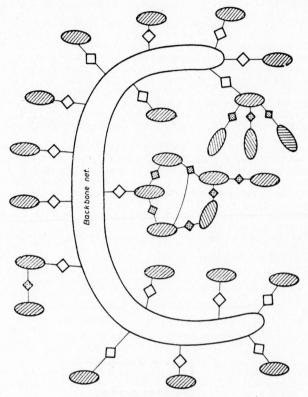

Figure 13
Broad Site Network. Tree oriented topology

The tree approach with its hierarchical flavor allows the gateways to have easy routing procedures. Moreover the problem of fragmentation and reassembly may be minimized if the maximum size of the packet on the backbone net is large. Notice also that the existence of a tree topology does not prevent the building of host-gateway if special situations exist. These shortcuts may be used only by private groups.

From the previous paragraphs it is clear that a broad site network will be based on local area networks with different technologies and performance characteristics. In a university, one is very likely to find an Hyperchannel-like network in the main computer centre, several Ethernet-like networks and rings networks with access strategies of various natures.

The global strategy to build a broad site net with such a collection of elements is to adopt a site-wide layer of protocol. The internet layer, upper layer at level 3 of the OSI model, is the most suitable layer. Such a layer may be easily put on top of the various LAN. To avoid undue complexity the most sound choice is to have this internet layer to achieve simply datagram passing between two stations. It is essential to avoid to put into this layer a lot of mechanisms that will prevent an easy implementation. The two basic functions of this layer will be routing and fragmentation/reassembly when it is needed.

CORPORATE NETWORK

The corporate network (CN) concept is concerned with the logical limit of
organized interaction. In a company located on a single building, the CN will be
the local area net. In a company located on a single large site, the CN will be
the broad site network just discussed. For a company with activities located
in a few location in various countries, the interconnection of all broad site
networks will be the CN.

The interest to introduce the concept of a CN is related to the existence of an
authority which is able to decide, not every detail of the global network but
the basic features to be followed by every basic element of the set.

At a corporate level, it is for instance possible to make standardisation
decisions. In the network area, the low levels of the OSI model are under the
technology pressure (hopefully things will remain that way...).

By adopting a well defined internet sublayer and a well defined transport protocol
any company will be able
- to integrate in the CN and benefit from any technological change likely to
  appear in the lowest levels
- to build on top of its transport service the necessary protocols for its own
  applications.

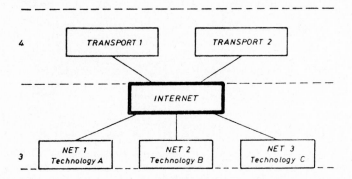

Figure 14
The Internet Sublayer in the OSI model

The datagram internet sublayer is seen by many as center part of a diabolo
(Figure 14). It provides the most simple communication service between two hosts.
It may be the ONLY element of commonality as applications may request several
transport services which will be offered by two classes of transport protocols.

Any corporate network will use the layer 4 as an end-to-end protocol. If the two
communicating entities are not located in the same site one has to provide a way
to get the communication between the two gateways located at the boundary of each
site (Figure 15).

From this Figure it is clear that we need a linking block which may be provided
- by an X.25/X.75 network (Figure 16 a)
- by a set of leased lines to interconnect the broad area net (Figure 16 b)
- by an X.21 satellite channel (Figure 16 c).

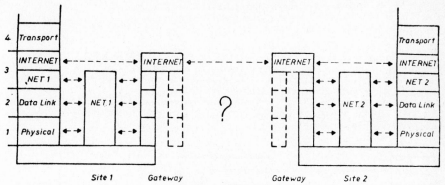

Figure 15
OSI model of a large corporate network

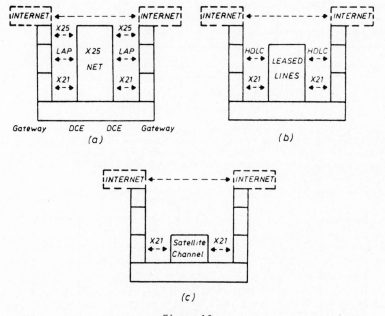

Figure 16
Linking blocks

Experience with widespread usage of data communication in the local area is just
beginning. It is therefore impossible to have now precise value about mean and
peak data rate which will have to be provided by the public networks. But having
a wide-band communication system based on datagram connected to a virtual
circuit of the X.25 type may create some problem of congestion in the gateway.
Some people may suggest to propagate the flow control inside the local area. This
approach which tends to get a problem under control by a complex mechanism must
be compared to the other approach which implies the suppression of the problem
by increasing the peak data rate of the missing block of Figure 15 or by

increasing the store and forward characteristic of the gateway.

OUTSIDE THE CN

A company or a university entirely located in a broad site area will have the
opportunity to build a CN without resorting to a common carrier. But a CN is not
closed construct. Communication will be necessary with the outside world to get
service from servers attached to public data networks. As it is very unlikely to
have the level 4 in the CN and in the servers entirely compatible, the communication will use the transport service to the limit of the CN and after rely on the
X.25 network (Figure 17).

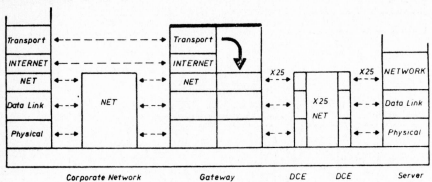

Figure 17
The CN and an outside server

Communication may also be needed between corporate networks. In the dreamful
situation where the two CN are using the same Internet and the Transport protocols
the situation of Figure 15 applies. In the more likely situation where each CN
has its own Transport and Internet protocols, the Teletex service will probably
be the most useful service (Figure 18).

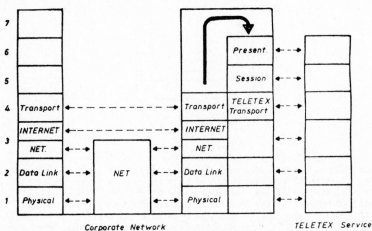

Figure 18
Using Teletex to communicate outside the CN

In the case of Figure 18 the gateway will have to make the necessary protocols conversion.

CONCLUSION

By extending the OSI model it is possible to unify the representation of the LAN and of the long-haul datagram and X.25 networks. The OSI model may also be used to discuss the issues related to the interconnection of LAN and of long-haul networks.

That the internet sublayer will play the central role described in this paper remains to be confirmed but the fast evolution of the LAN seems to indicate that one will not have to wait decades before getting this confirmation.

This research was partially supported by the Commission of the European Communities under contract n° X80-203.

REFERENCES

Boggs & al. (1980)
   Boggs David R., Shoch John F., Taft Edward A., Metcalfe Robert M., "PUP : AN INTERNETWORK ARCHITECTURE", IEEE Trans. on Communications, Vol. COM-28, nr 4, April 1980, pp 612-623.
Cerf & Kahn (1974)
   Cerf Vinton G., Kahn Robert E., "A PROTOCOL FOR PACKET NETWORK INTERCOMMUNI-CATION", IEEE Trans. on Comm., Vol. COM-22,5, May 1974, pp 637-648.
Cerf & Kirstein (1978)
   Cerf Vinton G., Kirstein Peter T., "ISSUES IN PACKET NETWORK INTERCONNECTION", Proc. IEEE, Vol. 66, 11, Nov. 1978, pp 1386-1408.
Danthine & Magnee (1980)
   Danthine André A.S., Magnée Francis, "TRANSPORT LAYER-LONG HAUL VERSUS LOCAL NETWORKS", Proc. of Local Networks for Computer Communications, Zurich, August 1980,(North Holland), pp 271-296.
Darpa (1980)
   Darpa, "DOD STANDARD INTERNET PROTOCOL", IEN 128 Defense Advanced Research Project Agency, Jan. 1980, Also in Computer Comm. Review, Vol. 10, 4, Oct. 1980, pp 14-51.
Dix (1980)
   Digital, Intel, Xerox, "THE ETHERNET, A LOCAL AREA NETWORK. DATA LINK LAYER AND PHYSICAL LAYER SPECIFICATIONS", Version 1.0,Sept. 1980 (82 pages).
IEEE 802 (1981)
   IEEE 802 Committee, LOCAL NETWORK STANDARD DRAFT B, Oct. 19,1981. Available from IEEE Computer Society, P.O. Box 639, Silver Spring MD 20901 USA.
ISO (1980)
   ISO/TC 97/SC 16 OPEN SYSTEMS INTERCONNECTION-BASIC REFERENCE MODEL, N 537 Revised November 1980.
McQuillan & Walden (1977)
   McQuillan J.M., Walden D.C., "THE ARPA NETWORK DESIGN DECISIONS", Computer Networks, Vol. 1, Aug. 1977, pp 243-289.
Postel (1980)
   Postel Jonathan B., "INTERNETWORK PROTOCOL APPROACH", IEEE Trans. on Comm., Vol. COM-28, 4, April 1980, pp 604-611

Postel & al. (1981)
    Postel Jonathan B., Sunshine Carl A., Cohen Dany, "THE ARPA INTERNET PROTOCOL",
    Computer Networks, 5, July 1981, pp 261-271.
Saltzer & al. (1980)
    Saltzer Jerome H., Reed David P., Clark David D., "SOURCE ROUTING FOR
    CAMPUS-WIDE INTERNET TRANSPORT", Proc. of Local Networks for Computer
    Communication, Zurich, August 1980, (North Holland), pp 1-23.
Schwartz & Stern (1980)
    Schwartz M., Stern T.E., "ROUTING TECHNIQUES USED IN COMPUTER COMMUNICATION
    NETWORKS", IEEE Trans. on Comm., Vol. COM-28, April 1980, pp 539-552.
Shoch (1978)
    Shoch John F., "INTERNETWORK NAMING, ADDRESSING AND ROUTING", COMPCON Fall
    1978, pp 72-79.
Shoch (1979)
    Shoch John F., "PACKET FRAGMENTATION IN INTER-NETWORK PROTOCOLS", Computer
    Networks, 3, Feb. 1979, pp 3-8.
Shoch & al. (1980)
    Shoch John F., Cohen Dany, Taft Edward A., "MUTUAL ENCAPSULATION FOR
    INTERNETWORK PROTOCOL", Trends and Applications: 1980, Computer Networks
    Protocols, NBS & IEEE, May 1980, pp 1-11. Also Computer Networks 5, 1981,
    pp 287-300.·
Sunshine (1977)
    Sunshine Carl A., "INTERCONNECTION OF COMPUTER NETWORKS", Computer Networks 1,
    3 Feb. 1977, pp 175-195

PROTOCOLS

LOCAL COMPUTER NETWORKS
P.C. Ravasio, G. Hopkins and N. Naffah (editors)
North-Holland Publishing Company
© IFIP, 1982

ON THE NAMING AND BINDING OF NETWORK DESTINATIONS

Jerome H. Saltzer

M.I.T. Laboratory for Computer Science
545 Technology Square
Cambridge, MA   02139
U.S.A.

This brief paper offers a perspective on the subject of names
of destinations in data communication networks. It suggests
two ideas: First, it is helpful to distinguish among four
different kinds of objects that may be named as the destination
of a packet in a network. Second, the operating system concept
of binding is a useful way to describe the relations among the
four kinds of objects. To illustrate the usefulness of this
approach, the paper interprets some more subtle and confusing
properties of two real-world network systems for naming
destinations.

WHAT IS THE PROBLEM?

Despite a very helpful effort of John Shoch[1] to impose some organization on
the discussion of names, addresses, and routes to destinations in computer
networks, these discussions continue to be more confusing than one would expect.
This confusion stems sometimes from making too tight an association between
various types of network objects and the most common form for their names. It
also stems from trying to discuss the issues with too few well-defined concepts
at hand. This paper tries a different approach to develop insight, by applying
a perspective that has proven helpful in the corresponding area of computer
operating systems.

Operating systems have a similar potential for confusion concerning names and
addresses, since there are file names, unique identifiers, virtual and real
memory addresses, page numbers, block numbers, I/O channel addresses, disk track
addresses, a seemingly endless list. But most of that potential has long been
rendered harmless by recognizing that the concept of binding provides a
systematic way to think about naming[2]. (Shoch pointed out this opportunity to
exploit the operating system concept; in this paper we make it the central
theme.) In operating systems, it was apparent very early that there were too
many different kinds of identifiers and therefore one does not get much insight
by trying to make a distinction just between names and addresses. It is more
profitable instead to look upon all identifiers as examples of a single
phenomenon, and ask instead "where is the context in which a binding for this
name (or address, or identifier, or whatever) will be found?", and "to what
object, identified by what kind of name, is it therein bound?" This same
approach is equally workable in data communication networks.

_____

This research was supported in part by the Defense Advanced Research Projects
Agency of the United States Government and monitored by the Office of Naval
Research under contract number N00014-75-C-0661.

To start with, let us review Shoch's suggested terminology in its broadest form:

-   a <u>name</u> identifies what you want,

-   an <u>address</u> identifies where it is, and

-   a <u>route</u> identifies a way to get there.

There will be no need to tamper with those definitions, but it will be seen that they leave a lot of room for interpretation. Shoch's suggestion implies that there are three abstract concepts that together provide an intellectual cover for discussion. In this paper, we propose that a more mechanical view may lead to an easier-to-think-with set of concepts. This more mechanical view starts by listing the kinds of things one finds in a communication network.

TYPES OF NETWORK DESTINATIONS, AND BINDINGS AMONG THEM

In a data communication network, when thinking about how to describe the destination of a packet, there are several types of things for which there are more than one instance, so one attaches names to them to distinguish one instance from another. Of these several types, four turn up quite often:

1.   <u>Services and Users</u>. These are the functions that one uses, and the clients that use them. Examples of services are one that tells the time of day, one that performs accounting, or one that forwards packets. An example of a client is a particular desktop computer.

2.   <u>Nodes</u>. These are computers that can run services or user programs. Some nodes are clients of the network, while others help implement the network by running forwarding services. (We will not need to distinguish between these two kinds of nodes.)

3.   <u>Network attachment points</u>. These are the ports of a network, the places where a node is attached. In many discussions about data communication networks, the term "address" is an identifier of a network attachment point.

4.   <u>Paths</u>. These run between network attachment points, traversing forwarding nodes and communication links.

We might note that our first step, the listing and characterization of the objects of discussion, is borrowed from the world of abstract data types. Our second step is to make two observations about naming of network objects, the first about <u>form</u> and the second about <u>bindings</u>.

First, one is free to choose <u>any</u> form of name that seems helpful--binary identifiers, printable character strings, or whatever, and they may be chosen from either a flat or a hierarchical name space. There may be more than one form of name for a single type of object. A node might, for example, have both a hierarchical character string name and a unique binary identifier. There are two semantic traps that one can fall into related to name form. First, the word "name" is, in the network world, usually associated with a printable character string, while the word "address" is usually associated with machine-interpretable binary strings. In the world of systems and languages, the term "print name" is commonly used for the first and "machine name" or "address" for the second, while "name" broadly encompasses both forms. (In this paper we are using the broad meaning of "name".) The second semantic trap is to associate some conventional form of name for a particular type of object as a property of that type. For example, services might be named by character strings, nodes named by unique ID's, and network attachment points named by hierarchical addresses. When one participant in a discussion assumes a particular name form is invariably associated with a particular type of object and another doesn't, the resulting conversation can be very puzzling to all participants.

The second observation about the four types of network objects listed above is that most of the naming requirements in a network can simply and concisely be described in terms of bindings and changes of bindings among the four types of objects. To wit:

1. A given service may run at one or more nodes, and may need to move from one node to another without losing its identity as a service.

2. A given node may be connected to one or more network attachment points, and may need to move from one attachment point to another without losing its identity as a node.

3. A given pair of attachment points may be connected by one or more paths, and those paths may need to change with time without affecting the identity of the attachment points.*

Each of these three requirements includes the idea of preserving identity, whether of service, node, or attachment point. To preserve an identity, one must arrange that the name used for identification not change during moves of the kind required. If the associations among services, nodes, attachment points and routes are maintained as lists of bindings this goal can easily be met. Whether or not all of the flexibility implied by these possibilities should be provided in a particular network design is a matter of engineering judgement. A judgement that a particular binding can be made at network design time and will never be changed (e.g., a particular service might always run at a particular node) should not be allowed to confuse the question of what names and bindings are in principle present. In principle, to send a data packet to a service one must discover three bindings:

1. find a node on which the required service operates,

2. find a network attachment point to which that node is connected,

3. find a path from this attachment point to that attachment point.

There are, in turn, three conceptually distinct binding services that the network needs to provide:

1. Service name resolution, to identify the nodes that run the service.

2. Node name location, to identify attachment points that reach the nodes found in 1.

3. Route service, to identify the paths that lead from the requestor's attachment point to the ones found in 2.

At each level of binding, there can be several alternatives, so a choice of which node, which attachment point, and which path must be made. These choices are distinct but can interact. For example, one might choose the node only

---

* This summary of network naming requirements is intentionally brief. An excellent in-depth review of these requirements can be found in a recent paper by Sunshine[3].

after first looking over the various paths leading to the possible choices. In
this case, the network tables may provide only a partial binding, which means
that an inquiry produces a list of answers rather than a single one. The final
binding choice may be delayed until the last moment and recorded outside the
three binding services provided within the network.

There is a very important sublety about bindings that often leads designers
astray. Suppose we have recorded in a network table the fact that the "Lockheed
DIALOG Service" is running on node "5". There are actually three different
bindings involved here but only one of those three is recorded in this table and
changeable by simply adjusting the table.

1.   The name "Lockheed DIALOG Service" is properly associated with a specific
     service, management, and collection of stored files. One does not usually
     reassign such a name to a different service. The association of the name
     with the service is quite permanent, and because of that permanence is not
     usually expressed in a single, easily changed table.

2.   Similarly, the name "5" is assigned to a particular node on a fairly
     long-term basis, without the expectation that it will change. So that
     assignment is also not typically expressed in a single, easily changed
     table.

3.   The fact that "DIALOG" is just now operating on node "5" is the one binding
     that our table does express, because we anticipate that this association
     might reasonably change. The function of our table is to allow us to
     express changes such as "DIALOG" is now operating at node "6" or the
     "Pipe-fitting Service" is now operating at node "5".

The design mistake is to believe that this table allows one to give the Lockheed
DIALOG service a new name, merely by changing this table entry. That is not the
function of this table of bindings, and such a name change is actually quite
difficult to accomplish since the association in question is not usually
expressed as a binding in a single table. One would have to change not only
this table, but also user programs, documentation, scribbled notes and
advertising copy to accomplish such a name change.

SOME REAL-WORLD EXAMPLES

Although the ideas outlined so far seem fairly straightforward, it is
surprisingly easy to find real-world examples that pose a challenge in
interpretation. In the Xerox/DEC/Intel Ethernet[5,6], for example, the concept
of a network attachment point is elusive, because it collapses into the node
name. A node can physically attach to an Ethernet anywhere along it; the node
brings with it a 48-bit unique identifier that its interface watches for in
packets passing by. This identifier should probably be thought of as the name
of a network attachment point, even though the physical point of attachment can
be anywhere. At the same time, one can adopt a policy that the node will supply
from its own memory the 48-bit identifier that is to be used by the Ethernet
interface, so a second, equally reasonable, view (likely to be taken elsewhere
in the network in interpreting the meaning of these identifiers) is that this
48-bit identifier is the name of the node itself. From a binding perspective
this way of using the Ethernet binds the node name and the network attachment
point name to be the same 48-bit unique identifier.

This permanent binding of node name to attachment point name has several network
management advantages:

     -   a node can be moved from one physical location to another without
         changing any network records.

- one level of binding tables is omitted. This advantage is particularly noticeable in implementing internetwork routing.

- a node that is attached to two Ethernets can present the same attachment point name to both networks, which simplifies communication among internet routers and alternate path finding.

But permanent binding also produces a curiosity if it happens that one wants one node to connect to two attachment points on the same Ethernet. The curiosity arises because the only way to make the second attachment point independently addressable by others is to allow the node to use two different 48-bit identifiers, which means that some other network records (the ones that interpret the ID to be a node name) will likely be fooled into believing that there are not one, but two nodes. To avoid this confusion, the same 48-bit identifier could be used in both attachment points, but then there will be no way intentionally to direct a message to one rather than the other. One way or another, the permanent binding of attachment point name to node name has made some function harder to accomplish, though the overall effect of the advantages probably outweighs the lost function in this case.

For another example, the ARPANET NCP protocol provides character string names that appear, from their mnemonics, to be node names or service names, but in fact they are the names of network attachment points[6]. Thus the character string name RADC-Multics is the name of the network attachment point at ARPANET IMP 18, port 0, so reattaching the node (a Honeywell 68/80 computer) to another network attachment point requires either that users learn a new name for the service or else a change of tables in all other nodes. Changing tables superficially appears to be what rebinding is all about, but the need to change more than one table is the tip-off that something deeper is going on. What is actually happening is a change of the permanent name of a network attachment point. We can see this more clearly by noting that a parallel attachment of that Honeywell 68/80 to a second ARPANET port would be achievable only by assigning a second character string identity; this requirement emphasizes that the name is really of the attachment point, not the node. Unfortunately, because of their mnemonic value, the ARPANET NCP name mnemonics are often thought of as service names. Thus one expects that the Rome Air Development Center Multics service is operated on the node reached by the name RADC-Multics. That particular assumption doesn't produce any surprises. But any of the four Digital PDP-10 computers at Bolt Beranek and Newman can accept mail for any of the others, as can the groups of PDP-10's at the USC Information Sciences Institute, and at the Massachusetts Institute of Technology. If the node to which one tries to send mail is down, the customer must realize that the same service is available by asking for a different node, using what appears to be a different service name. The need for a customer to realize that he must give a different name to get the same service comes about because in the ARPANET the name is not of a service that is bound to a node that is bound to an attachment point, but rather it is directly the name of an attachment point.

Finally, confusion can arise because the three conceptually distinct binding services (service name resolution, node name location, and route dispensing) may not be mechanically distinct. There is usually suggested only one identifiable service, a "name server". The name server starts with a service name and returns a list of network attachment points that can provide that service. It thereby performs both the first and second conceptual binding services, though it may leave to the customer the final choice of which attachment point to use. Path choice may be accomplished by a distributed routing algorithm that provides the final binding service without anyone noticing it.

CORRESPONDENCE WITH NAMES, ADDRESSES, AND ROUTES

With this model of binding among services, nodes, network attachment points, and paths in mind, one possible interpretation of Shoch's names, addresses, and routes is as follows:

1. Any of the four kinds of objects (service, node, network attachment point, path) may have a name, though Shoch would restrict that term to human-readable character strings.

2. The address of an object is a name (in the broad sense, not Shoch's restricted sense) of the object it is bound to. Thus, an address of a service is the name of some node that runs it. An address of a node is the name of some network attachment point to which it connects. An address of a network attachment point (a concept not usually discussed) can be taken to be the name of a path that leads to it. This interpretation captures Shoch's meaning "An address indicates where it is," but does not very well match Shoch's other notion that an address is a machine-processable, rather than a human-processable form of identification. This is probably the primary point where our perspectives differ on which definitions provide the most clarity.

3. A route is a more sophisticated concept. A route to either a network attachment point or a node is just a path, as we have been using that term. Because a single node can run several services at once, a route to a service consists of a path to the network attachment point of a node that runs the service, plus some identification of which activity within that node runs the service (e.g., a "socket identifier" in the PUP internet[4] or ARPA Internet[7] protocols). But note that a route may actually consist of a series of names, typically a list of forwarding node names or attachment points and the names used by the forwarding nodes for the paths between them.

Whether or not one likes this particular interpretation of Shoch's terms, it seems clear that there are more than three concepts involved, so more than three labels are needed to discuss them.

SUMMARY

This paper has argued that some insight into the naming of destinations in a network can be obtained by recognizing four kinds of named objects at or leading to every destination (services, nodes, attachment points, and routes) and then identifying three successive, changeable, bindings (service to node, node to attachment point, and attachment point to route). This perspective, modeled on analogous successive bindings of storage management systems (file--storage region--physical location) and virtual memories (object--segment--page--memory block) provides a systematic explanation for some design problems that are encountered in network naming systems.

ACKNOWLEDGEMENTS

Discussions with David D. Clark, J. Noel Chiappa, David P. Reed, and Dan Cohen helped clarify the reasoning used here. John F. Shoch provided both inspiration and detailed comments, but should not be held responsible for the result.

REFERENCES

1. Shoch, John F., "Inter-Network Naming, Addressing, and Routing," IEEE Proc.
    COMPCON Fall 1978, pp. 72-79. Also in Thurber, K. (ed.), Tutorial:
    Distributed Processor Communication Architecture, IEEE Publ. #EHO 152-9,
    1979, pp. 280-287.

2. Saltzer, J.H., "Naming and Binding of Objects," in: Operating Systems,
    Lecture notes in Computer Science, Vol. 60. Edited by R. Bayer, New York:
    Springer-Verlag, 1978.

3. Sunshine, Carl A., "Addressing Problems in Multi-Network Systems," to
    appear in Proc. IEEE INFOCOM 82, Las Vegas, Nevada, March 30-April 1, 1982.

4. Boggs, D.R., Shoch, J.F., Taft, E.A., and Metcalfe, R.M., "PUP: An
    Internetwork Architecture," IEEE Trans. on Comm. 28, 4 (April, 1980) pp.
    612-623.

5. (Anonymous), "The Ethernet, A Local Area Network: Data Link Layer and
    Physical Layer Specifications, Version 1.0," published by Xerox Corp., Palo
    Alto, Calif., Intel Corp., Sunnyvale, Calif., and Digital Equipment Corp.,
    Tewksbury, Mass., September 30, 1980.

6. Dalal, Y.K., and Printis, R.S., "48-bit Absolute Internet and Ethernet Host
    Numbers," Proc. Seventh Data Communications Symposium, Mexico City, Mexico,
    October 1981, pp. 240-245.

7. Feinler, E., and Postel, J., Ed., "ARPANET Protocol Handbook," SRI
    International, Menlo Park, Calif., January, 1978.

LOCAL COMPUTER NETWORKS
P.C. Ravasio, G. Hopkins and N. Naffah (editors)
North-Holland Publishing Company
© IFIP, 1982

CONNECTION-ORIENTED PROTOCOLS
OF NET/ONE

John M. Davidson

Ungermann-Bass, Inc.
2560 Mission College Blvd.
Santa Clara, CA 95050

INTRODUCTION

This paper describes the "connection-oriented" protocols of
Net/One. Net/One is a commercial local area network [1,2]
comprising a coaxial cable and a number of microprocessor-based
stations called Network Interface Units (NIUs). The NIU hardware
provides connectors for the attachment of serial and parallel
devices like computer ports, terminals, printers, modems, and
other peripheral equipment; the NIU software provides communication services to these attached devices so that they may select-
ively exchange data among themselves irrespective of their
individual points of attachment to the net.

The "connection-oriented" protocols are those which provide
the services ascribed to the Transport layer of the ISO Open Systems Interconnection (OSI) architecture--the layer which provides
reliable and orderly delivery of data between two network entities on a connection-oriented basis. There are four such protocols. Three are used to create, destroy, and ask questions about
connections; the fourth is used in carrying data on an established connection.

The paper presents a section on the NIU architecture to
establish some context, a section on the underlying datagram forwarding mechanism on which the first three connection-oriented
protocols depend, and then a section on each of the four protocols themselves.

ARCHITECTURAL OVERVIEW

Net/One comprises a collection of NIUs physically and logically interconnected by a broadcast communications medium such as
a coaxial cable. NIUs communicate with one another using point-
to-point, multicast, and broadcast techniques. Several versions
of Net/One are available which employ different data rates and
signalling techniques and distinct protocol repertoires; however,
for purposes of this paper, a hybrid description is presented
which assumes without loss of generality a baseband CSMA/CD coaxial cable implementation with Physical and Data Link layers
corresponding to those described for the 10 Mbps Ethernet specification [3]. Internetworks of Net/One systems may be constructed
by providing bridge NIUs which connect two or more Net/One segments in a mesh arrangement, as for example in [4]. The Network

protocol   layer   employs   Internet   Headers   to   facilitate   the
addressing of NIUs on distinct networks.

To facilitate understanding of the connection-oriented   protocols,   it   is   necessary to describe a few of the architectural
components   embodied   in   an   NIU.   Processor   boards,   software
processes,   and   the NIU interprocess communication mechanism are
discussed in the following paragraphs.

Processor Boards

There are currently two kinds of NIUs: the NIU-1 and   NIU-2.
ıhe   NIU-1   is   a   single   processor   system;   and the NIU-2 is a
multi-processor system. Each processor is contained on a distinct
printed   circuit board, so the NIU-1 has one processor board, and
the NIU-2 has up   to   four.   For   purposes   of   the   connection-
oriented   protocols   described   in   this paper, it is possible to
think of an NIU processor board as though it were a single   board
computer   attached   directly   to   the Ethernet.   No distinction in
service, in addressability, or in capacity or capability   can   be
discerned   between   a   processor board in an NIU-1 and any of the
boards in an NIU-2, even though the   NIU-2   boards   in   actuality
share   a single interface to the Ethernet.   Thus in this paper we
need consider only NIU-1s which we refer to generically   as   just
NIUs.

Each processor board provides a variey of serial and   parallel   connectors which can be used for the attachment of "foreign"
devices such as terminals, computer ports, printers, etc.

Software Processes

Each processor board provides an environment for the   execution   of   a   multitasking kernel.   The kernel in turn provides an
environment   for   the   execution   of   a   collection   of   tasks   or
"processes."   Each process on a given processor board has a board
relative unique 16-bit identity, called its process id, or <pid>.
The   three-tuple   <net, NIU, pid> is sufficient to uniquely identify all NIU processes in an internetwork of Net/One systems.

Interprocess Communication

The kernel provides a   form   of   interprocess   communication
(IPC)   which   allows processes to communicate with one another by
exchanging messages. When both sending and   receiving   processes
are on the same processor board, the Kernel supervises the entire
send/receive transaction.   When the two processes are on distinct
boards, the Kernel relies on an "IPC Forwarder" process to effect
the exchange.   Its job is to launch outgoing messages and receive
incoming messages; incoming messages are passed to the Kernel for
subsequent local distribution.   The Forwarder transports IPC messages   by unacknowledged datagrams, and thus the delivery of messages across the net is not   guaranteed.   Reliable   exchange   of
information   between   any two processes can of course be effected
by a higher level mechanism built upon this non-reliable IPC.

Overview of NIU Services

When processes need to communicate in a completely reliable fashion, they may elect to use "connections" instead of IPC messages. Connections are logical, full duplex data streams which allow the processes which employ them to send one another data. Connections can be created and destroyed dynamically. Requests for connection may be made by any process in the net, and the request may specify the interconnection of any two processes, not necessarily including the requestor. Connection initiation is performed by supervisory processes which employ IPC message exchanges to find one another and negotiate the creation of connections. The connections are implemented by designated "data-carrying" processes on each of the NIUs involved, and the processes which use the connection "plug into" it by byte stream or block oriented interface procedures provided by the data carriers.

One important type of process present on all NIUs is a device interface process. There is a device interface process for each device which is attached to an NIU. When two of these processes are joined in a connection, they forward data from their respective devices to one another. From the devices' perspective, this provides a service identical to that which they would have if they were attached directly to one another. A CRT and a computer port are examples of two "devices" which can clearly take advantage of this kind of service.

Device interface processes are not perpetual. In most cases, a new device interface process is created whenever a connection to its device is desired. At teardown of the connection, the processes involved typically destroy themselves.

Each device attached to an NIU is identified by a unique 32-bit number. The 32-bit number is a two-tuple, expressed as a <pid, rid> pair. The <pid> is the identity of a process known as the "device manager," and the <rid>, or "resource ID," is an identifier of a device which the device manager manages. The device manager ascribes to each of his attached devices a unique <rid> value. Then, when one or another protocol needs to talk about one or another device, it talks to the device manager <pid> specifying interest in device number <rid>. The way in which this is done is made clear in the subsequent presentation of the three IPC-based protocols.

NIU devices are uniquely identified in a global internet by a <net, NIU, <pid,rid>> three-tuple, or more simply a <net, NIU, device ID> three-tuple, called a "global device identifier".

Overview of the IPC-based Protocols

There are three protocols to be described. Each of them deals with global device identifiers. The Name-Inquiry Protocol (NP) performs a mapping function between ASCII name strings and device identifiers. The Rendezvous Protocol (RP) uses two device identifiers to initiate and teardown a connection. And the Connection-Inquiry Protocol (CP) uses two device identifiers in asking about the status of a network device.

In general, the three protocols are used as follows. When an NIU process wants to join two devices together in a connection, it must find the associated global device identifier of each. If it knows the string names of the two devices, it can determine the device IDs by repeated application of the NP. Then, through the use of the RP, it can arrange for the two devices to be joined in a connection. Any NIU process can afterwards cause the teardown of the connection by first using CP to determine a "handle" for the connection, and then using RP to initiate the dissolution.

In certain instances, information such as one or both of the device identifiers, or perhaps, say, the connection "handle", may be known ahead of time, so that one or more steps may be eliminated from the ritual depicted above. For example, a device interface process which knows its own device identifier, may need to use NP only to learn the ID of some remote NIU device in order to connect to it, and afterwards, knowing a handle for its own connection, may need only RP to cause the connection to be dissolved.

In the following sections, these three protocols are described in more complete detail.

NAME-INQUIRY PROCTOCOL

The Name-Inquiry Protocol, NP, may be used to provide mappings between ASCII name strings and global device identifiers. It is an internetworking protocol based on the IPC non-acknowledged datagram facility. The mappings may be performed in each direction--name string-to-ID or ID-to-name string.

In the description of the name-to-device ID mapping, it should be remembered that the NP is not a general purpose name server protocol (though it may later be extended in Net/One to include more functionality), but is really just a protocol designed to let processes connect to devices by using names instead of device IDs.

The data base for NP´s mapping function is generally distributed among the NIUs, with each processor board holding only that portion of the data base which relates to its own devices. Thus the NP mapping will generally only be performed for devices on active NIUs. The data base entries are generally simple; each entry specifying a <name string, device ID> pair. However, more complex entries are possible which associate one name string with a number of local device IDs, and there may also be multiple (simple or complex) entries which map distinct names to a single device ID. Recorded with each name string in the data base component is a bit which tells whether the name is unique within the local network, or not.

The goal of NP mapping is to associate name strings with IDs. In general, NP is used when one of these entities is known but not the other. When the name string is known, the NP function invoked is one which attempts to locate a device ID which can be used in an immediately following RP request for connection initiation. Since it is desired that the following connection attempt succeed, the mapping function is biased in favor of a device which is free and ready to partake in a connection whenever it is known that the given name string maps to more than one device. When the name string does not map to more than one device, the uniquely associated device ID is the ID returned.

When the device ID is the entity known, the ID-to-name mapping may be used. This mapping may yield one, or more than one, name strings for a given device ID. Since the data base entries are ordered, it is possible to ask for the 1st, 2nd, ..., nth entry which satisfies a given ID-to-name mapping. The current implementation of NP requires that the ID-to-name mapping be performed by the processor board to which the device is attached. This is a limitation which again is not considered too severe, given that NP is not a complete name server. The ID-to-name mapping is not employed in connection initiation or teardown, but needs to be supported on every NIU for the administrative services which employ CP.

Name Lookup

The name-to-ID mapping fuction of the NP works generally as follows. When a process desires to connect to a device whose name string is known (it may be one of many names that refer to the given device), it broadcasts to all NIU´s on the given network a "Name Lookup" request, asking each one to consult its data base component to see if the name is recorded therein. If an NIU has the name in its data base component, it performs two tests in order to decide whether to answer the Name Lookup request.

> (1) If the name is unique within the net, then the NIU returns a response.

> (2) If the name is not unique within the net, then the NIU scans the device IDs mapped by the name to determine if any is free. If one is free and ready to accept a connection, then the NIU returns a response.

In either case the returned response is a point-to-point IPC message which gives the device ID of the uniquely named device, or of the free device mapped by the non-unique name.

If the NIU does not have the name in its data base component, or if all the devices mapped by a non-unique name are unavailable for use in a new connection, then no response is generated.

If the requesting NIU does not receive a response within NP_TIMEOUT milliseconds (see Note 1.), it means one of three things. Either no active NIU has generated a response to the Name Lookup, or the Name Lookup request was lost in transit, or all subsequent responses were lost in transit. To determine with greater certainty whether messages were lost, the requesting process repeats its Name Lookup request up to NP_REPEAT additional times, each programmed to be NP_TIMEOUT milliseconds apart.

If a response is received after any one of the original or repeat transmissions, the name-to-device ID mapping has been performed and the protocol interactions are considered complete. If multiple responses are received, any of the mapped device IDs may

be used. Since multiple responses may be sent, provision must be
made at the requesting NIU to discard those that are not wanted.

If after NP_REPEAT+1 total requests, no response has been
received, the requesting process concludes that either no active
NIU has the name in its database component, or the name is non-
unique, and all the devices mapped by this name are busy. To
distinguish between these two possibilities, the requesting process broadcasts a "NU-Name Lookup" request to all NIUs asking
each one to consult its database component to see whether the
supplied name is present and registered as non-unique. If any
NIU determines the name to be non-unique it returns a response
showing one of the (busy) device IDs associated with the non-
unique name.

The requesting NIU waits NP_TIMEOUT milliseconds for a
response, and if it gets none, repeats its request NP_REPEAT
additional times, each NP_TIMEOUT milliseconds apart. If a
response is received after one of the original or repeat
transmissions, the requesting process concludes that the name is
non-unique and all devices associated with the name are busy.

If after NP_NUREPEAT +1 total requests, no response has been
received, the requesting process concludes that no active NIU has
the name in its data base component. The protocol interaction is
then considered complete.

Once the requesting process has begun to broadcast the "NU-
Name Lookup" request, subsequent responses to the Name Lookup
request are discarded, and once it has made its ultimate conclusion regarding the name_to_device ID mapping, subsequent
responses to the NU-Name Lookup are also discarded.

NP responses are associated with NP requests by the use of
unique sequence numbers. Responses to a request numbered "n"
must also be numbered "n." The sequence numbers used in NP
requests are incremented for each original transmission of a Name
Lookup or an NU-Name Lookup; repeated transmissions of either use
the same sequence number as the original.

Note that the responding NIU has no timeout requirements of
its own (for example it does not expect to receive requests at
any particular rate or time) except that it is expected to
respond to an NP request in a "timely fashion," which usually
means "quickly enough to keep the requesting NIU from timing
out."

Device ID Lookup

The ID-to-name mapping function of the NP works very much
like the name-to-ID mapping. However, instead of being a broadcast interaction, the ID-to-name mapping is strictly point-to-
point, since knowledge of the global device ID implies knowledge
of the NIU on which the appropriate data base component resides.
Here, as before, the individual interactions supported for this
mapping may be used as desired. The description in this section
shows how the NIU will employ these interactions in providing a
particular administrative service.

Generally the mapping function works as follows. When a process desires to know the name strings associated with a global device ID, it sends to the <net, NIU> portion of the <net, NIU, device ID> global ID an "ID Lookup" request, asking the receiving NIU to consult its data base component for one of the name strings associated with the ID. The ordering ascribed to the recorded names is as they are found in a forward sequential scan of the NIU's Name Descriptor Table. A parameter K is sent which selects the Kth name, 0 <= K <= 255.

If there is a Kth mapping between the ID and a name string, then the Kth mapped name is the one returned. If there is no Kth mapping, then an error response is returned.

When an NIU receives an ID Lookup request asking for the name used with the Kth ID-to-name mapping, it scans its data base component for the Kth entry which has the same local device ID as that specified in the lookup request. If there is no such entry, it returns an error response. If the entry exists, then the name recorded in the entry is returned along with a success indication.

A requesting NIU always starts out by issuing an ID Lookup with parameter K=0. If it does not receive a response within NP_TIMEOUT milliseconds it repeats its requests just as for Name Lookup.

If after all its requests, no response has been received, the requesting NIU concludes that the target NIU is not active and considers the protocol interactions complete. If a response is received after one of the original or repeat transmissions, the requesting NIU checks the response return code. If it indicates "success", then the Kth name string exists and is included in the response message. In this case, the requesting NIU increments the parameter K and repeats the protocol interaction with a new ID Lookup request.

If the returned response indicates a failure ("no Kth name"), then the requesting NIU considers the protocol interactions complete.

ID Lookup interactions employ a sequence number in precisely the same way that Name Lookup and NU-Name Lookup do to associate reponses with previous requests. Responses with sequence numbers not matching the sequence number of the current outstanding request, and responses arriving after the protocol interactions have completed, are discarded.

CONNECTION-INQUIRY PROTOCOL

The Connection-Inquiry Protocol, CP, may be used to determine the "status" of any device attached to an NIU. Most often, the status is checked in order to determine whether the device in question is involved in a connection--hence the protocol name. In Net/One, the CP is used by the network administrator to decide whether devices are free and can be joined in a connection or whether instead they are already engaged in a connection; in the latter case, he may follow up the CP interaction with a Rendez-vous interaction in order to tear down the connection if this is desired.

CP is an internetworking protocol based on the IPC non-acknowledged datagram facility. All CP interactions consist of a point-to-point request followed by a point-to-point response. The response is expected to be delivered in a "timely" fashion.

CP interactions proceed generally as follows. An NIU process is interested in the status of a remote network device. It sends a CP "Examine" request to the device maanger on the remote NIU to which the device is attached. The request specifies that the device manager examine the device in question and report its findings in an associated response message. Note that the requesting NIU most likely learned the global device ID of the device it is interested in by issuing a Name Lookup request for one of the device's name strings.

The receiver of an Examine request always returns a response to the requestor. The response can indicate a success or failure, with a success further detailing the status of the device (to be explained), and a failure indicating that the <rid> presented cannot be mapped to any device on the given NIU.

The request/response interactions can be used in any desired way since they are simply IPC datagrams, and there are no special constraints on these messages imposed by the CP. The way CP is used in the NIU is explained in the following.

A requesting NIU sends an Examine request to a destination device manager requesting that it examine a specified <rid>. If the requestor does not receive a response within CP_TIMEOUT milliseconds, it means one of three things. Either the destination process is not active (because it does not exist, or the NIU is not active), or the Examine request was lost in transit, or the subsequent response was lost in transit. To determine with greater certainty whether messages were lost, the requesting process repeats its Examine request up to CP_REPEAT additional times, each programmed to be CP_TIMEOUT milliseconds apart.

If a response is received after any one of the original or repeat transmissions, the Examine operation has been performed, and the protocol interactions can be considered complete. As in the Name-Inquiry Protocol, CP responses are associated with CP requests by the use of sequence numbers. The response to a request numbered "n" must also be numbered "n." The sequence numbers used in CP requests are incremented for each original transmission of an Examine request; repeated transmissions use the same sequence number as the original.

Devices attached to an NIU may be regarded as being in any of several distinct states. Two states of interest are

(1) Free state. The device is available for use in a connection.

(2) Connected state. The device has been claimed by a local device interface process which has an open connection established between itself and some other

remote (or local) device, i.e., the device is involved in a connection.

Devices attached to an NIU may also be classified on the basis of the service which their associated process has chosen to provide. There are a great many distinct services which device interface processes may provide in forwarding their data via a connection. The particular services are not described here, since they are not relevant to the protocol description; however the CP response returns information on these services and also returns the global device identifier of the remote connected device in the case where a connection is indicated.

RENDEZVOUS PROTOCOL

The Rendezvous Protocol, RP, may be used to help initiate and terminate connections between any two devices attached to an NIU. It is an internetworking protocol based on the IPC non-acknowledged datagram facility.

A connection is considered established when both endpoints of the connection know each other's complete address and some relevant demultiplexing information needed by the data carrying processes. This demultiplexing information includes "socket numbers" which help identify the participants in a connection, and "connection IDs" which help distinguish multiple connections between the same participants. The Rendezvous Protocol may be looked at (for the most part) as a protocol to be used in telling each end the other end's values for this information. Connection establishment takes place, then, not by the initial exchange of packets, but by the binding procedures inherent in the RP. No packets are sent on a connection until each party to the connection knows the complete binding for the other.

(In addition to the demultiplexing information which is bound by RP interactions, several other kinds of information can be negotiated and bound using RP as well. Although the mechanisms are not described in this paper, it should be readily apparent how RP can be augmented to reveal to one end the other's initial window settings, initial retransmission frequency, maximum receive buffer size, and other parameters associated with the data transport service that is being initiated.)

The Rendezvous Protocol appears to be the most complex of the protocols being described in this paper. What makes it appear complex is the fact that it often employs multiple IPC message exchanges in order to communicate the connection binding information. It does this solely in the interest of reliability, since the underlying IPC fowarding is not by itself reliable.

To achieve reliability, an NIU which wants to make an RP request of some other NIU first executes an exchange of IPC messages with the target NIU exactly as in an NP or CP interaction. The request in this interaction specifies a "HELLO", and the response indicates a "HELLOACK." Having opened a conversation with the target NIU, the requestor then communicates its "Bind-

ing" request under the terms agreed to for this conversation (to
be explained). The target responds to the Binding request with a
simple Binding response, in just the same way that the opening of
the conversation was performed. As a final step in the RP
interaction, the requestor sends a "GOODBYE" IPC message to the
target and waits for a "GOODBYEACK" response. Again, this is
just like all of the previously described request/response
protocol interactions.

It appears that RP is no more complicated in fact than execution of three back-to-back NP or CP request/response pairs. RP
is different, however, in the fact that the three
request/response interactions required to perform a rendezvous
function are all related to one another by the concept of a
"conversation number." Use of a common conversation number for
multiple IPC interactions forces the two participating NIUs to
maintain enough state concerning one another that there is no
possibility of duplicate Binding requests being accepted as ori-
ginals. The function performed at the instigation of a Binding
request is of course not idempotent, so receipt of undetected
duplicates could cause errors in connection setup.

There are several functions which the RP attempts to accomplish through the use of its hello/request/goodbye model for
interaction. To explain the various functions, it is useful to
consider why the RP was invented in the first place. The concept
is fairly simple. The devices attached to NIUs may not always
have the ability to interact (for example, through use of a
command language with their device interface processes) in order
to open connections between themselves and some other device.
In those cases where a device does not have this ability, it is
necessary for some other party to be able to initiate a connection on its behalf. The other party can of course be the other
end of the intended connection, but there are also cases where
the other end cannot perform this interaction either, or simply
does not know that the connection is desired. To accommodate
the case where neither end of an intended connection is able to
initate a connection to the other, the RP was created. RP allows
a third party to setup a connection between two devices without
either device having to take part in the setup. Once RP was in
place, of course, it became expedient to use it in all connection
setups, rather than to have two distinct mechanisms supported in
every NIU.

Two New Processes are Required

Since most connections between NIUs are in fact instigated
by devices which can interact with their device interface process, the "third party" who sets up connections is most often
just a process on the initiator's NIU. This process is called
the "operator" (after the old fashioned telephone operator who
plugs two parties into a connection via a simple patch panel.)
The device interface process acquires from its device the name
string of the desired remote endpoint, employs NP to acquire the
associated global device ID, and passes this ID and its own device ID to the operator saying "please join these two devices in a
connection." The operator uses RP to do so, and responds with
a success or failure indication to the requesting process at completion.

The administrator of a network of NIUs has access to a special command interpreter process which allows him to specify two devices (instead of just one with the other defaulted) which should be joined in a connection. This process uses NP twice to acquire the two associated global device IDs, and then passes these to the operator on its NIU with the same connection setup request. The operator complies as before. Note that it is the device interface process on an administrative station which is special, not the operator; the operator is identical on all NIUs.

In performing its third party connection setups, the operator needs to enlist the aid of another process on each of the NIUs which is involved. This other process is called the "representative" (after the telephone company's representative who you need to talk to get new lines installed); there is a single representative on every NIU.

The operator and representative are the two parties which perform the request and response roles in RP interactions. The operator is always the requestor, and the representative is always the responder. There are five binding operations which can be communicated as the middle request of an RP conversation:

(1) Setup Connection. ("What's yours?") The operator provides the representative with two global device IDs. One of the associated devices is on the representative's NIU and the other is remote. The representative creates a device interface process to service the local device, and attaches it to the local end of a connection. It returns to the operator the socket number and connection ID chosen for the local endpoint. The connection is only "half-setup", however, because the local end does not yet know the remote end's socket number and connection ID.

(2) Bind Connection. ("Here's his.") The operator provides the representative with all the binding parameters for both ends of a connection. If the representative recognizes the parameters for the local end as the parameters assigned to a half-setup connection, and recognizes the address of the remote end as the remote end address recorded previously in the Remote Setup request, it binds the remote socket number and connection ID into the connection. This results in a fully bound connection on the representative's end.

(3) Open Connection. ("Here's his, what's yours?") This operation performs the functions of both Setup and Bind in a single transaction. The operator provides the representative with the global device ID, socket number, and connection ID of an endpoint on a remote NIU, and the global device ID of a device on the representative's NIU. The representative creates a device interface process to service the local device, and attaches it to the local end of a connection. It binds the three remote parameters of the connection, and returns to the operator the socket number and connection ID of the local end.

(4) Spoil Connection. ("Please quit.") The operator
provides the representative with a socket number and
connection id for a connection endpoint on the
representative's NIU, and asks the representative to
have the associated device interface process initiate
connnection teardown.

(5) Close Connection. The operator provides the
representative with a socket number and connection ID
for a connection endpoint on the representative's
NIU, and asks the representative to delete the endpoint. The representative returns to the operator
the global device ID, socket number, and connection
ID of the remote endpoint of the associated connection.

The representative does not really delete the endpoint until
the local device interface process indicates it has finished
reading the data that may be residing in local buffers. In the
original NIU software, the process could announce it was through
only by asking its operator to issue a close. But since the
representative does not know (when it receives a Close Connection) whether the local process, the remote process, or even a
third party process has requested the close, it generally does
not delete the connection entirely until it has received two such
requests. It is guaranteed to receive (at least) two, since the
processes on each end request their operator to do a close whenever they are done with the connection.

These binding operations can probably be used in any combination, but the way they are used by NIU operators is as follows.
The details of the interactions have been simplified to keep the
paper at a manageable size.

When the operator is asked to connect two devices together,
it chooses one of the NIUs, A, (it is expedient to choose your
own first if one of the devices is local) and performs a
Setup Connection with the representative on A to acquire the
socket number and connection ID of one half of the connection.
If that operation is successful, the operator then performs an
Open Connection with the representative on the other NIU, B,
providing B with A's parameters, and acquiring B's in one
operation. If the Open Connection is successful, the operator
performs a Bind Connection with A in order to provide A with B's
socket number and connection ID. A successful Bind Connection
results in a completely established connection.

If the operator fails in A's Setup, the rest of the binding is not attempted. If it fails in B's Open, a Close Connection is sent back to A allowing it to inform its device interface process that the connection has been dissolved. (The device
interface process should generate the second close operation
required to really cause the connection's structures to be
released.) If it fails in A's Bind, a Close Connection is performed with B. No further interaction with A is attempted
since it is assumed a Close Connection interaction would meet
with no more success than did the Bind. If A really is alive,
it will have to time out a half-setup connection after it has
gone a (host-dependent) period of time without receiving a
Bind. The operator in most connection setup interactions runs
on the same NIU as representative A. Thus if the

representative has crashed, so will have the operator. The
"established" connection created on B will timeout by virtue of
the normal data carrying mechanisms.

    In some connection setups (for example the setups orches-
trated by the administrative command interpreter), the operator
will not be on the same NIU as either representative A or
representative B. In this case the failure of the operator prior
to the Remote Bind will lead to the time out and clean up
requirement noted above.

    When the operator is asked to close a connection, it is
given the address, socket number, and connection ID of one endpoint of the connection to be closed. It sends the representative on the designated NIU a Close Connection request, and gets
back the address, socket number, and connection ID of the party
that formed the other connection endpoint. It sends the
representative on that NIU a Close Connection request as well.
Teardown of an open connection is always instigated by one of the
processes involved in the connection. The notion to close the
connection comes to this process either because its task is all
done and it voluntarily decides to close, or because the connection has become unuseable and thus needs to be closed. A connection becomes unuseable to one end when it has been closed by the
other, or when it has been "spoiled" by administrative action.
Since each end of the connection requests a close from its
operator, each of two operators performs a Close Connection with
each of two representatives, and the necessary number of
closes are guaranteed.

    When an operator is unable to effect a Close Connection with
the remote representative, it repeats its Close Connection to the
local representative to guarantee it will have two.

    When it generates a "spoil" request, the administrator's
operator executes the same logic as when it does a close, but
uses Spoil Connection interactions instead of Close Connection
interactions (that is, "spoils" are sent to each of two representatives). It does not matter whether both representatives
receive a spoil, since it is enough to instigate teardown that
one end of the connection finds it unuseable.

DATA TRANSPORT PROTOCOL

    The Data Transport Protocol, DTP, is used to carry data
packets back and forth on open connections. As described earlier, DTP is not concerned with the initiation or teardown of
connections--just the reliable delivery of data on the connections while they exist. A full description of DTP awaits some
other opportunity; an overview is offered here for completeness
of the Transport layer's description.

    DTP is a protocol for the reliable exchange of packets
between two NIUs. Each packet sent contains both protocol information and (optionally) data. Data-carrying packets are assigned
a sequence number as they are sent so that they may be processed
in order as they are received. Non-data carrying packets employ
a sequence number so they may be located in their rightful place
in the packet procession, but they do not consume the number

since they do not need to be reliably transmitted--the protocol
information they contain will be repeated in the subsequent data
carrying packet that employs the same sequence number.

The protocol information consists principally of acknowledgment and flow control fields (plus connection identification
information which is needed by the DTP processes to demultiplex
incoming packets to the appropriate connection). These two
fields both contain sequence numbers. The acknowledgment field
holds the number of the latest data-carrying packet accepted by
the receiver; packets received out of order are held by the
receiver, but not accepted until all intervening packets have
also been received. Acknowledgments may thus be grouped, potentially reducing the number of non-data carrying packets which
need to be transmitted. The flow control field contains the
largest sequence number which the receiver will allow the oppos-
ing sender to transmit. It serves as an ever-advancing "window"
which allows the sender to potentially have multiple unacknowledged packets in flight simultaneously. The window value is
advanced as receive data buffers are made available after processing by the receiving client process.

The DTP process interlocks its operation with that of the
representative. Connections may appear or disappear between successive DTP invocations as commanded by RP interactions. An
advantage to this approach is that DTP can be streamlined to handle only data transport; it has no need to examine connection
setup or teardown requests in incoming packets, or to maintain
the attendant half-open/half-closed data structures. These functions can be done by the representative in background mode. DTP
can thus be a fast, frequently executed foreground task.

CONCLUSION

This paper has presented four protocol descriptions which
together implement a Transport service for Net/One processes.
The protocols are reminiscent of other Transport level protocols
like the original ARPANET Network Control Protocol or the DoD
Standard Transmission Control Protocol but have certain properties which distinguish them from these others because they are
designed for operation in a local area broadcast network whose
nodes are processor and storage limited in several respects.

The paper is not, of course, an implementation guide.
Nevertheless, the detail required to describe the protocols even
informally is fairly significant. To keep the paper at a manageable size, descriptions of the local and internet headers used in
Net/One were omitted, as were performance implications of the
given protocols, and additional architectural descriptions.

It may be of interest to state that the three IPC-based Protocols are largely independent, and were implemented in distinct
stages. RP was first, of course, followed by CP which is largely
an administrative tool. NP was not even present in the first
release of Net/One software; the command handling device interface processes in that release required users to know the global
device id of remote devices they wanted to connect to! In addition, there are now two distinct versions of DTP available in
different implementations of the network, though NP, CP, and RP
support both without change.

NOTE 1

Values for the various timeout and retry parameters in the
NP, CP, and RP protocols are of course variable, and can be set
to reflect desired degrees of responsiveness in the individual
interactions.   Typical values for the timeout parameters are 250
or 500 milliseconds; for the repeat parameters, 1, 2, or 3
repetitions.

ACKNOWLEDGMENTS

Mary Kay Carrico has been a wonderful help in entering and
editing the text of this paper. Tod Snook and Fred Sammartino
were both instrumental in the refinement of the paper and the
protocols.   Cary Wyman and Dick Broberg have contributed greatly
with these others to the NIU software, especially the kernel and
device interface processes.

REFERENCES

(1) John M. Davidson, "Interconnection Services of Net/One",
available from Ungermann-Bass, Inc.

(2) Charlie Bass, Joseph S. Kennedy, John M. Davidson, "Local
Network Gives New Flexibility to Distributed Processing", Electronics, Sept. 25, 1980, pp. 114-122.

(3) "The Ethernet, A Local Area Network: Data Link Layer and
Physical Layer Specifications", Version 1.0, September 30, 1980
(available from DEC, Intel, and Xerox).

(4) David R. Boggs, John F. Schoch, Edward A. Taft, and Robert M.
Metcalfe, "Pup: An Internetwork Architecture", IEEE Transactions
on Communications, April 1980.

LOCAL COMPUTER NETWORKS
P.C. Ravasio, G. Hopkins and N. Naffah (editors)
North-Holland Publishing Company
© IFIP, 1982

AN EFFICIENT ERROR DETECTION MECHANISM

FOR A MULTICAST TRANSPORT SERVICE ON THE DANUBE NETWORK

P. DECITRE[*], J. ESTUBLIER[**], A. KHIDER[**], X. ROUSSET DE PINA[**],I. VATTON[**]

  * Centre de recherche CII-Honeywell Bull BP53X 38041 GRENOBLE CEDEX
 ** Laboratoire IMAG, UNIVERSITÉ de GRENOBLE BP53X 38041 GRENOBLE CEDEX

ABSTRACT

This paper presents an error detection mechanism which has been developed at
GRENOBLE by the IMAG laboratory and the CII-Honeywell Bull research center.
It provides a new way of detecting errors in the transmission of messages
from several sources to several destinations. It has been designed to be
used at the transport station level to implement a reliable multicast
service. The main idea is to use the mutual exclusion provided by the transmission medium to create a numbering system which allows error detection without sending positive acknowledgements. This technique can be applied to
broadcast network such has CSMA/CD which has a hardware mutual exclusion mechanism provided by the contention algorithm.

Key-words : CSMA/CD networks, broadcast, multicast, error detection, transport protocol.

GOALS

The GRENOBLE IMAG Laboratory and the CII-Honeywell Bull research center have
started a study sponsored by KAYAK to design and implement a reliable multicast transport service ("conversation" service) on the DANUBE network. DANU-
BE is a CSMA/CD network similar to the ETHERNET network [5]. The first goal
of this study is to provide applications with a programmatic interface allowing multicast with the same reliability as the usual point to point transport protocol. The application layer must not be bothered by error detection
and recovery. This kind of service is useless to distributed applications
where distribution consists only in file transfers or terminal-to-program
connections. But it can largely simplify the application protocols involving
more than two co-operating processes.

Multicast service have been studied in the environment of packet switched
networks without broadcast medium [3,11]. Emphasis was on the broadcast problem itself. Here we deal with a network based upon a broadcast medium.

To this respect a second goal of this study, is to take advantage of the
broadcast facility provided by the network to design an efficient multicast
protocol. The multicast service must be capable of transporting information
to several points faster than would a set of point to point liaisons.

The "conversation" service.

The conversation service is provided to a set of co-operating application
entities by a transport station. It can be decomposed into four main parts :

connection, sending, receiving, deconnection. Connection allows the rendez-vous of several application entities. The sending service provides each entity with the possibility of sending a message to all the co-operating entities of the conversation. The receiving service allows an entity to receive all the messages broadcast on the conversation and ensures that every entity receives the messages in the same order.

The complete design of the conversation transport service has been motivated and directed by distributed applications developed at GRENOBLE (MICROBE [8], POLYPHEME [1], SCOT [9], SER [10] ...). All these distributed applications need to establish communications between several users or processes to create distributed activities. All the messages exchanged between the co-operating processes are not relevant to all of them, but a significant part of these messages are sent from one source to several destinations. Furthermore, in distributed database applications, the relative order between messages can be used to implement concurrency control. In the absence of a multicast transport protocol, this relative order is obtained using timestamp ordering [6].

The third goal of our multicast protocol is to provide applications with an absolute ordering between distributed events.

ERROR DETECTION.

Negative aknowledgement versus positive acknowledgement.

In this paper we present the most difficult technical part of the multicast protocols : the error detection. The complete description of our protocol can be found in [4]. The main difficulty raised by error detection in multicast is to avoid sending an acknowledgement after each message sent. In point to point liaisons, error detection is often done through sending positive acknowledgements from the destination to the source. Error detection can also be done with negative acknowledgements associated with a sequential numbering of messages at the sending time. An error is then detected by a missing number in the sequence of the numbers of the received messages. In the multicast case the sending of positive acknowledgements implies that for a given message there are as many acknowledgements as destinations. So the efficiency gained by the use of the broadcast hardware is hardly noticeable in the case of multicast between a small number of co-operating entities.

An alternative is to send negative aknowledgements whenever a destination has not received a message. This technique avoids concentration at a source of acknowledgements from the destinations, but raises a further difficulty as to how a destination can quickly detect the lack of a message. We can no longer apply the sequential numbering technique as there are several senders distributed on the network. The senders, having neither shared memory, nor exclusive lock on hypothetical "current message count", cannot generate consecutive message numbers.

We propose an error detection mechanism based upon the use of a "quasisequential numbering" associated with the broadcast of a "queue status". We shall prove that this technique detects all "single errors", and we beleive that most multiple errors can be detected. The negative acknowledgement technique needs to be associated with a periodical sending of null messages to detect that the receivers are still alive.

ARCHITECTURAL HYPOTHESES.

We suppose that the transport stations are in either a front end processor or in a host computer. They receive all the multicast traffic of the conversations in which they are involved, including the messages they have sent. They can send (receive) messages to (from) a device, called "BI", which ensures the transmission of the messages on the medium. They broadcast one message per conversation at a time, waiting for the reception of the last message before sending a new one.

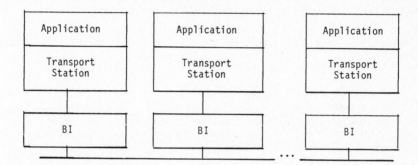

The transmission is performed on the medium in an exlcusive manner [2]. No two messages can pass simultaneously on the medium. This hypothesis, associated with the fact that a station receives its own packets, implies that all the stations receive the messages of a conversation in the same order.

We suppose that the mutual exclusion provided by the transmission medium is transparent to the transport station. They are asynchronous with the BI.

Multicast addressing.

On the DANUBE local network the addressing facility allows a message to be broadcast on the cable towards a general address completed by a name. Each site receives the message and checks wether the name belongs to a local name table. If so, the message is transmitted to the upper layer. We propose to use this mechanism to implement conversation addressing. In this paper we consider the traffic as being limited to one conversation. Error detection is at transport level, after filtering on names and on site addresses.

QUASI-SEQUENTIAL NUMBERING.

We call TS the transport station which provides the conversation service to the application and uses the DANUBE local network to communicate with other transport stations. The transport station is connected to the cable through a black box called BI in the DANUBE terminology. The BI is a box which hides the contention mechanism and introduces a de-synchronization between the TS and the cable. For example a message transmitted by station TS_1 to its BI at time t_1 can be retained in the BI whilst one or more messages transmitted at times later than t_1 are received by the BIs and delivered to the TS's.

Due to the exclusive access medium hypothesis the messages received in a
conversation are ordered by their passing order on the cable. This order is
visible to all the transport stations implied in the conversation, and is
called the "cable order". We propose to number the messages transmitted to
the BI's with a number as close as possible to their rank in the cable
order. To compute the number to be allocated to a message, each TS keeps,
for each conversation, a count R of the messages already received on it. The
number R+1 is assigned to the message being transmitted.

The initial value to be assigned to the counter R is not discussed here; we
shall suppose that all the TS's start <u>together</u> with a correct count value of
zero, and that they handle a single conversation.

The fact that each TS broadcasts messages independently of the others
implies :

-Possibility of duplicate numbers.

Let TS_j and TS_k be two TS's. At time t, the two counts R_j and
R_k are supposed as being equal to n, the two TS can transmit a message to their BI. If N_j and N_k are respectively the numbers assigned to the messages transmitted by TS_j and TS_k, we have :

$$N_j = N_k = n+1$$

-Possibility of holes.

In the previous case when q messages with the same number have been
transmitted on the cable, this numbering mechanism will not allocate the numbers n+1 to n+q-1.

-The sequence of numbers allocated does not necessarily always in-crease.

A message transmitted by a TS can be delayed in a BI and pass on
the cable behind messages which have been transmitted earlier by
other TS's. The order of transmission to the BI is not always equal
to the the cable order.

The figures 2, 3, 4 show these different irregularities. In those graphs we
represent the message number received by the station ST_k as a function of
the value R_k (rank of the received message).

Message numbers
as received by TS_k

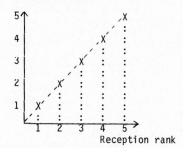

Fig 1 No irregularities

Message numbers
as received by TS_k

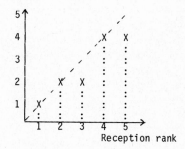

Fig 2 Duplicate numbers

Message numbers
as received by TS_k

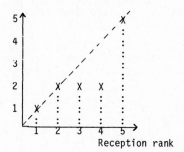

Fig 3 "holes"

Message numbers
as received by TS_k

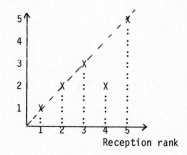

Fig 4 Decreasing part

When a TS transmits a message, it assigns a number to it such that, without the previously described irregularities, it should be represented by a point on the diagonal (see fig. 1).

An error can generate two kinds of irregularities on these graphs :

      a) A point is above the diagonal when TS_k has received fewer messages than the senders of the corresponding received message.

      b) If points <u>stay</u> below the diagonal the corresponding senders have received <u>fewer</u> messages than TS_k. Some messages may have been lost by the senders (fig 6).

Message numbers
as received by TS_k

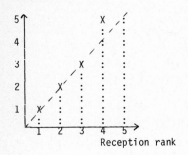

Reception rank

Fig 5 Point above the diagonal

Message numbers
as received by TS_k

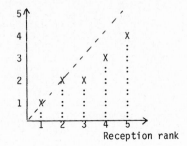

Reception rank

Fig 6 Points below

Error detection delay.

Theoretically a message can be delayed indefinitively by a BI. So a point can be very "far" below the diagonal. Likewise, all the TS connected to the cable can theoretically transmit a message with the same message number for a same conversation. This second case will imply a number of identical message numbers equal to the number of TS's.

To speed up the detection of errors of the type described in b) TS's ignore messages corresponding to a point which will be more than AD (Accepted Delay) units below the diagonal. This maximum accepted delay can be represented by a drop zone as in figure 7.

Message numbers
as received by TS_k

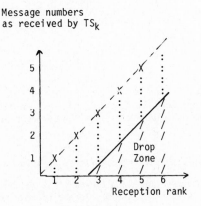

Reception rank

Fig 7 Drop zone.

Inefficiency of this numbering technique.

We present in this paragraph two examples showing the difficulties raised by the use of this numbering technique to detect errors.

Double errors.

Suppose that two and only two TS's connected to the cable have correctly received the messages numbered 1, 2, 3. TS_1 transmits the message numbered 4 ; this message is received by TS_1 but is lost by TS_2. Then TS_2 transmits the message numbered 4 which is received by TS_2 but not by TS_1. The result of this double error is that TS_1 and TS_2 are in an inconsistent state. But if we look to our graphs everything seems correct because in both cases the message 4 is on the diagonal, and the next message transmitted will be numbered 5 which will thus be on the diagonal (see Fig 8).

Heavy contention.

In the case of heavy contention due to an heavy load, distributed amongst several TS's, it may happen that the BI's always have a message to send, awaiting the cable. So the graph of message numbers can remain below the diagonal for a long time, without any message having being lost by the transport stations. This graph irregularity is very similar to the one generated by the error described in b).

It is impossible to base an error detection mechanism exclusively upon the numbering mechanism. We propose an additional control in order to cope with these two difficulties.

Message numbers
passing on the cable

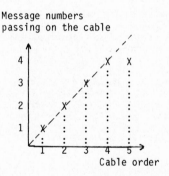

Fig 8 Numbers of the messages transmitted on the cable

Message numbers
as received by TS_1

Message numbers
as received by TS_2

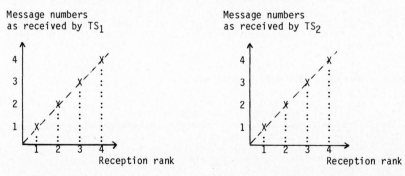

Fig 8.1 Sequence of message numbers
at TS_1

Fig 8.2 Sequence of message numbers
at TS_2

BROADCAST OF THE RECEPTION STATUS AT TRANSMISSION TIME.

We call "reception queue" the sequence of all multicast message headers
received in a TS. We suppose that the messages sent by a TS are received by
it and their headers stored in its reception queue. Thus the order in the
reception queue is the cable order previously described. In absence of error
all the reception queues are identical.

To enrich the numbering proposed in the previous section, we propose that
each TS inserts a short description of the last received messages into the
header of the message to be multicast. Each TS, looking to this message
header, will be able to compare the status of the sender's reception queue,
with the contents of its own reception queue.

Each TS will proceed as follows :

   1 - A message is uniquely identified by the couple MN/SS :
   message number/sending site number. The message numbers are assigned with the quasi sequential numbering described in the previous
   section. If we leave aside the problems due to modulo numbering
   these numbers are unique.

   2 - In each TS the reception queue gives the history of all received messages. This queue is composed of a small part of the message
   header : the couple MN/SS. The rank of a message is the position of
   the message in the queue.

   3 - When a TS transmits a message to its BI, it assigns to it a message number MN equal to the rank of the first free entry in the reception queue. This numbering is exactly the sequential numbering
   proposed in the previous section. This number is extended with the
   site number. The TS inserts in the message the queue status QS
   which is a copy of the last occupied entries in its queue.

   4 - When a site receives a message it checks its validity in regard
   to the accepted delay AD and drops the messages in the drop
   zone. Then it puts the message identifier MN/SS at the top of its
   reception queue and compares its queue to the queue status
   received. That is to say it compares the first rank MN-1 of its
   queue with the first couple MN/SS of the QS, and so on. A difference detects an error.

The message header is composed as follows :

                    CVID/type/MN/SS/QS/text/ with :
   type : message type (text, error recovery, connection, ...),
   CVID : conversation identifier,
   MN   : message number,
   SS   : sending site,
   QS   : reception queue status,
   text : remaining part of the message.

ERROR DETECTION AND LOCALISATION.

In this section we prove that the quasi-sequential numbering technique asso-ciated with the sending of the queue status allows detection of all the "single errors".

Definition of a "single error".

An error occurs when a message passing on the cable has been received by at least one of its recipients (the sender), but has not been received by all the recipients. This type of error can be due to a lack of buffers in the BI or in the TS, CRC errors, ... An error is called "single error" if all the messages transmitted after the error and before its detection are transmit-ted without error, and without any message having being dropped.

The rank of an error for the transport station TS_i is the position that the couple MN/SS of the lost message would have had in its reception queue if it had not been lost.

Detection of a single error of rank p.

Let (m,s) be the identifier MN/SS of the lost message. The set of transport stations (TS_i) connected to the cable can be divided into two parts.

P_1 : [TS_i / TS_i has received the message (m,s)]
P_2 : [TS_i / TS_i has not received (m,s)]

As a first step, in order to simplify the presentation, we shall assume that there is no contention, namely that no TS has numbered another message m. After reception of (m,s) the first free entry in the reception queues of P_1 are of rank p+1, while the first free entry of the queues of P_2 are of rank p. The next message transmitted will be received by all TS's (single error) and will have a message header with :

$\lfloor (k,TS_1);(h,TS_2)]$ where k=p+1, if this message was sent by P_1, or k=p if it was sent by P_2.

(k,TS_1) identifies this message and (h,TS_2) identifies the head of the queue (QS) of the site TS_1 at the time of the transmission of (k,TS_1).

If the receiving TS belongs to P_1 on the reception of $[(k,TS_1);(h,TS_2)]$ there are two possibilities :

TS_1 belongs to P_1 then k=p+1 and h=p. The reception status of TS is consistent with the queue of the sender TS_1. TS does not detect the error.

TS_1 belongs to P_2 then k=p and the message (h,TS_2) is of rank p-2 in the reception queue of TS. There is an inconsistency and TS de-tects the error.

In the same way if the receiving TS belongs to P_2 we have :

TS$_1$ belongs to P_1, then k=p+1 and k is greater than the rank of the first free entry of its reception queue (p). The point is above the diagonal. TS detects the error.

TS$_1$ belongs to P_2, then k=p and the queues of TS$_1$ and TS are consistent. TS does not detect the error.

In a second step we can introduce the contention. Several messages with a message number inferior or equal to p, can arrive at the sites TS$_i$. We note as previously :

$L(k,TS_1);(h,TS_2)]$ with k superior to p,

the identifier of the <u>first message received with k superior to p</u>. The transmission of this message to its BI was done after its sending TS had received the lost message or had received the message following the "hole". A station TS receiving this message will process it as follows :

If TS belongs to P_1 it examines the entry with rank k-1. There are two cases :

TS$_1$ belongs to P_1 and it finds (h,TS$_2$); no error detection.

TS$_1$ belongs to P_2, the transport station TS will not find (h,TS$_2$) with rank k-1 but with rank k-2. TS detects the error.

If TS belongs to P_2 :

TS$_1$ belongs to P_1 and the station TS does not find (h,TS$_2$) with rank k-1 but with rank k. TS detects the error.

TS$_1$ belongs to P_2 and it finds (h,TS$_2$) at the rank k-1. TS does not detect the error.

We see that in the case of "single errors", <u>an error is detected at the reception of the first packet transmitted by an ST to a BI after the error.</u> This detection is made by one of the parts P_1 or P_2.

Role of the maximum delay accepted AD.

As we have mentioned above, the messages arriving with an identifier (i,s) can be dropped if the rank k of the reception queue is greater than i+AD. This drop mechanism ensures that, if p stands for the rank of a lost message then identifiers stored at ranks greater than p+AD will have a message number greater than p in every reception queue.

So if we want to ensure the detection of every single error it is sufficient to <u>keep the last AD+1 elements in the reception queue.</u>

Localisation of an error.

An error is "localised" if the sender knows that its message has not been received by one of its recipients or if the identifier of the lost message is known by any of the transport stations which have not received it.

A sufficient condition to localise an error is to have simultaneously a description of the reception queue of a site belonging to P_1 and a description of a reception queue of a site belonging to P_2. By comparing of these descriptions, the identity of the missing message can be found. This condition allows errors to be readily localised by extending the message header to include a queue status describing the AD+1 message indentifiers of the last received messages.

Thus every reception of a message which reveals an error will also permit its localisation.

ERROR RECOVERY PRINCIPLE.

To recover from an error two cases have to be considered :

> 1) the error has been detected by the part which has not received the message. Every transport station in this part transmits a point to point negative aknowledgement to the message sender.

> 2) The error has been detected by the part which has received the lost message. The sender of this message belongs to this part, it repeats the message.

This kind of recovery mechanism raises several questions : how to avoid the synchronization of message sending after an error, under what condition a received message can be delivered to the application layer, how many errors must be recovered, ...

The synchronization of error recovery message sending can imply a high level of contention on the cable, forcing some of the BIs to a permanent error state. The simulation of our protocol has shown a low level of such synchronized message sending.

The delivery condition problem is still being studied. The difficulty is how to guarantee to the application that when a message is delivered to it, no lower ranking message will be delivered. Several delivery conditions have been proposed depending on the level of security requested by the application.

The complexity of the recovery algorithm increases very quickly with the number of errors taken into account. We have decided to limit the complexity of errors which will be recovered in order that a simpler recovery protocol can be designed. The uncorrectable errors will then lead to permanent errors, with disconnection of some of the co-operating entities.

STATE OF THE STUDY.

The protocol providing the multicast service on the DANUBE network is completely designed. Two simulation models, using QNAP [7] have exhibited the
main properties of the protocol. The main results will be published when
they are completed by experimental measurements. The prototype transport
station will be implemented in 1982 on mini and micro-computers connected to
the DANUBE network.

We intent to prove the efficiency of the error detection mechanism in the
case of multiple errors. We hope that we will be able to give the conditions
with which this kind of protocol is efficient.

CONCLUSION.

We have presented here the most interesting part of the study on reliable
multicast being undertaken at GRENOBLE. The error detection mechanism has
been proved for single errors and has been simulated in the case of multiple
errors. We think that this kind of error detection is applicable on a broadcast network providing a mutual exlusion mechanism through the transmission
medium. The use of such an error detection mechanism allows the design of
efficient multicast services which, in turn, should allow simpler design of
distributed application protocol especially in the case of more than two co-
operating processes.

BIBLIOGRAPHY

[1]   M. Adiba, J.M. Andrade, P. Decitre, F. Fernandez, Nguyen Gia Toan.
        "An experience in distributed database system design and
        implementation". International symposium on distributed databases.
        Paris. North-Holland. pp 67,84. March 1980.

[2]   J.S. Banino, C. Kaiser, H. Zimmerman. "Synchronization for distri-
        buted systems using a single broadcast channel". 1st Int. Conf. on
        Distributed Computing Systems. Huntsville Oct. 1979.

[3]   Y.K. Dalal. "Broadcast protocols in packet switched computer
        networks". PhD thesis. Stanford University, April 1977.

[4]   P. Decitre, J. Estublier, A. Khider, X. Rousset de Pina, I. Vatton.
        "Spécification du protocole de diffusion fiable sur le réseau
        DANUBE". Rapport de recherche IMAG CII-Honeywell Bull, published in
        1982.

[5]   R. Metcalfe, D. Boggs. "Ethernet : distributed packet switching for
        local computer networks." Comm. of the ACM, 19, 7, July 1976,
        pp. 395,404.

[6]   L. Lamport. "Time, clocks, and the ordering of events in a distri-
        buted system". CACM July 1978 Vol 21 #7.

[7]   D. Merle, D Potier, M. Veran. "A tool for computer performance
        analysis". Int. conf. on computer performance analysis. North Hol-
        land 1978.

[8]   Nguyen Gia Toan, G. Sergeant. "Distributed architecture and decen-
        tralized control for a local network database system". ACM interna-
        tional Computer symposium. London March 1981.

[9]   P. Decitre. "A concurrency control algorithm in a distributed
        environment". Proceedings NCC 81, pp 473,479. May 1981.

[10]   G. Sergeant, L. Treille. "SER : a system for distributed execution
        based on decentralized control techniques". ICCC 80, Atlanta, Oct.
        1980.

[11]   D.W. Wall. "Mechanisms for broadcast and selective broadcast".
        Tech. report n°190 Computer Laboratory. Stanford University, June
        1980.

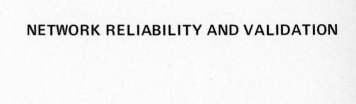

NETWORK RELIABILITY AND VALIDATION

LOCAL COMPUTER NETWORKS
P.C. Ravasio, G. Hopkins and N. Naffah (editors)
North-Holland Publishing Company
© IFIP, 1982

DEFINITION AND DEVELOPMENT OF A PROTOCOL FOR AN INDUSTRIAL PLANT CONTROL NETWORK

Walter Ansaldi   Marco Olobardi   Anna Maria Traverso

ANSALDO S.p.A.
Genova
Italy

A rich set of requirements and constraints was the premise for the application described in this paper. It was needed to provide means of connecting different kinds of equipment, in order to build an integrated system for instrumentation, measurement and automation for industrial process control environment. The local network we endeavoured to design, required prompt transmission error detection and recovery procedures, maximum delay constraints observance, and the capability of monitoring and dynamically reconfiguring the whole system. The solution proposed is a communication path consisting of a pair of coaxial cables; the access policy to these being governed, for each kind of equipment, by a microprocessor based interface, following the rules of an ad hoc developed protocol. The aim of the present paper is to focus on the aspects of description, formal definition and logical testing of the protocol afforded in the first stage of the project and also to illustrate the simulation techniques and tools which were employed step by step to extensively test the software implementing the protocol.

1 - INTRODUCTION

In recent years strong attention has been paid to the development of distributed process control systems. The availability of advanced low-cost microprocessors, with associated families of LSI peripheral chips, led to the implementation of small, powerful, local intelligent units, which relieve the main central computers from detailed regulation and control operations.

All units in a distributed process control system must be connected through a communication network in order to provide data exchange between them. A communication protocol is then charged to transform an error-prone connection medium into a relatively safe data path connecting the processes resident on the different nodes. This com-

---

This work was partially supported by the Italian   National Council of Research (CNR).

munication protocol is one of the most critical elements in the whole process control system because it must guarantee a very safe high speed data transmission in an industrial high noise environment |1|. In order to guarantee the fault tolerance characteristics required by the application , strong attention must be paid to the protocol design and verification phases. Special techniques, ranging from formal description and verification to simulation tests, can be used to achieve this goal.

This paper describes the development of the transport level of a communication protocol to be run on a local network for industrial process control application . In the following sections this level will simply be referred to as "protocol". The network is made of a serial multi-point communication line connecting controllers, regulators, supervisor units, process computers, etc. Each device is connected to the communication line by means of an intelligent interface handling the communication protocol.

After a comparative analysis of available design and verification techniques, a mixed approach was defined according to the following steps:

- careful analysis of the requirements and constraints imposed by the particular application;

- definition of the main functional features;

- protocol formal definition and preliminary logical consistency test;

- software simulator development; protocol correctness and fault tolerance verification through extensive simulation tests;

- coding.

Experience has shown that this approach allows a detailed and extensive verification of the protocol without requiring a great amount of resources. It can therefore be considered as a good trade-off between the requirements imposed by a practical industrial project and those of formal design techniques.

Section 2 is a short description of the local network architecture. Section 3 and 4 deal with service and transport description. Section 5 describes the protocol specification and development phases through formal description techniques. Section 6 describes protocol simulation tests.

2 - SYSTEM ARCHITECTURE

The system is a local network connecting mini, micro and multi-micro computers to monitor and control industrial plants.Typical areas of application are iron and steel industry, energy production, chemical and paper industry. The main features, imposed by the particular system application are:

- functional distribution. The place where the control functions are to be executed depends on the topological layout of the plant.
- Ease of connecting different nodes to the network. The implementation of the control system will require the use of different kinds of equipment connected to the network; e.g., supervisor nodes, operator interfaces, controllers, actuators and instrumentation.
- Redundancy. Plant safety requires the duplication of the system critical functions.

In fig. 2.1 the system architecture is shown.

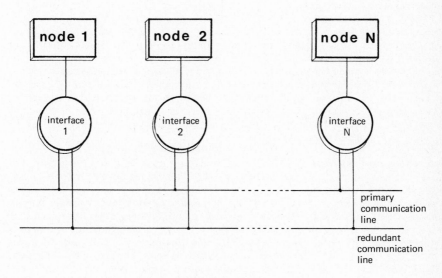

Figure 2.1

The network is built around a serial link which can achieve a transmission rate up to 1 M baud, using coaxial cable technology. In the future, optical fibre links would increase the transmission rate of about one order of magnitude. The physical transmission path is duplicated and, in case of a break, the flow of information is automatically switched to the redundant line. The line integrity control and possible switching are realized by hardware circuitry in a transparent way from the software viewpoint.

The same protocol is implemented on every interface. Therefore no
master node is defined at this level. This is done in order to
improve system modularity and reliability. Node hierarchy is
achieved, as is often needed in control applications, at some
higher level.

3 - SERVICE DESCRIPTION

This section describes what services the protocol provides for the
upper layers. Those services can be grouped into two basic functions: message delivery and monitoring of the network status.

The main function is the delivery of messages through the transmission line. Each message may have a maximum length of 512 bytes.
High priority messages whose maximum length is 128 bytes, can be
treated. They are sent on a different logical path providing a
lower transmission delay.

Error control is a function that must be offered at the IPC level
of a protocol |2|. Determining on which levels to implement error
control mechanism depends on some knowledge or assumption about
error types, frequency and cost effectiveness. In our case, efficiency and performance requirements suggested to us to implement
error detection and retransmission techniques at this low protocol
level. This dramatically reduces the probability of undetected
errors but leaves the responsability for providing perfect error
control to higher levels.

For the range of application the system is intended to cover, the
facility of easily connecting or disconnecting nodes to the network without altering the process control activity, is extremely
important. Moreover, it is often necessary that every node should
be able to know, as soon as possible, any change in the network
status. To achieve this requirement, the protocol keeps on every
interface an updated description of the network status and forwards
it to the node as soon as a network status change is detected.
This information is collected during a special "configuration"
phase (see section 4) while message delivery activity is temporar-
ily suspended. This guarantees that consistent status information
is kept on every node during normal protocol activity. The user is
allowed to force an updating of system tables in order to connect
new nodes to the network.

4 - TRANSPORT DESCRIPTION

The communication protocol has been designed according to the con-
trol passing scheme |3|. This means that only one interface at a
time can gain control of the line when owing a special token called

"sending-right"which is passed cyclically among the interfaces connected to the line. An interface which holds the sending-right is said to be in the "transmission mode". When receiving a sending-right the interface can transmit up to 4 messages; then the sending right is relinquished and sent to the next interface according to an ordering table stored in the interface local memory. If no message is available whenentering the transmission mode, the interface immediately transmits the sending-right.

Urgent information can be coded into a short high priority message and routed to the destination node through a "privileged path". The path is created by means of dedicated memory buffers and uninterruptable formatting procedures and by high priority transmission policies. The token passing mechanism,together with the privileged path, guarantees the delivery of urgent messages within a known finite time, as required by the application.

According to the need for security imposed by a system working in an industrial environment, the protocol is able to detect faults or failures occurring in the transmission line or in the nodes connected to it andto start suitable recovery procedures. Every message must be acknowledged by the receiving interface. Four types of aknowledgment messages can be sent back to the transmitting node according to the message CRC correctness or to the state of the destination node (see table 4.1).

TABLE 4.1

Type of acknowledgement	Meaning
Positive acknowledgement	Correct message
Negative acknowledgement	Wrong message
Busy acknowledgement	Message refusal due to internal interface buffer saturation
Death acknowledgement	Message refusal due to failure in the equipment con - nected to the interface

Depending on the acknowledgement type, different actions are taken by the transmitting interface. Upon reception of a negative acknowledgment the interface retransmits the message. Owing to the high message retransmission rate caused by the expected transmission error-prone industrial environment, messages are divided into packets of fixed length and sequentially transmitted. This is done in order to minimize the total retransmission overhead. In addition to the error-and-retransmission mechanism, the protocol performs a monitoring activity over the network status, in order to guarantee the status information referred to in the previous section. The monitoring activity of the protocol resident on every node consists of the following functions:

- monitoring of the node liveness. Through ad-hoc control messages the protocol can detect the node failure.
- monitoring of the network status. Anomalous events that can be caused by the failure of one or more nodes connected to the network are detected by the protocol. Such events are, for example, the repeated lack of acknowledgement of the same message or the loss of the token message.

Upon detection of some incorrect functioning of the system, a configuration procedure is started, thus enabling the updating of the system status information.Hardware mechanisms assure that only one node, at a given time, can start the configuration procedure. This node polls all the interfaces and builds a system status table which is then sent to the active nodes. In this way broken nodes are excluded from the token passing loop and thus virtually disconnected from the network. In the meantime, newly connected nodes are automatically made known to the active interfaces and inserted in the token passing loop.

5 - PROTOCOL FORMAL DESCRIPTION AND DEVELOPMENT

When dealing with communication protocols, the designer has to face a number of problems which are not found in common software design work. Synchronization and fault tolerance are in fact typical issues of complex protocols. Synchronization problems arise when communication modules that reside on different nodes must interact through a common transmission medium. Fault tolerance is obviously an important feature of good software products, but it becomes essential in communication protocols, when correct functioning must be guaranteed even in the presence of line errors and node failures.

During recent years a great amount of work has been done in the definition of tools and methodologies for formal description and validation of communication protocols. Common techniques are: finite state automata |4,5|, Petri nets |6|, grammars |7|, colloquies |8|, programming languages |9|, hybrid models |10,11|. A detailed survey of formal description and validation methods can be found in |12,13|. A complete bibliography is in |14|.

Many of these techniques were demonstrated to be very useful; however much of the work done refers to simple protocols (or simple aspects of a more complete protocol). The effort required for the complete formal specification and validation of a non trivial communication protocol is in fact quite heavy both in terms of time and work. For example, formal verification techniques based on transition graphs are very difficult to exploit when dealing with more than two protocol machines. This is due to the combinatorial "state explosion" of the graph which grows with the complexity of the proto col state model.On the other hand, the program proving approach has different major difficulties (15, like the formulation of asser- tions specifying protocol properties, the concurrency of multiple protocol modules and the modelling of unreliable message exchange between modules. Automated tools for state generation and assertion proving could simplify the task but they are not easily available.

For these reasons and due to the great amount of resources required by such an approach, we decided to choose a less formal solution for the specification and verification of our protocol. Neverthe less we tried to adapt existing methodologies in order to achieve a good and reliable protocol design. First, during the design phase, we carried out partial verification tests using some of the tech- niques described in the literature. Then the whole protocol code was tested by means of a simulator. This second step will be de- scribed later in section 6.

Examining the description and verification techniques surveyed in the literature, it is easy to realize that none of them can cover the range of all possible kinds of application, but each of them is expecially suited for a particular class of needs. Different aims such as definition, verification, implementation, completeness and congruency tests, suggest different choices among the available techniques. A top-down approach to the design of the protocol led to the identification of two abstraction levels that were described using two different specification techniques: transition graphs and process-based description.

Transition graph-based description

The protocol activity can be logically subdivided into three func- tional modules as shown in fig. 5.¹. The modules are connected through an "update of shared variables" relation |12|.

Fig. 5.1

The first module is a very simple half-duplex protocol itself and the second one is a collection of sequential activities to be scheduled and executed one at a time. The third one is the most critical set of functions and is discussed here. This module has been specified by a transition graph and successively verified with respect to general properties such as: freedom from deadlock, liveness, tempo blocking freedom, recovery from failures, self synchronization.

Six main states and a number of substates were identified:
- IDLE (I)   - the interface is not connected to the network;
- TRANSMITTING (T)   the interface owns the sending-right and may
                         address any other active node;
- RECEIVING (R)   - the interface is connected to the network and
                         can be addressed by any other active node;
- POLLING (P)   - the interface is polling the nodes in order
                         to build the system status table;
- SENDING TABLES (S)   - the interface is sending the updated system
                         status table to all the nodes recognized as
                         active;
- FAILURE (F)   - the interface is active but the equipment con
                         nected to it is out of order.

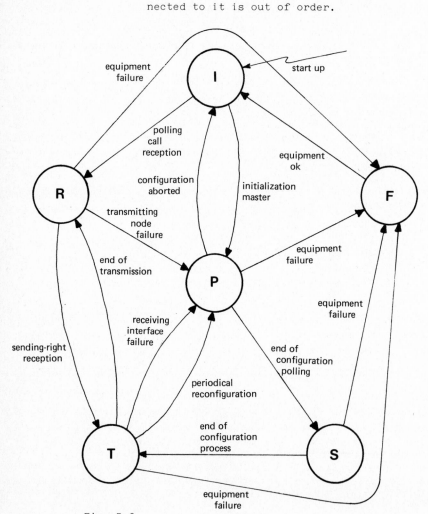

Fig. 5.2

Fig. 5.2 represents a simplified version of the transition graph where only the main states are shown. Each circle indicates a protocol state. Each arc shows the transition between two states and the corresponding label summarizes the event which fires the transition. Table 5.3 gives a brief overview of every event.

TABLE 5.3

START UP (--> I)
>   Power is given to the node.

INITIALIZATION MASTER (I --> P)
>   The interface starts the configuration process. It is from now the "configuration master".

POLLING CALL RECEPTION (I -->R)
>   The logically disconnected interface is polled and connected to the network.

SENDING RIGHT RECEPTION (R -->T)
>   The sending right is passed to the interface.

END OF TRANSMISSION (T -->R)
>   The interface has passed the sending right to the next active interface.

TRANSMITTING NODE FAILURE (R -->P)
>   The sending right has not been passed within a certain period of time. A timeout is designed to recover from system deadlock making the interface configuration master. Different timeout duration prevents two interfaces from concurrently starting the configuration.

END OF CONFIGURATION POLLING (P --> S)
>   All nodes have been polled. The system status table has been built.

END OF CONFIGURATION PROCESS (S -->T)
>   The system status table has been sent to all the active nodes.

CONFIGURATION ABORTED (P -->I)
>   The polling interface has received a negative answer from every node. The interface recognizes itself as out of work and disconnects itself.

RECEIVING INTERFACE FAILURE (T -->P)
>   The interface in the transmission mode has received two consecutive negative acknowledgements from the destination node. The interface starts a configuration process.

PERIODICAL RECONFIGURATION (T -->P)
>   The interface in the transmission mode starts a periodical reconfiguration procedure.

EQUIPMENT FAILURE (S or R or T or P --> F)
>   The failure of the equipment connected to the interface is revealed by the diagnostic procedures.

TABLE 5.3 (continued)

EQUIPMENT OK (F --> I)
        The equipment connected to the interface is OK again.

Starting from the local transition graph, a global transition graph
has been built. It was possible to verify the previously listed
general properties through manual analysis.   Deadlock   situations
were identified and timeouts introduced to avoid them. Fig. 5.4
shows a subset   of the global transition graph for a three node
network.

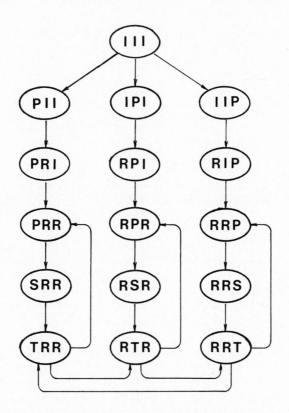

Fig. 5.4

Every global state is labelled with a triple (S1, S2, S3) represent
ing the states of three nodes. The subset refers to the situation
of normal functioning (e.g. without any failure of the nodes or
line errors).

An example of protocol behaviour in case of failure is shown in
the subset of fig. 5.5

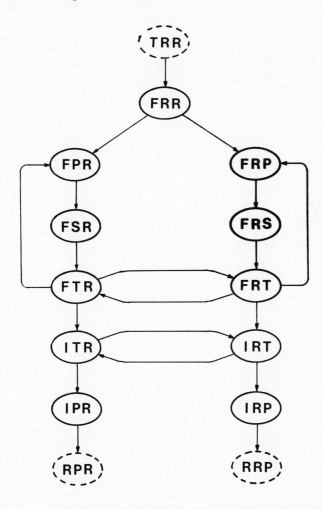

Fig. 5.5

The dotted lines represent normal functioning states. The transition
TRR ---> FRR represents the failure of an interface holding the send
ing right. The FRR state has been recognized as a deadlock state.
The recovery from deadlock is obtained through a timeout which
fires if no message is transmitted over the line for a certain
time. A reconfiguration procedure is then started. The timeout
duration is different for every interface to avoid the wrong transi
tion FRR --> FPP. After the configuration procedure the protocol
resumes correct functioning with only two active nodes. When the

broken node resumes (transition FTR -> ITR, or FTR -> IRT), periodical or supervisor- driven configuration procedures ensure that
the protocol will return to the normal functioning states of
Fig. 5.4 within a finite time. Other cases of system malfunctions
recovery were treated in the same way as in this example.

Process-based description

At the lower description level the concept of "process" was introduced to refine the protocol description. There was an intrinsic
parallelism of three classes of functions; those related to the
transmission of data along the line, to the internal activity and
to the managing of the communication with the equipment to which
the interface is connected,as shown in Fig. 5.1. Using a process-
based protocol description it is possible to explicitly represent
the concurrences of these activities inside the protocol itself.
Furthermore such a formalization allows the definition of different
priorities among different classes of functions. A priority mechanism
reflects the protocol behaviour with respect to system-dependent char
acteristics such as the different speeds on interface-line and in-
terface-equipment data exchange.

During the implementation phase of the protocol software, a process-
based description straightforwardly leads to:

- stepwise refinement;
- functional modularity: every logical function is performed by
  a well defined set of processes;
- information hiding.

These features result in a high degree of cohesion inside each
module and a low degree of connection among different modules
throughout clear and simple data interfaces.

Two different priority classes of processes were defined: back -
ground processes and interrupt-driven processes.

Background processes perform activities related to the treatment
of messages inside the interface and their exchange with the
equipment connected to it. They also provide diagnostic and error
recovery capabilities. Background processes lie on a lower priority
level with respect to the interrupt-driven processes and their execution can be suspended by any high priority process.

Interrupt-driven processes are activated in response to interrupts
generated by data transfer over the transmission line or by special
purpose time outs. An interrupt driven process cannot be interrupted by other processes. There are four types of interrupts:

LINE INPUT
          generated when the interface receives a message addressed
          to it.

END OF TRANSMISSION
> generated when the interface has ended the transmission of a message.

LINE TIME OUT
> generated when no message is transmitted over the line for a certain time. When the interface is in the re ceving state it means that the sending right message has been lost. In any other state , it means that no acknowledgement has been received for the last message sent.

EQUIPMENT TIME OUT
> generated when the equipment connected to the interface fails to transmit a diagnostic message.

An activation table associates each hardware interrupt with one from a set of interrupt driven processes, depending on the current protocol state. The activation table is shown in Fig. 5.6. Table 5.7 contains a list of the activated processes together with a short description.

TABLE 5.6

Interrupt type	Interface Status					
	I	T	R	P	S	F
Line input	PCØ	PC3	PC4	PC1	PC2	PC5
End of transmission	P22	P2Ø	P21	P2Ø	P2Ø	P21
Line time out	P17	P14	P15	P18	P19	
Equipment time out	Pv	Pv	Pv	Pv	Pv	

TABLE 5.7

PCØ	If it recognizes a polling message it sends back a positive acknowledgement and switches to the receiving state.
PC1	Updates the system status table according to the type of acknowledgement received and then goes on with the configuration procedure.
PC2	It manages to transmit the system status table.
PC3	If it recognizes an acknowledgement message it starts an ad hoc procedure according to the type of acknowledgement received.
PC4	Depending on the message received it switches to the transmission state (if a sending right is acquired) or

TABLE 5.7 (continued)

	sends an acknowledgement message.
PC5	Answers to a polling message with a death acknowledgement message.
P5	Stores in the interface buffers a low priority input packet.
P5A	Stores in the interface buffer an high priority message and prepares it to be passed to the equipment.
P6	Sends an acknowledgement message.
P7	Analyzes the internal buffers looking for a packet to transmit.
P7A	Sends the packet choosen by P7.
P8	(background) Prepares a message to be passed to the equipment.
P1∅	Sends the sending right message.
P11	Accepts a polling message.
P12	Accepts a sending right message. Starts to transmit on the line except when a periodical reconfiguration procedure is needed.
P14	Is activated when a line time out fires in the transmission state meaning that an acknowledgement packet is missing. It simulates the reception of a dummy negative acknowledgement.
P15	Is activated when a line time out fires in the receiving state meaning that the sending right is missing. It starts a reconfiguration procedure.
P17	Is activated when a line timeout fires in the idle state, meaning that the interface may start the configuration procedure. It starts the polling sequence.
P18	Is activated when a line time out fires in the polling state meaning that an acknowledgement to a poll message is missing. It simulates the reception of a dummy negative acknowledgement.
P19	Is activated when a line time out fires in the sending table state meaning that an acknowledgement to a system status table is missing. It simulates the reception of a dummy negative acknowledgement.
P2∅ P21 P22	Initialize hardware line interface for next input packet and time out circuitry according to the next expected input packet.
PT∅	Acquires the new system status table.
PTA	Prepares the new system status table to be passed to the equipment.

TABLE 5.7 (continued)

PR1	Sends a polling message.
PTM	Updates the messages stored in the interface buffers according to the new system status table.
PV	Switches to the Failure State.

The activation table has been expanded into a set of process activa tion flows, one for each pair (interrupt type, protocol status). They represent the processes activated by the hardware interrupts and the subsequent flow of processing activities.

An example of such expansion can be found in fig.5.8. It shows process activation flows when the protocol is in the receiving state.

The following graphical symbolism is used:

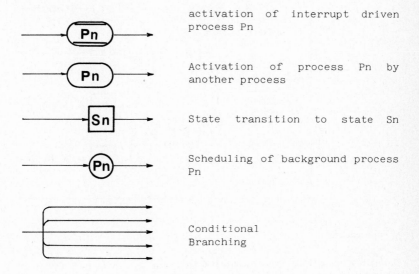

activation of interrupt driven process Pn

Activation of process Pn by another process

State transition to state Sn

Scheduling of background process Pn

Conditional Branching

In table 5.7 the mnemonics used for the interrupt handling processes are listed together with a brief description of their functions.

The possible changes of state, depending on the content of the re- ceived packet and the activities scheduled for later execution are syntetically summarized.

For instance, in the branch labelled "sending-right" three different choices are outlined. The first one considered in switching to the polling state to begin a periodical reconfiguration procedure. The second and third are selected depending on the availability of

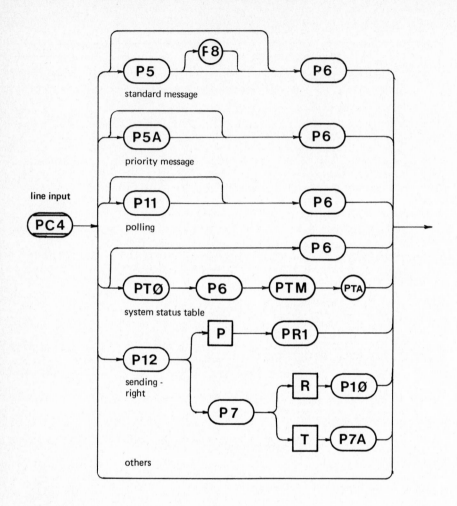

line time out

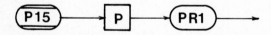

equipment time out

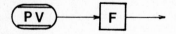

end transmission

FIG. 5.8

ready to send messages. If a message is found there is a transition to transmission state T and the execution of sending process P7A. Otherwise, the interface remains in the receiving state and process P10 is activated to provide the sending right transmission to another interface.

The processes realizing the protocol were coded using a Pascal-like pseudocode that was then extensively checked by walkthrough analysis.

6 - SIMULATION TESTS

Simulation tests took place as the final step of the protocol design. Using the hybrid approach described in the preceding sections it is not possible to exhaustively verify and validate the protocol. On the other hand, due to the lack of available hardware, it was not possible to run the protocol directly on the target system. Moreover such an in-field testing approach could not completely exercise the protocol routines.

For these reasons the simulation approach seemed to be a necessary solution for the testing problem|16,17|. Through simulation tests it has been possible to verify the correct functioning of the protocol in environments hardly reproduceable on the real system, without dealing with the problems associated with formal verification techniques.

A two-step simulation test was carried out during this phase. First, the protocol correctness was verified under normal conditions. Then the fault tolerance of the protocol was tested with respect to transmission errors on the line and to failures in the network nodes. Special attention was paid to particular critical situations such as: misunderstanding of critical message fields due to errors over the transmission line, failure of the interface holding the sending-right etc. In any case the protocol should guarantee error recovery or, at least, structural recoverability |6| i.e., return to normal operation state within a finite time.

The tests began with the activation and verification of single error situations, one at a time. Then the protocol tolerance with respect to the interacting effects of different kinds of errors was tested using a set of ad hoc error and failure mixes.

The simulation program allows the user to freely specify a set of parameters related to: the number of nodes connected to the network, the physical parameter of the interconnection link, the mean lenght of messages exchanged between the nodes, the mean times between message generation, node failures, errors over the transmission line, etc. By selecting different sets of input data the user can force the execution of a wide range of tests thus verifying any kind of critical situation.

Monitoring of protocol activity on every node is obtained through the output of execution traces showing significant events occurring during the simulation activity. The user can select different kinds of output traces with different levels of detail. He can therefore begin with an overview of the simulation process and then, simply by switching to the next output trace, concentrate on particular aspects of the protocol.

Fig. 6.1 gives a sample of a typical execution trace. On the left part of the picture the simulated events are listed. The time, symbolic name and sequential number are given for each of them, together with additional coded information. On the right side, a synthetic output shows the message history from origin to destination node. In the example of Fig. 6.1 the meaning of the synthetic output is as follows:

event 469   - high priority message (124 bytes) arrived at interface 2 from interface 5

event 471   - positive ack message (3 bytes) arrived at interface 5 from interface 2

event 473   - sending right message (3 bytes) arrived at interface 2 from interface 5

event 476   - high priority message (34 bytes) for node 5 is passed from node 4 to its interface

event 481   - message (128 bytes) arrived at interface 3 from interface 2

event 484   - positive ack message (3 bytes) arrived at interface 2 from interface 3.

7 - CONCLUSIONS

Several techniques can be developed for correct and reliable design of communication protocols. Formal techniques such as transition graphs, Petri nets, high level languages, formal grammars, etc., if correctly applied, can guarantee exhaustive validation and verification of the protocol software. On the other hand, such methods require a great amount of time and resources and are hardly appliable to practical industrial products.

A mixed approach consists of a careful, though not exhaustive, formal description and design phase, followed by extensive simulation tests. A hybrid description technique, consisting of a transition graph formalization and a high level language process based refinement, can be used for the initial verification of a protocol.

```
EVENTO ATTUALE:          0.4027 FINP1  16 35   17  3  5  20   3  1   XXX 466 XXX
ACPS =   0   3      4    20  3
EVENTO ATTUALE:          0.4027 INIPS  15 35   12  3  5  10 124  1   XXX 467 XXX
ACPS =   0   3      4    20  3
EVENTO ATTUALE:          0.4096 FINDMA          9  5  4  20   3  1   XXX 468 XXX   ARRIVA ALLARME  (124) A 2 DA 5
EVENTO ATTUALE:          0.4096 IDALIN 12 124  19  2  5  10 124  1   XXX 469 XXX   ARRIVA ACK POS. (  3) A 5 DA 2
ACPS =   1   3      5    15  2
EVENTO ATTUALE:          0.4110 FINDMA          9  2  5  10 124  1   XXX 470 XXX
ACPS =   1   3           20 15
EVENTO ATTUALE:          0.4110 IDALIN  0   0  19  5  2  15   3  1   XXX 471 XXX   ARRIVA SLITTA   (  3) A 2 DA 5
ACPS =   1   3      2
EVENTO ATTUALE:          0.4124 FINDMA          9  5  2  15   3  1   XXX 472 XXX
EVENTO ATTUALE:          0.4124 IDALIN  1   2  19  2  5  20   3  1   XXX 473 XXX
ACPS =   1 128      3     1   2
EVENTO ATTUALE:          0.4129 FINP1  16   0  17  1  5  20   3  1   XXX 474 XXX
ACPS =   0   3      0    16  1
EVENTO ATTUALE:          0.4129 INIPS  15   0  12  1  2   1 128  1   XXX 475 XXX
ACPS =   0   3      0    16  1
EVENTO ATTUALE:          0.4239 MEDAPP 34      2   4  0   0   0  0   XXX 476 XXX   NASCE ALLARME   ( 34) IN 4 PER 5
DAAP =   1          1          5
EVENTO ATTUALE:          0.4310 FINP1          17  5  2  20   3  1   XXX 477 XXX
ACPS =   0   3      2    20  5
EVENTO ATTUALE:          0.4330 FINP1  16   0  17  5  2  20   3  1   XXX 478 XXX
ACPS =   0   3      2    20  5
EVENTO ATTUALE:          0.4330 INIPS  15   0  12  5  2   1 128  1   XXX 479 XXX
ACPS =   0   3      2
EVENTO ATTUALE:          0.4388 FINDMA          9  2  5  20   3  1   XXX 480 XXX   ARRIVA PACKET   (128) A 3 DA 2
ACPS =   1   3      2    11  3
EVENTO ATTUALE:          0.4388 IDALIN 11 35   19  3  2   1 128  1   XXX 481 XXX
EVENTO ATTUALE:          0.4390 FINP1          17  2  5  10 124  1   XXX 482 XXX
EVENTO ATTUALE:          0.4402 FINDMA          9  3  2   1 128  1   XXX 483 XXX
EVENTO ATTUALE:          0.4402 IDALIN  0 124  19  2  3  11   3  1   XXX 484 XXX   ARRIVA ACK POS. (  3) A 2 DA 3
ACPS =   1 128      3
EVENTO ATTUALE:          0.4410 FINP1          17  2  5  10 124  1   XXX 485 XXX
ACPS =   0 128      3     2   2
EVENTO ATTUALE:          0.4415 FINP1  16 124  17  2  5  10 124  1   XXX 486 XXX
ACPS =   0 128      3     2   2
EVENTO ATTUALE:          0.4415 INIPS  15 124  12  2  2   2 128  1   XXX 487 XXX
DAAP =   1          1          2
EVENTO ATTUALE:          0.4466 MEDAPP 34       2  4  2   1 128  1   XXX 488 XXX
ACPS =   0   3      5    20  4
EVENTO ATTUALE:          0.4469 FINP1  16 57   17  4  5  10 124  1   XXX 489 XXX
```

Fig. 6.1

Simulation tests can then be used to completely verify the protocol correct functioning.

This approach has been applied to a transmission layer protocol for real-time process control applications, resulting in very useful help both in the design and verification phases.

8 - REFERENCES

|1| Technical committee N. 65 - IEC, Draft - Process Data Highway (PROWAY) for distributed process control systems. Part 1 - General introduction and functional requirements (1980).

|2| Watson, R.W., Distributed System Architecture Model, in : Lampson, B.W. et al. (eds.), Distributed System Architecture and Implementation (Springer Verlag, Berlin, 1981).

|3| Penney, B.K. and Baghdadi, A.A., Survey of Computer Communications Loop Networks: Part 1 - Part 2, Computer Communications, Vol. 2 N. 4,5 (1979), 165 - 176, 224 - 241.

|4| Bochmann, G.V., Finite State Description of Communication Protocols, Computer Networks, Vol. 2, Oct. 1978, 361 - 372.

|5| Zafiropulo, P. et al., Towards Analyzing and Synthesizing Protocols, IEEE Transactions on Communications, vol. COM 28, N. 4, April 1980, 651 - 660.

|6| Merlin , P.M. and Farber, D.J., Recoverability of Communication Protocols - Implications of a Theoretical Study, IEEE Transactions on Communications, Vol. COM 24, N. 9, Sept. 1976, 1036 - 1043.

|7| Harangozo, J., Protocol Definition with Formal Grammars, Proc. Computer Network Protocol Symp., Univ. Liege, Belgium, Feb. 1978, F6, 1 - F6, 10.

|8| LeMoli, G., A Theory of Colloquies, Alta Frequenza, Vol. 42 (1973), 493 - 223E - 500 - 230 E.

|9| Stenning, N.V., A Data Transfer Protocol, Computer Networks, Vol. 1, Sept. 1976, 99 - 110.

|10| Danthine, A., Bremer, J., Modelling and Verification of end-to - end Transport Protocols, Computer Networks, Vol. 2, Oct. 1978, 381 - 395.

|11| Bochmann, G.V., General Transition Model for Protocols and Communication Services, IEEE Transactions on Communications, Vol. COM 28, N. 4, April 1980, 643 - 650.

|12| Bochmann, G.V. Sunshine, C.A., Formal Methods in Communication Protocol Design, IEEE Transactions on Communications, Vol. COM 28, N. 4, April 1980, 624 - 631.

|13| Sunshine, C.A., Survey of Protocol Definition and Verification Techniques, Computer Networks, Vol. 2, Oct. 1978, 346 - 350.

|14| Day, J. and Sunshine, C.A., A Bibliography on the Formal Specification and verification of Computer Network Protocols, ACM SIGCOMM Computer Communication Rev., Vol. 9, Oct. 1979.

|15| Sunshine, C.A., Formal Techniques for Protocol Specification and Verification, Computer Magazine, Vol. 12, Sept. 1979, 20 - 27.

|16| LeLann, G. and LeGoff, H., Verification and Evaluation of Communication Protocols, Computer Networks, Vol. 2 (1978), 50 -69.

|17| Dyer, M., Software Development Practices, IBM System Journal, Vol. 19, N. 4, (1980).

LOCAL COMPUTER NETWORKS
P.C. Ravasio, G. Hopkins and N. Naffah (editors)
North-Holland Publishing Company
© IFIP, 1982

VALIDATION OF A TOKEN-RING PROTOCOL

Harry Rudin

IBM Zurich Research Laboratory
8803 Rüschlikon
Switzerland

The "token-ring" transmission subsystem of the local-area
communication network being architected and implemented at
the IBM Zurich Research Laboratory has been successfully
validated. The model of the token-ring protocol used for the
validation,the system used to validate this model, the
various error conditions used to stress the protocol, and
the results of the validation are described in this report.

INTRODUCTION

"Protocol validation" is an automated means of testing the protocols or rules which
specify how coordination and communication among a number of processes takes place.
These protocols are specified by the system architecture. Over some well-defined
region, protocol validation can be used to completely test the system architecture
in the sense that all possible permutations of event sequences within this region
will be examined. Validation is thus much more thorough than the use of a script of
test sequences applied to a particular implementation or the use of simulation techniques. In the first case, the script is usually incomplete and the results are in
any case limited to the particular implementation of the architecture. In the second
case, test coverage is random and therefore likely to be incomplete.

Several research efforts have been made in the area of protocol validation; a
summary of these is given in [1]. All of the techniques require a formal definition
of the protocols in some specification language. The specification technique used
in our approach is closely related to finite-state machines [2,3].

At the IBM Zurich Research Laboratory, we have applied automated validation with
success to a number of protocols: the CCITT X.21 protocol [4], the CCITT X.25
protocol [5], portions of IBM's System Network Architecture [6], and an early
version of the ARPANET IMP-IMP protocol [7]. The technique used in this work is an
exhaustive search of the global-state space [8]; in nearly all cases, errors were
found in the protocols by searching for various syntactic properties. The objective
of the present study is to apply validation to the token-ring protocol currently
being developed.

For the token-ring protocol under examination here [9] some new features have been
added to the earlier validation system [8]. One major change is modification to
facilitate the handling of synchronous protocols. The second major change is that
in addition to checking syntax as in the above examples, a series of programs has
been written to demonstrate that the protocol has various desirable functional
properties. This amounts to demonstrating various assertions about the protocols

[10]. Nearly all of these fall into the class of demonstrating recovery from
various transmission errors. The modified validation system is described more
fully in a forthcoming report [11].

THE MODEL FOR VALIDATION

The Ring

Figure 1 shows the topology of the token-ring considered here. There are two
terminals on the ring, A and B. The function of the token ring is to carry information from terminal to terminal. The flow on the ring is monitored by a single
active monitor. (For reasons to be explained below, the monitor is modeled as two
subprocesses, the monitor proper, M, and the phantom monitor, PM.) Finally, there
is an unruly demon which simulates transmission errors. We are particularly concerned with the effects of the errors introduced by the demon. The demon can be
moved to various positions around the ring.

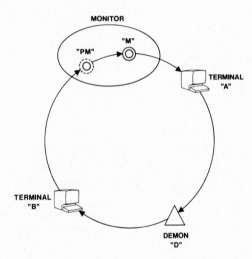

Figure 1
A Token Ring

The exact architecture of the token ring being implemented is described in [9].
The monitor, shown as a separate entity in Figure 1, is in reality a process which
could run in any of several terminals attached to the ring. Only one monitor is
active; the contention mechanism for determining the active monitor is not investigated here. The monitor's main function is ensuring that there is one and only
one token on the ring.

At the top of Figure 2, a typical frame on the ring is shown. The frame is
composed of a number of "messages"; most messages are used to control the ring;
the "data" message contains the user's information to be transported. The beginning
of the frame is indicated by a start-delimiter message or byte; this is followed
by a byte containing a token (either free or busy) and a monitor bit set either to
"0" or "1". (There is more information contained in this byte but it is not of

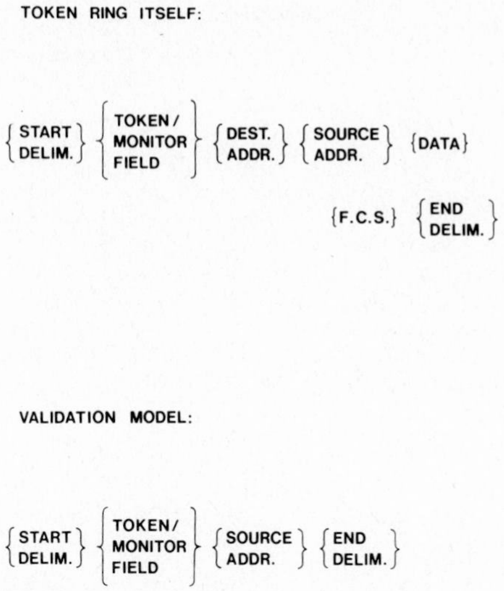

TOKEN RING ITSELF:

$$\left\{ \begin{matrix} \text{START} \\ \text{DELIM.} \end{matrix} \right\} \left\{ \begin{matrix} \text{TOKEN/} \\ \text{MONITOR} \\ \text{FIELD} \end{matrix} \right\} \left\{ \begin{matrix} \text{DEST.} \\ \text{ADDR.} \end{matrix} \right\} \left\{ \begin{matrix} \text{SOURCE} \\ \text{ADDR.} \end{matrix} \right\} \left\{ \text{DATA} \right\}$$

$$\left\{ \text{F.C.S.} \right\} \left\{ \begin{matrix} \text{END} \\ \text{DELIM.} \end{matrix} \right\}$$

VALIDATION MODEL:

$$\left\{ \begin{matrix} \text{START} \\ \text{DELIM.} \end{matrix} \right\} \left\{ \begin{matrix} \text{TOKEN/} \\ \text{MONITOR} \\ \text{FIELD} \end{matrix} \right\} \left\{ \begin{matrix} \text{SOURCE} \\ \text{ADDR.} \end{matrix} \right\} \left\{ \begin{matrix} \text{END} \\ \text{DELIM.} \end{matrix} \right\}$$

Figure 2
Actual and Abstracted Frame Sequences

interest to us here.) If the frame is a "free frame", these two bytes are sufficient; the initializing frame sent out by the active monitor is of this sort with
the monitor bit set to "0".

A terminal with information to transmit changes the token from free to busy and
adds the destination address, its own address as source, the data, a frame-check
sequence, and finally an end delimiter (see Figure 2). Each terminal on the ring
checks the destination address, and if equal to its own, makes a copy of the
appropriate portion of the frame. The unaltered frame continues. Upon passing
through the monitor, the monitor bit is set to "1". Finally, the frame is removed
by its source as the source effectively opened the ring when it began transmission.
Upon completed reception, the source terminal generates a new free frame and
reseals the ring.

In the validation, we are not concerned with the transported information, but with
the flow of control. For this reason, and so that there will be fewer system states
to explore, the frame at the top of Figure 2 has been abstracted to that shown at
the bottom. Thus, the model to be validated is a simplified version of the architected system. The claim made here, however, is that the flow of control-influencing
messages is the same in the simplified model and the architecture.

The various functions of the devices attached to the ring will be explained below
as part of the validation-model discussion.

Comments on the Modeling Technique

Figure 3 indicates some of the notions underlying the validator used specifically
for synchronous ring protocols [11]. The ring consists of a series of equal-length
buffers, say a single byte long, closed on itself. At each synchronous clock

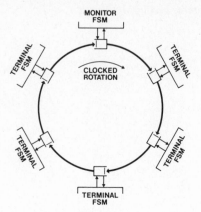

Figure 3
The Validator's Transmission Schema

interval, these bytes are advanced around the ring, the finite-state machines (FSM's)
associated with each buffer observe the buffer contents and then overwrite it or
not, as appropriate.

The processes representing the terminals, monitor and demon are described as finite-
state machines according to the scheme shown in Figure 4. The current state of each
process must have a departing arc labeled with the name of the event (+IN) in its
buffer. (The "+" symbol indicates event reception.) If there is no such departing
arc, there is a design error (a "reception error") which is automatically detected
and so flagged. Also associated with each arc is a label (-OUT) which indicates
the message to be placed into the buffer for delivery to the next entity on the
ring. ("The "-" symbol indicates event transmission.)

PROCESS N

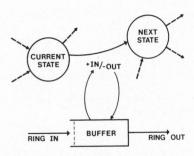

Figure 4
The Finite-State-Machine Representation

There is a case where the arc label (+IN/-OUT) may be omitted. This is when a state is labeled as a repeating state and would have arcs with the same "IN" and "OUT" labels looping back on itself for all possible messages. Such repeating states are labeled with an "R" in the figures. The presence of an explicit arc with a particular message label takes precedence over the repeating function. The repeating function plays a large role in ring systems.

The Terminal

Figure 5 shows the representation used for terminal A. Terminal B is identical except for responses to the various source addresses. Note that the state RPT is labeled with an "R" as a repeating state. Thus any message arriving will be repeated without a change of state – with the exception of the arc explicitly labeled +SDEL/-SDEL, which means that the start delimiter is repeated but accompanied by a change of state to the state START. If the terminal has nothing to transmit, the following message will return the terminal to the repeating state, RPT. If the terminal does have a message to transmit, the free token with monitor bit "0" (FO) will be converted to a busy token with monitor bit "0" (BO). The following two idle bytes (IDLE) will be converted to the source address (SORA) for terminal A and the end delimiter (EDEL), respectively. Terminal A then enters the WAIT state.

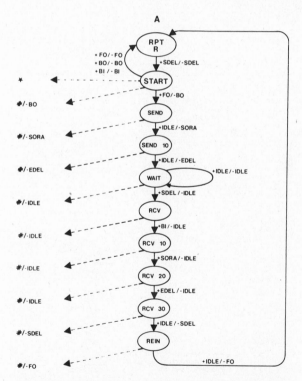

Figure 5
Model for Terminal A

In the WAIT state, terminal A expects either to see IDLE bytes or to start receiving the entire frame it transmitted. As it receives these bytes, it replaces them
with idle (IDLE) bytes until the ring has been flushed. Terminal A then sends a new
SDEL followed by a free token (FO).

Should any other pattern be observed, the terminal returns to the repeat state (RPT).
In doing so, the terminal sends the byte that it had already planned to send, there
being, in general, time constraints which prevent a terminal from responding to a
received byte in the same circulating time slot. The single active monitor will
then take corrective action.

The Monitor

The FSM diagram for the monitor is shown in Figure 6. At the top, the NULL messages
originally on the ring are replaced with the initial free frame: SDEL, FO, IDLE,
IDLE, and an imaginary TIME pulse [11], the purpose of which is discussed below.
(The NULL message or byte is used only to initiate the validator, it is not a part
of the protocol.) There are paths corresponding to the two standard sequences
starting from the state RPT near the top. One is for the free frame; the other is
for the busy frame. Note that the busy token with monitor field "0" is stamped

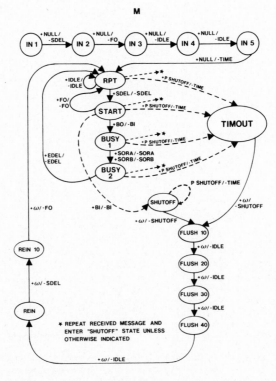

Figure 6
Model for the Monitor

"1", i.e., B0 is changed to B1. This is to guard against a perpetually circulating busy frame. Note that if a busy frame with B1 is received, the monitor enters
the state SHUTOFF, sends a SHUTOFF message followed by IDLE bytes to flush the ring,
and then reinitializes the ring with a free frame. The symbol "+ω" stands for the
reception of any message.

As in the terminal, any departure from the sequence expected is detected. In the
case of the monitor, the state SHUTOFF is then entered (see the asterisks in Figure
6), a SHUTOFF message is sent out on the ring which forces the receiving terminal(s)
into the RPT state, and the ring is flushed and reinitialized.

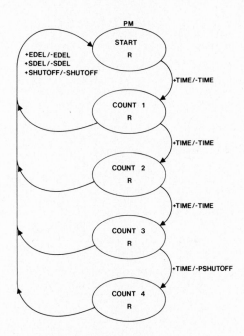

Figure 7
Model for the Phantom Monitor

There is also a timeout in the monitor. If no valid delimiter: start (SDEL), end
(EDEL), or shutoff (SHUTOFF) is detected by the monitor for a specified period of
time, the ring will be flushed and reinitialized. In the validation model, this
timeout function is simulated by the "phantom monitor", PM, Figure 7. The phantom
monitor makes use of the synchronously circulating TIME pulse, advancing its count
at the occurrence of every TIME pulse and resetting at the occurrence of every valid
delimiter. Should the timeout expire, the phantom monitor overwrites TIME with
PSHUTOFF. This "phantom" PSHUTOFF byte is detected by the monitor, replaced with
TIME, and the monitor enters the state TIMOUT (see dashed lines). The monitor
subsequently flushes and reinitializes the ring. An exception occurs, i.e., the
monitor ignores PSHUTOFF, when the ring is already being flushed.

The TIME pulse has no effect on any of the FSM's other than those just described.
In all other cases, it is simply repeated without the process involved changing

state. These TIME arcs are not specifically shown in the figures. Through this
trick, we have successfully modeled the required timeout [11].

The Demon

Part of the demon is shown in Figure 8. Specifically, only that portion of the demon
is shown which corrupts the free token, FO. Other, parallel arcs not shown in
Figure 8 model the other errors listed below. The demon is modeled so as to make a
sequence of a maximum of two errors of any of the types shown below in Table I.
An arbitrarily large number of errors cannot be considered because under these
circumstances error recovery could never be achieved.

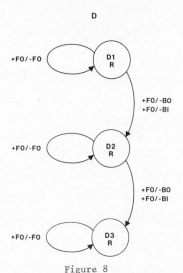

Figure 8
Part of the Model for the Demon

Table I   Error Types

Input		Output	Input		Output
SDEL	--->	SHUTOFF	SORB	--->	SORA
SDEL	--->	MUTIL			
			FO	--->	BO
EDEL	--->	SDEL	FO	--->	BI
EDEL	--->	SHUTOFF			
EDEL	--->	MUTIL	BO	--->	BI
			BO	--->	FO
SHUTOFF	--->	SDEL			
SHUTOFF	--->	EDEL	BI	--->	FO
SHUTOFF	--->	MUTIL	BI	--->	BO

The intention is to model the most likely and potentially most harmful errors.
These may or may not be separated by periods of errorless transmission. "MUTIL"
represents a mutilated delimiter.

Limitations of the Model

There are a number of points where the validation model differs from the architecture. The significant differences are listed here.

The actual frame has been shortened to the abstracted version shown at the bottom of Figure 2. Validation with the actual frame would bring the validation model closer to the architecture but, at the same time, would require the exploration of more states. Note also that given the one-field-per-connected-process basis for the validator, it is not possible to validate a frame longer than the ring. This is at variance with the architecture where the transmitting terminal opens the ring, and thus can generate frames longer than the ring length.

The architected frame shown in Figure 2 has fields which have various lengths, whereas for the validation model all have been modeled as having the same length, namely, a byte. The sequence remains the same but elapsed time is different in the architecture and validation model. The byte-size field itself is indivisible in the model. This imposes a granularity in time which does not necessarily exist in an implementation.

The fact that a ring with a specific number of terminals has been validated here is another restriction. Validation of a system with a specific number of terminals does not guarantee proper operation of a system with a larger number of terminals.

The timeout in the monitor has been modeled, whereas the timeouts in the terminals have not been modeled. The architecture specifies a timeout in the terminal to reseal the ring, should the terminal otherwise fail to do this. In the validation model the terminal never opens the ring so there was no need to include the terminal timeout.

THE VALIDATION PROCESS

The validation procedure consists again of first generating a global-state graph. (See Figure 9.) Reception errors and unexercised arcs (dead code) are automatically detected. (Given the defining conventions, static deadlocks cannot exist, in contrast to earlier work [3].) In addition, an attempt is made to prove that the protocol has the particular functional properties desired; this amounts to proving specific assertions about the protocol. Another validation system which uses assertions is the "APPROVER" [10].

To prove that the protocol has certain functional properties, the technique used here is to demonstrate that given a particular initial condition, another desirable condition is eventually reached regardless of what the particular connecting path in state space happens to be. Note the similarity between this notion and the "eventually" operator of temporal logic [12]. The most fruitful initial conditions to examine are the introduction of transmission errors by the demon. The goal is then to show that a satisfactory recovery occurs in all cases.

There are two attractive mechanisms which can be used to carry out such a demonstration. The first requires calculation of a reachability matrix showing which global states can be reached from all other global states. The second technique generates a trace of all the possible paths starting from those global states satisfying the specified initial condition. The trace continues until either the desired condition is reached - at which point the trace is successfully terminated - or until a specified number of iterations is reached without reaching the desired condition - at which point it is concluded that an error exists in the protocol.

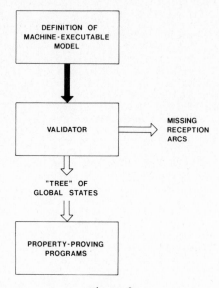

Figure 9
The Validation Procedure

We have found the latter technique - using traces - to be the more practical for two reasons. First, the reachability matrix does not have to be generated; this can be large and costly to calculate in terms of computer time. Second, the sequence of transitions along the trace can easily be displayed and this is most instructive for analyzing and repairing a faulty protocol. A graphical representation of a number of traces is shown in Figure 10.

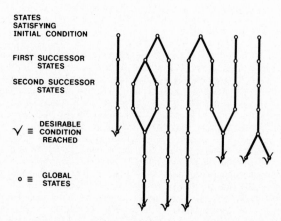

Figure 10
Demonstrating Functional Properties

RESULTS

The model described was validated. The demon was moved to various positions around the ring. A system of three terminals and a system with two demons at different locations were also validated. As one would anticipate, no missing reception arcs were identified. The reason can be seen from a consideration of the protocol's error-recovery design philosophy as follows. In essence, all of the processes expect to see a particular sequence of control messages. Error recovery consists of the detection of any and all variances from this expected sequence. The finite-state machines are thus fully specified - an action is listed in the specification for the reception of all messages.

On the other hand, there is typically a long list of unexercised arcs because of the same error recovery strategy. The list of unexercised arcs varies, of course, with different locations of the demon and terminals with respect to the monitor. Thus, in this case, the list of unexercised arcs provides us with little information.

As shown in Figure 9, the validator produces a tree of global states. The average number of global states (averaged over the various positions of the demon) is shown in Table II. Splitting the demon causes a substantial increase in the number of states because with the addition of another process, there are more bytes on the ring and correspondingly more ring states to be generated.

Table II Number of Global States

Condition	Average number of global states
Demon making no errors	38
Single demon making sequence of one error	341
Single demon making sequence of two errors	1487
Two demons each making sequence of one error	6514

The property-proving programs use the global-state tree as described above. The first demonstration made showed that when the demon made no errors, the control flow was correct, i.e., the transmitting terminal and the ring cycle properly through their states. First, the transmitting terminal gains access to the ring, transmits its control fields, enters the wait state, receives its control fields, flushes and finally reinitializes the ring. Note that no mention is made of the receiving terminal; the receiving terminal only makes a copy of the message when it detects the correct destination address, not a part of our model.

Eight other property-proving programs were used; these are listed in Table III below. The first program demonstrates that whenever the monitor gets to state SHUTOFF, as it does when an unexpected message is received, or whenever the monitor gets to state TIMOUT, as a result of a long interval without delimiters, then the system recovers in all cases, i.e., essentially the free sequence appears at either terminal A or B.

In all the other property-proving programs, in which we also want to show that recovery takes place, it is only necessary to show in some cases that one of these monitor states (SHUTOFF or TIMOUT) is reached. This saves a substantial amount of CPU time. In some cases, as many as six or seven hundred paths have to be examined so that a shortcut is advantageous.

Table III　Property-Proving Programs

Number	Initial conditions	Final conditions
1	M in TIMOUT or M in SHUTOFF	A or B gets initializing sequence
2	D changes BO or FO to BI	M in SHUTOFF or A or B gets initializing sequence
3	D changes SHUTOFF to EDEL or SDEL	"
4	D changes EDEL or SDEL to SHUTOFF	"
5	D changes BO or BI to FO	"
6	D changes SORA to SORB	"
7	D changes SORB to SORA	"
8	D changes SHUTOFF, EDEL, or SDEL to MUTIL	"

In all cases, i.e., for the single demon making single and double errors in the three different possible locations, and for a demon distributed into two halves making a single error in its possible locations, recovery was complete.

The property-proving programs also give an indication of recovery time. For example, the longest recovery sequence from SHUTOFF or TIMOUT is less than six ring cycles. Recovery from any of the other conditions listed is less than three ring cycles, giving an upper bound of nine ring cycles. It should be added that such a long recovery cycle requires the demon(s) to operate in a most demonic way! The optimum length for the timeout will be investigated in this way.

The software package put together [11] has a number of features which make it easy to learn about the operation of the token ring. One of these is a trace facility; a sample output is included here as Table IV. This trace gives a good understanding of just how the ring functions.

Table IV   A Typical Trace Output

	PM	M	B	A	D
1 ST->	START	IN1	RPT	RPT	D1
RING>	NULL	NULL	NULL	NULL	NULL
2 ST->	START	IN2	RPT	RPT	D1
RING>	NULL	NULL	SDEL	NULL	NULL
3 ST->	START	IN3	START	RPT	D1
RING>	NULL	NULL	FO	SDEL	NULL
4 ST->	START	IN4	RPT	START	D1
RING>	NULL	NULL	IDLE	FO	SDEL
11 ST->	START	IN5	RPT	SEND	D1
RING>	SDEL	NULL	IDLE	IDLE	BO
40 ST->	START	RPT	RPT	SEND10	D1
RING>	BO	SDEL	TIME	IDLE	SORA
97 ST->	START	START	RPT	WAIT	D1
RING>	SORA	BO	SDEL	TIME	EDEL
164 ST->	START	BUSY1	START	WAIT	D2
RING>	SDEL	SORA	BI	SDEL	TIME
256 ST->	START	BUSY2	RPT	RCV	D2
RING>	TIME	SDEL	SORA	BI	IDLE
361 ST->	COUNT1	SHUTOFF	RPT	RCV10	D2
RING>	IDLE	TIME	SDEL	SORA	IDLE
443 ST->	COUNT1	SHUTOFF	START	RCV20	D2
RING>	IDLE	IDLE	TIME	SDEL	IDLE
508 ST->	COUNT1	FLUSH10	START	RPT	D2
RING>	IDLE	IDLE	SHUTOFF	TIME	IDLE
560 ST->	COUNT1	FLUSH20	RPT	RPT	D2
RING>	IDLE	IDLE	IDLE	SHUTOFF	TIME
608 ST->	COUNT1	FLUSH30	RPT	RPT	D2
RING>	TIME	IDLE	IDLE	IDLE	SHUTOFF
650 ST->	COUNT2	FLUSH40	RPT	RPT	D2
RING>	SHUTOFF	TIME	IDLE	IDLE	IDLE
697 ST->	START	FLUSH40	RPT	RPT	D2
RING>	IDLE	SHUTOFF	TIME	IDLE	IDLE
743 ST->	START	REIN	RPT	RPT	D2
RING>	IDLE	IDLE	IDLE	TIME	IDLE
796 ST->	START	REIN10	RPT	RPT	D2
RING>	IDLE	IDLE	SDEL	IDLE	TIME
865 ST->	START	RPT	START	RPT	D2
RING>	TIME	IDLE	FO	SDEL	IDLE
931 ST->	COUNT1	RPT	RPT	START	D2
RING>	IDLE	TIME	IDLE	FO	SDEL
1021 ST->	COUNT1	RPT	RPT	RPT	D2
RING>	SDEL	IDLE	TIME	IDLE	FO
1122 ST->	START	RPT	RPT	RPT	D3
RING>	BI	SDEL	IDLE	TIME	IDLE
1213 ST->	START	START	RPT	RPT	D3
RING>	IDLE	BI	SDEL	IDLE	TIME
1286 ST->	START	SHUTOFF	START	RPT	D3
RING>	TIME	IDLE	BI	SDEL	IDLE
1340 ST->	COUNT1	FLUSH10	RPT	START	D3
RING>	IDLE	TIME	SHUTOFF	BI	SDEL
1390 ST->	COUNT1	FLUSH10	RPT	RPT	D3
RING>	SDEL	IDLE	TIME	SHUTOFF	BI
1429 ST->	START	FLUSH20	RPT	RPT	D3
RING>	BI	SDEL	IDLE	TIME	SHUTOFF

The top row displays the names of the various processes in the particular sequence validated: the two-part monitor (PM and M), terminals B and A, and the demon D. Below these labels are the states of the corresponding processes. Below and between the states are the messages on the ring flowing between the process on the left and that on the right. The message leaving the demon D is the input to the "phantom monitor" PM because of the ring topology.

As state 1 indicates (global-state numbers are at the far left) the ring originally contains null messages. As time passes (note the highlighted time pulses circulating on the ring) the monitor generates the free sequence: SDEL, FO, IDLE, IDLE. Terminal B lets this pass but terminal A has information to send and converts the free token FO to busy BO. Shortly thereafter, the demon corrupts the end delimiter EDEL into a start delimiter SDEL, changing from state D1 to D2. The monitor expects to see EDEL in state BUSY2; seeing SDEL, it initiates flushing of the ring by going to state SHUTOFF and subsequently by sending the SHUTOFF delimiter. The ring is flushed and reinitialized at state 865. Neither B nor A siezes the free token but the demon makes its second corruption of the frame by converting the free token FO to busy BI, in the process changing from state D2 to D3. Upon seeing the BI token, the monitor detects the condition for a circulating busy token and again proceeds to flush the ring by entering the state SHUTOFF. In the last state shown in this sequence, the monitor has started to flush the ring by sending out IDLE.

It is against errors such as these that the token-ring architects have tried to guard. The results obtained here indicate that they have been successful.

CONCLUSION

The validation process has been completed for the token-ring model defined here. No errors have been found.

The question arises, "Why were no errors found?" The answer has to lie in the design philosophy. This was to have all the processes involved expecting one of a small set of sequences. Any deviation results in passive behavior of all the processes involved, save one. The one active process (the monitor) then organized system recovery.

Finding no errors raises the question, "Was the undertaking worth the effort?" The answer is clearly "yes". The model validated here is the last in a series of models generated as the architecture developed. During the effort, there was intensive discussion between the architects and the author; many of these discussions were initiated by truly demonic sequences and it is fair to say that the refinement of the architecture clearly did profit from analysis of some of these early sequences.

ACKNOWLEDGEMENT

The author acknowledges with thanks the interaction and many discussions with Werner Bux, Felix Closs, Phil Janson, Colin H. West, and Pitro Zafiropulo.

REFERENCES

[1] Bochmann, G.V. and Sunshine, C., Formal methods in communication protocol design, IEEE Trans. Commun., Vol. COM-28 (April 1980) 624-631.
[2] Bochmänn, G.B., Communications protocols and error recovery procedures, ACM SIGOPS Operating System Review, Vol. 9 (1975).
[3] Zafiropulo, P., West, C.H., Rudin, H., Cowan, D.D. and Brand, D., Towards analyzing and synthesizing protocols, IEEE Trans. Commun., Vol. COM-28 (April 1980) 651-660.
[4] West, C.H. and Zafiropulo, P., Automated validation of a communications protocol: the CCITT X.21 recommendation, IBM J. Res. Develop., Vol. 22 (January 1978) 60-71.
[5] IBM Europe, Technical improvements to CCITT recommendation X.25, submission to Study Group VII (October 1978).
[6] Schultz, G.D., Rose, D.B., West, C.H. and Gray, J.P., Executable description and validation of SNA, IEEE Trans. Commun., Vol. COM-28 (April 1980) 661-677.
[7] Sherman, M. and Rudin, H., Using automated validation techniques to improve distributed software reliability, Proceedings of the Symposium on Reliability in Distributed Software and Database Systems, Pittsburgh, July 21-22, 1981.
[8] West, C.H., General technique for communications protocol validation, IBM J. Res. Develop., Vol. 22 (July 1978) 393-404.
[9] Bux, W., Closs, F., Janson, P.A., Kümmerle, K., Müller, H.R. and Rothauser, E.H., A local-area communication network based on a reliable token-ring system, Proceedings of the International Symposium on Local Computer Networks, Florence, Italy, April 19-21, 1982.
[10] Hajek, J., Automatically verified data transfer protocols, in Proceedings 4th Int. Conf. Computer Communications, Kyoto, Japan, Sept. 1978, 749-756.
[11] Rudin, H. and West, C.H., A validation technique for tightly-coupled protocols, submitted for publication, October, 1981.
[12] Hailpern, B.T. and Owicki, S.S., Verifying network protocols using temporal logic, Stanford University Computer Systems Laboratory Technical Report No. 192, Stanford, California (June 1980).

LOCAL COMPUTER NETWORKS
P.C. Ravasio, G. Hopkins and N. Naffah (editors)
North-Holland Publishing Company
© IFIP, 1982

METHODOLOGY FOR ASSESSING THE ROBUSTNESS
OF A LOCAL NETWORK BASED COMPUTER SYSTEM

Norman B. Meisner

Ungermann-Bass, Inc.*
One Burlington Woods Drive
Burlington, MA 01803
U.S.A.

This paper uses a specific example of a large multi-computer
system supported by a local network to examine a methodology
for evaluating the robustness of a distributed system. Robustness is evaluated in terms of availability. Two architectures
are explored, a hierarchical model and a planar model. In the
hierarchical model, users communicate to the higher level hosts
via intermediate level microcomputers. The planar architecture
has all machines on the same level, universally serving the
user's needs.

INTRODUCTION

One of the long standing promises of distributed processing connected by a local
network has been the potential robustness of the configuration. In this case we
are referring to the physical robustness or the ability of the system to with-
stand machine failure.

In this paper we begin a discussion of robustness by examining two specific network architectures representative of distinct alternatives in distributed architecture. These are hierarchical and planar architectures. The commonality is an
underlying local network.

The measure of robustness used is availability, which is the fraction of time
that the system is usable for its mission. Obviously, the term "usable" is
inadequate to precisely specify availability in a distributed system in which
machine failure may produce degraded operation rather than complete system
failure. Hence, the terminology is more precisely defined for each individual
architecture.

The specific example analyzed in this paper is that of a text entry and processing
facility akin to a newspaper office in form and function. There are 1400 operators whose job consists primarily of textual data entry. To facilitate this work
a low level of computer assistance is postulated. First a template is filled in
by the operator to identify the item and synopsize the text. This is followed by
a portion of free text. The text consists of an average of 5000 characters with
an upper limit of about 20,000 characters. The automated assistance to the
operator includes such features as automatic templates, simple editing by moving
of words and lines, overstriking to correct, and random access within the indivd-
ual message for search and correction. Major manipulation of portions of text
are not deemed necessary at this level.

_____

* Most of the work was accomplished while the author was with the
MITRE Corporation, Bedford, MA, U.S.A.

There are 200 editors and analysts who review the entered text, make changes and corrections, and compile related messages into reports. This group needs more sophisticated processing to accomplish its tasks. They must be able to execute data base searches on template information, manipulate and combine textual portions, and generally have text editing capability. Their job requires greater access to the total data base and more CPU intensive work than does the operator community.

ARCHITECTURAL ALTERNATIVES

The selected alternatives represent diverse points in the spectrum between resource specialization and resource sharing. In the resource specialization direction, machines are specified and sized to perform specific functions relying heavily on interprocessor communications to satisfy user needs. The resource sharing side of the spectrum dictates general purpose machines which provide all functions that a user requires with little reliance on other machines.

The hierarchical architecture described below represents a modest step toward resource specialization with microcomputers providing text editing support and serving as a viaduct for terminal access to more powerful machines. This architecture is illustrated in Figure 1 where BIU's are Bus Interface Units.

The architecture contains two levels of computers. The terminal support micro-computers provide the basic text editing support to the data entry operators. Access is maintained by a local network fully connecting the terminals and microcomputers. It is estimated for purposes of this exercise that 8 operators could be served by a microcomputer the size of a DEC LSI-11. Hence, 175 such machines are needed to serve the population.

The textual data and templates created at this level are stored in machines at the next layer in the hierarchical architecture. These layers are fully connected via a local network. This layer consists of larger host machines capable of storing the messages, performing data base management functions on them, and serving the 200 analysts for report generation and editing. Host machines of the IBM 4300 series class are postulated for this level. Benchmark testing reported by IBM indicates that 80-100 users can be supported by a 4341 computer. Since the analyst use is CPU intensive, for conservatism, three machines are postulated.

The second alternative is illustrative of the resource sharing mode of computer usage where each machine is capable of presenting all functions to the users. This is termed the planar architecture and is shown in Figure 2. While all users can access all machines, each user is assigned to a server up to the capacity of the server.

For this planar architecture, only the single machine class (IBM 4341) is used and it is assumed that 100 users can be accommodated by each machine since the majority of the users, the operators, do not require much service. The precise figures are not important as only trends in the robustness calculations will be examined.

Obviously, the hierarchical architecture can also be laid out in a planar motif and the hierarchical nature can be maintained by addressing and protocols. It is shown as a front end and back end configuration only to clearly differentiate it from the planar architecture.

ROBUSTNESS

System availability is the fraction of time the complete system is available for its mission. Since the mission's duration is an undefined interval, we use the

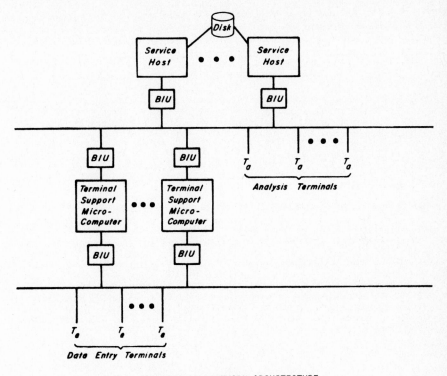

Figure 1 - HIERARCHICAL NETWORK ARCHITECTURE

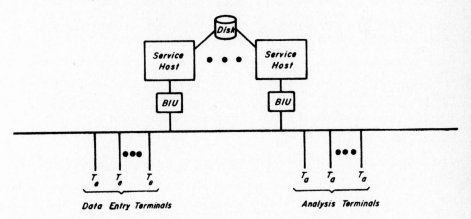

Figure 2 - PLANAR NETWORK ARCHITECTURE

steady state availability (A_{ss}) taken as the average of the instantaneous availability over a very long period:

$$A_{ss} = \lim_{t \to \infty} \frac{1}{t} \int_0^t A(t)dt \qquad [1]$$

where $A(t)$ is the instantaneous availability at any time t. When m out of n pieces of equipment need to be available for the system to be operable, the equation takes on the binominal form:

$$A(\frac{m}{n}) = \sum_{i=m}^{n} \binom{n}{i} A^i (1-A)^{n-i} \qquad [2]$$

where $A= \frac{b}{a+b}$, a is the equipment failure rate, and b is the equipment repair rate.

We apply this latter equation to evaluate the robustness of both the hierarchical and planar networks for this specifically sized network.

HIERARCHICAL NETWORK AVAILABILITY

Taking the hierarchical architecture first, we must allocate the required availability between the front end and back end networks. Assuming that they are physically independent, then the reliability of each is stocastically independent. Let the front end network availability be A_F, the back end network availability be A_B, and the overall availability be A_H. Then,

$$A_H = A_F A_B . \qquad [3]$$

Assuming for simplicity that the allocation of required availability will be the same for the front end and back end networks, then the target of A_H = 0.98 can be achieved if $A_F = A_B$ = 0.98995. Obviously, the allocation did not have to be equal and could have been biased toward higher reliability for that part which caused the more severe service loss when degraded by failure.

We first examine the front end network in this hierarchical scheme to determine how many additional machines are necessary to meet the requisite availability goal. Previously we made the assumption that testing and experience had indicated that 175 machines were necessary for full user support. For the purposes of this work, the machine is considered to be the microcomputer and the bus interface unit. A failure of either is considered a machine failure. It is obvious that the work could be extended to a separate availability allocation for just the network.

We will assume that actual performance measures, or for new equipment, design-to goals for reliability of each machine are

a = 0.001 per hour

b = 0.8 per hour

These numbers represent reasonable rates of both failure and repair. The value of (a) translates to two hours of downtime per year with 40 hour weeks and (b) translates to one hour and 15 minutes per repair, a quite reasonable time for isolating and replacing a failed board in this simple machine. We will investigate the sensitivity of the availability figures to these assumed rates later.

Using these rates, A = 0.99875. In order to exceed the target front end availability, A_F, then 177 machines must be used and A (175/177) = 0.99847. This is
based on a system of parallel redundancy, where the users of failed machines are
reassigned immediately to the spare machines. Hence, only when three or more
machines are concurrently in a failed state, has a front end network failure
occurred.

Turning our attention to the back end network, we recall that benchmark testing
has indicated that three machines (again including their associated bus interface
units) are necessary for operation. The allocated availability goal is A_B=0.98995.
Since these machines are substantial main frame computers with considerable
storage, the failure rate is higher and the repair time is longer than for the
front end machines. Again we select rates based on empirical observation or
design and we use the following values,

$$a = 0.01$$
$$b = 0.2$$

This leads to a back end machine availability of A = 0.95238. Using this in
equation, we see that five machines are needed to exceed A_B, yielding a back
end network availability of A_H = 0.998996 and, combining that with A_F, and overall
hierarchical network availability of 0.99747. This greatly exceeds the required
goal of 0.98 system availability. We can adjust this by noting that A_F was
0.99847 and using equation 3, A_B only needs to be 0.98150. The value of A_B is
exceeded when only four machines are used in the back end network when
A_B (3/4) = 0.98724. This yields A_H = 0.98573.

Hence, the hierarchical network requires 177 front end machines and 4 back end
machines to reach the stated availability goal.

PLANAR NETWORK AVAILABILITY

The robustness of the planar architecture is quantified in a similar way. In
this case, only one level of computers exists. The activity of 100 users was
assumed to be manageable by the machine, thus necessitating a minimum of 16
machines. Using the same failure and repair rates as for the back end machines
in the hierarchical case and again including bus interface unit reliability with
the computer reliability, we find that all 16 machines are available only 46%
of the time. Once again the task is to determine the level of redundancy necessary to improve that to 98%.

In this case, 19 machines are necessary since A_P(16/19) = 0.98879, where A_P is
the planar network availability.

NETWORK COMPARISON

One can now compare the two network designs for equally reliable operations.
For example, if the same front end machines cost about $30,000 each (typical of
a DEC LSI-11) and the large back end machine costs $500,000 (as per an IBM 4341),
than the hierarchical network costs $7.3 million and the planar network costs
$9.5 million.

However, much care must be exercised in using these numbers since they were based
on estimates for repair and failure rates. To see this, we vary the failure rate
for the front end machines in the hierarchical network. Recall that the repair
rate was 0.8 per hour and the failure rate was 0.001 per hour. Using 10 times
the failure rate (a = 0.01), we find that 182 front end machines used in conjunc-
tion with four back end machines yield A_H = 0.98519 (A_F = 0.99793 and A_B =
0.98724). Similarly, the failure and repair rates of the back end machines
should be varied between the extremes of the estimates to make certain that the

selected architecture remains the correct choice for the entire range of uncertainty.

SUMMARY

The work presented here merely scratches the surface of the efforts necessary to include robustness in the design of a local network based computer system. Obviously, the total system needs to be divided into subsystems such as the communications medium, the network interface units, and the computers. The effects of multiplexing through network interface units needs to be compared with the one unit per machine case presented here. Finally, the use of the system in a degraded mode should be permitted. Using the techniques in this paper which have been used for years in designing space vehicles and military hardware, the robustness of computer systems can be quantified and become a real factor in network design.

ACKNOWLEDGEMENT

The author would like to acknowledge the contribution of M. Stubican in suggesting this approach.

BIBLIOGRAPHY

[1] Myers, R., Wong, K., and Gordy, H., Reliability Engineer for Electronic Systems, John Wiley & Sons, New York, NY, 1964.

PERFORMANCE EVALUATION

LOCAL COMPUTER NETWORKS
P.C. Ravasio, G. Hopkins and N. Naffah (editors)
North-Holland Publishing Company
© IFIP, 1982

A LOCAL COMPUTER NETWORK FOR PERFORMANCE
MEASUREMENT OF LOCALLY DISTRIBUTED SOFTWARE[1]

Edward E. Balkovich
Dept. of Electrical Engineering
and Computer Science, U-157
University of Connecticut
Storrs, CT 06268, U.S.A.

Alexandru Soceanu
Computer Center
Universitat Regensburg
Rechenzentrum
8400 Regensburg, West Germany

1. INTRODUCTION

Local networks of microcomputers are frequently proposed as an implementation of distributed systems. The goals of a system may also require that control and information structures, implemented by software, be decentralized. Autonomous, communicating processes have been suggested [3,7,9,10,11] as building blocks for logically distributed control and data structures. The key features of such software are its potential for parallel execution and the communication required between software processes. It is necessary to understand these two features of the software in order to estimate the number of computers required to execute an application, to assign processes to execution by specific computers [4], or to select features of a suitable communication network.

An experimental distributed computer system was developed at the University of Connecticut to study these aspects of distributed system performance. This system is organized as a local network of microcomputers. The primary design objective was to produce a system that could be used to observe the behavior of distributed software structures. The remaining sections of this paper describe the hardware and software features of this network and how they can be used to observe the execution of logically distributed software.

2. THE PERFORMANCE MEASUREMENT FACILITY

The performance measurement facility can be described from three points of view: the hardware of the experimental distributed computer system, how software is expressed and executed by this system, and how the system is operated and observed.

2.1 The Experimental Distributed Computer System

The experimental distributed computer system is a local network of five LSI-11 microcomputers. These microcomputers are linked by two, independent communication networks. The first network is an example of a Direct, Dedicated and Complete (DDC) interconnection structure [1]. This network was implemented using commercially available components. The second network is an example of a Direct, Shared Bus (DSB) interconnection structure with decentralized control. The bus is a carrier sense, multiple access channel with collision detection (CSMA/CD) and is similar to the Ethernet proposed in [6].

---
[1] This work is supported by a grant from the National Science Foundation (MCS-8007466).

2.2 Logically Distributed Software

The experimental distributed computer system is used to execute programs
written in the language EPL [12,13]. EPL is an experimental programming
language for distributed computing. This language is used to express software
structures that may be executed as parallel processes. These processes cannot
share variables, and interact only through the transmission and receipt of messages. The interprocess communication mechanism of EPL transmits information
and synchronizes processes. It is similar to the rendezvous of Ada [5] and the
input/output commands described in [9].

The run-time support for EPL programs is provided by an operating system
kernel. The operating system kernel encapsulates the features of the local computer network. EPL programs do not distinguish between local interprocess communication and process interactions requiring the use of the communication network. The functions of the kernel are replicated at each computer. Logical
distribution of the kernel is achieved by partitioning the state information required to administer the processes of an EPL program. The kernel uses a communication protocol to update this state information [8].

2.3 Operation of the Facility

The experimental distributed computer system is hosted by a general purpose
computer. The host system is used for software development and to obtain and
analyze performance measurements. It provides facilities for compiling EPL programs, loading the distributed computer system, and interacting with programs
executed by the distributed computer system. The host system is also capable of
executing special purpose programs that can be used to capture, record, and
analyze performance data describing the behavior of the distributed computer
system.

The host computer is interfaced to the local computer network in several
ways. Serial interfaces of the host system are connected as the console devices
of each LSI-11 microcomputer. This allows the distributed computer system to be
conveniently operated from a single terminal attached to the host computer. An
additional group of high-speed, serial interfaces are used to report the current
processing element state to the host system. The host is also attached to the
shared bus. The bus can be passively monitored to collect data describing the
communication traffic generated by an EPL program. In addition to these facilities, the host provides centralized timing information that is available to each
microcomputer.

3. PERFORMANCE MEASURES

The potential for parallel execution of distributed software structures is
an important performance issue. Improvements in execution time will tend to mi-
tigate delays introduced by interprocess communication. The potential for
parallel execution is influenced by a number of factors that include the
features of the software, characteristics of the hardware, and scheduling decisions that determine the location of processes in the network and multiplexing
of individual computers.

The contribution of these factors to system performance may be studied by
observing their effects. Changes in the above factors are reflected in changes
in the completion time (or cycle time) of an algorithm. Variations in the above
factors are also reflected in direct measures of the simultaneous activity of
multiple microcomputers.

The experimental distributed computer system allows these effects to be measured in several ways. Direct timing of events can be accomplished by having the host system observe the time between state changes. Because timing and measurements are centralized, measurements may begin and end with processes executed by different microcomputers. Measures of parallel activity can be obtained by having the host simultaneously sample the states of all microcomputers. These samples may be obtained as often as once every 50 microseconds and do not interfere with the system under observation. This role of the host computer is analogous to that of a conventional hardware monitor.

A second, and perhaps more important area for performance measurements is the communication traffic generated by distributed software. Communication between processes represents a source of overhead required to decentralize an application. Characteristics of interprocess communication play a significant role in explaining overall system behavior.

Communication between processes may be examined from a network dependent or a network independent point of view. Measures such as the distribution of message lengths and the patterns of computation required to generate or receive messages are independent of the characteristics of the communication network used to transport them. Measures such an network utilization, delay, or collision frequency are obviously dependent on the implementation of a network.

Communication in the experimental distributed computer system can be observed in two ways. Each microcomputer can obtain measurements of its contribution to communication traffic. This form of measurement presents several problems. Collecting or reporting (to the host system) data describing the communication traffic interferes with the activities of a processing element. This may significantly alter the behavior of a benchmark program by using processor resources or by altering the pattern of CPU-I/O overlap for a processing element. In addition, the messages observed by a single processing element are uncorrelated with those observed by other processing elements. This makes it difficult, if not impossible to reconstruct a complete picture of how processing elements are used. A second approach to measure communication traffic is to use the host computer system to passively observe messages sent via the shared bus. Reception of messages can be time-tagged using the timing facilities of the host system. This form of measurement does not interfere with the system being observed. The data obtained presents a correlated, global view of the usage of the communication network. It can be used to analyze the usage of the bus and to correlate events occuring in different computers. In addition, sequences of messages can be used as the input to trace-driven simulations of other designs. This simulation technique was used in a related study [14] that obtained trace data from a single-computer system.

4. STATUS OF THE SYSTEM

The experimental distributed computer system is operational. Both the DDC and DSB communication networks have been constructed. An operating system kernel that provides run-time support for EPL programs has been developed [8] and adapted to use either communication network.

At present, the system is capable of collecting performance data obtained locally by each microcomputer. This data includes measures such as event counts, average message lengths, and state samples. The host system is being revised to interface with the DSB network. Special purpose software is being written to capture and reduce data obtained from the bus.

The experimental distributed computer system is being actively used to support efforts to model the performance of logically distributed software. This work attempts to develop and evaluate models that explain the parallel activities and communication traffic that are observed for logically distributed algorithms and data structures. These modelling activities are supported by data that has been obtained for a number of benchmark programs written in EPL [2].

5. REFERENCES

[1] Anderson, G.A., and E.D. Jensen, "Computer Interconnection Structures: Taxonomy, Characteristics and Examples", ACM Computing Surveys, 7, 4, (Dec. 1975), pp. 197-213.

[2] Balkovich, E.E., and D.S. Lane, Performance Measurements of Logically Distributed Software, Department of Electrical Engineering and Computer Science, University of Connecticut, Storrs, CT, (1981).

[3] Brinch Hansen, P., "Distributed Processes: A Concurrent Programming Concept", Communications of the ACM, 21, 11, (Nov. 1978), pp. 934-941.

[4] Chu, W.W., et.al., "Task Allocation in Distributed Processing", Computer, 13, 11, (Nov. 1980), pp. 57-69.

[5] Department of Defense, Reference Manual for the Ada Programming Language, (July 1980).

[6] Digital Equipment Corp., Intel Corp., and Xerox Corp., The Ethernet, A Local Area Network, Data Link and Physical Layer Specifications, Version 1.0, (Sept. 1980).

[7] Enslow, P.H., Jr., "What is a 'Distributed' Data Processing System?", Computer, 11, 1, (Jan. 1978), pp. 13-21.

[8] Fontaine, S.C., A Distributed Operating System Kernel, Department of Electrical Engineering and Computer Science, University of Connecticut, Storrs, CT, (1980).

[9] Hoare, C.A.R., "Communicating Sequential Processes", Communications of the ACM, 21, 8, (Aug. 1978), pp. 666-677.

[10] Jones, A.K., and K. Schwans, "Task Forces: Distributed Software for Solving Problems of Substantial Size", Proceedings of the 4-th International Conference on Software Engineering, Munich, Germany, (Sept. 1979), pp. 315-330.

[11] Liskov, B., "Primitives for Distributed Computing", Proceedings of the 7-th Symposium on Operating System Principles, Pacific Grove, CA, (Dec. 1979), pp. 33-42.

[12] May, M.D., R.J.B. Taylor, and C. Whitby-Strevens, "EPL - An Experimental Programming Language", IEEE Conference on Trends and Applications: Distributed Computing, Gaithersburg, MD, (May 1978), pp. 69-71.

[13] May, M.D., and R.J.B. Taylor, The EPL Programming Manual, Distributed Computing Report No. 1, Department of Computer Science, University of Warwick, Coventry, England (1979).

[14] Souza, R., and E.E. Balkovich, "Impact of Hardware Interconnection Structures on the Performance of Decentralized Software", 8-th Annual Symposium on Computer Architecture, Minneapolis, MN, (May 1981), pp. 357-365.

LOCAL COMPUTER NETWORKS
P.C. Ravasio, G. Hopkins and N. Naffah (editors)
North-Holland Publishing Company
© IFIP, 1982

PERFORMANCE EVALUATION OF THE CSMA/CD (1-persistent) CHANNEL-ACCESS PROTOCOL IN COMMON-CHANNEL LOCAL NETWORKS

Nachum Shacham
V. Bruce Hunt

SRI International
Menlo Park, CA   94025

A probabilistic model for the 1-persistent CSMA/CD channel access protocol similar to the one used by the standard Ethernet is developed, and the throughput-delay characteristics of the protocol is presented. Performance graphs illustrating these characteristics, with parameters in the range applicable to the proposed Ethernet standard are extracted from the general performance curves. A new phenomenon applicable to heavy traffic conditions is predicted. In that region the model predicts the existence of a channel-capture effect, where a single station can hold the channel for long periods of time while others try unsuccessfully to gain access. To verify the capture effect predicted by the exact model, a simplified model is developed which illustrates the capture phenomenon.

I. INTRODUCTION

Local computer networks connect terminals, computers, and peripherals which exist in geographical proximity and allow them to communicate to perform complex tasks or share expensive resourses. There are several ways to interconnect these elements; among them are the ring and the star configurations .[1] In this paper we study the common-cable configuration, packet-switching network, as exemplified by the Ethernet .[2] In the configuration shown in Figure 1, all network interface modules (henceforth called NIM) are connected to a single cable using a single frequency band, so that each NIM can communicate directly with every other NIM. Since no more than one transmission at a time can be carried on the cable, the NIMs have to share the channel by means of a channel-access protocol.

Under the 1-persistent CSMA protocol, such as used in Ethernet, a NIM that has a packet ready for transmission, examines the channel prior to transmission. If it senses no transmission on the cable, it transmits the packet immediately; otherwise, it waits until the channel goes idle and then transmits the packet. While transmitting, the NIM continues to monitor the channel, and, if it senses a transmission by another NIM, it aborts transmission and schedules its packet for transmission after a random time delay. This protocol, a combination of 1-persistent CSMA[3] and collision detection, uses random access to resolve user contention for channel access. In this protocol the mean of the retransmission delay is an important parameter that strongly affects the network's performance. It is well known that, when the mean is too small, collisions among packet transmissions occur more frequently and as a result, channel utilization remains low. Thus, in Ethernet, a NIM increases the mean of the retransmission delay time as a function of collisions, in an attempt to reduce the probability of collision. This scheme is known as exponential backoff.

* This work was supported by the Olivetti Advanced Technology Center under SRI Project 1592.

Several models for Ethernet CSMA/CD schemes have been constructed in the past. Metcalfe and Boggs[2] considered the heavy traffic condition of network operation but did not take into account the fact that, in that condition, new and retransmitted packets are treated differently. Further, their analysis considered only channel throughput and did not consider packet delay. Hunt and Tobagi[4] constructed a model for CSMA/CD for all regions of operation; however, they considered a non-persistent CSMA protocol while Ethernet uses a 1-persistent protocol. Lam[5] obtained expressions for the user's buffer queue size, but in his model he assumed that there is a constant probability that a transmitted packet is received successfuly. That assumption rules out the possibility to consider the channel-access protocol itself.

In this paper we develop an accurate model for the 1-persistent CSMA/CD protocol under all levels of traffic intensity. Our model differs from the proposed standard Ethernet protocol by assuming exponentially distributed retransmission delay rather than a uniform distribution with a mean that increases after every collision. The general model is developed in Section 2; in Section 3 expressions for the channel throughput and the average packet delay are derived. In Section 4 we discuss the network performance as obtained from the numerical solution of the model's equations. In Section 5 we concentrate on the behavior of the network under heavy traffic. An approximate model is constructed to yield the throughput-delay charcteristics in that condition of operation. Section 6 contains some concluding remarks.

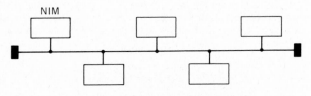

FIGURE 1   ETHERNET CONFIGURATION

II. THE MODEL

The packet-switching network under consideration consists of M NIM interconnected on a common cable. When two transmissions overlap in time, a collision occurs, and none of the colliding packets can be retrieved. However, if a packet is transmitted without interference, it is received correctly. Thus this model assumes that the only means of interference is multiple transmissions; otherwise the medium is perfect. The NIM monitor the channel at all times, even while transmitting. Thus, several NIM that transmit simultaneously, detect the collision and consequently abort their transmissions.

The packets transmitted in the network are of fixed length, T seconds each. The one-way propagation delay on the cable is T_p and it takes T_a seconds for the NIM to abort their transmission once a collision is detected.

Each NIM has a buffer that can hold, at most, one packet. Once a NIM generates a packet for transmission, it is retained until successfully transmitted. Given that a NIM has an empty buffer, the time until it generates a packet is exponentially distributed with parameter q. Following a collision, the NIM schedules its packet to be ready for transmission after a random delay, exponentially distributed with parameter p. A NIM with a previously collided packet in its buffer is called a blocked NIM.

From the protocol description above, it follows that the channel can be in one of three types of transmission intervals: successful transmission, a collision, and idle. It is assumed that all NIM detect the beginning and end of a carrier on the channel. However, due to their separation, it takes some time for signals to propagate between NIM. For the sake of simplicity in analysis, we assume the worst case of an end-to-end propagation delay between any two NIM. Thus our model will give lower bounds on performance. Thus, if we denote by 0,1,2 the successful transmission, collision, and idle transmission intervals, respectively, and the length of these intervals by $T(y)$ $(y \epsilon 0,1,2)$ then

$$T(0) = T + T_p \tag{1.a}$$

$$T(1) = T_a + 2 T_p \tag{1.b}$$

$$T(2) = T_p. \tag{1.c}$$

That is, when a packet is successfully transmitted, it takes an extra T_p seconds to detect the end of carrier by all the NIM. Similarly, a collision interval consists of the transmission time T_a, plus twice the propagation delay.

Using the assumptions about the packet generation and retransmission processes and the fixed interval lengths, it follows that, if a NIM has an empty buffer at the end of the $(k-1)$ interval and the $k-th$ interval is of type y, then at the end of the $k-th$ interval the NIM will have a packet with probability $q[T(y)]$ where

$$q[T(y)] = 1 - e^{-qT(y)}. \tag{2}$$

Similarly, if a NIM has a previously collided ("blocked") packet, that packet becomes ready during the $k-th$ interval with probability $p[T(y)]$ where

$$p[T(y)] = 1 - e^{-pT(y)}. \tag{3}$$

In both cases, the packet that either becomes ready or is generated during the $k-th$ interval is transmitted in the $(k+1)$ interval. The NIM retains an empty buffer during a type y interval with probability $1-q[T(y)]$ and does not schedule its blocked packet during such interval with probability $1-p[T(y)]$.

Another assumption we use is that, even when a NIM transmits its packet, it continues the scheduling process for that packet. If the transmission is successful, the scheduling is, of course, unnecessary since the packet is discarded at the end of the successful transmission. However, if the packet collides, then with probability $1-e^{-pT(1)}$ it is scheduled for transmission again in the following interval.

Denote by $n(k)$ the number of blocked NIM, either ready, or not ready, for transmission at the end of the $k-th$ interval, and $y(k)$ the type of the $k-th$ interval. Then $\{(n(k),y(k)), k=1,2,3...\}$ is a Markov chain.

We first observe that, out of the $3(M+1)$ possible states, three cannot occur: $(0,1)$, $(1,1)$, $(M,0)$. The first two are not possible since a collision occurs $(y=1)$, only if at least two packets are in the system. The third, $(M,0)$ cannot occur, since at the end of an interval with a successful transmission $(y=0)$, at least one NIM must have an empty buffer. All other states are feasible, thus the Markov chain studied here has $3 M$ states. This chain is irreducible and aperiodic; thus it is ergodic. Denote by X the state space and by $\overline{\pi}$ the vector of steady state probabilities; then

$$\bar{\pi} = \bar{\pi} P \tag{4.a}$$

and

$$\sum_{i \in X} \pi_i = 1, \tag{4.b}$$

where P is the matrix of transition probabilities computed in the appendix.

III. THROUGHPUT-DELAY ANALYSIS

The channel throughput S is the proportion of time a successful transmission is carried over the channel; it is given by:

$$S = \frac{\sum_{n=0}^{M} \pi(n,0) T(0)}{\sum_{i \in X} \pi_i T_i} \tag{5}$$

where $\pi(n,0)$ is the steady state probability of the state that represents n blocked NIM at the end of a successful transmission. T_i is the length of the interval corresponding to state i. Note that in the numerator the states are designated by the ordered pair (n,y), while in the denominator they are ordered linearly.

The average packet delay D is calculated from Little's theorem[6]

$$D = \frac{N}{S} \tag{6}$$

where N is the average number of packets in the system and S equals the input rate since no packets are lost and all are eventually transmitted. Following the method described in ,[7] N can be written as

$$N = \frac{\sum_{i \in X} \pi_i E[Z|i]}{\sum_{i \in X} \pi_i T_i} \tag{7}$$

where Z is the cumulative time spent by all packets in an interval and $E[Z|i]$ is the conditional expectation of Z given the state at the end of the interval is i. This expectation is the sum of the average cumulative time, Z_b, spent by the packets that exist at the beginning of the interval and the average cumulative time, Z_n, spent by the packets generated during that interval. Thus

$$E[Z|i] = E[Z_b|i] + E[Z_n|i]. \tag{8}$$

Let $m(i)$ be the number of blocked NIM at the end of the interval in which the state is i and y is the type of that interval, i.e., i corresponds to the pair $[(m(i),y)]$. All the $m(i)$ packets in the blocked NIM waited from the beginning of the interval whose length is $T[y]$. If the interval contains successful transmission (type 0) that packet, too, waited during the interval. Thus

$$E[Z_b|i] = T[y] [m(i) + \delta_{0,y}] \tag{9}$$

where $\delta_{i,j}=1$ for $i=j$ and 0 otherwise. To calculate $E[Z_n|i]$ we first observe that since, $m(i)$ blocked packets are in the system at the end of the interval, only $M-m(i)-\delta_{0,y}$ NIM could generate a new packet during that cycle. Those packets are generated independently of each other thus

$$E[Z_n|i] = [M-m(i)-\delta_{0,y}]E[z|i] \tag{10}$$

where $E[z|i]$ is the average time spent in the system by a packet that is generated during the interval. Using the assumption that the time until a packet is generated is exponentially distributed, we get

$$E[z|i] = \int_0^{T[y]} [T[y]-t]qe^{-qt}dt \tag{11}$$

$$= T[y] - \frac{1}{q}\left[1 - e^{-qT[y]}\right]$$

Substitution of Equations (8)-(11) in (7) allows us to calculate N from which D is found.

IV. DISCUSSION OF NUMERICAL RESULTS

The model's equations were solved numerically and the results are shown in Figures 2-4. In those runs standard Ethernet parameters were used. The wave velocity on the cable is 4.33 nsec/meter. The jam transmission time when collision is detected is 48 bits. The transmission data rate is 10 megabits per second. The number of NIM is 25. All these are assumed to be constants. The varying parameters are the cable length, the packet length and p, the inverse of the mean of the retransmission distribution.

Both the cable length, which determines the propagation delay, and the packet transmission time, affect the channel utilization. It is well known[3,4] that, for CSMA-type protocols, it is the ratio of the propagation delay to the packet transmission time that determines the channel utilization. In the graphs presented, we have taken these ratios to be:

0.0423 - This corresponds to a packet length of 2048 bits when the cable has a length of 2000 meters. This is the minimum allowable ratio for the standard ethernet.

0.2114 - This corresponds to a packet length of 512 bits for a 2500 meter cable.

0.3383 - This corresponds to a packet length of 256 bits for a 2000 meter cable.

We observe that the ratio exhibits similar bahavior here. For example, for $p=0.1$ and ratios .0423, .2114, .3383 the maximum throughput is about 8.3 megabits/second, 5.2 megabits/second, and 4.0 megabits per second, respectively. Similar changes are observed for other values of p.

Different p for the same ratios of propagation delay to packet length yield a different maximum channel utilization. Indeed, if we are free to choose p, we can increase the throughput obtained. For example, a throughput of 9.2 megabits/second for the ratio .0423 is achieved, as seen in Figure 2. The corresponding p is 0.001. Similarly, when the ratio is .2114, $p=0.06$ achieves throughput of 5.4 megabits/second.

In channel-access protocols based on random access, the effect of p is to control the collision probability. When decreased, p tends to spread the retransmissions and, thus, to reduce the probability that two packets that have collided will collide again. However, decreasing p also forces the previously collided packets to wait longer and their delay consequently increases. Thus, it was found[8] that, in slotted ALOHA, p should be large when the input rate is low, to reduce the expected packet delay while it should be small when the input rate is high (heavy traffic) to ease contention for the channel.

In the model studied here, changing p has the expected effect on the throughput-delay performance when the input rate is small. Figure 2 shows that, when the throughput is small, decreasing p merely increases the average packet delay while not affecting the throughput. In this region, therefore, p should be kept large. Yet, the exact value is not important if a little more delay can be tolerated.

In the heavy traffic region, i.e., when the input rate is high, the value of p is very important since it strongly affects both the throughput and the delay, as can be seen from Figures 2-4. When p is too large, e.g., $p=0.2$ in Figure 3, the probability of collision is high, and, thus, an excessive number of transmissions and retransmissions will cause the throughput to decrease sharply while increasing the average packet delay. As a result, for that value of p we obtain the familiar curve of random access.[8] When p is reduced (0.06 in Figure 3), the throughput and the delay increase with the input rate, and, beyond some value of q, both stay virtually the same. The channel does not collapse in this case since the number of NIM is finite, and a retransmission parameter can always be found such that contention is not too large.

From the preceding discussion it seems that, whenever the traffic intensity increases, it is sufficient to reduce p to bring the network back to proper operation. This is the reason for incorporating the exponential backoff mechanism in Ethernet. However, if p is decreased too much in the 1-persistent CSMA/CD protocol, another phenomenon is observed in the heavy traffic region. There, when p is small as the input rate increases, the throughput increases while the average packet delay decreases. See, for example, the curve for $p=0.01$ in Figure 3. This behavior, which seems paradoxical, is due to channel capture by one of the NIM. That NIM transmits a long series of packets at a very small delay while all the other NIM try, in vain, to gain access to the channel. This phenomenon is discussed in the next section.

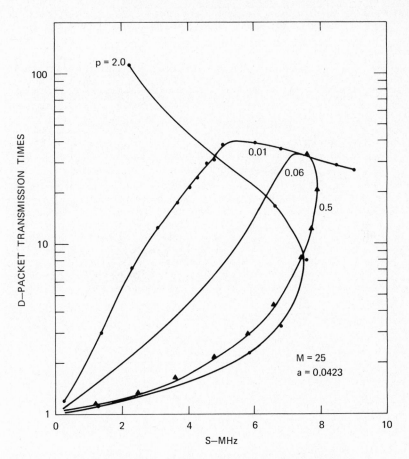

FIGURE 2 THROUGHPUT-DELAY PERFORMANCE

N. Shacham and V.B. Hunt

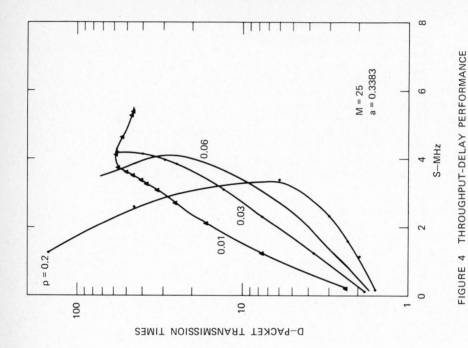

FIGURE 4 THROUGHPUT-DELAY PERFORMANCE

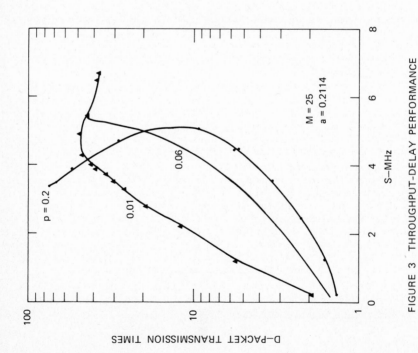

FIGURE 3 THROUGHPUT-DELAY PERFORMANCE

V. HEAVY TRAFFIC ANALYSIS OF 1p-CSMA/CD

In the previous sections, on the accurate model we observed an unexpected behavior in the heavy traffic region where the rate of packet generation is large. In that region a decrease in average packet delay is seen while the throughput increases. Normally it would be expected that the average packet delay would increase with rising input packet rate while the throughput would first increase to a maximum and then decrease. Such behavior was observed in previously studied random-access protocols .[3,4,8] In those protocols the delay increases and the throughput decreases in the heavy traffic region because of excessive interference among packet transmissions. Since the Ethernet protocol under consideration here resolves contention by random access, we expected it to behave similarly.

Consider the case where the generation rate of new packets is sufficiently high that, at the end of a successful transmission cycle, each station has a packet in it's buffer. Most of these packets are likely to be blocked. All NIM continue to schedule their packets during the successful transmission, and all those who schedule during the cycle will, according to the 1-persistent protocol, begin transmission in the next cycle. If there is more than one such packet, a collision occurs. During this collsion the NIM that just completed the successful transmission will continue its packet generation process while the other NIM continue to schedule their blocked packets. Thus there are two processes contending over the channel: one is the generation of a new packet by the recently successful NIM and the other is the scheduling of the blocked packets. If a new packet is generated before a blocked packet is successfully scheduled, the recently successful NIM will transmit again - provided it does not collide with a blocked packet scheduled for that cycle. However, if a blocked packet is scheduled successfully (with no interference) before a new packet is generated, then another NIM will gain the channel. It might also happen that the new packet collides with a blocked packet, and, in this case, all NIM will continue scheduling blocked packets until one is scheduled successfully.

From the above discussion it follows that, when the first event has higher probability than the other two events, we can expect to observe a sequence of repeated transmissions by the same NIM. All the other NIM will thus have to wait for long periods of time to transmit their packets. We call this phenomenon channel capture. On the other hand, if the probability of the first event is small then the probability is high that a different NIM will gain the channel. In this case all NIM have equal access to the channel.

From the explanation in the paragraph above, it follows that, for a given p, the capture effect increases as the ratio of propagation delay to packet transmission time decreases. This trend is shown in Figure 5. There, throughput-delay characteristics of the three networks with the sets of parameters discussed above are compared. In all these networks $p=0.06$. For a ratio of 0.0423 the S-D curve bends to the right, indicating a strong capture. For a ratio of 0.2114, the capture is much weaker, and for 0.3383 it is barely detected.

The standard Ethernet protocol requires the network users to increase the mean of the retransmission delay each time they transmit and collide. This is done in an attempt to ease the contention for the channel. However, such an action tends also to increase the capture effect. Thus, as one of the users captures the channel for some time, the other users collide and increase their retransmission mean, making it easier for the "lucky" user to continue holding the channel. Note, that in standard Ethernet, after 16 transmission attempts that fail with collision, a NIM will discard the packet. If the new packet is generated during a successful transmission of the NIM that captures the channel, the new packet will probably join the other blocked packet since it collides at the end of the successful transmission.

To further characterize this capture phenomenon and to determine what elements affect the channel capture, we develop an approximate model for the network behavior at that region.

Consider the time instant where a successful transmission ends. We assume that at that time the other $M-1$ NIM are blocked. The NIM that has just completed the successful transmission has another packet for transmission with probability q^*. Note that, in the former model, we assume $q^*=0$ by modeling each NIM with one packet buffer and nonzero time until a new packet is generated.

To simplify the analysis we assume that the length of an interval containing a collision equals the length of an empty interval. Thus, the probability of scheduling a previously collided packet during an empty interval and during a successful transmission are $p[T(1)]$ and $p[T(0)]$ respectively which is given by Equation (3). Likewise, the probability of generating a new packet during an empty cycle is given by $q[T(1)]$, see Equation (2). We denote these terms p_c, p_s, q_c respectively.

The probability of a collision among the blocked packets right after the successful transmission is the probability of more than one blocked packet being scheduled during the successful transmission cycle. This probability is given by

$$1-[1-p_s]^{(M-1)}-(M-1)p_s[1-p_s]^{(M-2)} \tag{12}$$

In the heavy traffic region, for packet sizes sufficiently large to make the 1P-CSMA/CD protocol attractive (i.e., $T(0)/T(1)<0.10$) and for more than a few stations (i.e., $M>5$) this probability is very close to one.   Thus we assume that the first cycle following a successful transmission contains a collision.

Denote by P_M the probability that there is no successful scheduling by the $M-1$ blocked NIM during a collision or empty cycle. That is

$$P_M=1-(M-1)p_c[1-p_c]^{(M-2)} \tag{13}$$

As discussed above, the first cycle following a successful transmission almost certainly contains a collision. This assumption can be relaxed; however, it simplifies the analysis while not severely affecting the results.

Let n be the number of cycles from the end of the first cycle (the collision that follows a successful transmission) until another successful transmission. Since the first cycle always contains a collision, $n+1$ represents the number of short cycles (collision or empty) separating two successful transmissions.

The probability that the NIM that has previously transmitted will transmit successfully again after n cycles is given by:

$$P_{new}(n)=(1-q^*)P_M^{n-1}(1-q_c)^{n-1}(1-p_c)^{M-1}q_c \tag{14}$$

As discussed above, capture is the event where the same NIM that previously successfully transmitted regains the channel. The probability of this event is the sum over all n of $P_{new}(n)$. Thus

$$P_{capture}=\sum_{n=1}^{\infty} (1-q^*)P_M^{n-1}(1-q_c)^{n-1}(1-p_c)^{M-1}q_c$$

$$=\frac{q_c(1-p_c)^{M-1}(1-q^*)}{1-P_M(1-q_c)} \tag{15}$$

The probability of successful transmission at the n-th cycle by either a blocked NIM before the new packet is generated or after the two processes merge is:

$$(1-q^*)(1-q_c)\,^nP_M^{n-1}(1-P_M)+q^*\,P_{M+1}^{n-1}(1-P_{M+1})$$

$$+(1-q^*)\sum_{m=1}^{n-1}P_{M+1}^{n-m-1}(1-P_{M+1})[P_M(1-q_c)]^{m-1}q_c\left[1-(1-p_c)^{M-1}\right] \tag{16}$$

The probability, $P_{succ}(n)$ of successful transmission after n cycles is given by the sum of Equations (14) and (16).

We define an epoch to last from the end of one success through the next success. In the heavy traffic region we assume that, at the end of an epoch, there are $M-1$ blocked NIM. Thus all epochs are statistically identical. Therefore it is enough to consider a single epoch. The average channel utilization for an epoch is calculated as follows. The expected length of an epoch is:

$$E(epoch) = T(0)+\sum_{n=0}^{\infty}T(1)\,(n+1)P_{succ}(n) \tag{17}$$

and hence the channel utilization is

$$S_h = \frac{T}{E(epoch)} \tag{18}$$

where, as defined before, T is the packet transmission time.

To compute the average packet delay in the heavy traffic region, we observe that, at every epoch, the $M-1$ packets held by the blocked NIM add to their delay the epoch length. In addition, the newly generated packet adds delay equal to the length of the time interval from its generation to the end of the epoch. Denote by $E[D]$ the average packet delay. It can be shown that

$$E[D]=[(M-1)E(epoch)+E(D_{new})]\,/\,M \tag{19}$$

where

$$E[D_{new}]=\sum_{n=1}^{\infty}T[P_{new}(n)+(1-q^*)(1-q_c)\,^nP_M^{n-1}(1-P_M)]+[(n+1)T(1)+T(0)]q^*\,P_{M+1}^{n-1}(1-P_{M+1})$$

$$+[(1-q^*)\sum_{m=1}^{n-1}[(n-m)T(1)+T(0)]P_{M+1}^{n-m-1}(1-P_{M+1})[P_M(1-q_c)]^{m-1}q_c\left[1-(1-p_c)^{M-1}\right] \tag{20}$$

We note here that Equation (20) contains the approximation that a new packet is generated in the first cycle of T if a blocked NIM gains the channel.

In order for capture to occur, the station that just completed the successful transmission must regain the channel prior to a blocked NIM acquiring the channel. The number of cycles that are captured by a single NIM is geometrically distributed so the expected number of cycles for a capture string is:

$$E[Capture\ Length]=\frac{P_{capture}}{[1-P_{capture}]} \tag{21}$$

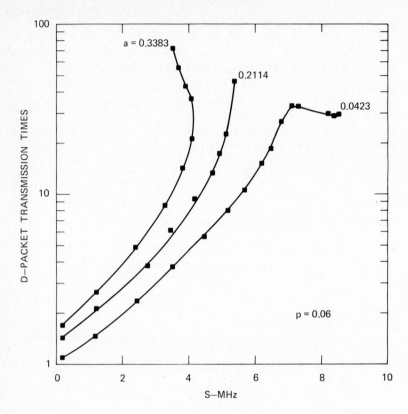

FIGURE 5   EFFECT OF a ON THROUGHPUT-DELAY PERFORMANCE

VI. CONCLUDING REMARKS

An analytic model for the channel access-protocol used by Ethernet was presented. This model covers all the operating regions of the network. The model shows the effect on network performance of the cable length, the packet length, and the mean of the retransmission delay. The effect of the first two factors is well understood from previously published works in this area, and this model contributes to that knowledge by quantifying the effects for the 1-persistent CSMA/CD protocol. However, in studying the effect of the third factor, the model reveals a new phenomenon, i.e., the capture of the channel by a single user for long periods of time. Thus, when the channel carries heavy traffic, changing the retransmission delay can cause a sharp decrease in throughput (if p is too large), or channel capture (when p is too low). Proper choice of p will cause the network to operate in stable conditions giving equal access to all NIM.

APPENDIX : TRANSITION PROBABILITIES

The transition probabilities of the chain are the conditional probabilities

$$Pr[n_2,y_2|n_1,y_1] = Pr[nbk+1=n_2,y(k+1)=y_2|nbk=n_1,y(k)=y_1]$$

where $n_1, n_2 \epsilon \{0,1,2...M\}$ and $y1, y2 \epsilon \{0,1,2\}$.

Recalling that the states $(0,1),(1,1),(M,0)$ cannot occur, we first calculate the transition probabilities for which $y_2=0$, i.e., the $(k+1)$ interval contains a successful transmission. These probabilities are 0 when $n_1 > n_2$ since that condition implies that more than 1 packet was generated during the $k-th$ interval. Thus, the $(k+1)$ interval contains collision. The transition probabilities are also 0 for $n_1 < n_2-1$ since no more than one packet can leave the system in one interval. $n_1=n_2$ implies that exactly one new packet is generated during the $k-th$ interval, and none of the blocked packets is scheduled for transmission during that interval. This cannot happen when $n_1=M$ since then no new packets can be generated.

$$P[n_1,0|n_1,y] = \begin{cases} (M-\delta_{0,y}-n_1)q[T(y)][1-q[T(y)]]^{M-\delta_{0,y}-n_1-1}[1-p[T(y)]]^{n_1} & 0 \leqslant n_1 < M \\ 0 & n_1=M \end{cases}$$

Similarly for $n_2=n_1-1, n_1>0$

$$P[n_1-1,0|n_1,y] = [1-q[T(y)]]^{(M-n_1-\delta_{0,y})}n_1p[T(y)][1-p[T(y)]]^{n_1-1}.$$

For $y(k+1)=1$, i.e., the $(k+1)$ interval contains a collision

$$P[n_2,1|n_1,y] = 0, \quad 0 \leqslant n_1 \leqslant 1$$

and for $2 \leqslant n_1 \leqslant M$

$$P[n_2,1|n_1,y] = \begin{cases} 0 & n_2 < n_1 \\ P[n_n=0|n_1,y]\{1-P[n_s=0|n_1,y]-P[n_s=1|n1,y]\} & n_2=n_1 \\ P[n_n=0|n_1,y]\{1-P[n_s=0|n_1,y]\} & n_2=n_1+1 \\ P[n_n=r|n_1,y] & n_2=n_1+r \end{cases}$$

where n_n and n_s are the numbers of the packets, generated and scheduled, respectively, during the $k-th$ interval. Similarly, for $0 \leqslant n_1 \leqslant M$

$$P[n_2,2|n_1,y] = \begin{cases} 0 & n_2 \neq n_1 \\ P[n_n=0|n_1,y]P[n_s=0|n_1,y] & n_2=n_1 \end{cases}$$

where

$$P[n_n{=}r\,|\,n_1,y] = \begin{pmatrix} M-\delta_{0,y}-n_1 \\ r \end{pmatrix} q\,[T(y)]^r[1-q\,[T(y)]]^{(M-\delta_{0,y}-n_1-r)}$$

and

$$P[n_s{=}r\,|\,n_1,y] = \begin{pmatrix} n_1 \\ r \end{pmatrix} p\,[T(y)]^r[1-p\,[T(y)]]^{(n_1-r)}.$$

REFERENCES

1. D. C. Clark et. al., "An Introduction to Local Area Networks," *Proceedings of the IEEE*, pp. 1497-1517 (November 1978).

2. R. M. Metcalfe and D. R. Boggs, "ETHERNET: Distributed Packet Switching for Local Computer Networks," *Communications of the ACM* **19**(7), pp. 395-403 (1976).

3. L. Kleinrock and F. A. Tobagi, "Packet Switching in Radio Channels: Part I - Carrier Sense Multiple-Access Modes and Their Throughput Delay Characteristics," *IEEE Trans. on Communications* **COM-23**(12), pp. 1400-1416 (December 1975).

4. F. A. Tobagi and V. B. Hunt, "Performance Analysis of Carrier Sense Multiple Access with Collision Detection," pp. 217-244 in *Proc. of the Local Area Communication Networks Symposium*, The MITRE Corp. (May 1979).

5. S. S. Lam, "A Study of CSMA Protocol in Local Networks," pp. 141-154 in *Proc. of 4-th Berkeley Workshop on Distributed Data Management and Computer Networks*, Lawrence Berkeley Laboratory (August 1979).

6. J. D. C. Little, "A Proof of the Queueing Formula: L=λW," *Operations Research* **9**(2), pp. 410-423 (March-April 1961).

7. N. Shacham, "Preferred Access in Packet Switching Radio Networks," Ph. D. Dissertation, University of California, Berkeley (August 1980).

8. L. Kleinrock and S. S. Lam, "Packet Switching in a Multiaccess Broadcast Channel: Performace Evaluation," *IEEE Trans. on Communications* **COM-23**(4), pp. 410-423 (April 1975).

LOCAL COMPUTER NETWORKS
P.C. Ravasio, G. Hopkins and N. Naffah (editors)
North-Holland Publishing Company

A Theoretical Performance Analysis of Polling and Carrier Sense Collision Detection Communication Systems

E. Arthurs
B. W. Stuck

Bell Laboratories
Murray Hill, New Jersey 07974

1. Introduction

This work is motivated by two application areas of communication networks connecting computers and terminals over a geographic region of several kilometers diameter or less, so called *local area networks**:

- A set of terminals, processors, and secondary storage devices are connected by a high speed communications link. How many terminals, processors, and secondary storage devices can the system support and still meet traffic handling goals?

- Multiple processors are connected together by a high speed communications link. How many processors can the link handle to meet performance criteria?

A mathematical abstraction of model of such a situation is dealt with here. A serially reusable data link must be scheduled to handle demands from diverse sources. We wish to examine the performance of the scheduling policy for a given workload, i.e., for a given set of arrival statistics and message length statistics. The points we wish to make are

- If we fix the mean number of messages per unit time that we *attempt* to transmit, and the mean overhead per message, then each design considered here has an intrinsic limit, called the *maximum mean throughput rate* of transmitting messages through the link

- If we fix the mean number of messages per unit time that we *attempt* to transmit, and the mean overhead per message, and allow the *number* of stations connected to the network link to become infinite, then certain designs can have a *finite* maximum mean throughput rate but the mean delay to transmit a message can be *infinite!* Other designs (not discussed here, e.g., Capetanakis, 1977; Hayes, 1978) can have both a *finite* maximum mean throughput rate and a *finite* mean delay to transmit a message

- If we fix the mean number of messages per unit time that each station attempts to transmit, the maximum mean throughput rate as a function of number of stations increases *linearly* for small numbers of stations and then is *constant* for sufficiently large numbers of stations

- If we fix the mean number of messages per unit time that each station attempts to transmit, the lower bound on the mean delay for transmitting a message is *constant* for small numbers of stations and then increases *linearly* with the number of stations (for sufficiently many stations)

---

* The interested reader is referred to tutorials (Clark, Pogrąn, Reed, 1978; Kryskow, Miller, 1981)

The local network is used for two purposes, *control* and *data transmission*. Two approaches are examined here:

- *polling* which is a special type of *priority arbitration policy* where control is passed from station to station around the network, so conceptually the control is a token, and whatever station owns the token has highest priority (even this has variations: a central controller may interrogate each of the stations, or the stations may pass the token by themselves, so called *hub* polling, presumably named so because polling càn be thought of as moving about a wheel)

- *carrier sense collision detection* where all stations sense the energy in the carrier associated with a successful message transmission, and attempt to transmit when no carrier is sensed but may fail because one or more other stations attempt transmission within a specified time interval, and hence this collision must be detected and some appropriate action taken

These *logical* abstractions for control must be mapped onto *physical* devices or networks: here we deal with two distinct physical topologies

- *bus* --every station transmits and receives from and to every other station with both *decentralized* control such as in hub polling and *centralized* control such as in low speed data terminal controllers

- *ring* --every station transmits and receives from just one other station with control either *decentralized* and passed from station to station or *centralized* where one station determines who will be allowed to transmit next

For the polling arbitration, we see that a given amount of time is required to handle passing control, and then a certain amount of time is required for message transmission. We find it useful to define the following parameters:

- *TPROP*--time for a message to propagate between the two farthest stations

- *BLINK*--link speed in bits per second

- *BMESS*--mean message size in bits

- $TCON(I,I+1)$--time to hand control over from station I to station $I+1$

If the physical link is topologically isomorphic to a straight line, then the total maximum round trip time to visit one station repetitively, denoted *TCYCLE*, for this so called *token bus* is

$$\max TCYCLE = TPROP + N\ BMESS/BLINK \quad \textit{token bus}$$

Under light loading, at most one station at a time will be active, and the mean cycle time is then roughly one half a propagation time plus one messge transmission time:

$$\min TCYCLE = \tfrac{1}{2}\ TPROP + BMESS/BLINK \quad \textit{token bus}$$

On the other hand, if the physical link is topologically isomorphic to a circle, then the total maximum round trip time to visit one station for this so called *token ring* is

$$\max TCYCLE = \sum_{I=1}^{N} TCON(I,I+1) + N\ BMESS/BLINK \quad \textit{token ring}$$

On physical grounds, we see that the total mean time to hand control over through all the stations is roughly one round trip propagation time:

$$\sum_{I=1}^{N} TCON(I,I+1) \approx 2\ TPROP$$

Under light loading, the mean cycle time is roughly one half a round trip propagation time plus a message transmission time:

$$\min TCYCLE = \frac{1}{2} TPROP + BMESS/BLINK \quad \text{token ring}$$

For carrier sense collision detection, one additional parameter must be specified, the carrier sense collision detection time interval *TDETECT*. For local networks, this is typically much smaller than the mean message transmission time; on the other hand, for space satellite communications, this equals the mean message transmission time.

As the transmission speed increases, the overhead time required to resolve contention becomes relatively more important compared to the mean message transmission time if token passing polling or carrier sense collision detection are used, but the opposite is true for token ring technology.

Using variations on polling or carrier sense collision detection involves making a decision at the completion of each successful message transmission about which station will next gain control. We emphasize that there need be no relationship between which station *logically* will next gain control and the *physical* location of a station.

Two regions of operations are evident in the above discussion:

● The light loading regime, where typically one station at most has a message to transmit

● The heavy loading regime, where a large fraction of the stations have a message to transmit

One policy can work well in one region and poorly in another, as the analysis here will show: carrier sense collision detection has a smaller mean delay per message than polling in the light loading regime, and the opposite in a heavily loaded regime. One question is how we can blend the best of these two different modes of operation together. Fundamentally, groups of stations are examined to see if thre is one or more messages to transmit (cf pioneering work of Hayes, 1978): carrier sense collision detection assumes that most of the time the group consists of *all* stations, i.e., that at most one station out of all stations has a message, while polling assumes that most of the time the group consists of *one* station, i.e., that every station has a message. Numerous other policies lie within these extremes. Furthermore, these policies do not even bound the space of admissible scheduling rules: we have implicitly assumed that once a station begins to transmit successfully, it will empty its buffer of all messages; we could demand that messages be broken up into packets of a maximum size or less, and that once a station begins to transmit successfully, it may transmit only up to a given number of packets.

Avi-Itzhak et al (1963) were among the first to address this problem for two queues that were polled cyclically and emptied of all work. Sykes (1970) extended that work to account for overhead time in switching from one queue to the other. Eisenberg (1972) extended earlier work to encompass polling an arbitrary but finite number of queues either exhaustively or nonexhaustively for work, with arbitrary overhead in switching from queue to queue. Pack and Whittaker (1976) studied and compared a number of variants on polling in a multidrop communications context. Kuehn (1979, 1980) dealt with multiple queues and nonexhaustive service, with renewal arrival streams, not simply Poisson, as in all the previous work.

The literature on carrier sense collision detection arbitration begins apparently with Abramson (1972) proposing this technique for a space satellite application. Boggs and Metcalfe (1976) studied this technique for a coaxial cable system connecting terminals within a complex of building.

We stress that the level of analysis presented here is (deliberately) quite high, suitable for a rough sizing of system traffic handling characteristics, that can be refined successively as development proceeds in a variety of ways. The limitations presented here are fundamental to understanding system performance; on the other hand, a number of other factors have been ignored that should only further degrade performance beyond that described here, suggesting that designers should allow additional margin at an early stage of development for uncertainty.

2. Problem Statement

In order to specify the mathematical abstraction of a real situation we must describe

- arrival statistics for each transaction type
- processing time statistics for each type of transaction
- arbitration or scheduling policy when multiple transactions are present for the serially reusable resource

Time can be either *discrete* (time is marked with so called *slots)* or *continuous* (the time scales of interest are much greater than any basic granularity due to clocking and synchronization).

The physical topology dealt with here can be a *ring* where each station receives messages from only one station and transmits messages to only one station, or a *bus* where every station can transmit and receive from every other station.

The arrival statistics for the so called *finite source* model of each station are as follows:

- each of N stations are either idle or active
- the idle times for each station form a sequence of independent identically distributed exponential time intervals

The arrival statistics for the so called *infinite source* model of each station are as follows:

- the interarrival times between messages for each station form a sequence of independent identically distributed exponential random variables

The principal difference is that the station cannot transmit any more messages until it returns to the idle state in the finite source model, while the infinite source model does not have this restriction. Both models will be of use: the finite source model in many cases can quite closely approximate first order behavior of a station, but the resulting analytic complexities lead us to analytically tractable models such as the infinite source model. It is gratuitous to claim that one model is better than another in a given situation unless one compares measurements with analysis. If we start with a set of N sources with mean idle time $TIDLE$ and allow both N and $TIDLE$ to become infinite while their ratio is fixed, then the resulting arrival stream obeys infinite source arrival statisitcs.

The message lengths can be statistically characterized as follows:

- the active transmission times for each source form a sequence of independent identically distributed time intervals drawn from an arbitrary distribution

Each station is assumed to have an infinite capacity buffer for storing messages from this point on. The scheduling or arbitration policies considered here are as follows:

- *Noncollision--* Messages are transmitted without interference or collisions between messages from different stations, either in a cyclical sequence, by polling stations in a fixed order with the option of visiting a station one or more times during a polling cycle and removing up to a fixed maximum number of messages from the buffer associated with each station for holding messages; polling stations in a fixed order until a message is transmitted and then returning to poll in a fixed order is called *static priority* arbitration, because each station is assigned a priority or urgency based on the order in which it is polled; polling stations in a cyclic order until a message is transmitted and then polling the next station on the list is called polling from this point on; once message transmission is initiated it is not interrupted, i.e., we confine attention to *nonpreemptive* arbitration policies

- *Carrier sense collision detection*-- Each station senses the state of the transmission medium; if it is idle, and a station has a message, it begins transmission, and either succeeds or contends with one or more other stations that are also attempting to transmit; a variety of actions are possible if contention is detected, such as assigning stations fixed or randomized time intervals following contention detection to begin retransmission. Two techniques are available, one involving spreading out the time interval between retransmission attempts in order to lessen the possibility of collisions between the same set of stations, and the second involving probing groups of stations to see if a group has a message or not, and then thinning the group by a variety of techniques and repeating.

3. Symmetric Stations Using Token Passing Arbitration

The operation of a polling system may be thought of as passing a token from station to station, with the owner of the token possessing control of the transmission medium, i.e., as a time varying priority arbitration scheme. We analyze two different mathematical abstractions of this system, one involving a set of N stations each of which is either idle (no message) or active (waiting to transmit or transmitting a message), and one where messages are generated at N stations according to simple Poisson arrival statistics. The first model may be thought of as having a buffer at each station that can only hold one message at most, while the second model involves infinite buffering of arbitrarily many messages. In the queueing literature, the first model of arrival statistics is called the *finite source* model while the second model is called the *infinite source* model that results from allowing the number of finite sources to become infinite while the mean idle time per source also goes to infinite but the *ratio* of the number of sources divided by the mean idle time is constant.

3.1 Finite Source Model

- N identical stations attempt to transmit messages; each station is either idle or is active (either waiting to transmit or transmitting). The idle times for all stations form a sequence of independent identically distributed exponential random variables with mean idle time $1/\lambda$

- the message lengths transmitted by each station form a sequence of independent identically distributed random variables, with associated transmission time $T_{message}$ which has an associated moment generating function $\gamma_{T_{message}}(z)$ defined by

$$E[exp(-zT_{message})] = \gamma_{T_{message}}(z)$$

- the policy for operating the communications link is as follows: each station is polled according to a cyclic order, and when its turn in the polling sequence arrives each station transmits a message if it has one or passes control onto the next station in the polling sequence. The time to pass control on to the next station is a random variable; in our analysis we will be concerned with the distribution of the random variable denoting the time for all stations to be polled once assuming *no* station has any message to transmit. This random variable, denoted by $T_{overhead}$, is assumed to be drawn independently from an arbitrary distribution with moment generating function $\gamma_{T_{overhead}}(z)$ defined by

$$E[exp(-zT_{overhead})] = \gamma_{T_{overhead}}(z)$$

In practice $T_{overhead}$ may equal a constant plus a term that is linearly proportional to the number of stations on the link, for example.

The mean rate of completing messages is simply the fraction of time the link is actively transmitting messages divided by the mean time to transmit one message. We denote by *UTIL* the link utilization, while $E(T_{message})$ is the mean message transmission time, and see

$$mean\ throughput\ rate = \frac{UTIL}{E(T_{message})})$$

Since each station is either idle or active, the mean cycle time for one station to go from idle to active and back to idle is simply

$$mean\ station\ cycle\ time = E(T_{idle}) + E(T_{delay})$$

and by definition the mean throughput rate is the number of stations divided by the mean cycle time per station:

$$mean\ throughput\ rate = \frac{N}{E(T_{idle}) + E(T_{delay})}$$

Equating these two expressions, we see

$$E(T_{delay}) = \frac{N\ E(T_{message})}{UTIL} - E(T_{idle})$$

Elsewhere we show that the mean utilization is given by

$$UTIL = \frac{FRACT\ E(T_{message})}{E(T_{overhead})/N + FRACT\ E(T_{message})}$$

where

$$FRACT = \frac{\sum_{J=0}^{N-1} \binom{N-1}{J} \prod_{K=0}^{J} [exp(\lambda(T_{overhead} + K\ E(T_{message}))) - 1]}{1 + \sum_{J=1}^{N} \binom{N}{J} \prod_{K=0}^{J-1} [exp(\lambda(T_{overhead} + K\ E(T_{message}))) - 1]}$$

For the limiting special case of negligible overhead compared to the service time per job, we see that the mean flow time for cyclic polling matches that for service in order of arrival: in both cases we are computing the Laplace Stieltjes transform of the service time distribution at evenly spaced points, as expected, and unlike the analysis in the appendix.

3.2 Infinite Source Model with Exhaustive Service Number in System

Now we develop a more comprehensive theory for arbitrating contention among N stations using polling. Our development here will focus on identical stations with simple Poisson arrival streams, but it will be straightforward to extend this to encompass

- batch or compound Poisson arrival streams, where the interarrival times of batch sizes are independent identically distributed exponential random variables, and at each arrival epoch we sample independently from a common discrete distribution the number of messages arriving, to allow for phenomena such as control packets followed by data packets

- multiple visits to the same station during a polling cycle, to allow load balancing: more heavily loaded stations are visited more frequently (in a subsequent section we examine the other possibility for load balancing: only removing a finite number of messages on each visit, with the number removed being proportional to the load)

- Different amounts of overhead in moving from station to station, to encompass a variety of higher level protocol activity that might require different amounts of processing time depending upon the type of station

We denote by the vector $(j_1, j_2, ..., j_{N-1})$ the number of messages remaining at stations two through N, respectively, at the completion of a visit to station one: note the cyclic permutation of the indices! At the completion of a visit to station one there are no messages left there waiting to be transmitted. We denote by $(k_1, ..., k_{N-1})$ the number of messages at stations three, four, five,...,N and one, respectively, at the completion of a visit to station two: again, note the cyclic (modulo N) permutation of the indices! The time interval from the completion of a visit to station one until the completion of a visit to station two is broken up into a time interval for overhead following by a time interval for transmitting messages from station two, both all the messages present at arrival to station two plus all subsequent messages that arrive during the transmission of messages. We will find it useful to define four new quantities, the long term time averaged fraction of time the system is in state j $\pi(j)$ with associated multivariate generating function $\hat{\pi}(\underline{x})$ where j is the vector with entries $j_m, m=1,...,N-1$:

$$\hat{\pi}(\underline{x}) = \sum_j x_1^{j_1} x_2^{j_2} \cdots x_{N-1}^{j_{N-1}}$$

and the long term time averaged fraction of time the system is in state $\underline{l}$ upon the start of transmission at station two, denoted by $p(\underline{l})$, where $\underline{l}$ is the vector with entries $l_m, m=1,...,N$ are the number of messages waiting to be transmitted at stations two, three,...,N and one, upon arrival to station two; the associated moment generating function $\hat{p}(\underline{y})$ is given by

$$\hat{p}(\underline{y}) = \sum_l p(\underline{l}) y_1^{l_1} y_2^{l_2} \cdots y_N^{l_N}$$

By definition,

$$E[x_1^{k_1} \cdots x_{N-1}^{k_{N-1}}] =$$

$$\sum_{j_1,...,j_{N-1}} \pi(j_1,...,j_{N-1}) x_1^{j_2} \cdots x_{N-1}^{j_{N-1}} exp[-\lambda T_{overhead}(N - x_1 - \cdots - x_{N-1})/N]$$

In terms of our earlier notation, we see

$$\hat{p}(y_1,...,y_N) = \hat{\pi}(y_1,...,y_N) exp[-\lambda T_{overhead}(N - y_1 - \cdots - y_N)/N]$$

$$\hat{\pi}(x_1,...,x_{N-1}) = \hat{p}[E(exp(-B(\lambda(N - x_1 - \cdots - x_{N-1})),x_1,...,x_{N-1}]$$

$$E[exp(-zB)] = E[-T_{message}(z + \lambda - \lambda E[exp(-zB)])]$$

The stations are identical; we are interested in the waiting time statistics at any one station, say station one, which is simply the marginal distribution of $p(\underline{y})$ for y_1:

$$\hat{p}(x_1,1,1,...,1) = E[exp(-V(\lambda - \lambda x_1)]$$

Rearranging, we see

$$E[exp(-zV)] = \hat{p}(1 - \frac{z}{\lambda},1,1,...,1) \quad x_1 = (\lambda-z)/\lambda$$

from whence we can compute $E(V)$ and $E(V^2)$, which is what we need to calculate the mean delay as we saw earlier. $\hat{p}$ is given by the following implicit expression:

$$\hat{p}(x_1,...,x_N) exp[\lambda T_{overhead}(N - x_1 - \cdots - x_N)/N] =$$

$$\hat{p}[E[exp(-B(\lambda(N - x_1 - \cdots - x_{N-1})],x_1,...,x_{N-1}]$$

To compute $E(V)$ involves one equation in one unknown, while to compute $E(V^2)$ involves two equations in two unknowns.

For the special case of total symmetry, each of N stations having the same mean message arrival rate λ, with each station sampling independently from an identical message length distribution, and a constant amount of overhead for polling cycle $E(T_{overhead})$ the mean waiting time can be explicitly calculated (e.g., Konheim, Meister, 1974):

$$E(T_{wait}) = \frac{N\lambda E(T_{message}^2)}{2(1 - N\lambda E(T_{message}))} + \frac{1}{2}E(T_{overhead}) \frac{1 - \lambda E(T_{message})}{1 - N\lambda E(T_{message})}$$

This gives us a *lower* bound on the mean waiting time with polling:

$$E_{polling}(T_{wait}) = E_{order\ of\ arrival}(T_{wait}) + E_{overhead}(T_{wait}) \geq E_{order\ of\ arrival}(T_{wait})$$

The second term in the mean waiting time expression using polling is due to irregularities or fluctuations in the cycle times.

The mean delay, queueing plus transmission, is given by

$$E(T_{delay}) = E(T_{wait}) + E(T_{message})$$

3.3 Asymmetric Arrival Statistics and Message Length Statistics

What if the arrival statistics differ at each station, or the message length statistics vary from one station to the next, or both? What if the flow of messages is from *sets* of stations to *sets* of stations, not just one station to one other station, e.g., many messages intended for one or a few stations, or one station broadcasting to a given set of stations? Each of these three different types of asymmetries can impact the traffic handling characteristics of the system in different ways:

- If each station has Poisson arrival statistics with the same mean interarrival time between messages at each station, and each station has arbitrary but identical message length statistics, then the mean delay encountered in a token bus system will be greater for every station than if we set the mean arrival rate to *one* station equal to the *sum* of the individual mean arrival rates, with *zero* arrivals to all other stations. The import here is that the exhaustive service policy results in *higher* mean delays for symmetric traffic than for asymmetric traffic, in this sense. In fact, the two cases just outlined, perfectly symmetric and perfectly asymmetric traffic, give the largest and smallest mean delay of any exhaustive service policy.

- The impact on traffic handling characteristics due to message length statistics asymmetry and due to traffic flow asymmetry are still open at present.

3.4 Infinite Source Model for One Station with Nonexhaustive Service

In order to assess the sensitivity of our results due to underlying assumptions, we consider a model of operation as seen from one station. An analysis of the multiple station case is apparently open at the present time, but the best available evidence suggests that the insight gained in the single station case can be applied to the multiple station problem.

- the arrival statistics to the queue are simple Poisson, i.e., the interarrival times are independent identically distributed exponential random variables with mean interarrival time $1/\lambda$ (the extension to batch Poisson is straightforward and is omitted)

- the service required of each task is random, with the service times forming a sequence of independent identically distributed random variables drawn from an arbitrary distribution with moment generating function $\gamma_{T_{message}}(z)$

- the processor serves up to a maximum of S tasks at the buffer and then leaves for an intervisit time interval, with the intervisit random variable denoted V, and the sequence of intervisit times being independent identically distributed random variables drawn from a distribution with moment generating function $\gamma_V(z)$

- all tasks are served in order of arrival, first come, first served

- the tasks are stored in an infinite capacity buffer

This model captures the fluctuations in the cycle time distribution, but not the correlation in polling cycles due to surges of work at a particular queue.

In order for a nontrivial equilibrium distribution to exist, we demand that

$$\lambda \left[\frac{SE\left(T_{message}\right)+E\left(V\right)}{S} \right] < 1$$

must be satisfied. Note that for $E(V)=0$ this is simply that the mean arrival rate must be less than the mean service rate.

The method of analysis draws on techniques pioneered in fluctuations of sums of random variables (e.g., Feller, 1966). An alternate approach to this problem is algorithmic in nature (Neuts, 1979) but is not pursued here in the interest of brevity.

3.4.1 Maximum Number of Messages Transmitted per Visit=1 (S=1) The simplest case is where the processor does one task and then leaves for an arbitrary time interval (to do work elsewhere). This lengthens the service required for each task. The moment generating function of the long term time averaged waiting time distribution is given by

$$E\left[exp\left(-zT_{wait}\right)\right] = \frac{[1-\lambda(E\left(T_{message}\right)+E\left(V\right))]z}{z-\lambda[1-\gamma_{T_{message}}(z)\gamma_V(z)]} \; \frac{1-E\left[exp\left(-zV\right)\right]}{zE\left(V\right)}$$

where the second term is due to the fact that a task might arrive during the absence of the processor and thus must wait for it to return. The flow time is simply the sum of the waiting time plus the service time for a task, and hence the moment generating function of the long term time averaged flow time distribution is given by

$$E\left[exp\left(-zT_{delay}\right)\right] = E\left[exp\left(-zT_{message}\right)\right] \times E\left[exp\left(-zT_{wait}\right)\right]$$

The mean waiting time is given by

$$E\left(T_{wait}\right) = \frac{\lambda E\left[\left(V+T_{message}\right)^2\right]}{2(1-\lambda[E\left(V\right)+E\left(T_{message}\right)])}$$

while the mean flow time is

$$E\left(T_{delay}\right) = E\left(T_{wait}\right) + E\left(T_{message}\right)$$

The moment generating function of the number in system process is given by

$$E\left[x^N\right] = E\left[exp\left(-\lambda(1-x)T_{delay}\right)\right]$$

and hence the mean number in system is

$$E(N) = \lambda \; E\left(T_{delay}\right)$$

3.4.2 Maximum Number of Messages Transmitted per Visit=2 (S=2) The extension of these results from $S=2$ to $S>2$ is straightforward once the basic ideas developed here for this special case have been mastered, and thus we concentrate on a moderately thorough discussion of this case.

We consider a sequence of independent random variables $\{X_k\}$ where

$$E\left[exp\left(-zX_k\right)\right] = \begin{cases} \gamma_{T_{message}}(z)\gamma_V(z)\dfrac{\lambda}{\lambda-z} & k \; even \\[2mm] \gamma_{T_{message}}(z)\dfrac{\lambda}{\lambda-z} & k \; odd \end{cases}$$

We also define a random walk with partial sums denoted by S_k where

$$S_k = S_{k-1} + X_k \quad k \geq 1$$

$$E\left[exp\left(-zS_0\right)\right] = \frac{\lambda}{\lambda-z} \; \frac{1-\gamma_V(z)}{1-\gamma_V(\lambda)}$$

We define a new random variable T as the smallest value of k such that $S_k < 0$. Finally, we define $\phi_i(z)$ as

$$\phi_i(z) = E\left[exp(-zS_i) \; ; \; T>i\right]$$

We do so because the long term time averaged waiting time distribution has moment generating function given by

$$\lim_{n \to \infty} E\left[exp(-zT_{wait,n})\right] = \frac{\Phi(z)}{\Phi(1)}$$

$$\Phi(z) \equiv \sum_{i=0}^{\infty} \phi_i(z)$$

It is useful to define an auxiliary generating function

$$\Theta_i(z) = E\left[exp(-zS_i) \; ; \; T=i\right]$$

which obeys the following recursions:

$$\phi_i(z) + \Theta_i(z) = \phi_{i-1}(z)\gamma_{T_{message}}(z) \qquad i \; odd$$

$$\phi_i(z) + \Theta_i(z) = \phi_{i-1}(z)\gamma_{T_{message}}(z)\gamma_V(z) \qquad i \; even$$

We can rewrite these recursions as follows:

$$\sum_{i=0}^{\infty} \phi_{2i+1} + \frac{\lambda}{\lambda-z}\sum_{i=0}^{\infty} PROB\,[T=2i+1] = \frac{\lambda\gamma_{T_{message}}(z)}{\lambda-z}\sum_{i=0}^{\infty} \phi_{2i}(z)$$

and

$$\phi_0(z) + \sum_{i=1}^{\infty} \phi_{2i}(z) + \frac{\lambda}{\lambda-z}\sum_{i=1}^{\infty} PROB\,[T=2i] =$$

$$\frac{\lambda\gamma_{T_{message}}(z)\gamma_V(z)}{\lambda-z}\sum_{i=0}^{\infty} \phi_{2i+1}(z) + \frac{\lambda\gamma_V(z)}{\lambda-z}\sum_{i=0}^{\infty} \phi_{2i+1}(z) + \frac{\lambda}{\lambda-z}\frac{1-\gamma_V(z)}{1-\gamma_V(\lambda)}$$

If we solve for $\Phi(z)$ we find that

$$\Phi(z) = \frac{NUMERATOR}{(1-\gamma_V(\lambda))[(\lambda-z)^2 - \lambda^2\gamma_p^2(z)\gamma_V(z)]}$$

where *NUMERATOR* is given by

$$NUMERATOR = -\lambda(\lambda-z)[\gamma_V(z)-\gamma_V(\lambda)] + \lambda^2\gamma_{T_{message}}(z)[1-\gamma_V(z)] - [1-\gamma_V(\lambda)] \times$$

$$\lambda^2\gamma_{T_{message}}(z)[\gamma_V(z)PROB\,[T \; odd] + PROB\,[T \; even]]$$

where we have used the obvious notation for the probability of the events that T is even and T is odd respectively.

We note that the denominator is zero for some real value of $z, Re(z) > 0$ but since $\Phi(z)$ is a moment generating function, it is an analytic function for $z > 0$ and hence the numerator must also be zero at the same point. Thus, we have two conditions that must be satisfied:

• Cancellation of the zero in the denominator with the zero in the numerator

• Normalization, i.e., the moment generating function evaluated at $z=0$ must be unity

Satisfying both conditions is equivalent to evaluating the unknown constants for the probability of the event T is even and the event T is odd. While this is numerically tractable, little analytic insight is available at present into the formulae, even after considerable algebraic manipulations.

What is the analysis required for $S>2$? First, $S-1$ zeroes in the denominator that must be cancelled by the same zeroes in the numerator. The (S-1) constants involve evaluating the probability of the event $T=k$ for $k=0,1,...,S-2$ which will be implicitly evaluated by the (S-1) zero cancellations plus the normalization condition. We leave this as an exercise.

The flow time is the sum of the waiting time plus service time, and hence the moment generating function of the long term time averaged flow time distribution is given by

$$E[exp(-zT_{delay})] = E[exp(-zT_{message})] \, E[exp(-zT_{wait})]$$

Using a generalization of Little's law, we find that the moment generating function of the long term time averaged distribution of number in system is given by

$$E[x^N] = E[\exp(-\lambda(1-x)T_{delay})]$$

There are a variety of numerical methods for approximating the waiting and flow time distributions as well as their associated moments. At the present time little insight is available into the probabilistic significance of the (S-1) roots or how they relate back to the original model parameters.

In a pioneering paper, Boudreau et al (1962) showed that if the service time is zero then as the utilization of the serially reusable resource approaches unity, the roots obey an *equidistribution* type theorem, i.e., the roots asymptotically are uniformly spaced about the unit disk. Moreover, they showed that the mean waiting time and mean number in system are a simple function of these roots. For the case where the intervisit time is constant and of duration T while the mean arrival rate is λ they showed that the flow time is given by

$$E(T_{delay}) = \frac{T}{2(S-\lambda T)} + \frac{T}{2} - \frac{S-1}{2\lambda} + \frac{1}{\lambda} \sum_{K=1}^{S-1} \frac{1}{1-ROOT(K)}$$

which makes it clear how important the S-1 roots are in determining system performance.

3.4.3 Exhaustive Service ($S=\infty$) Given all the previous assumptions, the moment generating function for the long term time averaged waiting time distribution is given by

$$E[exp(-zT_{wait})] = \frac{[1-\lambda E(T_{message})]z}{z-\lambda[1-E(exp(-zT_{message}))]} \frac{1-E[exp(-zV)]}{zE(V)}$$

This random variable has a mean of

$$E(T_{wait}) = \frac{\lambda E(T_{message}{}^2)}{2(1-\lambda E(T_{message}))} + \frac{E(V^2)}{2E(V)}$$

The flow time, the time from arrival until departure, is denoted by the random variable T_{delay} with associated moment generating function

$$E[exp(-zT_{delay})] = E[exp(-zT_{message})] \times E[exp(-zT_{wait})]$$

$$E(T_{delay})=E(T_{wait})+E(T_{message})$$

The moment generating function for the number in the system at arrival epochs, completion epochs, or arbitrary time epochs, is given by

$$E(x^N) = E(exp(-(\lambda(1-x)T_{delay})))$$

$$E(N) = \lambda E(T_{delay})$$

4. Carrier Sense Collision Detection Contention Arbitration

We now analyze the traffic handling characteristics of a class of contention arbitration policies called *carrier sense* (because all stations are always sensing the carrier to see if the link is busy) and *collision detection* because if two or more stations are simultaneously transmitting figuratively speaking their messages will collide and this situation must be detected and an appropriate action taken.

This arbitration policy encompasses a type of positive feedback: if contention occurs, no station succeeds in transmitting its message, and will retry later, when possibly other stations will begin to compete for available transmission time. This suggests we should first investigate the question of the stability of operation, in order to gain insight, before treating other aspects of the problem.

4.1 Stability

We have been dealing with long term time averaged quantities here. How do we know these exist when we carry out various limiting operations? What is the definition of *stability* that will be of most use in characterizing performance? Earlier work by Lam (1974) pointed out the problem area; work by Capetanakis (1977) and Hayes (1978) has refined these earlier notions. Several definitions are possible:

- If we examine the mean throughput rate of successfully transmitted packets, then we might demand that as we increase the number of stations or sources without bound, while fixing the mean idle time between transmissions for each station, then the mean throughput rate of successfully transmitted packets increases *monotonically*. On the other hand, we might demand that for a fixed number of stations, as we reduce the mean idle time between transmissions to zero, that the mean throughput rate of successfully transmitted packets increases *monotonically*. Both these definitions of stability follow immediately from the definition of mean throughput rate for the finite source model. It is *not* clear that these definitions of stability follow immediately using infinite source arrival statistics. For example, if we use a retry policy of attempting to retransmit a packet immediately after detecting contention, then we see that (on intuitive grounds that can be made precise) the mean throughput rate will increase as we increase the mean arrival rate of messages, but then will drop as contention builds up, eventually reaching zero.

- Granted that we have agreement on stability of the mean throughput rate of successfully transmitted packets, we still need to define more precisely what is meant by long term time averaged delay per successfully transmitted packet: one approach might be to study the mean time interval between successful message transmissions, $E(T_{success})$, because the mean utilization is given by

$$UTIL = \frac{E(_{message})}{E(T_{success})}$$

If the system is not stable, then $E(T_{success}) \to \infty$, and otherwise it is stable, with a finite mean delay between transmissions. The problem is that a certain amount of time is required to establish control of the channel for each message, and we must be precise in describing the interaction of the time the channel is used for control (including collisions) and data transmission.

How might we quantify these intuitive notions? Here is one approach, suggested by J.Lagarias. N stations are competing for transmission: each has a message to send. In order for message transmission to be successful, we need to have a time interval of duration $2\ TOV$ on either side of the start of transmission, in order to insure that one station can successfully seize the transmission medium. We will examine a time interval that is of fixed duration, say $M\ TOV$ where M is an integer. $P(K), K=0,...,M-1$ denotes the probability that a single source produces an arrival in the time interval $[K\ TOV, (K+1)TOV]$. For a given retry policy, we can in principal calculate the set of numbers $\{P(K), K=0,...,M-1\}$. A necessary (but not sufficient) condition for successful seize of the transmission medium is that no more than one message arrives in a given interval. We confine attention to those subintervals of $[0, M\ TOV]$

such that $P(K)>0$, i.e., there is a positive probability of an arrival. We index the associated index K with a subscript I; we suppose that S_I sources are in a retry mode in the time interval with index I. The fraction of time there is more than one arrival in the interval $[K_I TOV,(K_I+1)TOV]$ is given by

$$PROB\,[more\ than\ one\ arrival\ in\ [K_I TOV,(K_I+1)TOV]] =$$

$$1 - (1-P(K_I))^{S_I} - S_I P(K_I)(1-P(K_I))^{S_I-1} = 1 - (1-P(K_I)-S_I P(K_I))(1-P(K_I))^{S_I-1}$$

We choose some number $\epsilon>0$ that is arbitrarily small. We now choose S_I sufficiently large such that the probability of more than one arrival in the Ith time interval is greater than $1-\epsilon$, i.e., abitrarily close to one:

$$S_I:(1-P(K_I)-S_I P(K_I))(1-P(K_I))^{S_I-1}<\epsilon$$

Finally, we recall that we had a total of N stations contending in this time interval, so that N is the sum of all the S_I over the entire time interval. If we have a total of L time intervals such that $P(K_I)>0,I=1,...,L$ then we can choose all the subintervals out of the total interval such that

$$PROB\,[all\ subintervals\ have\ more\ than\ one\ arrival] > (1-\epsilon)^L$$

Hence, we can show that the fraction of time that a successful transmission requires more than $M\ TOV$ time units is arbitrarily close to one:

$$PROB\,[successful\ transmission\ starts\ after\ M\ TOV\ time\ units]>(1-\epsilon)^L$$

What have we shown? If we fix the total mean *offered* load, the mean number of messages offered to the transmission medium per unit time, and if we fix the time interval *TJAM* required to seize the carrier per message, then the mean time interval between successful message transmissions becomes arbitrarily large as we increase the number of stations, so the mean delay between successful message transmissions becomes infinite! On the other hand, the long term time averaged rate of successfully transmitting messages approaches a constant.

Thus, we are arguing that for a large class of arrival statistics, that tend to approximate actual data, operation will be in two modes:

- a transient regime of low message mean throughput rate and low message mean delay

- a persistent regime of high message mean throughput rate and very long message mean delay

Why is this so? Is there an intuitive or heuristic argument to explain this? This is because the overhead per station to transmit a message is constant, i.e., we need a time interval of duration $2\ TOV$, and hence as we increase the total number of stations we spend all our time doing this overhead relative to doing successful message transmissions, even though the total mean load offered to the system is fixed.

Some reflection will show that if we carry out the same analysis for a polling system, where we fix the total mean offered load and the mean overhead per station, and allow the number of stations to become infinite, then the mean delay will become arbitrarily large to successfully transmit a message, because we spend all our time doing overhead of passing from station to station. Hence, both carrier sense collision detection and polling as discussed in the previous section are *unstable* in the sense just defined.

What is more surprising is that there exist arbitration policies that have both a finite nonzero maximum mean throughput rate of successful message transmission *and* a finite nonzero mean delay per message, if we fix the total offered load. One example of such a policy is service in order of arrival, which is unrealizable. A second class of examples is due to Capetanakis (1977) and Hayes (1978).

4.2 Renewal Theoretic Analysis of Unslotted Carrier Sense Collision Detection

Our goal is to calculate the maximum mean throughput rate of successfully transmitting messages over an unslotted or unsynchronized transmission medium using carrier sense collision detection. We do so via different methods than used in the previous sections, in order to assess the sensitivity of our conclusions to the underlying assumptions.

Let X denote the random variable associated with the interarrival time of transmission attempts; these time intervals are independent identically distributed random variables drawn from a distribution denoted by $G_A(.)$. Let S denote the random variable associated with the time the transmission interval is busy attempting to transmit or successfully transmitting a message; these time intervals are independent identically distributed random variables drawn from a distribution denoted by $G_S(.)$. The transmission medium is busy either attempting to transmit a message but failing since two or more attempts are made during a time interval of duration $T_{slot}/2$ with probability $G_A(T_{slot}/2)$ or is successful transmitting a message with probability $1-G_A(T_{slot}/2)$. The duration of time to transmit a message is the sum of two independent random variables, the message transmission time and the interframe gap time interval. The duration of time the transmission medium is busy with resolving contention between two or more sources is the sum of three independent random variables, a slot time, a jam time, and an interframe gap time. Combining all this, we see the distribution for S is given by

$$G_S(Y) = [1 - G_A(T_{slot}/2)][G_{T_{message}}(Y)^*G_{T_{defer}}(Y)]$$
$$+ G_A(T_{slot}/2)[G_{T_{defer}}(Y)^*G_{T_{slot}}(Y)^*G_{T_{jam}}(Y)]$$

where * denotes convolution.

If we examine the state of the transmission medium at an arbitrary time, say t, then the random variable F_t denotes the time interval from this arbitrary point until the next attempt epoch. Let $H_F(t,X)$ denote the fraction of time that F_t is greater than X:

$$H_F(t,X) = PROB[F_t>X] = \int_0^t [G_A(t-y+X)-G_A(t-y)]d_y \sum_{K=0}^\infty G_A^{*K}(y)$$

where the last expression follows from known results (Feller, p.354, (3.8)).

The transmission medium is either idle or busy (where busy comprises time intervals devoted to control and resolution of two or more simultaneous attempts and to data transmission). Let Z denote the time interval measured from the arrival epoch to an idle medium to the next arrival epoch to an idle medium. This sequence of random variables is a renewal sequence, i.e., the random variables are independent and identically distributed, with distribution given by

$$G_Z(X) = PROB[Z \leq X] = \int_0^X [1-H_F(Y,X-Y)]dG_S(Y)$$

The mean rate of successful message transmissions is the fraction of time the transmission medium is busy successfully transmitting messages, $1-G_A(T_{slot}/2)$, multiplied by the total mean message transmission rate (including both unsuccessful and successful attempts). However, the total mean message transmission rate is simply the reciprocal of the mean of Z:

$$\textit{mean successful message transmission rate} = \frac{1-G_A(T_{slot}/2)}{E(Z)}$$

In order to illustrate the utility of this approach, we consider an example. Each of N stations is either idle for a mean time interval T_{idle} or active, attempting to transmit or transmitting a message. The sequence of idle times for each station are independent identically distributed exponential random variables. The mean of Z is given by

$$E(Z) = \frac{N}{T_{idle}} + e^{-(N-1)T_{slot}/2T_{idle}}[T_{message}+T_{defer}]$$
$$+ [1-e^{-(N-1)T_{slot}/2T_{idle}}][T_{slot}+T_{jam}+T_{defer}]$$

The mean rate of successfully transmitting messages is given by

$$mean\ successful\ message\ transmission\ rate = \frac{exp\,(-(N-1)T_{slot}/2T_{idle})}{E(Z)}$$

If we *fix* T_{idle} then as $N \to \infty$ the mean successful message transmission rate approaches zero. If we allow T_{idle} to depend upon N, i.e., to be adaptive, then the mean successful message transmission rate approaches a positive value as $N \to \infty$. Numerical studies suggest that for $N > 5$ if we attempt to maximize the mean throughput rate of successfully transmitting messages then T_{idle} is directly proportional to N. Hence, from this point on, we fix $N/T_{idle} = \lambda$ and see

$$mean\ throughput\ rate = \frac{exp\,(-\lambda T_{slot}/2)}{E(Z)}$$
$$E(Z) = \frac{1}{\lambda} + e^{-\lambda T_{slot}/2}[T_{message}+T_{defer}] + [1-e^{-\lambda T_{slot}/2}][T_{slot}+T_{jam}+T_{defer}]$$

4.3 Analysis of Slotted P-Persistent Carrier Sense Collision Detection

The parameters need to describe the operation of this policy are

- $T_{message}$ -- The mean transmission time of a successful message

- T_{jam} -- The mean time to jam or reinforce contention between two or more messages for a time slot

- T_{ibs} -- The mean interburst spacing or time interval after a message transmission

- T_{mrtd} -- The maximum round trip time delay for energy to propagate from one end of the system to the other and back again

- T_{slot} -- The time required for the transmission medium to become quiescent, which should be roughly $(3/2)T_{mrtd}+T_{jam}$, because in a worst case scenario one station will attempt to transmit, its signal will propagate to the other end in at most $(1/2)T_{mrtd}$, just before the signal arrives there a station will transmit and its signal will propagate back to the other station in at most $(1/2)T_{mrtd}$, and finally the original station will transmit a sequence of bits to jam or reinforce this collision, which will require at most a time interval $(1/2)T_{mrtd}$ to propagate to the other end of the line.

P denotes the probability that a station will attempt to transmit in the next time slot, given that it has a message. The sequence of attempts are independent identically distributed random variables from source to source and time slot to time slot. The probability that K sources will attempt to transmit in the next time slot is denoted by Q_K where

$$Q_K = PROB\,[K\ attempts\ in\ next\ time\ slot] = \frac{N!}{(N-K)!K!}\,P^K(1-P)^{N-K}$$

The mean value S denotes the mean time between attempts that could capture the transmission medium to send a message, given an attempt was made at time zero that resulted in a collision between two or more attempts. Four events comprise S:

- A mean time interval of duration T_{ibs} follows the collision time slot

- A message is successfully transmitted in the next time slot with probability Q_1

- Two or more sources collide in the next time slot with probability $1-Q_1-Q_0$

- There are no attempts in the next time slot with probability Q_0

If all N stations have a message to transmit, then the mean time between attempts that could in fact capture the channel is given by

$$S = T_{ibs} + \frac{Q_1}{1-Q_0}T_{message} + \frac{1-Q_1-Q_0}{1-Q_0}[T_{slot}+T_{jam}] + \frac{Q_0}{1-Q_0}T_{slot}$$

The mean throughput rate of successfully transmitting messages is the reciprocal of S, but this must be multiplied by the probability that one source tried, given that at least one tried:

$$mean\ throughput\ rate = \frac{1}{S}\frac{Q_1}{1-Q_0}$$

$$= \frac{1-Q_0}{Q_1}T_{ibs} + T_{message} + \frac{1-Q_1-Q_0}{Q_1}[T_{slot}+T_{jam}] + \frac{Q_0}{Q_1}T_{slot}$$

The analysis in the previous section is quite parallel to this analysis, except that it was for an unslotted system, while the analysis here is for a slotted system. In terms of the notation used in this section, we see that assuming each of N stations has a message, with the interarrival times between message attempts for each station independent identically distributed exponential random variables with mean $1/\lambda$, we find that

$$S = T_{ibs} + e^{-(N-1)\lambda T_{mrtd}/2}T_{message} + [1-e^{-(N-1)\lambda T_{mrtd}/2}][T_{mrtd}+T_{jam}] + \frac{1}{N\lambda}$$

The mean throughput rate is simply the reciprocal of the mean time between successful message transmissions, multiplied by the probability that one source is successful:

$$mean\ throughput\ rate = \frac{1}{S}\ exp\left[-(N-1)\lambda T_{mrtd}/2\right]$$

4.4 Unslotted Persistent Carrier Sense Collision Detection Maximum Mean Throughput Rate

We now present a model and analyze its maximum mean throughput rate as a function of different parameters for a so called *unslotted* bus with no synchronization or timing between different stations that uses a *persistent* policy of attempting to seize the transmission medium but if it is busy with a successful transmission waiting until the medium becomes available.

We assume N stations are connected, and that each station always has a message to transmit; once a successful transmission is completed, a new message is immediately available for transmission. The key ideas to keep in mind are that the transmission medium can be in one of three states, idle, busy with a successful transmission, or busy with a collision, and that the mean duration of each is denoted by T_{idle}, T_{mess}, and T_{coll} respectively, while the total number of each type of event during a given observation interval is N_{idle}, N_{mess}, and N_{coll}, respectively, so the mean throughput rate of successfully transmitting messages is

$$mean\ throughput\ rate = \frac{N_{mess}}{T_{idle} + T_{mess} + T_{coll}}$$

$$= \frac{N_{mess}}{\dfrac{T_{idle}}{N_{idle}}\dfrac{N_{idle}}{N} + \dfrac{T_{mess}}{N_{mess}}\dfrac{N_{mess}}{N} + \dfrac{T_{coll}}{N_{coll}}\dfrac{N_{coll}}{N}} \qquad N = N_{idle} + N_{mess} + N_{coll}$$

We see that the mean duration of each type of time interval is simply the total time of each type divided by the number of each type of interval,

$$mean\ interval\ duration = \frac{T_{state}}{N_{state}} \qquad state = idle\ ,success\ ,collision$$

The fraction of each type of time interval is simply the ratio N_{state}/N. Our goal is to predict each of these quantities based on model parameters, and then relate them to actual measurements. The delicate analysis arises from showing existence of these ratios as the observation interval becomes infinite; here we focus on the engineering aspects, i.e., how to carry out the calculation. The extension to other arbitration techniques such as slotted using persistent or nonpersistent policies will be presented elsewhere.

N stations attempt to access a serially reusable resource. The physical topology is such that after $t_1 = T_{prop}$ time units all stations will know that one station has successfully seized the transmission medium, while after $t_2 = T_{prop} + T_{jam} + T_{guard}$ time units all stations will recognize that two or more stations have simultaneously seized the transmission medium and reinforced this with a jam signal and a guard time has passed to insure circuitry has settled. The message transmission times are independent identically distributed random variables with common distribution $G_M(X) = PROB[M \leq X]$, and $G_M(2\,T_{prop}-) = 0$. All stations have a nonempty queue of messages; if a station is involved in a collision, retry is calculated after the end of the guard time. The retry times are independent identically distributed exponential random variables with mean retry time for each station $1/\alpha$. Finally, we will find it useful to define a multinomial kernel Q:

$$Q(L,K,Y) = \begin{pmatrix} L \\ K \end{pmatrix} (1-e^{-Y})^K e^{-(L-K)Y} \qquad L=0,...,N; K=0,...,L; 0 \leq Y < \infty$$

The transmission medium will have zero, one,... on up to N stations attempting to use it. The underlying Markov renewal process will have $I=0,...,N$ states, one for each of these conditions. We denote by T_I the random variable for the sojourn time in state I.

Our goal is to calculate the mean sojourn time in each state, and the fraction of each type of state, averaged over a suitably long time interval. To do so, we will first calculate the transition probabilities from state to state. When these quantities are averaged over a suitably long time interval, we can calculate the mean throughput rate; we use the transition probabilities to calculate the fraction of each type of state over a suitably long time interval.

First, the state where all stations are in retry is particularly simple to characterize, with the following mean sojourn time:

$$E[T_0] = \frac{1}{N\alpha}$$

The transition probabilities out of this state are given by

$$P(0,J) = \delta_{1,J} = \begin{cases} 1 & J=1 \\ 0 & J \neq 1 \end{cases}$$

Next, the state where one station is active will involve either a successful transmission or a collision:

$$E(T_1) = E(T_1, success) + E(T_1, collision)$$

$$E(T_1, success) = e^{-(N-1)\alpha t_1} \int_0^\infty x\,dH(x)$$

$$E(T_1, collision) = [t_1 + t_2][1 - e^{-(N-1)\alpha t_1}]$$

The transition probabilities out of this state are given by

$$P(1,0) = \sum_{K=1}^{N-1} Q(N-1,K,\alpha t_1)Q(N-1-K,0,\alpha t_2)$$

$$P(1,J) = Q(N-1,0,\alpha t_1)\int dH(x)Q(N-1,J-1,\alpha(x-t_1))$$

$$+ \sum_{K=1}^{N-1} Q(N-1,K,\alpha t_1)Q(N-1-K,J,\alpha t_2) \quad J>0$$

For $I>2$, we see

$$E(T_2) = t_1 + t_2$$

$$P(I,J) = \sum_{K=0}^{N-I} Q(N-I,K,\alpha t_1)Q(N-I-K,J,\alpha t_2)$$

We next compute the invariant measure $\pi(I), I=0,...,N$ associated with these transition probabilities:

$$\sum_{I=0}^{N} \pi(I)P(I,J) = \pi(J) \quad J=0,...,N \quad 0\le\pi(J)\le 1$$

The mean throughput rate of successfully transmitting messages is given by

$$mean \; throughput = \frac{\pi(1)e^{-(N-1)\alpha t_1}}{\sum\limits_{I=0}^{N}\pi(I)E[T_I]}$$

This can be maximized over the admissible set of retry rates α.

It is interesting to allow the number of stations to become infinite while the mean retry time goes to zero such that the total mean rate of transmission attempts averaged over a suitably long time interval is fixed at λ:

$$\lambda = \alpha N <\infty \quad N\to\infty \quad \alpha\to 0$$

This so called *infinite* source asymptotic analysis will simplify the above analysis, and allow us to gain insight into system performance. The transition probabilities now become:

$$P(I,J) \to \hat{P}(I,J) \quad \alpha N=\lambda=constant; \quad N\to\infty$$

$$\hat{P}(0,J) = \delta_{1,J}$$

$$\hat{P}(1,0) = [1-e^{-\lambda t_1}]e^{-\lambda t_2}$$

$$\hat{P}(1,J) = e^{-\lambda t_1}\int_0^{\infty} dH(x)e^{-\lambda(x-t_1)}\frac{[\lambda(x-t_1)^{J-1}}{(J-1)!} + [1-e^{-\lambda t_1}]\frac{(\lambda t_2)^J}{J!}e^{-\lambda t_2} \quad J>0$$

$$\hat{P}(I,J) = \frac{(\lambda t_2)^J}{J!}e^{-\lambda t_2} \quad I>1$$

We now wish to solve for the invariant measure associated with this new set of transition probabilities:

$$\hat{\pi}_0\hat{P}(0,0) + \hat{\pi}_1\hat{P}(1,0) + \sum_{I=2}^{\infty}\hat{\pi}_I\hat{P}(0,I) = \hat{\pi}_0$$

$$\hat{\pi}_0\hat{P}(0,1) + \hat{\pi}_1\hat{P}(1,1) + \sum_{I=2}^{\infty}\hat{\pi}_I\hat{P}(1,I) = \hat{\pi}_1$$

$$\hat{\pi}_0\hat{P}(0,J) + \hat{\pi}_1\hat{P}(1,J) + \sum_{I=2}^{\infty}\hat{\pi}_I\hat{P}(J,I) = \hat{\pi}_J \quad J>1$$

A fundamental observation is that for I>1, $\hat{P}(I,J)$ is independent of I, and depends only on J. Using this, we can write a new set of aggregated transition probabilities and aggregated states (the states are now zero attempting seizure, one attempting seizure, and more than one attempting seizure):

$$\tilde{\pi}_0 = \hat{\pi}_0 \quad \tilde{\pi}_1 = \hat{\pi}_1 \quad \tilde{\pi}_2 = \sum_{I=2}^{\infty} \hat{\pi}_I$$

$$\tilde{P}(I,J) = \hat{P}(I,J) \quad I,J=0,1,2; \tilde{P}(I,2) = \sum_{J=2}^{\infty} \hat{P}(I,J) \quad I=0,1,2$$

The mean sojourn time in each state is now

$$E[\tilde{T}_0] = \frac{1}{\lambda} \quad E[\tilde{T}_1] = e^{-\lambda t_1} \int_0^{\infty} x dH(x) + [1-e^{-\lambda t_1}][t_1 + t_2] \quad E[\tilde{T}_2] = t_1 + t_2$$

Finally, the mean throughput rate is given by

$$mean \; throughput \; rate = \frac{\tilde{P}_1 e^{-\lambda t_1}}{\tilde{P}_0 E[\tilde{T}_0] + \tilde{P}_1 E[\tilde{T}_1] + \tilde{P}_2 E[\tilde{T}_2]}$$

4.5 Analysis of Slotted P-Persistent Upper Bound on Delay

Now we analyze to a limited extent the delay characteristics of a slotted P-persistent carrier sense collision detection arbitration policy. This appears to be analytically tractable and may give insight into the delay characteristics of more sophisticated policies.

N stations are connected to a common transmission medium or bus. A clock with period T is transmitted over the bus. Each station can buffer an infinite number of messages. Messages are transmitted in order of arrival from each station. The link or transmission medium arbitration policy is as follows:

• All stations sense the state of the transmission medium at all times to see if it is busy

• If the transmission medium is not busy, then with probability P a station will attempt to transmit a message (if it has one) in the next time slot, and with probability $1-P$ will wait until the subsequent time slot and repeat this process

• If one station successfully seizes the transmission medium for one time slot, it will hold it for the duration of the message transmission

• If two or more stations attempt to seize the transmission medium during one time slot, neither will succeed, and both will retry in the next time slot with probability P and will not retry in the next time slot with probability $1-P$, with the process repeating itself

We will find it useful to define an auxiliary variable, the probability that a given station is successful in seizing the transmission medium, given that a total of K stations actually have messages to transmit:

$$Q_K = PROB[a \; given \; station \; out \; of \; K \; successfully \; seizes \; a \; time \; slot] = p(1-p)^{K-1}$$

We focus on the traffic handling characteristics of the system by assuming that every station but one, i.e., the other (N-1) stations, always has a message to transmit, while the last station has messages arriving according to simple Poisson arrival statistics with mean arrival rate λ. If the modified system reaches a nondegenerate statistical equilibrium, then the delay (waiting time plus transmission time) of messages at this last station will *upper bound* the delay of messages at all stations in the actual system. We assume from this point on that the message length statistics are identical for all stations, with the message lengths forming a sequence of independent identically distributed random variables. The message transmission time distribution has moment generating function $E[exp(-zP)]$ given by

$$E[exp(-zP)] = \sum_{K=1}^{\infty} F(K)exp(-zKT) \quad \sum_{K=1}^{\infty} F(K) = 1, 0 \leq F(K) \leq 1$$

If we denote the message transmission delay random variable in the modified and actual system by $D_{modified}$ and D_{actual} then we see by definition

$$PROB[D_{modified} > X] \geq PROB[D_{actual} > X]$$

By definition, the system we wish to analyze consists of a single server, the transmission medium, with an infinite buffer capable of storing messages at the node or station of interest. The interarrival times are independent identically distributed exponential random variables. The service times are independent identically distributed arbitrary random variables. The sequence of times the server is absent are independent identically distributed arbitrary random variables. The random variable for the delay in the modified system is the sum of the forward recurrence time of the intervisit time, $V_{forward\ recurrence}$, plus the time spent waiting to transmit all messages queued ahead of it, plus the actual transmission time:

$$D_{modified} = V_{forward\ recurrence} + W + \tilde{P}$$

The moment generating function is the product of the individual moment generating functions:

$$E[exp(-zD_{modified})] = E[exp(-zV_{forward\ recurrence})]E[exp(-zW)]E[exp(-z\tilde{P})]$$

The moment generating function of the forward recurrence time of the intervisit time distribution is given by

$$E[exp(-zV)] = \frac{1-G_V(z)}{zE(V)} \quad G_V(z) = (N-1)Q_{N-1}E[exp(-zP)] + [1-(N-1)Q_{N-1}]e^{-zT}$$

The moment generating function for V follows from observing that the transmission medium will be busy transmitting messages successfully from each of the other (N-1) stations or will waste one time slot in a message attempt collision between two or more stations.

The waiting time moment generating function is given by the Pollaczek-Khintchine formula:

$$E[exp(-zW)] = \frac{z(1-\lambda E(\tilde{P}))}{z-\lambda[1-E[exp(-z\tilde{P})]}$$

The final moment generating function, for the message transmission time, involves taking into account that with probability Q_N the last station will succeed and hold the transmission medium for an interval of duration P, with probability $(N-1)Q_N$ one of the other (N-1) stations will succeed and hold the transmission medium for an interval of duration $\tilde{P}$ and then the last station will succeed and hold the transmission medium for an interval of duration P, and with probability $1-NQ_N$ there will be a collision consuming a time slot followed by a time interval of duration $\tilde{P}$:

$$E[e^{-z\tilde{P}}] = Q_N E[e^{-zP}] + (N-1)Q_N E[e^{-zP}]E[e^{-z\tilde{P}}] + [1-NQ_N]E[e^{-z\tilde{P}}]e^{-zT}$$

$$E[exp(-z\tilde{P})] = \frac{Q_N E[exp(-zP)]}{1-(N-1)Q_N E[exp(-zP)] - [1-NQ_N]exp(-zT)}$$

The mean of the modified delay process is given by

$$E[D_{modified}] = E(V) + E(W) + E(\tilde{P})$$

$$E(V) = \frac{(N-1)Q_{N-1}E(P^2) + T^2[1-(N-1)Q_{N-1}]}{2(N-1)Q_{N-1}E(P) + 2T[1-(N-1)Q_{N-1}]}$$

$$E(W) = \frac{\lambda E(\tilde{P}^2)}{2(1-\lambda E(\tilde{P}))}$$

$$E(\tilde{P}) = NE(P) + \frac{T(1-NQ_N)}{Q_N}$$

$$E(\tilde{P}^2) = NE(P^2) + (N-1)E(P)E(\tilde{P}) + \frac{1-NQ_N}{Q_N}[T^2+2TE(\tilde{P})]$$

A nontrivial distribution, averaged over a suitably long time interval, exists provided that the following sufficient conditions holds:

$$\lambda E(\tilde{P})<1$$

The largest mean arrival rate to one queue that can still result in a nondegenerate statistical equilibrium distribution is to choose $P=1/N$ and then

$$\lambda < \frac{1}{N[E(P)+T(e-1)]}$$

The attached figures plot this upper bound versus mean arrival rate where P is chosen to equal $1/N$.

Acknowledgements

The authors gratefully acknowledge the support, encouragement and interest expressed by F.S.Dworak, J.Lagarias and R.W.Lucky of Bell Laboratories, V.Tarassov of Western Electric, and T.Phinney of Honeywell throughout the course of this work. All errors, omissions, and other oversights are the sole responsibility of the authors.

References

[1] B.Avi-Itzhak, W.L. Maxwell, L.W.Miller, *Queueing with Alternating Priorities*, Operations Research, **13**, 306-318 (1963).

[2] D.R.Boggs, R.M.Metcalfe, *Ethernet: Distributed Packet Switching for Local Computer Networks*, C.A.C.M., **19** (7), 395-404 (1976).

[3] Werner Bux, *Local Area Subnetworks: A Performance Comparison*, IFIP Conference on Local Networks, Zurich, Switzerland, August 1980.

[4] J.Capetanakis, *The Multiple Access Broadcast Channel: Protocol and Capacity Considerations*, M.I.T.Department of Electrical Engineering Ph.D.Dissertation, 1977; *Tree Algorithms for Packet Broadcast Channels*, IEEE Transactions on Information Theory, **25** (5), 505-515 (1979).

[5] D.D.Clark, K.T.Pogran, D.P.Reed, *An Introduction to Local Area Networks*, Proceedings IEEE, **66** (11), 1497-1517 (1978).

[6] M.Eisenberg, *Queues with Periodic Service and Changeover Time*, Operations Research, **20** (3) 440-451 (1972).

[7] J.F.Hayes, *An Adaptive Technique for Local Distribution*, IEEE Transactions on Communications, **26** (8), 1178-1186 (1978).

[8] J.F.Hayes, *Local Distribution in Computer Communications*, IEEE Communications Magazine, **19** (2), 6-14(1981).

[9] M.Kaplan, *A Sufficient Condition for Nonergodicity of a Markov Chain*, IEEE Transactions on Information Theory, **25** (4), 470-471 (1979).

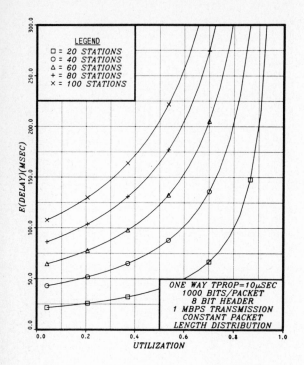

*UPPER BOUND
ON MEAN DELAY
VS LINK UTILIZATION
P=1/N PERSISTENT
SLOTTED CSMA/CD*

*UPPER BOUND
ON MEAN DELAY
VS LINK UTILIZATION
P=1/N PERSISTENT
SLOTTED CSMA/CD*

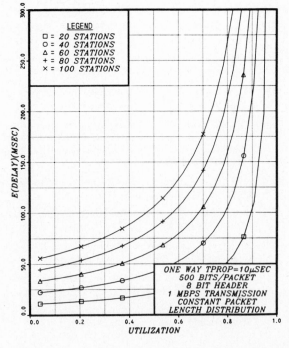

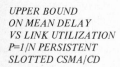

[10] J.M.Kryskow, C.K.Miller, *Local Area Networks Overview--Part I: Definitions and Attributes,* Computer Design, 22-35 (February, 1981), *Local Area Networks Overview--Part II: Standards Activities,* Computer Design, 12-20 (March, 1981).

[11] P.J.Kuehn, *Multiqueue Systems with Nonexhaustive Cyclic Service,* Bell System Technical Journal, **58** (4), 671-698 (1979).

[12] P.J.Kuehn, *Performance of ARQ-Protocols for HDX-Transmission in Hierarchical Polling Systems,* Fifth International Conference on Computer Communication, Atlanta, Georgia, 27-30 October 1980

[13] C.D.Pack, B.A.Whittaker, *Multipoint Private Line (MPL) Access Delay Under Several Interstation Disciplines,* IEEE Transactions Communications, **24** (3), 339-348 (1976).

[14] A.G.Pakes, *Some Conditions for Ergodicity and Recurrence of Markov Chains,* Operations Research, **17**, 1059-1061 (1969).

[15] I.Rubin, *Group Random Access Disciplines for Multi-Access Broadcast Channels,* IEEE Transactions on Information Theory, **24** (5), 578-592(1978).

[16] I.Rubin, *Message Delays in FDMA and TDMA Communication Channels,* IEEE Transactions on Communications, **27** (5), 769-777(1979).

[17] I.Rubin *Access Control Disciplines for Multiaccess Broadcast Channels: Reservation and TDMA Schemes,* IEEE Transactions on Information Theory, **25** (5), 516-536(1979).

[18] J.Sykes, *Simplified Analysis of an Alternating Priority Queuing Model with Setup Times,* Operations Research, **18** (6), 1182-1192 (1970).

[19] F.Tobagi, *Multiaccess Protocols in Packet Communication Systems,* IEEE Transactions on Communications, **28** (4), 468-488 (1980).

LOCAL COMPUTER NETWORKS
P.C. Ravasio, G. Hopkins and N. Naffah (editors)
North-Holland Publishing Company
© IFIP, 1982

PERFORMANCE PREDICTION OF A FLOW CONTROL SYSTEM USING
AN ANALYTIC MODEL

P.G.Harrison

Department of Computing
Imperial College
London SW7 2BZ
ENGLAND

A Markov model of a message processing node with batch arrivals, window
size constraints and an additional flow control based on allocation of
credits is presented. The model is sufficiently general for modelling many
nodes which represent servers or sub-systems in any queueing network with
congestion controls. Its principal application is the representation of
network-independent flow control of messages between networks which may
have quite different message sizes and protocols: a "gateway". Model
structue is much simplified by alternative representation of certain node
characteristics and direct solution of the balance equations becomes
practicable. Validation is by comparison with simulation tests.

1. INTRODUCTION

In communication networks, flow control schemes are necessary to ease congestion which
would otherwise cause any of a variety of problems. These include speed mis-matching
(different processing rates at the sending and receiving nodes), deterioration in
efficiency (e.g. throughput degradation), loss of security or reliability (e.g. due to
buffer overflow at some node), unfairness (in the sense that certain classes of message
may be allowed to dominate). Various strategies have been proposed and sub-sets of these
implemented in some actual networks; e.g. pacing control, [KLEI80], window size constraint
as in SNA, DECNET and ARPANET, [KLEI80], buffer size limitation at individual nodes,
[LAM79,WECK80], and isarithmic control, [DAVI72]. Performance prediction of flow
controlled networks is important in the comparison of such schemes, with the aim of
choosing the most efficient (always subject to adequate attainment of the original
objective of the flow control).

We address this via an analytic model, constructed initially to represent a node, the
message processor, connecting separate communication networks with possibly quite
different characteristics, such as message size or protocol; a gateway. Flow control in
the gateway is independent of the characteristics of each network and uses:
  (i)   Window size restriction;
  (ii)   Buffer size limitation via assignment of a threshold value for the number of
         messages therein;
  (iii) Message acceptance protocol based on the availability and issue of credits,
         accumulated on completion of processing of a message unit by the message processor.
         This is a pacing control.

The analytic model was developed within a Markovian framework and results in balance
equations with many global dependencies in the sense that certain state transition
probabilities depend on several state vector component values; in particular, blocking is
present. The credit-based control scheme is shown, in 2.1, to be equivalent to operation
by the node in modes, representing congestion levels, each with its own buffer capacity.
In this way, the problem specification is greatly simplified, and the state space much
reduced, since credit handling need no longer be modelled explicitly. The approach taken
is to make realistic approximations to further reduce the size of the state space, the

number of dimensions in particular. The global state dependence, e.g. blocking, is still present, but the resulting small size of the state space permits direct numerical solution of its balance equations for the state space probabilities. From these, important performance measures follow immediately. The physical realism of the approximations made retains the original parameters of the model in an intuitively significant way, preserving an accurate representation. Thus the precision of predictions is expected to be good. Validation is performed by comparison with the results of simulation tests, although ultimately validation is only relevant when based on data measured on actual networks. Nevertheless, the consistency shown with the simulated results does increase confidence in the model; its approximations in particular.

The model has great generality in that it is the solution of raw balance equations, so that all its parameters can have any (global) state dependencies; in particular state dependent service rates. Thus it can be applied to a variety of queueing network nodes in the contexts of communications and computer systems. For example, whole sub-systems of physical nodes may be represented by one with state dependent service rate and/or customer acceptance protocol; indeed any system with a congestion control scheme which can somehow be represented realistically by a single (possibly very complex) processor is a suitable application.

In the following section, the gateway node modelled is defined and the analysis resulting in the reduced state space discussed. The balance equations for the underlying Markov Process then follow directly, from which the state transition probability matrix may be obtained. Some computational aspects are considered in section 3, which is followed by a description of our validation exercise. Finally in section 5, we suggest applications of the model and extensions which could be made to increase its generality, allowing representation of more sophisticated, stabilized congestion control schemes.

2. THE NODE MODEL

2.1 NODE DESCRIPTION

The node, shown in Figure 1, accepts batches of messages from a number of classes, each of which has its own batch size and input stream. Incoming message batches from each stream enter a common hold queue from which batches are released into the server queue of the message processor, whence they are served on a first-come-first-served (FCFS) basis. Messages are processed one message at a time and the following flow control schemes are operative:

    (i)   Window control. Each message class is assigned a maximum number of batches allowed in the server and hold queues, its window size;

    (ii) Isarithmic control or buffer size limitation. The server queue has an associated threshold value such that no messages are accepted when the queue size reaches this level and a congested mode is entered whereby message acceptance is restricted according to credit availability as discussed next in (iii);

    (iii) Pacing control. Once the threshold has been reached messages are accepted only if sufficient credits have been accumulated, until the queue again becomes empty. The number of available credits is set to zero for queue sizes greater than or equal to the threshold value. One credit is issued whenever a message's processing is completed with a resulting queue length less than the threshold value. Batches of messages are accepted from the hold queue, on a FCFS basis, when the number of accumulated credits is greater than or equal to the batch size of the class at the front of the hold queue. On such a message acceptance a number of credits equal to the batch size is consumed, reducing the number of accumulated credits correspondingly. If the server queue size becomes zero, non-congested mode of operation is restored until the threshold is again crossed.

This is basically the node described in [KERM80] with variable message sizes and no time-out mechanism. The time delay involved in the issue of credits, arising from their own transmission on a network in the physical system, is not represented.

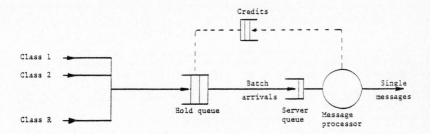

Figure 1
The flow controlled network

NOTATION:

Number of message classes: R
Message processor service rate: μ messages/unit time
Queueing discipline: FCFS (both queues)
Class arrival rates: λ_r batches/unit time ($1 \leq r \leq R$)
Class batch sizes: b_r messages ($1 \leq r \leq R$)
Class window sizes: w_r batches ($1 \leq r \leq R$)
Threshold of server queue: T messages

These parameters may be state dependent in any Markov model, in particular queue length dependent. The direct representation of this system in terms of a Markov process involves a state space with dimensions corresponding to
(i)   ordering of batches in the hold and server queues in terms of their classes;
(ii)   number of messages in the server queue;
(iii) number of credits accumulated.

The balance equations have no closed form solution because of the global state dependencies of state transition matrix entries on more than one state vector components, c.f. [CHAN77], [LAM77]; for example due to blocking. Furthermore, direct solution of the balance equations is infeasible due to the size of the state space. We therefore simplify the formulation of the specification for a model to represent the system so as to reduce the state space size to such an extent that explicit solution of the new balance equations becomes a practicable proposition. The global state dependencies do not vanish so that a closed form solution still cannot be derived.

The following observations may be made:
(i)   The system operates in either of two modes:
       * congested, when the server queue has not been empty since the last time the threshold was reached;
       * uncongested, otherwise.
(ii)   Uncongested mode may be represented by some maximum server queue size, C say, where $C \geq T$. Of course it is meaningless to have $C > T-1+\max(b_r)$ since queue lengths greater than the r.h.s. of this inequality can only occur after an arrival to a queue of length greater than T-1, when no batches are accepted.
(iii) Congested mode may be represented by
       * no arrivals for server queue lengths greater than or equal to T.
       * arrivals subject to maximum queue length T for server queue length less than T. This is because on a service completion resulting in a queue length below the threshold, ı single credit is issued corresponding to a single message completed. Also, when a batch is accepted, the number of credits consumed is equal to the number of messages in the batch. Thus the sum of the number of

accumulated credits and the server queue length is constant, equal to T since at the threshold there are zero credits available by definition. This is equivalent to (ii), uncongested mode, with C set to T.

The state space, slightly generalised from this description, is now defined in terms of mode and server queue length; the credit-based control becomes _implicit_ and the model specification greatly simplified.

2.2 THE STATE SPACE

The state space, S, is the set of ordered pairs defined by
$$S = \{(n,m):1\leq n\leq C_m;1\leq m\leq M\}$$
where
M is the number of different modes (2 in the previous section);
m is the mode corresponding to state vector (n,m), with $m=1$ representing congested mode;
C_m is the maximum queue length permitted in mode m, the mode's _capacity_, so that $C_1=T$;
n is the queue length corresponding to state vector (n,m).

This state space permits a more general flow control scheme than that described in the previous section:
(a) Any number of modes is possible, i.e. $M\geq2$;
(b) Mode changes may occur when the queue becomes empty (n=0). Initially, n=0 and m>1; C_m>T for a realistic system, otherwise congestion will never occur in the mode m. Subsequently, on entry to a state with n=0 from a state $(1,m')$, a _mode transition_ to mode m occurs with probability $\pi_{mm'}$. Thus, in the scheme defined in the previous section,
$$\pi_{mm'} = \begin{cases} 1 & \text{if } m=2 \\ 0 & \text{if } m=1 \end{cases}$$
Additional modes may be used to provide stability in the system by introducing intermediate capacities, preventing the immediate onset of repeated congestion. In fact the scheme can be generalised further, providing more stability, via multiple thresholds as discussed in 5.3
(c) A batch from message class r at the front of the hold queue is accepted into the server queue in state (n,m) iff the queue capacity would not be exceeded, i.e. iff $n+b_r\leq C_m$. Hence a form of blocking is present even in our approximate model.
(d) On crossing the threshold, congested mode is entered, i.e. a transition to a state (n,m) with $n\geq T$ causes m to be set to 1.

2.3 IMPLICIT REPRESENTATION OF THE CONGESTION CONTROL MECHANISMS

The window flow control scheme of the node is represented implicitly in the parameterization of the following two quantities for each class k, $1\leq k\leq R$:
(a) p_k, the probability that any given message in the hold or server queues belongs to class k. This is chosen to be proportional to the _window size_ as well as the _arrival rate_ of class k. Thus, $p_k \propto \lambda_k w_k$. The value of p_k will also be influenced by the window control through λ_k, as described next.
(b) u_k, the constraining factor on the arrival rate, λ_k, of class k batches, $0<u_k\leq1$. These constraints result from the rejection of class k message batches when their number in the hold and server queues is equal to their window size; the effective reducing of λ_k to 0. The _constrained arrival rate_ for class k is then $u_k\lambda_k$.
The value of u_k depends critically on transmission protocol. It is unity if re-transmission is attempted immediately after rejection, or equivalently if rejected batches are stored until they do become acceptable after further processing of sufficiently many class k messages. However, more commonly and inevitably if the total unconstrained message arrival rate (from all classes) exceeds the message processing rate, u_k depends on the distribution of batch classes in the hold and server queues. We denote the constraining factor for class k in state (n,m) by

$u_k(n)$: independent of m since the window control is mode-independent.
The approximation given below for $u_k(n)$ is based on the mean value of the length of the combined hold and server queues. We assume that the total number of messages in these queues has the same probability distribution, Z, as the length of the steady state M/M/1 single server queue with arrival

rate $\sum\limits_{k=1}^{R} u_k(n)\lambda_k b_k$, processing rate μ , and capacity $\sum\limits_{k=1}^{R} w_k b_k$,

henceforth denoted by Q. Thus $\{u_k(n)\}$ are defined recursively (and non-linearly) and may be determined iteratively, each being set to 1 initially and successively updated to the required precision. Convergnce is not considered formally here. Our approximation for $u_k(n)$ is derived as follows.

Let $\overline{q}(n)$ be the mean combined length of the hold and server queues in state (n,m). Thus,

$$\overline{q}(n) = \frac{\sum\limits_{j=n}^{Q} j\, Z(j)}{\sum\limits_{j=n}^{Q} Z(j)}$$

Then the corresponding <u>mean number of batches</u> in the hold and server queues is

$$\overline{m}(n) = \frac{\overline{q}(n)}{\sum\limits_{i=1}^{R} p_i(n) b_i} + 1/2$$

where $p_i(n) \propto u_i(n)\, \lambda_i w_i$ and we use the value of $u_i(n)$ given by the previous iteration to compute $p_i(n)$. The addition of 1/2 allows for the batch currently being processed.
The probability of the queues containing w class k batches, given total length m(n), is therefore

$$\binom{\overline{m}(n)}{w} \{p_k(n)\}^w \{1-p_k(n)\}^{\overline{m}(n)-w} \qquad (\overline{m}(n) \geq w)$$

and we define

$$u_k(n) = \begin{cases} \sum\limits_{w=0}^{w_k} \binom{\overline{m}(n)}{w} \{p_k(n)\}^w \{1-p_k(n)\}^{\overline{m}(n)-w} & (\overline{m}(n) \geq w_k) \\ \\ 1 & (\overline{m}(n) \leq w_k) \end{cases}$$

<u>Notes</u>:
(i) In general, $\overline{m}(n)$ is not an integer, and the generalized factorial function is used in the combinatorials to provide an interpolated estimate for $u_k(n)$ as a function of mean queue length.
(ii) This approximation assumes primarily that the hold queue length is always the same for any given server queue length. A more precise analysis which does not require this assumption is given in [HARR81a].

The credit allocation control scheme is reflected implicitly in the effective batch arrival rate in state (n,m),

$$\Lambda_{nm} = \frac{\displaystyle\sum_{\substack{i=1 \\ n+b_i \le C_m}}^{R} u_i(n)\,\lambda_i b_i}{\displaystyle\sum_{\substack{i=1 \\ n+b_i \le C_m}}^{R} p_i(n)\,b_i}$$

so that $\displaystyle\sum_{n+b_i \le C_m} u_i(n)\lambda_i b_i$ = overall message arrival rate in state (n,m)

= (effective batch arrival rate)
* (mean accepted batch size)

as required. Note that for degenerate b_i's or w_i's,

$$\Lambda_{nm} = \frac{\displaystyle\sum_{n+b_i \le C_m} u_i(n)\,\lambda_i}{\displaystyle\sum_{n+b_i \le C_m} p_i(n)}$$

again as required.

Note too that if batch arrival rates are unconstrained by window control, i.e. if $u_k(n)=1$ for each message class k and queue length n, Λ_{nm} may be inaccurate since, for example, one arrival stream may dominate through its high arrival rate and yet have a small, highly constraining window size.

2.4 THE BALANCE EQUATIONS

2.4.1 FURTHER DEFINITIONS

Before the balance equations can be derived, some more definitions are required:

$B_{nm}(k)$ = probability that the system is blocked in state (n,m) waiting to accept a batch of class k from the front of the hold queue, $1 \le k \le R$;

B_{nm} = probability of any blocking in state (n,m)

$= \displaystyle\sum_{k=1}^{R} B_{nm}(k)$;

We make the following (intuitively sound) approximation:

$$B_{nm}(k) = \begin{cases} A_{nm}p_k(n) & \text{if } b_k > C_m - n \\ 0 & \text{otherwise.} \end{cases}$$

where A_{nm} is the probability that there is at least one arrival of any class outstanding in the hold queue in state (n,m). The parameter A_{nm} is important in that its choice of value allows various different message batch acceptance protocols to be represented.

Some examples of relevant value assignments are:

(i)   For a re-transmit batch acceptance protocol in which a message batch is discarded if it cannot be accepted into the server queue immediately, no blocking occurs and A_{nm} = 0 for all $(n,m) \in S$.

Such a protocol is good as regards buffer protection and no hold queue is required. Throughput is not reduced significantly and it is the easiest case to model; the credit control scheme is redundant. However, the protocol is unfair to large batches which do not have bounded waiting time for service and suffer severely if there is heavy small batch traffic.

(ii) Hold queue with FCFS discipline and unbounded buffer size (unlimited queue length).

For state $(n,m) \in S$, let $\Lambda(n) = \sum\limits_{k=1}^{R} b_k \lambda_k u_k(n)$,

the total, window-constrained, external message arrival rate in state (n,m).

If $\Lambda(n) \geq \mu$, the system is overloaded and there will <u>always</u> be a blocked arrival; i.e. $A_{nm} = 1$.

If $\Lambda(n) < \mu$,

$A_{nm} = \text{Prob}$(total no. of messages in hold & server queues > n :

server queue length = n)

Considering the whole system as an M/M/1 single server queue, this yields

$A_{nm} = \text{Prob}$(queue length > n : queue length $\geq$ n)

$$= 1 - \frac{Z(n)}{\sum\limits_{j=n}^{Q} Z(j)}$$

in the notation of 2.3. This is the parameterization we choose for our model.

Clearly, further approximation has been introduced, but note that the result is exact for $\Lambda(n)=0$ and as $\Lambda(n) \to \infty$ with maximum allowed queue size approaching infinity. Furthermore, one would expect the inaccuracy introduced to be considerably less than that arising from the other approximations in the model.

With the problem now fully defined it is a relatively simple matter to write down the balance equations for the scheme. The node is assumed to be in a state of equilibrium with state space probability P_{nm} for state (n,m). In the forthcoming formulation, the batch arrival rate and the service rate of the message processor are taken to be constant for the sake of clarity; it will be noted that extension to state dependent $\lambda_k(n,m)$, $\mu(n,m)$ for $(n,m) \in S$ and $1 \leq k \leq R$ is a simple matter, the raw balance equations being considered directly.

2.4.2 SUPER-THRESHOLD STATES

Above the threshold, the mode m must be 1 by definition and the queue length $n \geq T$. The balance equations are then

$$\mu P_{n,1} = \sum\limits_{\substack{k=1 \\ b_k > n-T}}^{R} \sum\limits_{\substack{m=1 \\ C_m \geq n}}^{M} p_k(n-b_k) \Lambda_{n-b_k,m}(1-B_{n-b_k,m}) P_{n-b_k,m}$$

$$+ \mu \sum\limits_{\substack{k=1 \\ b_k > n+1-T}}^{R} \sum\limits_{\substack{m=1 \\ C_m = n}}^{M} B_{n+1-b_k,m}(k) P_{n+1-b_k,m}$$

$$+ \delta_{nT} \mu \sum\limits_{\substack{k=1 \\ b_k = 1}}^{R} B_{T,1}(k) P_{T,1}$$

$$+ \mu P_{n+1,1} \qquad\qquad\qquad (\delta \text{ is the Kronecker delta})$$

$P_{nm} = 0$ for $m > 1$.

NOTES ON THE TERMS ON THE R.H.S.

(i)   The factor $p_k(n-b_k) \, \Lambda_{n-b_k,m}$ is used in the first term as the arrival rate in state $(n-b_k,m)$ rather than λ_k to represent the window control mechanism;

(ii) The factor $(1-B_{n-b_k,m})$ is required since no arrivals are allowed if the node is in a blocked state;

(iii) The second term represents situations where the network <u>was</u> in a blocked state <u>below</u> the threshold, $(n+1-b_k,m)$, but on one service completion the waiting batch (of class k) can be accepted;

(iv) The third term is actually a special case of the second with $b_k=1$ and the mode $m=1$. It is considered separately for consistency with the numerical representation of the equations, see section 3.

2.4.3 SUB-THRESHOLD STATES

(a) For $1 \leq m \leq M$, $0 < n \leq T-1$,

$$\{ \mu + \Lambda_{nm}(1-B_{nm}) \sum_{b_k \leq C_m-n} p_k(n) \} \, P_{nm} =$$

$$\sum_{\substack{k=1 \\ b_k \leq n}}^{R} p_k(n-b_k) \, \Lambda_{n-b_k,m}(1-B_{n-b_k,m}) P_{n-b_k,m}$$

$$+ \, P_{n+1,m}\{1- \sum_{b_k=C_m-n} B_{n+1,m}(k)\} \, \mu$$

NOTES:

(i)   The coefficient of P_{nm} on the l.h.s. is the total transition rate from state (n,m). The factor $(1-B_{nm})$ is the probability that transitions are not invalid due to congestion, and the factor $\sum_{b_k \leq C_m-n} p_k(n)$ is needed since not all arrivals to the hold queue cause a transition in view of the credit control;

(ii) The first r.h.s. term represents regular external arrivals in a non-blocked state;

(iii) The second r.h.s. term represents a message service completion such that a waiting batch does not become acceptable as a result. For $n=T-1$, this term vanishes for $m \neq 1$ and requires $b_k=1$ for $m=1$;

(iv) There are no transitions to a sub-threshold state from a <u>blocked state,</u> as in (iii) of the previous section. Otherwise it would have occurred already on a previous service completion or as an intervening arrival.

(b) For $n=0$, $m>1$,

$$\Lambda_{0m}P_{0m} = \sum_{i=1}^{M} P_{1,i} \, \pi_{im} \, (1-B_{1,i}) \mu$$

Note here the mode transition, represented by the matrix $\underline{\underline{\pi}}$, on entry to a state with empty queue.

(c) $P_{01} = 0$.

3. NUMERICAL SOLUTION

3.1 THE STATE TRANSITION MATRIX AND STATE SPACE PROBABILITIES

The terms of the state transition matrix are simply written down straight from the balance equations. Suppose we have generalised balance equations with state space probability $P(\underline{s})$ for state vector $\underline{s}$ in state space S,

$$\Lambda(\underline{s})P(\underline{s}) = \sum_{\underline{t} \in S} P(\underline{t}) \, \mu(\underline{t} \to \underline{s})$$

where $\mu(\underline{t} \to \underline{s})$ is the flow rate from state $\underline{t}$ to state $\underline{s}$,
and $\Lambda(\underline{s})$ is the total flow rate out of state $\underline{s}$.
Then the normalised state transition probability matrix, $\underline{M}$, is given by

$$M_{\underline{ts}} = \frac{\mu(\underline{t} \to \underline{s})}{\Lambda(\underline{t})}$$

The state space probabilities, $\underline{P}$, are then the solution of the equations $\underline{P} = \underline{P}.\underline{M}$. Thus, given a suitable computer representation of the matrix $\underline{M}$, $\underline{P}$ and hence the usual resource based performance measures (see 5.1) may be derived according to the parameter values of the model.

3.2 NUMERICAL REPRESENTATION

The mapping between the states of S and the integers is fairly trivial, and once established permits immediate construction of the state transition matrix, and so computation of the state space probabilities. The 1-1 mapping is as follows:
For $n < T$, $1 \le m \le M$,

$\qquad (n,m) \dashrightarrow (m-1)T + n + 1$

For $n \ge T$, $m=1$,

$\qquad (n,m) \dashrightarrow (M-1)T + n + 1$

For $n \ge T$, $m > 1$, $P_{nm} = 0$ so these states are not represented.
This causes some minor programming problems, notably separate consideration of terms in the balance equations representing transitions across the threshold; see 2.4.2 (iv) and 2.4.3 (iii).

The size of the state space is $(M-1)T + \max_{1 \le m \le M} C_m + 1$, and the number of
elements in the transition matrix is the square of this value. Typically, M will be small, e.g. 2 in our original specification, and T and $\{C_m : 1 \le m \le M\}$ not large with respect to computational feasibility; in any case, the state space size is only _linear_ in T.

No storage optimization techniques have been found necessary, but the transition matrix is clearly suitable for sparse matrix processing techniques. These could be enhanced further using certain properties of the model. For example by considering separately the mode changes which can occur only in very few states; the intervening states enterable may then be considered to have only one component, the queue length. In particular, the state $(n,1)$ with $n > T$ can transit only to the state $(n-1,1)$ and thence, eventually, to $(T,1)$. Thus all super-threshold states could be lumped together into a single composite state. This would produce a more efficient implementation with respect to both execution time and storage, but results in loss of potentially important detail, viz. the queue length distribution above the threshold.

4. VALIDATION

4.1 THE SIMULATION MODEL

The analytic model defined in the previous sections was validated by comparing its predictions with those of a simulation model which represents the node's operating characteristics explicitly (although very much less efficiently). Whilst it is conceded that ultimate validation must be based on data monitored on at least one existing physical node, agreement with simulated results certainly supports confidence in our model; its implementation, but most importantly its approximations.

The simulation model is an algorithmic representation of the node defined in 2.1. It models explicitly the flow of messages in each class and the window flow control mechanism as well as the credit allocation/threshold congestion control scheme which is equivalent to two modes of congestion. All interarrival times and the message processor service times are drawn from negative exponential probability distributions (consistent with our Markov model), and messages rejected due to window flow constraints are discarded: a stream's arrival rate is effectively shut down to zero when it attempts to violate its window size limit.

The durations of the time periods simulated were chosen to be long enough to yield sufficiently small standard error estimates on the derived performance measures: of the order of 5%, see 4.3. Both the analytic formulae and simulation are simply programmed in APL, and run on an IBM 5100, the efficiency of which is conducive to performance evaluation by wrist watch! The analytic results for each test case required around 5 minutes of CPU time, whereas the corresponding simulation runs lasted some 10 hours.

4.2 NODE TEST CASES

In any test, the total message arrival rate from all classes must be at least close to the message processor's service rate in order that any congestion control become operative. Relatively low arrival rates were used to validate the implementations of the models - giving results close to those of corresponding M/M/1 queues, as required.

Similarly, for a node with all batches consisting of only a single message, the maximum queue length in all modes is the threshold value, since congested mode will be entered as soon as the queue reaches this size: the modes are degenerate. Here, the node is precisely a regular single server queue (M/M/1 under our Markovian assumptions) with the super-threshold states aggregated into one. Thus, for a single arrival stream of unit-sized batches with window size Q, in the notation of 2.3, we should have

$$P_i = Z(i) \qquad \text{for } 0 \le i < T$$
$$P_T = \sum_{j=T}^{Q} Z(j)$$

where we drop the redundant mode subscript. Now, batches can be blocked in the hold queue only in state $(T,1)$ and so the balance equations for our analytic model reduce (via the conventional method for the M/M/1 analysis) to

$$P_{i+1} = \rho(i)P_i \qquad \text{for } 0 \le i < T-1$$
$$P_T = (1-A_T)^{-1}\rho(T-1)P_{T-1}$$

where $\rho(i) = \Lambda(i)/\mu(i+1)$
for message arrival rate $\Lambda(i)$ and processing rate $\mu(i)$ in state $(i,1)$, and A_T is the probability of there being a batch waiting in the hold queue in state $(T,1)$, see 2.4. Now, $Z(i+1)=\rho(i)Z(i)$ for $0 \le i < Q$, so we require

$$\{1-A_T\}^{-1}Z(T) = \sum_{j=T}^{Q} Z(j)$$

which is satisfied by our definition of A in 2.4.

Numerical results are in agreement, but this merely provides some validation of the implementations of the analytic and simulation models. Note that although the modes are degenerate, for finite window sizes the arrival streams are not; they result in a multi-class single server queue.

The following selection of nodes defined for our validation was chosen to demonstrate the most significant characteristics of the flow controls:

(1) A node with 2 arrival streams and the threshold value sufficiently high for both the credit allocation and window flow control schemes to have significant effects. Note that a threshold above the sum of the products of the window size and batch size for each class would <u>never</u> be reached.

(2) The same node with the threshold reduced so that the credit allocation control scheme becomes dominant.

(3) The node with total (unconstrained) message arrival rate much higher than the message processor's service rate - a <u>saturated</u> node.

(4) A node with a third arrival stream of single message batches with relatively high arrival rate and window size. Such a stream allows the server queue length to remain at its threshold value after a service completion (in congested mode, of course), due to acceptance from the hold queue of a message batch of unit size.

The numerical parameterizations of these specifications are given in the tables of results below, along with their performance predictions. These test cases are a sub-set of a much more comprehensive set, revealing our most significant results as discussed in later sections.

4.3 ESTIMATION OF PERFORMANCE MEASURES

The primary performance measure, computed by both the analytic and simulation models for each test case (4.2), is the probability distribution of the server queue length. Secondary quantities then follow immediately, for example throughput, mean and standard deviation of queue length, expected message waiting time (through Little's Law). In some simulation runs, we also estimated the proportion of time that:

(a) Each arrival stream is inactive due to the window contol. In this way the validity of our approximation for $\{u_k(n)\}$, 2.3, could be judged directly.

(b) The hold queue is non-empty, with a class k batch at the front, $1 \leq k \leq R$. Hence the accuracy of our assignment of values to $\{A_{nm}\}$, 2.4, can be assessed for cases more complex than that discussed in 4.2.

(c) The node is in each mode. This can provide further validation by comparison with the appropriate marginal state space probabilities of the analytic model.

In each simulation run, initially both the hold and server queues are empty and the node is in non-congested mode. No data is collected until a period of 5 time constants has elapsed. The value used for the time constant is the reciprocal of the mean state transition rate, averaged over all states in the analytic model. We used primarily the sampling or "snapshot" method of data collection, described below, for our statistical analysis. Cumulative techniques were also used to provide an alternative approach, but the resulting estimates are not significantly different from, in fact are almost identical to, those based on the snapshot data. The cumulative variant is described in [HARR81b].

Snapshots of the node's state were sampled at a set of time points uniformly spaced at intervals of 2 time constants, the first at time equal to 5 time constants. If server queue length i is observed n_i times in a sample of N snapshots, the estimate for the equilibrium probability of queue length i is $\hat{p}_i = n_i/N$, $0 \leq i \leq I$, where I is the maximum possible queue length. Assuming that the sample is independently identically distributed according to true queue length probabilities $\{p_i : 0 \leq i \leq I\}$, n_i has binomial distribution with mean $N p_i$ and variance $N p_i (1-p_i)$.

Thus, $\hat{p}_i$ has expected value p_i (as required) and variance $p_i(1-p_i)/N$. Hence, $\hat{p}_i$ has standard error estimate

$$\sigma[\hat{p}_i] = \{\hat{p}_i(1-\hat{p}_i)/N\}^{0.5}$$

Since N is proportional to the (simulated) duration of the run, D say, the standard errors are proportional to $D^{-0.5}$. Thus to reduce the standard error estimates by a factor of f, the simulation run time must increase by a factor of f^2.

The <u>mean</u> queue length is estimated as $\sum_{i=1}^{I} i\hat{p}_i$ and so has standard errror

$$\{ \sum_{i=1}^{I} (i \, \sigma[\hat{p}_i])^2 \}^{0.5}$$

A numerical comparison of these performance measures as computed by the analytic and simulation models is presented in the tables below, with the goodness-of-fit assessed by the chi-squared test. Histograms derived for the server queue length probability distributions are shown in Figure 2.

4.4 ANALYSIS AND INTERPRETATION OF THE NUMERICAL RESULTS

4.4.1 OVERVIEW AND GENERAL OBSERVATIONS

From the tables and plots (Figure 2) it can be seen that the analytic and simulation results exhibit the same general characteristics: in terms of mean queue length, the distribution itself and their standard errors. The distribution is essentially bimodal (with the exception of the case with high arrival rate discussed below), decreasing from the idle probability (queue length zero) to a trough before the threshold queue length, increasing to a maximum at or immediately below the threshold and falling away sharply for queue lengths above the threshold. The corresponding single server queue results, with window flow controlled arrival rate and all super-threshold states lumped into one, bear little resemblance.

Apart from the general bimodal shape, there are other more local variations in the distributions. Denoting the probability of queue length n by P(n), for test cases 1-3, P(0)>P(1)<P(2)>P(3)<P(4), whereas in case 4 the probabilities are <u>monotonically</u> decreasing for sub-threshold queue lengths. This is simply explained by the absence of a single message batch stream in all cases but the fourth. The (queue length) transition 0->1 is then invalid and queue length 1 can only result from a transition 2->1, on a message completion. Thus P(1)<P(2) and the effect propagates to P(3) for precisely the same reason. Similarly in cases 1-3, P(T-1)>P(T) for threshold value T. This follows since the transition T->T is invalid (acceptance of a blocked single message batch on service completion) and so all super-threshold states must transit monotonely to state (T-1,1). Propagation analogous to that discussed above results in P(T-3)>P(T-2)<P(T-1) in cases 1 and 2, the effect being less pronounced in case 3 because of the counteracting high arrival rate.

In contrast, note that in case 4, the presence of the unit sized batches allows the transition T->T, yielding very emphatically P(T)>P(T-1). Furthermore, P(T-1)<P(T-2), explained by the existence of (T-1)->T (blocked arrival) transitions: no similar transition is possible from queue length T-2 and the effect is outweighed by the others in cases 1-3.

4.4.2 GOODNESS-OF-FIT

It is clear from our tables and graphs that there is very variable agreement between the analytic and simulation results: from very good (test case 1) to poor (case 3). The <u>mean</u> queue lengths for cases 1,2,4 certainly do not differ significantly (in terms of their standard error estimates); even case 3 is not outrageous here. However, more rigorous quantitative testing must be based on whole distributions. The proportion of analytically computed probability points lying outside the 2 x standard error confidence bands on the simulation results (Figure 2) are 0, 37, 100 and 12 per cent for cases 1-4 respectively. Excluding case 3, only one point differs by more than 3 standard errors (queue length 0 in case 2). Case 3 is the saturated node and is discussed in some detail in the next section.

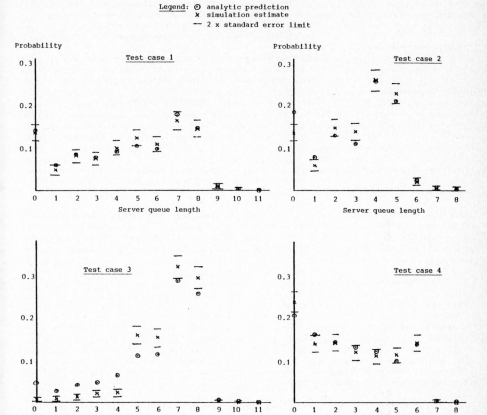

Figure 2

Predicted server queue length probability distributions

Note here that although quantitatively poor, its analytic predictions still exhibit general characteristics not inconsistent with the simulation.

Our primary statistical test for goodness-of-fit is the chi-squared test. This again reflects the variability of agreement, with values of the test statistic in the range 12-200 on 8-11 degrees of freedom. The corresponding percentage points indicate a fit which is good for case 1 (about 75%), reasonable for case 4 (96%) and poor for case 2 (99.9%); effectively 100% for case 3. These results are not too impressive in themselves, indeed rather surprising in case 2. But the chi-squared test is well known for its extreme and unforgiving sensitivity: just one or two points differing significantly yield a large contribution in the test statistic which consequently shows a poor fit regardless of the sizes of the contributions from the other points. This is precisely the situation in test cases 2 and 4, as well as many others not reported here, with particularly large contributions from small queue lengths (see the last columns in the tables). If such points are corrected or omitted, a good fit is indicated. Thus, although the chi-squared test may suggest a model worthless, it may be that for a (majority) sub-set of queue lengths the model provides a good representation - actually supported by this self-same test which may reject a whole theory on the basis of one point.

Our model, then, appears to provide a good, statistically supported representation of queue length behaviour if underload situations are excluded. This is especially true near the threshold, precisely where the control schemes modelled are most crucial and prediction is most important. Some possible causes for the inadequacies identified in the model are revealed next.

4.4.3 INTERPRETATIONS

(1) For many of the node specifications examined, cases 1-3 here, the simulation predicted a sharper peak in the queue length distribution at (or just below) the threshold. This is quite consistent with its lower predictions for the probability of zero queue length in that non congested mode would be entered less frequently. Thus the queue capacity would be greater than the threshold value less often, and hence the threshold will provide a more dominating constraint. In more general terms also, some smoothing of the peak in the analytic model is consistent with the aggregate type of representation of window control: discussed further below.

(2) As expected, the credit allocation control (CAC) dominated cases give the best agreement, e.g. case 1: CAC is modelled explicitly and in greater detail than the window flow control (WFC), represented only in terms of aggregate effects on arrival rates. Moreover the WFC has representation independent of the CAC and so of the threshold value. Thus, if it is inadequate, the analytic model cannot be expected to be accurate since its own input (arrival rate) parameters would be incorrect. This applies regardless of the threshold value, so that by a "CAC dominated" test case we really mean one in which WFC has little effect on arrival rates and not necessarily merely one with low threshold.

The good agreement obtained in case 1 is consistent with this argument, but greater positive support is provided by the poor results of test case 3 in which batch arrival rates were high and consequently adjusted by the WFC to a considerable extent. Certainly the significant probabilities predicted for queue lengths 0 and 1 are counter-intuitive, and we postulate that the inaccuracy arises from our representation of WFC. Exploring this possibility further, we tested a case with two arrival streams, one with much greater arrival rate but small window size. The resulting adjustments to the batch arrival rates were therefore substantial, even though the node was not overloaded. This test gave a chi-squared statistic of around 500 on 9 degrees of freedom, strongly suggesting that our arrival rate adjustment formula (2.3) is inadequate.

On re-computing the analytic results for this node specification and test case 3, using the WFC-constrained arrival rates estimated by monitoring the corresponding simulations (4.3 (b)) in place of the adjustment formula, much better agreement was obtained. A need for improvement in our representation of WFC is clearly identified, and may be provided to some extent through a refinement of our aggregate approach, [HARR81a]. A more detailed representation would be preferable, but recall that it is impractical for this to be fully explicit (2.1). Note that another similar possible source of inaccuracy is the formulation of the batch class selection probabilities, $\{p_k(n)\}$ of 2.3.

(3) Finally, and in the same vein as (2), the parameterisation of the blocking probabilities through $\{A_{nm}\}$ may lead to imprecision. Again the WFC representation is also significant through $\{p_k(n)\}$, as well as $\{A_{nm}\}$ to a lesser extent. However, tests using values for the blocking probabilities estimated in corresponding simulation runs (compare (2)) were inconclusive.

5. APPLICATIONS AND ENHANCEMENTS OF THE MODEL

5.1 PERFORMANCE METRICS

Most of the required performance measures can be derived from the state space probabilities, $\underline{P}$. These are as follows:
(i)   Server queue length probability distribution, marginal probabilities of the joint probability distribution, $\underline{P}$;
(ii) Server utilization, following directly from (i);
(iii) Server throughput;
(iv) Mean and standard deviation of the server queue length;
(v)   Distribution of the time delay for a message batch to pass through the message processor, a simple weighted convolution;
(vi) The power of the node, defined as

$$\frac{\text{Throughput of node}}{\text{Mean message time delay in both queues}}$$

$$= \frac{(\text{Throughput})^2}{\text{Sum of mean queue lengths}}$$

by Little's Law. Now the throughput may be derived from the node's state space probabilities and the sum of the mean queue lengths obtained by considering the whole system as an M/M/1 single server queue with window flow constrained arrival rate (2.3).

5.2 EXPERIMENTATION

Having derived expressions or algorithms for the performance measures listed in the previous section, one can attempt to optimize the node's performance in various ways, by selection of appropriate parameter values. For example,
(i)   In the graphs of throughput and power vs. mean time delay or mean queue length (related by Little's Law) for messages in the system, one can identify a knee and a peak respectively. Optimization would involve choosing model parameters to achieve positioning of these points which is best according to some objective; e.g. maximum throughput subject to some upper bound on mean time delay (reflecting provision of some pre-determined minimal service quality).
(ii) The distribution of the server queue length is important, particularly if service rate depends on queue size. Clearly a low probability of zero queue length is required (minimal idle time). In addition, the "spread" of the distribution should not be too great, otherwise the variance of the number of messages in the queue will be high, reflecting a highly variable message delay time and possible instability; a most undesirable effect, psychologically at least. Thus the ideal shape for the queue length distribution is that of a sharp peak at a length greater than zero. Furthermore, for a queue length dependent service rate, one would like to be able to choose parameter values such that the peak was located near the queue length yielding maximum service rate (the queue is finite, recall); in this way, throughput should be optimized also.

Considerable experimentation with parameter values, such as the threshold, mode capacities, batch and window sizes, is possible, since the significant characteristics of the flow control scheme are parameterized explicitly. Particular examples are suggested in [HARR81a].

5.3 EXTENSIONS TO THE MODEL

An immediate extension is to incorporate state-dependent parameters into the model; arrival and service rates in particular. Much more sophisticated optimization may then be undertaken, as in 5.2. Dynamic flow control schemes are being used increasingly, particularly in networks with distributed control functions. The parameters of such schemes are adjustable according to the current state of the network. For example, as congestion increases at any particular node, the node can reduce, or even shut down to zero in severe cases, the window sizes of some or all message classes. Of course the physical mechanism would involve transmission of control information on the network, requiring much more complex modelling which would be impracticable in our case. However it is a simple matter to incorporate queue length or mode dependent window sizes, w_r, represented by p_r and u_r in the balance equations. In this way, the distribution of messages with respect to class, entering the message processor queue may be controlled according to the current state.

State dependent mode capacities may be used to model stabilizing mechanisms which may operate physically by issuing variable (fractional or multiple) credits. Indeed in general, mode capacity is equivalent to the size of credits issued on sub-threshold message completion. Although a less trivial change, the balance equations are easily modified to accomodate such dynamic mode capacities. A form of dynamic message acceptance protocol is represented in this way.

A novel stability mechanism may be provided by the use of multiple thresholds. In our model, there is only one threshold, the only significance of which is that the mode, or queue capacity, may change when it is reached from below. The mode always becomes 1, congested, but there is no analytical reason for this restriction or why a mode transition probability matrix similar to $\underline{\pi}$ could not be used. Furthermore, such transitions are quite realistic and feasible, and capable of representation in the balance equations, on approaching the threshold from above as well as below; one could view the existing model as having unit mode transition matrix on reaching the threshold from above.

Using the possibility of a mode change at a queue length of n as the defining criterion for a threshold, the empty queue is also a threshold. Extending this argument, any number of thresholds may be defined, the mode being subject to change at any; approaching from above or below. In this way, stabilizing mechanisms may be represented via entry to intermediate modes or use of a threshold band to delay reversion to the old mode on returning through a threshold. The threshold band operates as follows:
    (i)   The band consists of two values for the queue length, T_A and T_B with $T_A < T_B$ for thresholds A and B respectively.
    (ii)   On reaching threshold B from below, the mode may change; to a "more congested" mode. For example, m may change from 2 to 1 in our test case with M=2 at the threshold with value T. On approach from above, no mode change occurs.
    (iii) Similarly, on reaching A from above, the mode may change; to a "less congested" mode. In the same example, m may change from 1 to 2 when the queue becomes empty. On approach from below, no mode change occurs.

It can be seen that this mechanism will prevent instability caused by oscillation of the queue length about a single threshold value having inverse mode transitions for approach from opposite directions. In fact in our example we have precisely a threshold band, with $T_A = 0$ and $T_B = T$, but far greater generality is possible.

6. CONCLUSION

An analytic model has been developed which can represent a wide range of nodes or subsystems in queueing networks with congestion control schemes. The equivalence of the credit- and mode-based control schemes, together with certain approximations yield a state space sufficiently small to permit feasible, direct, numerical solution of its balance equations; even for complex nodes with large buffer sizes. At the same time, enough detail of a modelled system, in terms of its parameters, is retained to achieve great generality; mainly through the acceptability of unrestricted state dependence of the parameter values.

The type of control modelled is node-to-node rather than end-to-end, based on single buffer capacity constraints and restrictions on the arrival processes to one processor. The control is <u>localized</u>, reflecting message pacing and single node protection, and is eminently suitable for application to networks with distributed flow control. End-to-end flow control is modelled via the window size parameters, although its explicit implementation is not.

Validation to date is encouraging, suggesting that our model provides a good analytic representation of nodes' behaviour, for server queue lengths near the threshold in particular. The choices of threshold value and mode capacities are crucial for optimizing performance, and this domain is the most important for prediction purposes. We therefore expect that the model can be a suitable tool for performance prediction in the next stage of our research effort: experimentation with multiple modes and thresholds in the development of dynamic stability mechanisms, see 5.3.

Perhaps of less obvious importance, it should be pointed out that in addition to providing a rich class of models, this modelling process has increased insight into and understanding of the corresponding physical processors; resulting in the proposals for new or extended congestion control schemes. A network consisting of nodes all of which possess flow control mechanisms of these types could provide dynamically well paced, efficient, fair and secure communication between end users.

ACKNOWLEDGEMENTS

The research reported in this paper originated during my recent visit to IBM Watson Research Center, Yorktown Heights, New York. I would like to extend my thanks to Frank Moss, Mischa Schwartz, Paul Green, but above all to Parviz Kermani, for all their help and advice.

REFERENCES

[CHAN77]   Chandy, K.M., Howard, J.H., Towsley, D.F., "Product Form and Local Balance in Queueing Networks", J.ACM 24,2.

[DAVI72]   Davies, D., "The Control of Congestion in Packet Switching Networks", IEEE Transactions on Communications, Vol. COM-20, No. 3, June 1972.

[HARR81a] Harrison, P.G., "Analytic model of a Communication Network Node with Flow Controls", IBM Research Report RC8832, Research report DoC81/9, May 1981, Department of Computing, Imperial College, London SW7 2BZ, England. Also submitted to <u>Computer Networks.</u>

[HARR81b] Harrison, P.G., "Performance Prediction of a Flow Control System using an Analytic Model", Research report DoC81/10, June 1981, Department of Computing, Imperial College, London SW7 2BZ, England.

[KERM80]   Kermani, P., Bharath-Kumar, K., "A Congestion Control Scheme for Window Flow Controlled Computer Networks", IBM Research Report No. RC8401.

[KLEI80]   Kleinrock, L., Gerla, M., "Flow Control: A Comparative Survey", IEEE Transactions on Communications, Vol. COM-28, No. 4, April 1980.

[LAM77]   Lam, S.S., "Queueing Networks with Population Size Constraints", IBM J. Res. Develop., July 1977.

[LAM79]   Lam, S.S., Reiser, M., "Congestion Control in Store and Forward Networks by Buffer Input Limits", IEEE Transactions on Communications, Vol. COM-27, No. 1, January 1979.

[WECK80]   Wecker, S., "DNA: The Digital Network Architecture", IEEE Transactions on Communications, Vol. COM-28, No. 4, April 1980.

Tables of results

NODE SPECIFICATION: 1

MESSAGE CLASSES: 1   2

ARRIVAL RATES   5.000   3.000
BATCH SIZES   2   4
WINDOW SIZES   3   2

MESSAGE PROCESSING RATE = 20.000
THRESHOLD VALUE =   8
NON-CONGESTED MODE CAPACITY = 11

QUEUE LENGTH	PROBABILITY: ANALYTIC	PROBABILITY: SIMULATION	STANDARD ERROR	PROBABILITY: M/M/1 QUEUE	CHI SQUARED CONTRIBUTION
0	.142	.137	.010	.068	.224
1	.060	.048	.006	.074	3.287
2	.086	.082	.008	.080	.239
3	.078	.075	.007	.086	.152
4	.092	.101	.009	.090	1.092
5	.106	.124	.009	.092	4.147
6	.099	.110	.009	.091	1.535
7	.178	.165	.010	.087	1.174
8	.147	.146	.010	.331	.009
9	.008	.010	.003	.000	.332
10	.003	.003	.001	.000	.098
11	.001	.000	.000	.000	1.222

SAMPLE SIZE = 1250
LENGTH OF TIME PERIOD SIMULATED = 112.095

MEAN QUEUE LENGTH
ANALYTIC: 4.497
SIMULATED: 4.562
STD ERROR: .140

CHI-SQUARED STATISTIC = 13.510 WITH 11 DEGREES OF FREEDOM

NODE SPECIFICATION: 2

MESSAGE CLASSES: 1   2

ARRIVAL RATES   5.000   3.000
BATCH SIZES   2   4
WINDOW SIZES   3   2

MESSAGE PROCESSING RATE = 20.000
THRESHOLD VALUE =   5
NON-CONGESTED MODE CAPACITY =   8

QUEUE LENGTH	PROBABILITY: ANALYTIC	PROBABILITY: SIMULATION	STANDARD ERROR	PROBABILITY: M/M/1 QUEUE	CHI SQUARED CONTRIBUTION
0	.184	.136	.010	.068	15.122
1	.078	.059	.007	.074	5.592
2	.129	.148	.010	.080	3.516
3	.110	.138	.010	.086	9.025
4	.257	.260	.012	.090	.054
5	.211	.228	.012	.602	1.790
6	.022	.021	.004	.000	.076
7	.007	.006	.002	.000	.281
8	.003	.004	.002	.000	.022

SAMPLE SIZE = 1250
LENGTH OF TIME PERIOD SIMULATED = 126.505

MEAN QUEUE LENGTH
ANALYTIC: 2.954
SIMULATED: 3.144
STD ERROR: .091

CHI-SQUARED STATISTIC = 35.477 WITH   8 DEGREES OF FREEDOM

NODE SPECIFICATION: 3

MESSAGE CLASSES:	1	2

ARRIVAL RATES	10.000	6.000
BATCH SIZES	2	4
WINDOW SIZES	3	2

MESSAGE PROCESSING RATE = 20.000
THRESHOLD VALUE = 8
NON-CONGESTED MODE CAPACITY = 11

QUEUE LENGTH	PROBABILITY: ANALYTIC	PROBABILITY: SIMULATION	STANDARD ERROR	PROBABILITY: M/M/1 QUEUE	CHI SQUARED CONTRIBUTION
0	.046	.006	.002	.001	42.705
1	.026	.008	.003	.002	15.091
2	.041	.013	.003	.003	24.282
3	.047	.021	.004	.005	17.867
4	.064	.023	.004	.007	33.280
5	.110	.159	.010	.010	27.326
6	.113	.153	.010	.016	17.901
7	.287	.320	.013	.024	4.589
8	.256	.294	.013	.932	7.401
9	.006	.002	.001	.000	4.576
10	.003	.001	.001	.000	1.680
11	.001	.000	.000	.000	1.068

SAMPLE SIZE = 1250
LENGTH OF TIME PERIOD SIMULATED = 104.202

MEAN QUEUE LENGTH
ANALYTIC: 5.881
SIMULATED: 6.516
STD ERROR: .162

CHI-SQUARED STATISTIC = 197.765 WITH 11 DEGREES OF FREEDOM

NODE SPECIFICATION: 4

MESSAGE CLASSES:	1	2	3

ARRIVAL RATES	8.000	2.000	2.000
BATCH SIZES	1	2	3
WINDOW SIZES	6	2	1

MESSAGE PROCESSING RATE = 20.000
THRESHOLD VALUE = 6
NON-CONGESTED MODE CAPACITY = 8

QUEUE LENGTH	PROBABILITY: ANALYTIC	PROBABILITY: SIMULATION	STANDARD ERROR	PROBABILITY: M/M/1 QUEUE	CHI SQUARED CONTRIBUTION
0	.204	.237	.012	.163	6.567
1	.160	.139	.010	.146	3.500
2	.143	.142	.010	.131	.013
3	.131	.118	.009	.117	1.782
4	.121	.109	.009	.105	1.628
5	.098	.112	.009	.094	2.319
6	.138	.141	.010	.244	.098
7	.003	.003	.002	.000	.024
8	.001	.000	.000	.000	.868

SAMPLE SIZE = 1250
LENGTH OF TIME PERIOD SIMULATED = 88.029

MEAN QUEUE LENGTH
ANALYTIC: 2.672
SIMULATED: 2.637
STD ERROR: .090

CHI-SQUARED STATISTIC = 16.798 WITH 8 DEGREES OF FREEDOM

LOCAL COMPUTER NETWORKS
P.C. Ravasio, G. Hopkins and N. Naffah (editors)
North-Holland Publishing Company
© IFIP, 1982

THROUGHPUT - DELAY ANALYSIS OF THE
NON SLOTTED AND NON PERSISTENT
CSMA-CD PROTOCOL

Thien Vo-Dai
Département d'informatique
Université Laval
Québec, P.O.
CANADA

This paper provides a throughput - delay analysis of the non
slotted and non persistent CSMA-CD protocol. An expression for
channel throughput as function of channel offered traffic is
obtained and its behavior is studied. The retransmission process is analysed and an optimal collission control algorithm is
obtained. An analytical expression for average transmission
delay is derived. Numerical results show that the CSMA-CD protocol is appropriate for local area networks in terms of channel capacity, transmission delay and channel stability.

INTRODUCTION

Local area networks are frequently thought of as the backbone for the office of
the futur and, as such, they are in rapid development [1]. A local area network
is conceptually a communication channel to which users access by a multiple access protocol [2,3]. The CSMA-CD (carrier sense multiple access with collision
detection) protocol as proposed for Ethernet [4] and proposed for standardization by the IEEE Society [5] appears to be appropriate for local area networks
and has been implemented in other local area networks such as Net/one [6] and
Localnet [7]. Performance measurement on an experimental Ethernet has proved
CSMA-CD to be an effective multiple access protocol for local area networks [8].

Three principal variants of the CSMA-CD protocol have been proposed, namely, the
non-persistent version, the P-persistent and the one-persistent [9]. In the
non-persistent CSMA-CD scheme, a station with a packet ready for transmission
senses the channel. If the channel is sensed idle, the station initiates transmission, listens for collision and if during transmission a collision is detected, the station aborts transmission and schedules retransmission according to
a collision control algorithm. If the channel is sensed busy, the station schedules transmission at some later time.

In Ethernet there is a collision concensus enforcement procedure in which a station, upon detection of a collision, momentary jams the channel. In the one
persistent CSMA-CD scheme [9], a station with a packet ready for transmission
senses the channel and proceeds as in the non-persistent CSMA-CD protocol, except
that, when the channel is sensed busy, it monitors the channel until it is sensed
idle and then initiates transmission of the packet.

The CSMA-CD protocol as described above has been analysed by Tobagi and Hunt 9
and Lam [10]. Metcalfe and Boggs [4] have proposed a model for estimating the
channel capacity of the Ethernet. The analyses in [9] and [10] assume that the
channel is time slotted and stations are synchronized such that tranmission must
start at the beginning of a time slot. The model proposed in [4] approximates
the channel as a slotted one during a collision conflict resolution period. However, in actual implementation, the channel is not time slotted so that network
persormance may be different from that assessed by these analyses.

The purpose of this paper is to perform a throughput-delay analysis of the non
slotted, non persistent CSMA-CD protocol. The one-persistent CSMA-CD protocol
can be analysed by the same techniques employed here and will be the subject of
a forth comming report. In section 2, some CSMA-CD terminologies are explained
and modelling assumptions are presented. In section 3, the throughput analysis
is treated. In section 4, a delay analysis for the CSMA-CD protocol is carried
out. Numerical results and discussion are presented in section 5.

DEFINITIONS AND ASSUMPTIONS

At any time the channel can be in one of the three possible states, namely, idle,
contention and transmission. In the idle state the channel carries no signal, in
the contention state it carries signals resulting from packets in collision or
jamming signals, and in the transmission state, it carries signals generated by
a packet progressing toward a successful transmission. The durations of an idle
state will be referred to as an idle period, that of a contention state a contention slot and that of a transmission state transmission interval (see fig. 1).

The points in time at which packets are scheduled for transmission form a sto-
chastic point process. They will be referred to as arrival times of the channel
traffic. As can be seen in Figure 1, in the CSMA-CD scheme, a transmission initiated at the end of an idle period goes through a vulnerable period called a
collision window in which collisions can take place. The size of a collision
window is the maximum end-to-end propagation delay between any two stations.
Packets in collision and jamming signals from the collision consensus enforcement
occupy the channel for the duration of a contention slot so that another transmission can be initiated only at the end of the idle period following this contention slot.

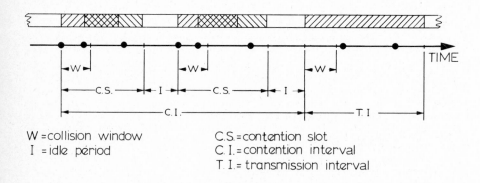

W =collision window   C.S.=contention slot
I = idle period   C.I.=contention interval
                             T.I.= transmission interval

Figure 1
Channels States

Many successive contention slots each of which separated by an idle interval, may
be generated before a successful transmission results. The time between the
beginning of the first and the end of the last of a series of successive contention slots will be referred to as a contention interval.

Our analysis of the CSMA-CD protocol will based on the following assumptions:

Assumption 1: Channel traffic is generated from an infinite population and has a Poisson arrival process with time invariant parameter.

Assumption 2: All transmissions initiated within a collision window collide.

Assumption 3: Propagation delays between any two stations are identical and jamming time is constant.

Assumption 4: Each station can transmit one packet at a time.

Assumption 5: The system has a steady-state.

Assumption 6: The channel is error free in the sense that packets are only lost through collisions.

Assumption 3 can be relaxed but the mathematical analysis would become much more complicated. Assumption 5 is necessary for delay analysis. Other assumptions necessary for delay analysis are discussed in section 4.

We will adopt the following notation for system parameters:

λ = parameter of the arrival process of channel traffic (in packets per unit time);

τ = collision window (end-to-end propagation delay);

π = average packet length (in bits);

σ = jamming time;

δ = $2\tau + \sigma$;

g = $\lambda\pi$ (normalized channel traffic intensity);
a = τ/π (normalized propagation delay);
d = δ/π.

The following notations will be used for system random variables:

I = length of an idle period;

X = length of a contention slot;

L = length of a contention interval;

T = length of a transmission interval (packet length);

Y = $X + I$.

Time unit is the channel bit-transmission time.

THROUGHPUT ANALYSIS

Channel throughput is usually defined as the fraction of channel bandwidth devoted to successful transmission. We identify the channel throughput as the probability that the channel is found in a transmission state.

We will prove the following theorem:

Theorem 1:

Channel throughput of a non-persistent CSMA-CD protocol is given by:

$$S = \frac{qe^{-ag}}{(1 + g)\, e^{-ag} + (ag + dg + e^{-ag})\,(1 - e^{-ag})}$$

□

To prove this theorem, we will need some propositions.

Proposition 1:

The length of a contention slot has following probability distribution:

$$\Pr\{X \le \delta + x\} = \begin{cases} 0 & \text{if } x < 0, \\ e^{-\lambda\tau}\,(1 - \dfrac{x}{\tau}) & \text{if } 0 \le x < \tau, \\ 1 & \text{if } x \ge \tau. \end{cases}$$

□

PROOF:

Let there be a transmission initiated at time 0 (see Figure 2). By the Assumption (2), there will be collision if there are other packets sche- culed for transmission within the collision window following time 0. Let this be the case. By the Assumption (3) (identical propagation delays), at time τ all stations transmitting within the collision window will de- tect collision (with the packet initiated at time 0) and jam the channel. The jamming signal will last until time δ. Thus the channel cannot be free before time δ.

The station initiating transmission at time 0 is the last to detect colli- sion. It will detect collision before time x + τ if all other stations initiate transmission before time x. In this case its jamming signal will die before time δ + x with x ≥ 0.

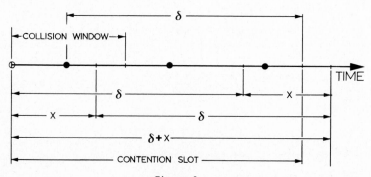

Figure 2
A Contention Slot

By the Assumption 1, if there are n arrivals in the collision window, they are uniformly distributed in the time interval $[0, \tau]$. Thus, the probability that a transmission is initiated in the time interval $[0, x]$ given that there are n transmissions initiated in the interval $[0, \tau]$ is x/τ. Thus:

Pr {channel free at $\delta + x$ | n arrivals in $[0, \tau]$}.

$$= \left(\frac{x}{\tau}\right)^n, \ 0 \leq x < \tau. \tag{1}$$

By eq. (1) and by the Assumption (1), the probability that the channel is free at time $\delta + x$ is:

$$F_X(x) = Pr\{X \leq \delta + x\},$$

$$= \sum_{n=0}^{\infty} \left(\frac{x}{\tau}\right)^n \frac{(\lambda\tau)^n}{n!} e^{-\lambda\tau}, \ 0 \leq x < \tau, \tag{2}$$

$$= e^{-\lambda\tau(1 - \frac{x}{\tau})}, \ 0 \leq x < \tau.$$

Since the latest transmission initiated within the collision window is at most at time τ, the channel must be free at time $\delta + \tau$:

$$F_X(x) = 1, \ if \ x \geq \tau. \tag{3}$$

By Assumption (1), the contention slots form a renewal process. This observation together with Eqs. (2) and (3) imply proposition 1. □

Proposition 2:

The length L of a contention interval is given by:

$$L = Y_1 + Y_2 + \ldots + Y_N$$

where N is a discrete random variable independent of the Y_i and has geometric distribution with parameter $p = (1 - e^{-\lambda\tau})$ and the Y_i are identically and independently distributed with:

$$Y_i = X + I.$$

□

PROOF: Let $X_1, X_2, \ldots, X_N$ be the successive contention slots in a contention interval and $I_1, I_2, \ldots, I_N$ be the idle periods alternating between these contention slots.

Let

$$Y_i = X_i + I_i \tag{4}$$

Then:

$$Y = Y_1 + Y_2 \ \ldots + Y_N. \tag{5}$$

By the assumption (1), the Y_i form a renewal process and N is independent of Y_i. By the assumption (2), N is a Bernoulli trial process with success parameter p being the probability that a collision window contains at least one arrival. By the assumption (1), we have:

$$p = (1 - e^{-\lambda\tau}). \tag{6}$$

□

PROOF OF THEOREM 1: By a well known result from the theory of renewal processes, we have:

$$S = \frac{E[T]}{E[I] + E[L] + E[T].} \tag{7}$$

By assumption 1, we have:

$$E[I] = \frac{1}{\lambda}. \tag{8}$$

By assumption 4, we have:

$$E[T] = \pi. \tag{9}$$

From proposition 2 and the independence of Y and N, we have:

$$E[L] = E[Y]E[N], \tag{10}$$

where

$$E[N] = \frac{1 - e^{-\lambda\tau}}{e^{-\lambda\tau}} \tag{11}$$

and $$E[Y] = E[I] + E[X]. \tag{12}$$

But from proposition 1, it is trivial to prove that:

$$E[X] = \frac{1}{\lambda} (e^{-\lambda\tau} + \lambda\tau - 1) + \delta \tag{13}$$

Combining Eqs. 8 - 13, we have theorem 1. □

Corollary 1.1:

Channel throughput of a non-persistent CSMA protocol (without collision detection) with fixed packet length can be obtained from theorem 1 by putting $a = 1 + v/\pi$ and $d = 1 + (2v/\pi)$ where v is the end-to-end propagation delay. □

PROOF: In the CSMA protocol, the vulnerable period following a transmission lasts for the whole duration of the packet transmission plus the propagation delay to all other stations. Thus, the collision window has a length of $\tau = v + \pi$, where v is the propagation delay. Furthermore, each transmission initiated in a collision window engenders a busy period which lasts for a time equal to

$\delta = 2v + \pi$. $\square$

Corollary 1.2:

The channel throughput S is a bell-shape function of g and tends to zero when $g \to \infty$. The channel capacity (maximum throughput) C admits an upper-bound given by:

$$C < \frac{1}{1 + Z_0 \,(a + d)}$$

where Z_0 is a solution of the equation:

$$Z \ln (1 + Z) = \frac{a}{a + d} ,$$ $\square$.

PROOF: See the Appendix $\square$.

Corollary 1.2 tells us that when the offered channel traffic gets very large the channel throughput tends to zero, the channel capacity may be found by maximizing S with respect to g, and the channel capacity is inferior to 1.

DELAY ANALYSIS

We define channel delay as the mean elapsed time from the time a packet is ready for transmission until it is successfully transmitted. Channel delay depends very much on the retransmission control mechanism. We will first analyse the retransmission process in order to make reasonable assumptions about the retransmission control algorithm which will allow us to obtain an analytical expression for channel delay.

Retransmission control mechanism

In the CSMA-CD protocol a transmitting station, upon detection of a collision, jams the channel for a period of σ time units, waits until the jamming signal reaches all other station, then schedules for retransmission according to some probability distribution. Taking the time origin as the time at which the station initiates transmission, as measured by the station's own clock, the time to the next retransmission is determined by the following:

Assumption 7:   if a collision is detected, the station scheduled a retransmission at a later time sampled from a uniform distribution in the interval (δ, Σ).

When a number of stations initiate transmission in an interval of τ time units, they will all experience packet collision. We have:

Proposition 3:   given that there are n stations all initiating transmission in the interval $(0, \tau)$, their scheduled retransmission times R_1, R_2, ... R_n measured from time origin 0 has the following probabilily density function:

$$f \,(r_1, r_2, \ldots r_n) = n! \prod_{i=1}^{n} f \,(r_i),$$

where we have adopted the ordering of the retransmission times such that $R_1 \leq R_2 \leq \dots \leq R_n$ and where:

$$f(r) = \begin{cases} \dfrac{r-\delta}{\tau(\Sigma-\delta)}, & \delta \leq r < \tau+\delta, \\[2ex] \dfrac{1}{\Sigma-\delta}, & \tau+\delta \leq r < \Sigma, \\[2ex] \dfrac{\Sigma+\tau-r}{\tau(\Sigma-\delta)}, & \Sigma \leq r < \Sigma+\tau. \end{cases}$$

PROOF: let Z be the sampled retransmission time obtained by a station. By Assumption 7, Z has the following probability density function:

$$g(z) = \begin{cases} \dfrac{1}{\Sigma-\delta} & \text{if } \delta \leq z \leq \Sigma, \\[2ex] 0 & \text{otherwise.} \end{cases} \qquad (14)$$

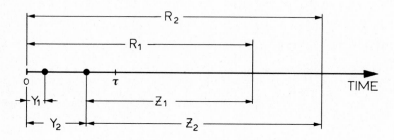

Figure 3
Retransmission Control Mechanism

Let Y be the time measured from origin 0 to the time at which a station detects collision. The relationship between Z and Y and R is shown in fig. 3. By Assumption 1, Y has a uniform probability density function:

$$h(y) = \begin{cases} \dfrac{1}{\tau}, & 0 \leq y < \tau \\[2ex] 0 & \text{otherwise.} \end{cases} \qquad (15)$$

The retransmission time for a station which detects a collision in the interval $(0, \tau)$ is just a random variable $R = Z + Y$ admitting the probability density function:

$$f(r) = \int_0^\infty g(r)\, h(r-y)\, dy \qquad (16)$$

By integration and by Eqs (14) and (15), we obtain the function f given in the proposition. The joint probability density function for the retransmission times is just that of the order statistics $R_1 < R_2 < \ldots < R_n$ for n samples of R. ☐

Proposition 4: Given that there are n stations all initiating transmission in the interval $(0, \tau)$, the probability that a retransmission success at the earliest time $R_1 = r$ is given by:

$$h(r) = nf(r) [(1 - F(r + \tau)]^{n-1}$$

where $F(x)$ is the cummulative distribution corresponding $f(x)$, provided that there be no other transmission initiated before time $R_1 = r$. ☐

PROOF: By proposition 3, the joint probability density function for R_1 and R_2 can be obtained by integration as:

$$f(r_1, r_2) = n(n - 1) f(r_1) f(r_2) [1 - F(r_2)]^{n-2} \tag{17}$$

Let $R = R_1$ and $Q = R_2 - R_1$, the joint probability density function for R and Q can be obtained from Eq. 17 as:

$$g(r, q) = n(n - 1) f(r) f(r + q) [1 - F(r + q)]^{n-2} \tag{18}$$

We are interested in the probability $h(r)$ that the retransmission scheduled at time $R_1 = r$ succeeds. Since a success will result if $R_2 - R_1 > \tau$, we have, by applying Eq. 18:

$$h(r) = \int_{\tau}^{\Sigma + \tau} g(r, q) \, dq$$

$$= nf(r) [1 - F(r + \tau)]^{n-1}. \quad ☐$$

When a number of stations having initiated transmission detect collision and sample the retransmission times, we say that they participate in collision conflict resolution. We say that a conflict resolution is <u>potentially successful</u> if, given that there is no other transmission scheduled before the time R_1 e.g. due to a new packet, the retransmission initiated at the earliest scheduled time R_1 succeeds.

Theorem 2:

Given that there are n stations participating in a collision conflict resolution, the probability that the resolution is potentially successful is:

$$P = \left[1 - \frac{\tau}{2(\Sigma - \delta)} \right]^n$$

PROOF: By proposition 4, the probability of success at the earliest retransmission time is given by:

$$P = \int_{\delta}^{\Sigma + \tau} h(q)\, dq$$

$$= \left\{ [1 - F(r + \tau)]^n \right\}_{\delta}^{\Sigma + \tau}$$

$$= [1 - F(\tau + \delta)]^n$$

But by proposition 3, we have:

$$F(\tau + \delta) = \frac{1}{2}\, \tau \cdot \frac{1}{\Sigma - \delta} \cdot \square$$

Let $K = 2(\Sigma - \delta)/\tau$. Then $P \to 0$ when $n \to \infty$ if K is independent of n. Thus, under heavy load the number of packets queueing for transmission would increase indefinitely if the retransmission mechanism is not dynamically controlled. The retransmission control algorithm should make K dependent on n such that the success probability $P = [1 - 1/K(n)]**(n)$ remains finite in the limit $n \to \infty$. An optimal choise in terms of retransmission delay for the function $K(n)$ is given by:

> Assumption 8: the collision control algorithm adjusts the mean retransmission delay such that $K = 4 \alpha n$.

Then we have:

$$\lim_{n \to \infty} P = e^{-\frac{1}{4\alpha}} \tag{19}$$

For finite n, $P < \exp(-1/4\, \alpha)$.

Assumption 8 implies that the number of stations participating in a collision conflict resolution is exactly known to the collision control algorithm. In practice this number can only be estimated by some algorithm.

So far we have discussed only the retransmission mechanism for collision conflict resolution. Retransmission when the channel is sensed busy is governed by:

> Assumption 9: if the channel is sensed busy, the station schedules a retransmission at some later time sampled from a distribution with fixed mean β.

Channel delay

Let γ be the channel input rate measured in terms of number of packet per time unit. By assumption 5, γ must equal the channel output rate:

$$\gamma = \frac{S}{\pi} \tag{20}$$

The channel can be pictured as a queueing system in which the service time includes packet transmission time and collision conflict resolution time. Let $\overline{W}$ be
channel delay (average waiting time) and $\overline{N}$ be the average number of packet in our
queueing system. An application of Little's formula yields:

$$\overline{N} = \gamma \overline{W} . \tag{21}$$

By Assumption 1, the probability that an arbitrary packet offered to the channel
is successfully transmitted is given by:

$$P_S = \frac{S}{g} . \tag{22}$$

The average number of retransmission per packet is $g/_S - 1$.

Thus channel delay is given by:

$$\overline{W} = (\frac{g}{S} - 1) \overline{D} + \pi, \tag{23}$$

where $\overline{D}$ is the average elapsed time between two successive retransmission. The
random variable D will be referred to as retransmission delay.

When a retransmission is scheduled because the channel is sensed busy, the average retransmission delay is (by the Assumption 9):

$$D_B = \beta \tag{24}$$

When a retransmission is scheduled because a collision is detected, the average
retransmission delay depends on the average number of packet's queueing for
transmission, $\overline{N}$, and is given by Assumptions (7) and (8):

$$D_C = \delta + \frac{1}{2} (\Sigma - \delta) \tag{25}$$

$$= \delta + \overline{N}\alpha\tau .$$

Given that a packet is offered to the channel when it is in a contention interval,
the probability that the packet experiences a collision is:

$$P_C = \frac{\tau}{E[X]} = \frac{\text{collision window}}{\text{average contention slot}}$$

$$= \frac{\lambda\tau}{e^{-\lambda\tau} + \lambda(\tau + \delta) - 1} \tag{26}$$

Taking into account of the probabilities of possible events we can write an expression for the average retransmission delay as:

$$\overline{D} = SD_B + (1 - S) [P_C D_C + (1 - P_C) D_B]$$

$$= S\beta + (1 - S) [P_C (\delta + \overline{N} \alpha \tau) + (1 - P_C) B]. \tag{27}$$

Eqs. (21), (23), (27) allow us to solve for $\overline{N}$, $\overline{D}$ and $\overline{W}$ and obtain:

> Theorem 3: The normalized channel delay incurred by the CSMA-CD protocol is given by:
>
> $$\frac{W}{\pi} = \frac{1 + N_R \{Sb + (1 - S) [P_c d + (1 - P_c) b]\}}{1 - N_R \alpha P_c (1 - S) Sa}$$

where $N_R = g/S - 1$, $b = \beta/\pi$. □

The normalized channel delay depends on g, the channel traffic, which in term depends on S. Corresponding to a fixed value of S, Theorem 1 allows on to determine two values for g, say g_1 and g_2, for channel traffic. The smaller traffic, g_1, will be assumed to correspond to the operation point for the channel and channel delay will be based on g_1.

NUMERICAL RESULTS AND DISCUSSION

We plot channel throughput as a function of channel traffic for various values of normalized propagation delay in Fig. 4. For a = 1, channel capacity is about 16%, for a = 0.1, it is about 68% and for a = 0.001 it reaches 99%. Channel capacity increases very slowly with decreasing propagation delay below the value 0.01, i.e. for a < 0.01. At a = 0.01 it already reached 95%.

Since in local area networks, the propagation delay is in the range 0.01 - 0.001, the CSMA-CD protocol is therefore a very effective multiple access protocol for local area networks. For a < 0.01, channel capacity is very close to the upper bound established in Corollary 1.2 for all cases shown in Fig. 4. Therefore, for a ≪ 0.01 and d = 2a, we can use the formula

$$C \simeq \frac{1}{1 + .75 *3a}$$

to obtain a good approximation for channel capacity.

For fixed values of network parameters a and d, Theorem 1 establishes three regions for channel traffic (Fig. 5). With traffic in the region $(0, G_c)$ which we call operational region, channel throughput increases with channel traffic. For traffic in the region (G_C, G_{max}) which we call unstable region, channel throughput decreases as channel traffic increases. When traffic is in the region $G > G_{max}$ which we call unfeasible region, channel throughput is zero.

For an input rate corresponding to a channel throughput S_0, the retransmission mechanism adopted by the network can make the channel operate in principle with channel traffic at G_0 in the operational region or at G_u in the unstable region. In practice the input rate behaves in such a way that channel traffic would fluctuate. If the channel operates at traffic G_0, channel throughput would fluctuate in the same direction as channel traffic so that channel throughput would fluctuate about the equilibrium level, S_0. At traffic level G_u, channel throughput decreasing as channel traffic increases above G_u, channel traffic tends to accumulate and finally pulls the channel into the unfeasible region.

From the proceeding discussion, it can be seen that any CSMA-CD channel is potentially unstable in the sence that statistical fluctuation can push channel throughput beyond the level G_c from which the channel can tend to the zero-throughput state. Hence G_c is a good measure of the channel stability and we will refer to it as critical traffic.

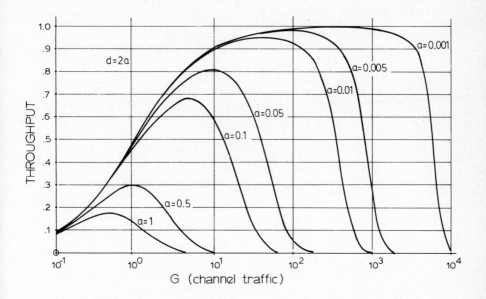

Figure 4
Throughput Characteristics

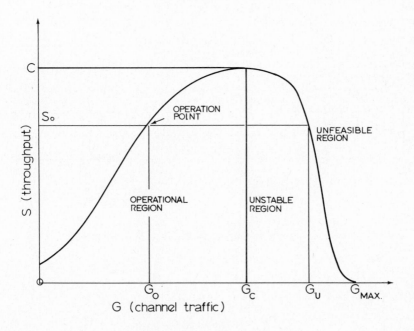

Figure 5
Operational Region for CSMA-CD

From Fig. 4, we see that although channel throughput is gained quite unsignificantly by decreasing a below the value 0.01, critical traffic is considerably gained by doing so. Thus, channels with very small propagation delay are expected to be stable. Since for local area networks a is in 0.01 - 0.001, the CSMA-CD protocol is very appropriate to them.

In Fig. 6, the throughput curves are plotted for various well-know multiple access protocol including CSMA-CD, for slotted as well as non-slotted versions. It can be seen that, for CSMA-CD, the throughput behavior is practically the same for slotted and non-slotted versions in the operational region. The slotted CSMA-CD protocol is a little more stable than the non-slotted one.

We plot normalized channel delay as a function of throughput for a = 0.01, 0.005 and 0.001. The delay curve are typical of queueing delay and are practically the same for channel operating at these propagation delays for channel throughput up to 90%. Channel delay is about 2 times the average packet transmission time for S = 60%, about 5 times for S = 80% and about 10 times for S = 90% (see Fig. 7).

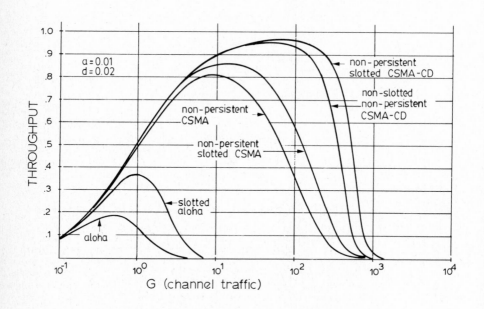

Figure 6
Comparison of Throughputs of Various Multiple Access Protocols

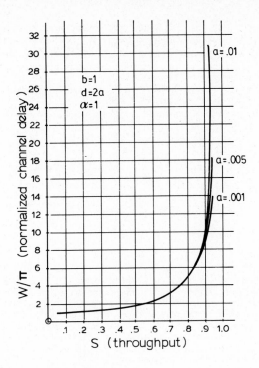

Figure 7
Delay Characteristics

CONCLUSION

The non persistent and non-slotted CSMA-CD protocol offers excellent channel capacity to networks in which the end to end propagation delay between any two stations is small in comparison with the mean packet transmission time. For typical local area networks, channel capacity is above the 95% level. The normalized propagation delay is an important factor for channel stability and we observe
that, although channel capacity does not increase significantly by decreasing the
normalized propagation delay below the value 0.01, channel stability is considerably gained. Our results show that local area networks operating with CSMA-CD
are expected to be stable.

For channels with normalized propagation delay equal to 0.01, the throughput
behavior is practically the same for slotted and non-slotted CSMA-CD protocols.
We expect the same behavior for channel with smaller normalized propagation delay.

Our analysis of the retransmission process shows that an optimal choice for the
mean retransmission delay when collision is detected is to make it proportional
to the number of packets in collision. With this collision control mechanism,
channel delay is quite small for typical local area networks.

ACKNOWLEDGEMENT

The author would like to acknowledge helpful discussions with A. Dubuque, M. Finley and G. Simian. He would like to thank G. Turcotte for computational assistance. The referees' comments have helped improve the presentation of this paper. This work is supported partly by the National Research Council of Canada under grant number A 3380 and by the F.C.A.C. program of the Ministère de l'Education du Québec, Canada, under grant number EQ - 1981.

APPENDIX

Proof of corollary 1.2

We proceed by a graphical method. Put $x = \exp(-ag)$, Theorem 1 implies:

$$g = g(x) = \frac{Sx\,(2 - x)}{[1 - S\,(1 - a - d)]\,x - S\,(a + d)} \, . \tag{A.1}$$

But by definition of x, we have:

$$ag(x) = -\ln x \tag{A.2}$$

Thus, for a given value of $S < 1$, x is a solution to Eq. (A.2) which can be found by a graphical method (see Figure A.1). The function $ag(x)$ is rational, admitting the straight line $x = x_0 = 1/[1 + (1 - S)\,/S\,(a + d)]$ as an asymptotic and is monotonically decreasing from $x = x_0$ to $x = \infty$. In general, for a given value of S, Eq. (A.2) may have two solutions, x_1 and x_2, corresponding to two values, $g(x_1)$ and $g(x_2)$, of g (this is true because the function $-\ln(x)$ is also monotonically decreasing function for $x > 0$). When $S \to 1$, $x_0 \to 1$, and x_1 and x_2 get closer and closer together. There is one value of S, S_{max}, for which $x_1 = x_2$. When $S > S_{max}$, the curve representing the function $ag(x)$ does not intercept with the curve representing the function $-\ln(x)$.

We have just proved that the throughput S is a bell-shape function of g. We now establish an upperbound for the throughput.

Let $y = \frac{1 - S}{S}$. Let y_1 be the interception of the straight line $x = x_0$ with the curve representing the function $-\ln(x)$ and let $y_2 = ag(1)$ (see Figure A.1). We have:

$$y_1 = \frac{a}{y} \, ,$$

and

$$y_2 = -\ln \left(\frac{1}{1 + \frac{y}{a + d}} \right)$$

From Figure A.1, we have:

$$y_1 < ag(x_2) < ag(x_1) < y_2 .$$

When S increases, y decreases, y_1 gets closer to y_2 and $y(x_1)$ gets closer to $y(x_2)$. The maximum value of S, C, is such that $y(x_1) = y(x_2)$. Thus, C must be less than the value of S, S_0, for which $y_1 = y_2$, i.e.:

$$\frac{a}{y} = - \ln \frac{1}{1 + \frac{y}{a + d}} \cdot \qquad (A.3)$$

Putting $Z = y/(a + d)$, Eq. (A.3) becomes:

$$Z \ln(1 + Z) = \frac{a}{a + d} \cdot \qquad (A.4)$$

Let Z_0 be a solution to Eq. (A.4). By the definition of Z, we have:

$$\frac{1 - S_0}{S_0} = Z_0 (a + d)$$

so that:

$$S_0 = \frac{1}{1 + Z_0 (a + d)} \cdot$$

Hence $C < S_0$.

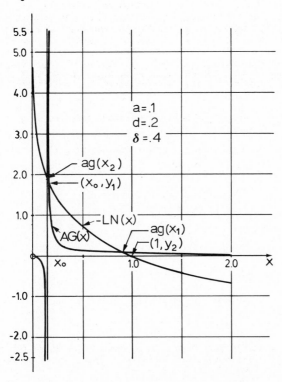

Figure A.1
Graphical Interpretation of the Relationship Between Channel Throughput and
and Channel Traffic

REFERENCES

1. Thurber J.T. and Freeman A.F., Tutorial Local Computer Networks. IEEE Compu-
    ter Society, 1980.

2. Tobagi F.A., "Multiacces Protocols in Packet Communication System", IEEE Trans.
    Com., COM-28, 4, p. 468-488, 1980.

3. Lam S.S., "Multiple access protocols", Computer Communication: State of the
    Art and Direction for the Future, edited by W. Chou, Prentice-Hall, 1980.

4. Metcalfe M. and Boggs, "Ethernet: distributed packet snitching for local com-
    puter networks", Com. of the A C M, Vol. 19, 7, p. 395-404.

5. IEEE 802 DLMAC Working Group on CSMA/CD, "IEEE 802 CSMA/CD Media Access Stan-
    dard", Draft of working group report, Jan. 1981.

6. Bass C., Kennedy J.S. and Davidson J.M., "Local Network gives new flexibility
    to distributed processing", Electronics, Sept. 1980.

7. Gravis H., "Local networks prove practical for datacom systems in closed
    proximity", Datamation p. 98, March 1981.

8. Shoch J.R., and Hupp J.A., Comm. of the ACM, vol. 23, no. 2, December 1980.

9. Tobagi F.A., and Hunt V.B., "Performance Analysis of Carrier Sense Multiple
    Access with Collision Detection", Computer Networks, Vol. 4, N. 5, pp. 245-
    259, 1980.

10. Lam, S.S., "A Study of the CSMA protocol in local networks", Proc. Fourth
    Berkeley Conference on Distributed Date Management and Computer Networks,
    San Francisco, August 1979.

LOCAL COMPUTER NETWORKS
P.C. Ravasio, G. Hopkins and N. Naffah (editors)
North-Holland Publishing Company
© IFIP, 1982

PERFORMANCE ANALYSIS OF LOOP COMPUTER NETWORKS

Gojko A. Babić

Institute for Computer and Information Systems
IRIS - Energoinvest
Sarajevo
Yugoslavia

In this paper, we develop a new approach to analyzing
loop computer networks. It is simple and general, and can
be efficiently used to analyze a symmetric or asymmetric
loop computer network having any number of hosts and
using any transmission mechanism (DLCN, Newhall or Pierce).
We illustrate our approach by analyzing the loop computer
network to support transaction processing against a distributed data base and analytical expressions for calculating
different network parameters are derived. Also, we describe
corresponding simulation models. Results obtained from
analytical and simulation models are compared and agreement
between these results is reasonable and for some parameters
very good.

I. INTRODUCTION

In this paper, we present a performance analysis of a loop computer
network consisting of a loop communication network and attached components (hosts) with associated terminals (figure 1). Meaningful
analyses of loop computer networks require the use of quantitative
analytical tools. Queueing-theoretic models of centralized computer
systems consisting of one or more CPU's, several I/O processors,
terminals and other peripherals have been studied intensively (e.g.,
/BAS75, BRO75, BRO77, LIP77/). Also, queueing analyses of different
kinds of loop communication networks have been performed by many
researchers (e.g., /KON72, SPR72, YUE72, KAY72, ROB74, CAR77, HAY71/).

However, all of these papers dealt only with either centralized
computer systems or loop communication networks, none of them
considered a loop computer network as a unified system. A paper by
Labetoulle, et al. /LAB77/ is the only work that analyzed a loop
computer network, but their approach is applicable only to homogeneous (symmetric) loop computer network (a network with identical
hosts characteristics) with few hosts using the Newhall transmission
mechanism /FAR69/. Here in this paper, we introduce our simple and
general approach to analyzing loop computer networks. Our approach
is iterative and can handle a heterogeneous (asymmetric) loop computer
network (a network with different host characteristics) with any
number of hosts and any kind of transmission mechanism.

The paper is organized in the following way. In Section II, the
approach is described. In the succeeding sections, we illustrate our
approach by analyzing the loop computer network to support a distributed data base. The third section contains a functional description
of the system under consideration and the network of queues obtained

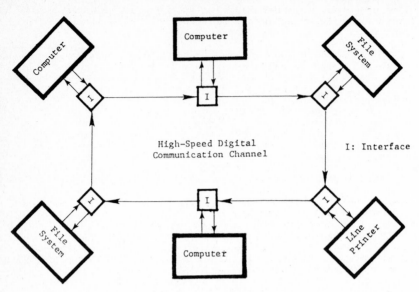

Figure 1
Hardware Structure of Loop Computer Network

as a corresponding analytical model. In the fourth section, we derive
closed-form analytical expressions for calculating several design
parameters, viz., average response times to users, average queue
lengths and utilization of processors. The technique that we develop
is applied to a symmetric network and to an asymmetric network. In
Section V, in order to verify and evaluate our approach, analytical
results are compared to a simulation model. It turns out that the
results agree over a wide range of interest, supporting the validity
of our approach. Finally, in Section VI, a summary of the paper is
given.

II. APPROACH TO ANALYSIS OF LOOP COMPUTER NETWORK

The successful analysis of a loop communication network is crucial
for the analysis of a loop computer network. This point is illustrated
in the work by Labetoulle, et al. /LAB77/, where they analyzed a homogeneous loop computer network using the Newhall transmission mechanism, exemplified by MININET /MAN77/. The lack of analytical results
for the average message delay in the Newhall loop was an important
reason why they were only able to model accurately a loop computer
network including few hosts. They concluded that it was unwise to
attempt to predict the behavior of a multi-host network with a high
percentage of remote requests using their current analytical model.

On the other hand, our approach can be used for the analysis of a
heterogeneous loop computer network having an arbitrary number of
attached hosts and using any kind of transmission mechanisms. In our
studies, we analyze loop computer networks in a steady state only, and
do not consider transitory periods. The parameters of interest are
average response times to users, average queue lengths, and utilization of processors, as functions of locality of references, system load,

and service rates. In order to focus on these aspects, we assume that there is neither equipment failure nor transmission errors in the system.

There are two main reasons underlying our choice of approach. The first reason, which we call the incompatibility problem, is peculiar to the analysis of the DLCN communication system /REA75/, but its solution has also implications to the analyses of other types of communitation networks. The queueing network model of the DLCN communication network has the distinguishing characteristic that a customer may be simultaneously served by more than one server. As discussed in /LIU77/, this is quite different from conventional networks of queues considered in queueing theory. Conventional networks of queues are appropriate for modeling hosts (centralized computer systems), where a customer can be served by only one server at a time. The implication is that these two kinds of queueing networks are incompatible.

The second reason, which we call the complexity problem, is found in the analysis of a loop computer network with any transmission mechanism. If a loop computer network were modeled by simply adding host models to the queueing model of a loop communication network, the size of the model (the number of queues) might become very large, when the number of hosts is large. Consequently, the analysis of this model might be very complex or even intractable.

In summary, our approach consists of two basic concepts:

1. modeling of the entire communication network by a single server, as a solution to the incompatibility problem, and

2. using the method of iterations for solving the queueing model of the computer network, as a solution to the complexity problem.

A. Solution to incompatibility problem

In our approach, we resolve the incompatibility problem by approximating the entire loop communication network by one server with service time exponentially distributed. Our simulations of the DLCN communication network show that message delay histograms display approximetely exponential shapes, thereby supporting our assumption. For other loops, similar results are reported in /JAF78/. Note that we did not examine in details how good this approximation is in a statistical sence. Some of later discrepancies between analytical and simulation results might be partly due to this approximation. We also assumed that the interarrival time of messages sent from a host to a loop commincation network is distributed exponentially. Studies of computer statistics /JAC69,FUC70/ indicate that this assumption may be realistic. Under those assumptions the server approximating the loop communication network can be modeled as an M/M/1 queueing system.

If a loop communication network has been properly analized, a mean of the exponential service distribution of this server can be easily derived. The average queueing time T (the average time that customers spend in the queue plus service time), for an M/M/1 queueing system, with a service rate μ and an arrival rate λ, is given by

$$T = \frac{1}{\mu - \lambda} \tag{1}$$

Values of parameters T and λ are obtained from the analysis of a loop communication network (hence the importance of that analysis). Then, from (1) the mean of service distribution $1/\mu$ can be calculated.

/LIU77/ containes such an analysis of the DLCN communication network.
In /HAY71/, the Pierce loop communication network /PIE72/ has been
fully analyzed and good approximate expressions of average loop
message delay are derived. These results are later used in our analysis of the DLCN system and the Pierce loop computer network. We do
not analyze the Newhall loop computer network, because appropriate
analytical expressions of average message delay for the Newhall
communication network are not available.

B. Solution to Complexity Problem

The approximation of a loop communication network by one server not
only makes compatible the two kinds of queueing networks mentioned
above in the analysis of the DLCN system, but also reduces the number
of queues in the model. The second reason underlying the choice of
our approach is concerned with the size of the model of a loop
computer network. Further reduction in the number of queues is
accomplished by the use of iterations (to be discussed in the following paragraph), which is the main characteristisc of our approach
to analyzing loop computer networks. The use of iterations makes the
size of queueing models definitely smaller and more manageable.

Our approach basically considers at each step (called iteration) only
one host at a time, interacting with all other hosts and the loop
communication network through three message streams. As shown in
Figure 2, the ith host interacts with other hosts through streams
A(i) and B(i), and with the loop communication network modeled as a
single server through stream C(i).

In the model, it is assumed that for a given request from terminals
to the ith host (requests arrive at the rate $\lambda(i)$) only one response
is returned (responses return to terminals also at the rate $\lambda(i)$).
Requests are satisfied either locally or remotely. Server 1 of the
ith host (with the parameter $\mu(1,i)$) represents the loop communication

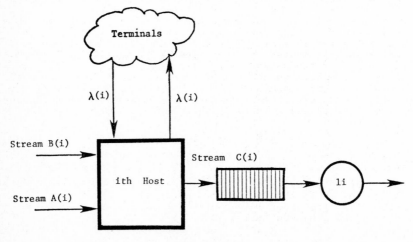

Figure 2
Conceptual Model Considered at Each Iteration

network model as seen by the ith host. A detailed model of the host
is not given here because it is not important at this level of
abstraction. Stream B(i) contains responses returning to the ith
host from all other hosts in the network on remote requests made by
the ith node. Stream A(i) consists of remote requests made by all
other nodes to be satisfied at the ith host. Stream C(i) consists of
responses to requests from stream A(i) and remote requests made from
the ith node to all other hosts. We assume that streams A(i) and
B(i) are generated by Poisson processes, thereby allowing further
analysis to be tractable. Methods for calculation parameters of
those streams (arrival rates) are given later. The model can be analyzed as a centralized computer system using standard queueing
theoretic tools. Once the system in Figure 2 is solved for a particular host (the first iteration), another host can be taken into
consideration (the second iteration), then the third host (the third
iteration), and so on until all hosts in the network are included.
It is intuitively clear why iterations are idependent and why the
solution to one iterativn does not affect neither the previous nor
the later iterations. Note that the number of iterations is N, where
N is the number of hosts in the system. The order in selecting hosts
is arbitrary. Finally, many network design parameters can be easily
calculated by using the results from these iterations.

III. DESCRIPTION AND MODEL OF SYSTEM UNDER CONSIDERATION

In this and the following sections, for purpose of evaluation and
illustration, the approach is used in analysis of a particular loop
computer network which includes an arbitrary number of hosts and any
kind of transmission mechanism. We consider the loop computer network
to support transaction processing against a distributed data baze.
We emphasize that we are not interesed in a detailed modeling of
hosts, but rather in evaluating the validity of our approach to analyzing loop computer networks consisting of a loop communication
network and attached hosts with associated terminals. For this reason,
we do not consider complex host models with different customer
classes, and assume that all servers in the queueing model have exponential services and use the FCFS priority discipline.

Under the assumptions we have made above, the networks of queues to
be considered are of the Jacksonian type /JAC57,JAC63/, i.e., all
external interarrival times of customers and all service times are
exponentially distributed. As background information, we include the
basic result from the Jackson's theorem. Each node (consisting of a
server and an associated queue) in a Jacksonian network of queues
(including N nodes) behaves as if it ware an independent M/M/1 system
with the assumed service rate and the Poisson input rate d(i) calculated from the following system of linear equations

$$d(i) = b(i) + \sum_{j=1}^{N} r(j,i)d(j) \qquad (2)$$

i = 1,2,...,N.

In the expressions (2), b(i), i = 1,2,...,N, is the external arrival
rate of customers to the ith node, and r(j,i), j,i = 1,2,...,N, is
the probability that upon leaving the jth node a customer then
proceeds to the ith node (transition probability).

We should point out that more accurate analyses of real systems would
probably introduce different classes of customers and more types of

servers, so that results of Baskett et. al. /BAS75/ should be used.
However, as mentioned, this is not our main interest.

A. Description of System

The system, we analyze, is identical to that considered in /LAB77/.
As shown in Figure 3, the host model consists of the File Machine
(FM) and the Data Host (DH). In addition a certain number of terminals are connected to each File Machine. A request from a terminal is
handled locally if possible; otherwise, it is put in a standard form
and sent through the loop to the appropriete remote component (host),
which services the request and returns a response through the loop
back to the local component (host). It is assumed that all required
data is transferred along with the remote request, so no further
communication activity is necessary to satisfy that request. The
File Machine receves requests from terminals, preprocesses them, and
sends them to the local Data Host if requests can be satisfied locally,
or to the loop if service of a remote Data Host is needed. Each Data
Host can serve both local and remote requests. The Data Host models
a disc storage system, and to serve a request several disc accesses
may be required. This implies that the same request may pass several
times through and be served by the Data Host. Responses to local
requests are postprocessed at the File Machine and then returned to

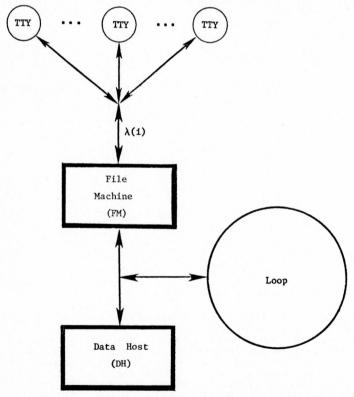

Figure 3
Functional Organization of Attached Host

terminale. After the arrival at a remote host, each request is again preprocessed, i,e., a remote request does not procead directly to the remote Data Host for processing. Afterwords, the postprocessing is only done at the host where the prosessing is obtained, i.e., the postprocessing of remote requests is only performed at the remote host. Consequently, responses to remote requests after arriving at their local hosts return directly to the terminals without any post-processing at the local host.

The preprocessing of requests from terminals at the File Machine consists of data conversion, formating and other protocol overhead, determining locality of request, etc. The processing at the Data Host performsan appropriate retrieval or update. Responses to requests are application program responses, query answers, etc. The postprocessing of responses at the File Machines consists of different protocol functions, etc.

B. Queueing Model of System

The detailed queueing model of the system under consideration is presented in Figure 4. For purpose of clarity, only two host models with associated parts of a loop communication network are included in the figure. The number of queues implies that the analysis of this model would be very complex. As emphasized in the previous section, in our approach only one host should be analyzed at a time. Figure 5 shows a detailed queueing model being considered at each iteration used in our approach. One can see considerable difference in complexity of models in Figure 4 and Figure 5, that implies considerable differences in complexity of analyses of models, too.

We concentrate on the model in Figure 5. It is assumed that inter-arrival times of requests from terminals are exponentially distributed. The routing of requests and responses through the model is now described in more details. Requests enter the ith host from terminals at the rate $\lambda(i)$ and queue for preprocessing at the local File Machine (Server 2 of the ith host, at the rate $\mu(2,i)$). There they compete for service with remote requests from other hosts (stream A(i)), requesting preprocessing, and with local responses and responses to requests from stream A(i), both requesting postprocessing. If the requests can be satisfied locally, they are passed to the local Data Host for processing (Server 3 of the ith host, at the rate $\mu(3,i)$). At the local Data Host they compete for service with remote requests from other hosts (stream A(i)). After the processing at the Data Host, a request may, with the cetain non-zero probability, join the Data Host queue to obtain additional processing. Afterwords, responses to local requests go to the local File Machine for postprocessing. This time, they compete for service with local requests and remote requests from other hosts (stream A(i)), both requesting preprocessing and responses from stream A(i), requesting postprocessing. After servicing, these responses return to terminals.

Should the requests from terminals associated with the ith host be satisfied remotely, after preprocessing they must be delevered to the loop (Server 1 of the ith host, at the rate $\mu(1,i)$). There they compete for service with responses returning from the ith host to the requests from other hosts (responses to requests from stream A(i)). Remote requests made by the ith host then go to some other hosts (as a part of stream C(i)). At remote hosts, they ask for preprocessing at remote File Machines, and then they are processed at remote Data Hosts. After postprocessing at remote File Machines, corresponding responses to those requests are returned through the loop (as stream

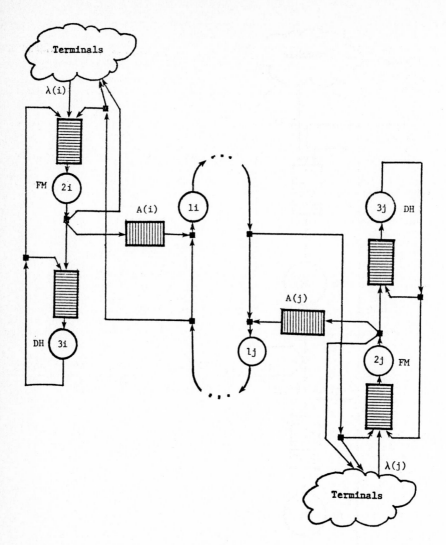

Figure 4
Queueing Model of Loop Computer Network Under Consideration

B(i)) to the ith hosts. Responses to remote requests return to the
terminals without any postprocessing at the local hosts. Note that
streames B(i) do not influence behavior of the network of queues
under investigation.

IV. ANALYTICAL RESULTS

In this section we derive closed-form expressions for average queue
lengths, average response time to users, and utilization of servers
associated with the loop computer network under investigation. First,

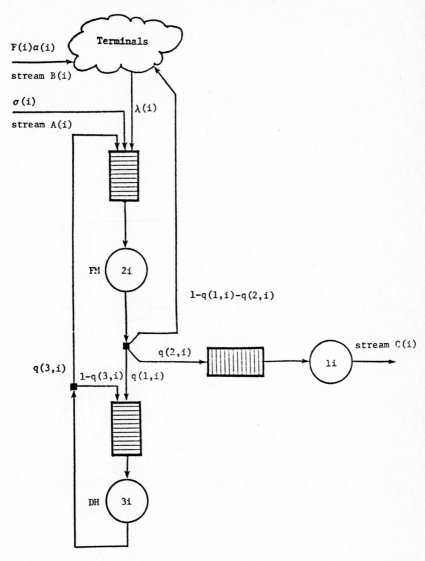

Figure 5
Model of Host Considered at Each Iteration

we describe some parameters such as average service times and arrival rates, which are assumed to be given. Second, transition probabilities are calculated. Third, the set of simultaneous equations equivalent to (2) is obtained and solved. Fourth, we calculate loop parameters. Finally, closed-form expressions for calculating design parameters of interest are derived.

Definitions and Assumptions. It is assumed that the following parameters are known and given:

1. The request service matrix $\Psi = /f(i,j)/$, where, $f(i,j)$, $i,j=1,2,\ldots,N$, is the fraction of requests generated at the ith node (i.e., generated from terminals associated with the ith host) to be satisfied at the jth host; note that $f(i,i)$, $i = 1,2,\ldots,N$, is the fraction of requests to be processed locally, and

$$f(i,i) = 1 - \sum_{\substack{j=1 \\ j \neq i}}^{N} f(i,j)$$

(3)

2. $\lambda(i)$, $i = 1,2,\ldots,N$, the Poisson arrival rate of requests from terminals associated with the ith host;

3. $\mu(2,i)$ and $\mu(3,i)$, $i = 1,2,\ldots,N$, the Poisson service rates of Server 2 (the File Machine) and Server 3 (the Data Host) of the ith host, respectively;

4. $1/\xi(i)$, $i = 1,2,\ldots,N$, the average length of exponentially distributed messages sent from the ith host to the communication network;

5. C, the capacity of high-speed communication channel;

6. B, the size of message address field; and

7. $C(i)$, $i = 1,2,\ldots,N$, the average number of disc accesses per request at the ith host.

Then the next two parameters can be calculated:

1. $F(i)$, $i = 1,2,\ldots,N$, the fraction of requests generated at the ith node to be satisfied remotely, and

$$F(i) = \sum_{\substack{j=1 \\ j \neq i}}^{N} f(i,j)$$

(4)

(Note that the arrival rate of stream B(i) is $F(i)\lambda(i)$), and

2. $\sigma(i)$, $i = 1,2,\ldots,N$, the arrival rate of remote requests from all other hosts in the network to be satisfied at the ith host, and

$$\sigma(i) = \sum_{\substack{j=1 \\ j \neq i}}^{N} f(j,i) \ (j)$$

(5)

(Note that arrival rate of streams A(i) and C(i) are $\sigma(i)$ and $\sigma(i) + F(i)\lambda(i)$, respectively).

In the case of a symmetric system, we have

$$f(i,j) = \begin{cases} f & i \neq j \\ 1 - (N-1)f & i=j \end{cases}$$

(6)

$$F = (N-1)f$$
$$\sigma = (N-1)f = F$$

where $\lambda = \lambda(i)$, $F = F(i)$, and $\sigma = \sigma(i)$, $i = 1,2,\ldots,N$.

Transition Probability Calculation. We define the following transition probabilities:

1. $q(1,i)$, $i=1,2,\ldots,N$, the probability that upon being served by Server 2 of the ith host, a customer goes to Server 3 of the same host;

2. $q(2,i)$, $i = 1,2,\ldots,N$, the probability that upon being served by Server 2 of the ith host, a customer goes to Server 1 of the same host; and

3. $q(3,i)$, $i = 1,2,\ldots,N$, the probability that upon being served by Server 3 of the ith host, a customer goes to Server 2 of the same host.

We use similar arguments in calculating of these transition probabilities, as used in /LAB77/. The transition probability from node X to node Y is obtained as the ratio of the rate of customers arriving to node Y from node X and the total rate of customers leaving node X.

Output from Server 2 of the ith host consists of the fellowing streams:

1. stream a, requests from terminals to be satisfied remotely, leaving at a rate $F(i)\lambda(i)$;

2. stream b, requests from terminals to be satisfied locally, leaving at a rate $(1 - F(i))\lambda(i)$;

3. stream A(i), leaving at a rate $\sigma(i)$;

4. stream c, responses to local requests, leaving at a rate $(1 - F(i))\lambda(i)$;

5. stream d, responses on remote requests, leaving at rate $\sigma(i)$.

Among those, only streams b and A proceed to Server 3, and $q(1,i)$ is given by

$$
\begin{aligned}
q(1,i) &= \frac{(1 - F(i))\lambda(i) + \sigma(i)}{F(i)\lambda(i) + (1 - F(i))\lambda(i) + \sigma(i) + (1 - F(i))\lambda(i) + \sigma(i)} \\
&= \frac{(1 - F(i))\lambda(i) + \sigma(i)}{(2 - F(i))\lambda(i) + 2\sigma(i)}
\end{aligned} \tag{7}
$$

Similary, streams a and d go to Server 1, and for $q(2,i)$ we have

$$
\begin{aligned}
q(2,i) &= \frac{F(i)\lambda(i) + \sigma(i)}{F(i)\lambda(i) + (1 - F(i))\lambda(i) + \sigma(i) + (1 - F(i))\lambda(i) + \sigma(i)} \\
&= \frac{F(i)\lambda(i) + \sigma(i)}{(2 - F(i))\lambda(i) + 2\sigma(i)}
\end{aligned} \tag{8}
$$

In order to obtain the expression for $q(3,i)$, we nave to use diferent reasoning. Since every $c(i)$th output from the Data Host qoes to the File Machine, then $q(3,i)$ is obteined as

$$
q(3,i) = \frac{1}{c(i)} \tag{9}
$$

Calculation of $a(i,j)$'s. Corresponding to (2) we have the following system of linear equations in the matrix form for the network of queues in Figure 5,

$$
\begin{bmatrix} a(1,i) \\ a(2,i) \\ a(3,i) \end{bmatrix} = \begin{bmatrix} 0 \\ \lambda(i) + \sigma(i) \\ 0 \end{bmatrix} + \begin{bmatrix} 0 & q(2,i) & 0 \\ 0 & 0 & q(3,i) \\ 0 & q(1,i) & 1 - q(3,i) \end{bmatrix} * \begin{bmatrix} a(1,i) \\ a(2,i) \\ a(3,i) \end{bmatrix} \tag{10}
$$

where $a(r,i)$, $r = 1,2,3$, is the arrival rate of customers to Server r of the ith host. The solution of this system of linear equations is

$$a(1,i) = \sigma(i) + F(i)\lambda(i)$$
$$a(2,i) = (2 - F(i))\lambda(i) + 2\sigma(i) \qquad (11)$$
$$a(3,i) = c(i)((1 - F(i))\lambda(i) + \sigma(i))$$

In this analysis, we have assumed that the general structure of host models is identical although parameters are different. Thus, in future iterations, transition probabilities, matrix equations, and solutions of matrix equations should have the forms identical to (7)-(9), (10) and (11), respectively. Therefore, in this case, expressions (7)-(11) are valid for $i = 1,2,\ldots,N$.

When host configurations are different (this is quite possible in a real situation), each host is considered separately, implying that transition probabilities and a matrix equation corresponding to (2) are separately calculated for each host. In general, the size of matrix equations to be solved in each iteration is $M(i)$, where $M(i)$ is a number of servers at the ith host, including a server approximating the communication network. If the whole network were considered at one time, a system of $\sum M(i)$ simulataneous equations should be solved.

In a symmetric case, we have

$$q(1) = \frac{1}{2 + F} \qquad (12)$$

$$q(2) = \frac{2F}{2 + F} \qquad (13)$$

$$q(3) = \frac{1}{c} \qquad (14)$$

$$a(1) = 2F$$
$$a(2) = (2 + F)\lambda$$
$$a(3) = c \qquad (15)$$

where $q(1) = q(1,i)$, $q(2) = q(2,i)$, $q(3) = q(3,i)$, $a(1) = a(1,a)$, $a(2) = a(2,i)$, $a(3) = a(3,i)$, and $c = c(i)$, $i = 1,2,\ldots,N$.

It can be easily checked that expressions for parameters coresponding to our $a(i,j)$'s obtained by Labetoulle et al. /LAB77/ for the symmetric Newhall loop computer network are identical to expressions (15). Also, it can be noticed that our approach is simpler(it considers only one host in each iteration instead of the whole system at once)and more general (it can be applied to a loop network with any number of hosts and any kind of transmission mechanism)than theirs.

Loop Parameters Calculation. As already mentioned, we approximate the loop communication network by one server with exponential service time. It is assumed that the arrival rate of messages from the ith host is Poisson and lengths of those messages are exponentially distributed. Parameters of those two distributions are $a(1,i)$ (already calculated and equal to $a(i)$) and $1/\xi(i)$ (assumed to be known·), $i = 1,2,\ldots N$. Also, it is assumed that the capacity C and the size of message address field B are given. Beside these parameters, we need to determine the traffic matrix $P = /P(i,j)/$, where $P(i,j)$, $i,j = 1,2,\ldots,N$, denotes the fraction of remote traffic generating from the ith host that is destined for the jth host. $P(i,j)$ is given by

$$P(i,j) = \begin{cases} \dfrac{f(i,j)\lambda(i) + f(j,i)\lambda(j)}{F(i)\lambda(i) + \sigma(i)} & i \neq j \\ 0 & i = j \end{cases} \qquad (16)$$

Note that (16) is general and does not depend upon a particular host configuration or loop transmission mechanism of a loop computer network under consideration.

Now all parameters required in the analysis of a loop communication network are defined and calculated. In the case of the DLCN or Pierce communication network, the average message delay T can be calculated using results from /LIU77/ or /PIE72/, respectively. If another message transmission mechanism is used, such as Newhall's, the average message delay would be calculated, using the appropriate analysis. From (1) it follows that

$$\mu(1,i) = \frac{1}{T} + a(1,i) \qquad (17)$$

$i = 1,2,\ldots,N$.

In a symmetric case, we have

$$P(i,j) = \begin{cases} \dfrac{1}{N-1} & i \neq j \\ 0 & i = j \end{cases} \qquad (18)$$

$$\mu(i) = \frac{1}{T} + a(1) \qquad (19)$$

where $\mu(1) = \mu(1,i)$, $i = 1,2,\ldots,N$.

Note that if $a(i,j) \geqslant \mu(i,j)$, for any $i = 1,2,3$ or $j = 1,2,\ldots,N$, the system under investigation would be unstable. In that case average response times and queue lengths would grow without bound.

As already pointed out, in a Jacksonian network of queues, each node can be viewed as an independent M/M/1 queueing system. Now that we have derived expressions for all parameters of the model in Figure 5, we can proceed to calculate several design parameters of interest (utilization of processors, average queue lengths and average response times to users), using well known solutions for an M/M/1 queueing system.

Utilization. Utilization of processors and a loop communication channel are important design parameters. The utilization of a high-speed communication channel is calculated in the loop communication network analysis and is not considered here. For processors, we have the following expressions for their utilization,

$$U(i,j) = \frac{a(i,j)}{\mu(i,j)} \qquad (20)$$

where $U(i,j)$, $i = 2,3$ and $j = 1,2,\ldots,N$, is the utilization of the ith server at the jth host.

In a symmetric case, we have

$$U(i) = \frac{a(i)}{\mu(i)} \qquad (21)$$

where $U(i) = U(i,j)$, $\lambda(2) = \lambda(2,j)$, and $\lambda(3) = \lambda(3,j)$, $j = 1,2,\ldots,N$.

<u>Queue Lengths</u>. Average queue lengths, i.e., average numbers of
messages (requests and responses) in the queues, are other important
design parameters used to determine sizes of corresponding buffers
in the system. The size of the output buffer should be calculated
using results from the analysis of a loop communication network. The
average number of messages at the ith server of the jth host
$N(i,j)$, $i = 2,3$, and $j = 1,2,...,N$, is given by

$$N(i,j) = \frac{a(i,j)}{\mu(i,j) - a(i,j)} \tag{22}$$

In a symmetric case, we have

$$N(i) = \frac{a(i)}{\mu(i) - a(i)} \tag{23}$$

where $N(i) = N(i,j)$, $j = 1,2,...,N$.

<u>Response Times</u>. A user of the computer system is mostly interested
in the response time for his/her request, defined as a time elapsed
between the arrival of a request from a terminal to the local File
Machine and the return of the corresponding response to the terminal.
This parameter is derived below.

First, the average queueing time at the ith server of the jth host
$TQ(i,j)$, $i = 1,2,3$ and $j = 1,2,...,N$, is given by

$$TQ(i,j) = \frac{1}{\mu(i,j) - a(i,j)} \tag{24}$$

Note that the average message delay T is equal to $TQ(i,j)$ for all
$j = 1,2,...,N$. From (24) we can calculate the average response time
of remote requests from the ith node to be satisfied at the jth host
$TR(i,j)$, $i \neq j$ and $i,j = 1,2,...,N$. This average response time
consists of;

1. $TQ(2,i)$, the average preprocessing time at the local host;
2. T, the average message delay to deliver a request from the ith
   host to the jth host;
3. $TQ(2,j)$, the average preprocessing time at the remote host;
4. $c(j)*TQ(3,j)$, the average processing time at the jth host;
5. $TQ(2,j)$, the average postprocessing time at the jth host;
   and
6. T, the average message delay to deliver the response from the jth
   host back to the ith node.

$$\begin{aligned} TR(i,j) &= TQ(2,i) + 2(T + TQ(2,j)) + c(j)TQ(3,j) \\ &= 3TQ(2,i) + 2T + c(j)TQ(3,j) \end{aligned} \tag{25}$$

Next, we can derive the average response time of remote requests from
the ith host, $TR(i)$, $i = 1,2,...,N$, given as

$$TR(i) = \frac{1}{F(i)} \sum_{\substack{j=1 \\ j\neq i}}^{N} TR(i,j)\, f(i,j) \tag{26}$$

The average response time of remote requests, TR, is obtained from
the following expression

$$TR = \frac{\sum\limits_{i=1}^{N} F(i) \cdot \lambda(i) \cdot TR(i)}{\sum\limits_{i=1}^{N} F(i) \; \lambda(i)} \qquad (27)$$

The average response time of local requests at the ith host, TL(i), i = 1,2,...,N, consists of:

1. TQ(2,i), the average preprocessing time at the ith host;
2. c(i)*TQ(3,i), the average processing time at the ith host; and
3. TQ(2,i), the average postprocessing time at the ith host.

Thus, we have

$$TL(i) = 2TQ(2,i) + c(i)TQ(3,i) \qquad (28)$$

Therefore, the average response time to satisfy any local request, TL, is

$$TL = \frac{\sum\limits_{i=1}^{N} (1 - F(i)) \; \lambda(i) \; TL(i)}{\sum\limits_{i=1}^{N} (1 - F(i)) \; \lambda(i)} \qquad (29)$$

Finally, the average response time to satisfy any request from the ith node, TD(i), is given by

$$TD(i) = F(i) \; TR(i) + (1 - F(i)) \; TL(i) \qquad (30)$$

and the average response time of the system, TD, is given by

$$TD = \frac{\sum\limits_{i=1}^{N} \lambda(i) \; TD(i)}{\sum\limits_{i=1}^{N} \lambda(i)} \qquad (31)$$

Note that expressions (26), (27), (29), (3o) and (31) are general and independent on host configurations.

In a symmetric case, we have

$$TQ(i) = \frac{1}{\mu(i) - \lambda(i)} \qquad (32)$$

where TQ(i) = TQ(i,j), j = 1,2,...,N. Thus,

$$TR = 3TQ(2) + 2T - cTQ(3) \qquad (33)$$

$$TL = 2TQ'(2) + cTQ(3) \qquad (34)$$

$$TD = F \; TR + (1 - F) \; TL \qquad (35)$$

where TR = TR(i) = TR(i,j), TL = TL(i) and TD = TD(i), i,j = 1,2,...,N.

This concludes the derivation of closed-form expressions of several design parameters for the particular loop computer network. In the following section, we compare simulation results and analytical results obtained from expressions derived in this section.

V. SIMULATION AND COMPARISON

In order to carry out queueing analysis, we had to make several
assumptions and approximations. Thus, to verify our approach and our
analytical results, we also performed a simulation. Our simulation
attempts to mirror as closely as possible the actual operations of
loop computer networks. We model loop computer networks having hosts
of given configuration and using the DLCN or the Pierce transmission
mechanism. The primary quantities of interest in these simulation
studies are average response times, average queue lengths, and
utilization of processors and a loop, although, many other data are
gathered. Simulation models are written in the GPSS simulation
programming language and run on an IBM 370/168 computer.

A. Description of Simulation Models

The general characteristics and some details of the simulation
models are now given. Although a bit would be a more precise measure
for message lengths, in order to perform efficient and economical
simulations, we have to use a character as the unit of message
lengths. Consequently, all timing is in arbitrary character-time
units. All times and message lengths in the system are exponentially
distributed. Simulation models consist of ten hosts attached to the
communication network using DLCN or Pierce message transmission
mechanism with channel capacity C = 10, 20 or 50 Kbit/sec. Each
message multiplexed onto the loop consists of a constant part (800
bits) and an exponential part with a mesn of 480 bits, with the
maximum length of exponential part equal to 4800 bits. Propagation
delay on the communication channel is ignored, while each interface
contributes 2 units of delay for the message addrese checking. In
the model of DLCN communication network, the size of delay buffer
equals 5600 bits, because this size must be at least as large as the
longest message to be generated by the assocoated attached component.
For models of Pierce communication networks, the packet size of
720 bits (90 characters) is chosen for the given average message
length. Note that we do not take into account the packet header. It
was decided to place just one complete packet onto the loop, as has
been done in prior simulation studies of the Pierce communication
network /AND72, HAY73/. Since the ten loop interfaces together
introduce 20 units of delay, a delay box of 70 time units is placed
between the last and first interface. In this way, an entire packet
interval of 90 time units is formed, corresponding to the time
required to transmit one packet of 90 characters.

Twenty-five terminals are connected to each host, with the average
think time (a time elapsed between the arrival of the last response
to a terminal and the sending of the next request from the same
terminal) equal to 90 sec. Note that in the queueing analysis, we
have assumed that requests are generated by an infinite Poisson
process, with mean 25/90 = 0.277 requests/sec. Both symmetric and
asymmetric loop computer networks are simulated. In the symmetric
case, for all hosts, the average preprocessing, processing and postprocessing times are 3.2, 32.0, and 3.2 msec., respectively. Remote
requests from each host are uniformly addressed to the other 9 hosts.
In the asymmetric case, we consider a network consisting of one large
computer and 9 midi-computers. Characteristics of the midi-computers
are identical to those of hosts in the symmetric case, except that
they send all their remote requests to the large computer. Requests
from terminals associated with the large computer are always satisfied

locally. The average preprocessing, processing, and postprocessing times of the large computer are 1.6, 12.8, and 1.6. msec., respectively.

We assume and incorporate in the simulation models that a number of disc accesses per request is uniformely distributed between 1 and 29, with a mean $c(i)$ equal to 15. In this case, the uniform distribution is a relatively accurate and realistic assumption, which is used in /LAB77/. Recall that in our queueing analysis we take $q(3,i) = 1/c(i) = 1/15$, as the probability that a request does not rejoin the queue of the Data Host. This implies that we assume a geometric distribution for the number of disc accesses per request. It is a well-known fact that the variance of this distribution is larger than the variance of the uniform distribution. Consequently, our analytical models are more conservative than our simulation models. We emphasize that there is no known method to incorporate a uniform distribution into the models of network of queues.

B. Comparison and Evaluation

In Figures 6 - 9, we plot analytical results obtained from the closed-form expressions (solid lines) and results obtained from our simulation (special indicators) for the DLCN system. Those figures show graphs of the average loop utilization UL (symmetric and asymmetric cases), and the average response time of the system TD (symmetric and asymmetric cases), as functions of the fraction F of requests to be satisfied remotely, and the capacity of communication channel C. The graphs of the Pierce computer network, corresponding to graphs of the DLCN system in Figures 6 - 9, are given in Figures 10 - 13. Figure 14 shows utilization of the requests servers $U(3,i)$ (asymmetric case), as a function of the parameter F. Note that $U(3,i)$ does not depend on channel capacity and the message transmission mechanism.

It is interesting to note, that in asymmetric cases response times to remote requests, Figures 9 and 13, show that in certain ranges response time decrease as a fraction of requests increase. This happens because in those ranges it takes more time to serve requests locally in midi-computers than remotely in the large computer, including communication delays.

It can be seen that for both symmetric and asymmetric cases, results of utilization of communication channel and processors obtained by analysis and by simulation agree very closely, Figures 6, 7, 10, 11 and 14. Agreement of analytical and simulation results for average response times is reasonable. As Figures 8, 9, 12 and 13 indicate that for higher values of C agreement is good. Some discrepancy exists for lower valves of C, especially for higher fractions of remote requests. The comparison of intermmediate results indicates that in those cases the contribution of the average message delay in a communication network to average response times is considerable and the discrepancy is due to that parameter. In the stady of DLCN communication network /LIU77/, it is concluded that analytical results for the average message delays are consistently conservative (i.e. analytical curves always lie above simulation results), supporting our cenclusion. Some of the discrepancy in our results is also due to the assumption of Poisson arrivals of streams A(i) and B(i), and the assumed distribution of the number of disc accesses per request.

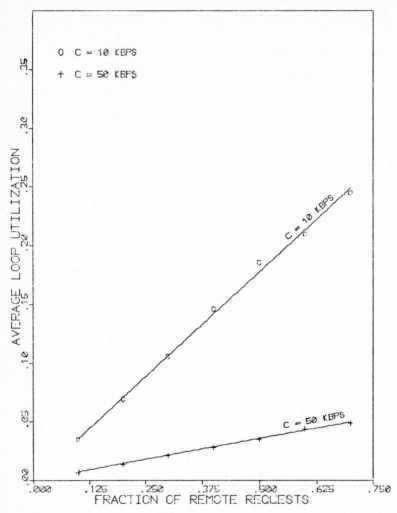

Figure 6
DLCN System (Symmetric Model) - Average Loop Utilization

VI. SUMMARY

In this paper, our approach to the analysis of loop computer networks, consisting of a loop communication network and attached components (hosts) with associated terminals, is presented. It consists of two basic concepts: 1) modeling the entire communication network by a single server, and 2) solving the computer network queueing model iteratively, considering only one host at each iteration. Its generality also suggests that computer networks of general topology could be analysed in the same way. It is worth emphasizing that modeling and solving the computer network is reduced to queueing analysis of a single centralized computer system with the addition of one FCFS server and two Poisson input streames. We believe that the analysis

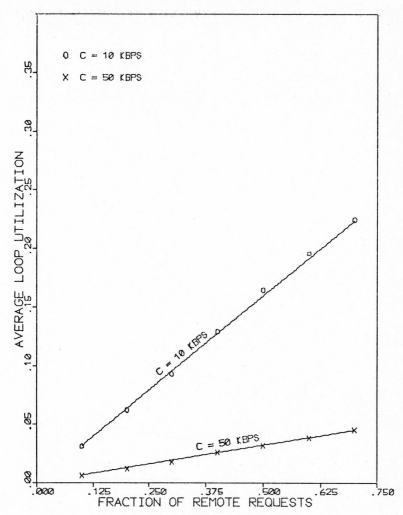

Figure 7
DLCN System (Asymmetric Model) - Average Loop Utilization

of this system is not considerable more complex than that of the
centralizd system alone. Also, we think that our approach is a
significant contribution to analysis of computer networks in particular and distributed processing systems in general. We illustrate
our approach by analyzing the loop network of computers
to support transaction processing against a distributed data base.
The host configuration is relatively simple because of our interst
in the analysis of host interactions, the evaluation of the approach
and clarity of presentation, but not in the analysis and simulation
of a centralized computer system. For a loop computer network having
hosts of these configurations, we derive closed-form expressions for
several design parameters of interest, viz., average response times,
mean queue lengths, and utilization of processors. Comparison of

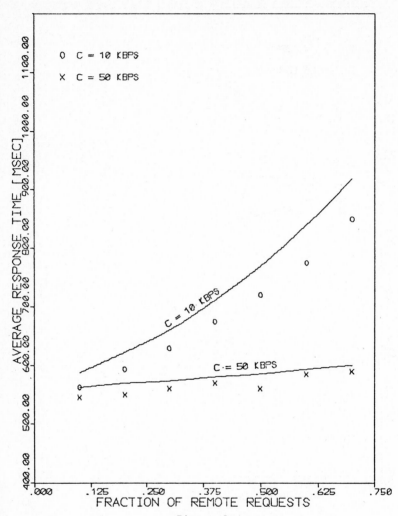

Figure 8
DLCN System (Symmetric Model) - Average Response Time in System

analytical and simulation models is performed for the loop computer
network using the DLCN or the Pierce transmission mechanism. The
agreement between analytical and simulation results is reasonable
and for some parameters very good, implying validity of our approach.

REFERENCES

AND72 R.R. Anderson, J.F. Hayes, and D.N. Sherman, "Simulated Perfor-
       mance of a Ring-Switched Data Network," IEEE Trans. on Comm.,
       COM-20, June 1972, pp.576-591.

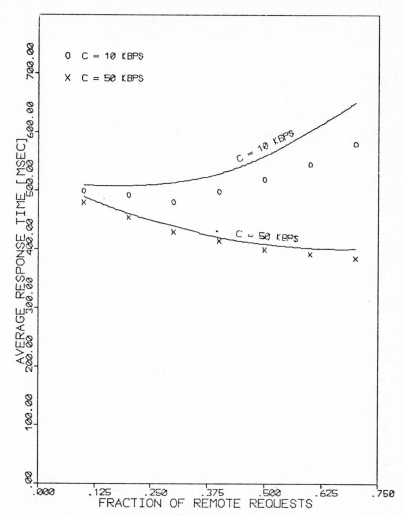

Figure 9
DLCN System (Asymmetric Model) - Average Response Time in System

BAS75 Baskett, et al., "Open, Closed, and Mixed Networks of Queues with Different Classes of Customers," JACM, Vol. 22, pp. 248-26o, 1975.

BRO75 J.C. Browne, et al., "Hierarchical Techniques for the Development of Realistic Models of Complex Computer Systems," Proc. IEEE, Jun 1975, pp. 966-976.

BRO77 R.M. Brown et al., "Memory Management and Response Time," CACM, March 1977, pp. 153-165.

CAR77 R.T. Carsten, et al., "A Simplified Analysis of Scan Times in an Asymmetric Newhall Loop with Exhaustive Service," IEEE Trans. on Comm., September 1977, pp. 951-957.

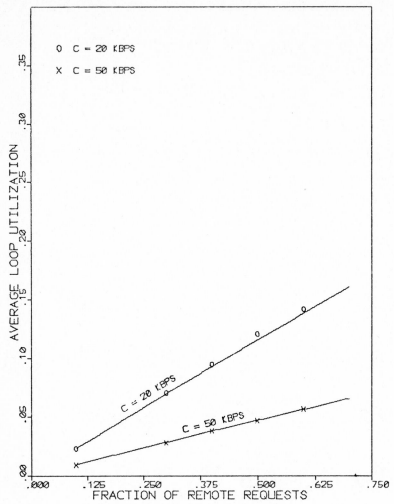

Figure 10
Pierce Network (Symmetric Model) - Average Loop Utilization

FAR69 W.D. Farmer and E.E. Newhall, "An Experomental Distributed
       Switching System to Handle Bursty Computer Traffic," Proc.
       ACM Conf. on Data Comm., October 1969, pp. 1-33.

FUC70 E. Fuchs and P.E. Jackson, "Estimates of Distribution of
       Random Variables for Certain Computer Communication traffic
       Models," CACM, December 197o, pp. 752-757.

HAY71 J.F. Hayes and D.N. Sherman, "Traffic Analysis of a Ring
       Switched Data Transmission System," Bell System Tech. Journal,
       November 1971, pp. 2947-2978.

HAY74 J.F. Hayes, "Performance Models of an Experimental Computer
       Communication Network," Bell System. Tech. Journal, Vol. 53,
       February 1974, pp. 225-259.

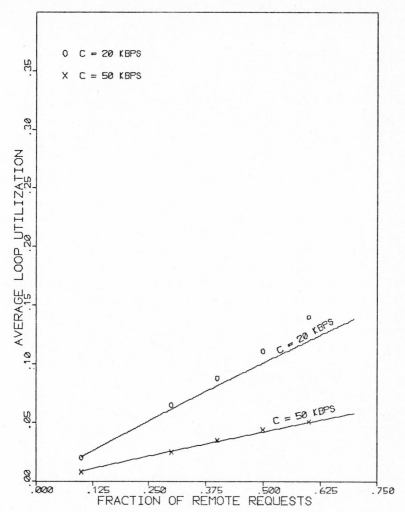

Figure 11
Pierce Network (Asymmetric Model) - Average Loop Utilization

JAC57 J.R. Jackson, "Networks of Waiting Lines," Operations Research, 1957, pp. 518-521.

JAC63 J.R. Jackson, "Jobshop-like Queueing Systems," Management Science, 1963, pp. 131-142.

JAC69 P.E. Jackson and C.D. Stubbs, "A Study of Multi-Access Computer Communications," Proc. SJCC, May 1969, pp. 491-5o4.

JAF78 H. Jafari, et al., "A New Modular Loop Architecture for Distributed Computer Systems," Trends and Applications: 1978 Distributed Processing, May 1978, pp. 72-77.

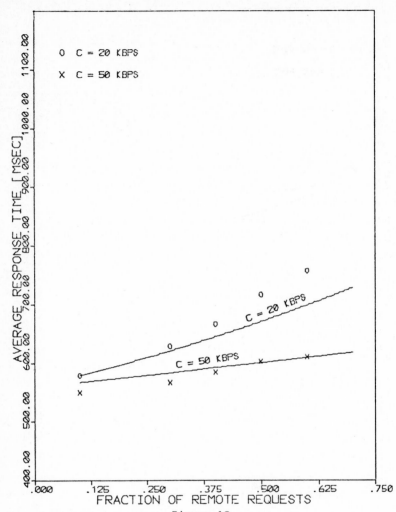

Figure 12
Pierce Network (Symmetric Model) - Average Response Time

KAY72 A.R. Kaye, "Analysis of a Distributed Control Loop for Data
       Transmission," Proc. Symp. on Computer-Communication Networks
       and Teletraffic, April 1972, pp. 47-58.

KON72 A.G. Konheim and B. Meister, "Service in a Loop System,"
       JACM, January 1972, pp. 92-1o8.

LAB77 J. Labetoulle, E.G. Manning and R.W. Peebles, "A Homogeneous
       Computer Networks: Analysis and Simulation," Computer
       Networks, May 1977, pp. 225-24o.

LIP77 L. Lipski and J.D. Church, "Applications of a Queueing
       Network Model for a Computer System," Computing Surveys,
       September 1977, pp. 2o5-221.

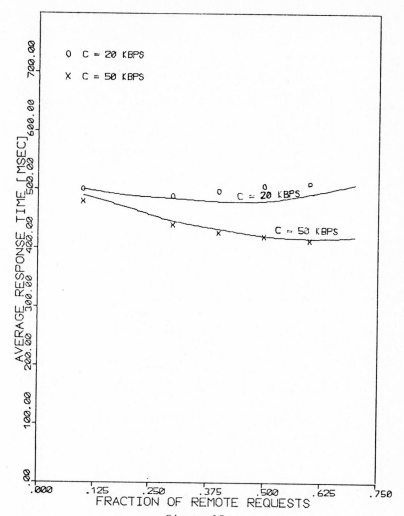

Figure 13
Pierce Network (Asymmetric Model) - Average Response Time in System

LIU77 M.T. Liu, G.A. Babić and R. Pardo, "Traffic Analysis of the Distributed Loop Computer Network (DLCN)," National Telecommunication Conf., December 1977, pp. 31:5(1-7).

MAN77 E.G. Manning and R.W. Peebles, "A Homogeneous Network for Data Sharing: Communications," Computer Networks, May 1977, pp. 211-224.

PIE72 J.R. Pierce, "Network for Block Switching of Data," Bell System Tech. Journal, July/August 1972, pp. 1133-1145.

REA75 C.C. Reames and M.T. Liu, "A Loop Network for Simultaneous Transmission of Variable-Length Messages," Proc. Second Annual Symp. on Computer Architecture, January 1975, pp. 2-12.

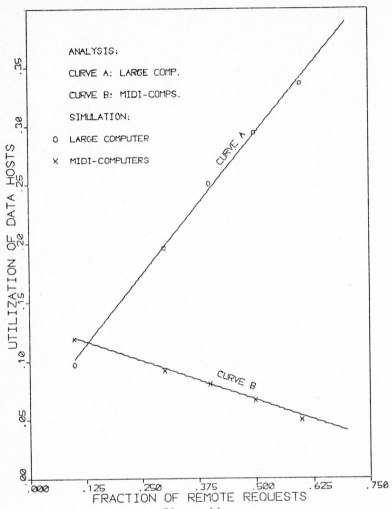

Figure 14
Asymmetric Model - Utilization of Data Hosts

ROB74 P.N. Robillard, "An Analysis of a Loop Switching System with Multirank Buffers based on the Markov Process," *IEEE Trans on Comm.*, November 1974, pp. 1772-1778.

SPR72 J.D. Spragins, "Loops Used for Data Collection," *Proc. Symp. on Computer-Communication Networks and Teletraffic*, April 1972, pp. 59-76.

YUE72 M.L. Yuen, et al., "Traffic in a Distributed Loop Switching System," ibid., pp. 29-46.

ADDITIONAL PAPERS

LOCAL COMPUTER NETWORKS
P.C. Ravasio, G. Hopkins and N. Naffah (editors)
North-Holland Publishing Company
© IFIP, 1982

PERFORMANCE ANALYSIS
OF THE UNIDIRECTIONAL BROADCAST SYSTEM

RAPHAEL ROM

SRI International
Menlo Park, California

ABSTRACT

This paper describes and analyzes a round-robin algorithm for scheduling subscribers attached to a random access channel. As a round robin algorithm a bounded (and low) maximum delay is guaranteed. The algorithm is particularly efficient as it utilizes the geometry of the system to achieve a very small changeover time between users independent of the number of users or the end-to-end delay. Ther performance of the system is compared with the performance of the more traditional nonpersistent and 1-persistent CSMA-CD algorithms.

I. INTRODUCTION

Multiple access schemes for computer networks have been abundant in recent years. These schemes regulate the shared usage of a communications channel among contending subscribers. An excellent survey of some of the most common ones is given in.[1]

Several of theses schemes, notably the random-access ones such as ALOHA, CSMA, and CSMA-CD suffer considerable performance degradation, and even a total channel collapse, when the load on the channel increases beyond a certain limit. Moreover, the random-access schemes that are based on a statistical approach cannot guarantee a bounded delay even under stable operating conditions. This last requirement is instrumental in the transport of packetized speech particularly when voice and data are mixed on the same channel.

Another cause of performance degradation in many random access algorithms is the relation between message length, channel rate, and end-to-end delay. Most of these algorithms require that the message duration (in the nominal channel rate) be much longer than the channel's end-to-end propagation delay to assure acceptable system performance. This rules out the use of channels with very high data rates (e.g., fiber optics) or those that span a large geographical distance (e.g., CATV).

In this paper we describe and analyze a round robin algorithm for which the changeover time (or "walking time") is very short, is independent of the number and location of the ready subscribers, and has low dependence on propagation delay.

II. UNIDIRECTIONAL BROADCAST SYSTEMS

in a unidirectional broadcast system (UBS) transmission signals are forced to propagate in only one direction on the cable. This may be achieved, for example, by using unidirectional media (e.g. fiber optics) or by the use of taps that considerably attenuate the signals in the opposite direction (CATV technology utilizes such taps which have also been used by such systems as MITRIX[2]).

The entire system consists of two interconnected channels--the forward (or outbound) channel and the reverse (or inbound) channel. Subscriber devices are connected to both channels via passive taps. The tap on the forward portion of the cable is used for message transmittal, while the tap on the reverse portion is used for message reception. The channel interconnection can be simply implemented by folding a single cable. Broadcast communication is accomplished because all signals traverse the entire inbound channel to which all receivers are attached. Figure 1 displays the system topology schematically.

In the UBS considered here, in addition to transmission capability on the outbound channel, we assume that subscribers can also sense activity on that channel in a way similar to that required in other channel-sensing systems such as CSMA.[3] This capability results in an interesting feature. Assume subscribers are numbered sequentially S_1, S_2, S_3, etc., and that subscriber S_1 is defined as the "farthest," i.e., has the longest distance between its inbound and outbound taps (see figure). Because of the unidirectional property, S_2 is able to sense signals generated by S_1 on both the inbound and the outbound channels whereas the converse does not hold; that is, S_1 can sense signals generated by S_2 only on he inbound channel. This assymmetry can be used to establish the ordering in a round- robin scheme, which we proceed to do in the following sections.

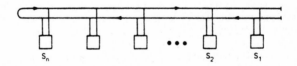

S_n S_2 S_1

FIGURE 1   UNIDIRECTIONAL BROADCAST SYSTEM (UBS)

III. THE ALGORITHM

In this section we describe an efficient round-robin algorithm which can be easily implemented on a UBS. We also show how the algorithm can be adapted for implementation on a biidirectional broadcast system (BBS) such as the ETHERNET.[4]

Round-robin channel-access algorithms are a family of algorithms in which access to a shared channel is granted sequentially to all subscribers that wish to access the channel. No subscriber will be granted a second access before all others have had a chance to access the channel. We define a "round" as that period within which every subscriber is given a single chance to access the channel.

Our network consists of subscribers each with two buffers on the send side--the arrival buffer and the transmission buffer. Packets generated by the subscriber will fill the arrival buffer. At the beginning of each round these buffers are exchanged, i.e., the transmission buffer becomes the arrival buffer and vice versa. During the following round each subscriber is scheduled for transmission exactly once, at which time it will transmit the contents of its transmission buffer. The end of the round is signified by having all transmission buffers empty.

In the scheme described here, a subscriber can be in one of three states. A subscriber whose transmission buffer is empty at the beginning of the round is considered in the IDLE state for the rest of the round. A non-IDLE subscriber, called a ready subscriber, can assume one of two states--ACTIVE if it has not transmitted its message in the "current round" or DORMANT if it has transmitted and is now waiting for completion of the round. To achieve the round-robin scheduling, DORMANT subscribers defer to all ACTIVE subscribers. Consequently, we are assured that no subscriber will transmit its second message before other ready subscribers have a chance to transmit their first ones. Eventually all ready subscribers will have transmitted their messages (i.e., all will have become DORMANT); this constitutes the end of a round, at which time all reset their state and a new round starts.

While each subscriber distinguishes between its DORMANT and ACTIVE states (with a 1-bit flag), arbitration among active subscribers must be provided by additional means. To that end each ACTIVE subscriber transmits a short burst of unmodulated carrier after the end of the previous message to indicate its ACTIVEness and, at the same time, it senses the outbound channel. All but one ACTIVE subscriber will sense the outbound channel busy during this transmittal (because of transmission from lower indexed subscribers--see figure 1) thus singling out the next subscriber to transmit. As explained earlier, we make use here of the timing asymmetry between the outbound and inbound channels. If a given subscriber senses the outbound channel busy during the transmission of the reservation burst, there exists at least one ready subscriber "ahead" of it which generated that signal; a subscriber will always defer its transmission in favor of those "ahead" of it.

The duration of the burst of unmodulated carrier should be sufficiently long to allow its detection by subscribers and avoid mistaking channel noise for the reservation burst. On the other hand it must be kept small as its duration affects the intraround message separation. We denote by b the time required to detect the end-of-message, transmit a reservation burst, and possibly detect another concurrent reservation burst. This is exactly the intraround message separation and its duration is typically much shorter than the round trip delay a, or $b \ll a$.

An ACTIVE subscriber will operate as follows:

1. It waits until the next end-of-carrier (EOC) is detected on the outbound channel at the end of a message.
2. It transmits a short burst of unmodulated carrier and listens to the out-

bound channel for a period of duration b.

3. If the outbound channel is sensed idle during the entire period, the subscriber immediately transmits its message and moves to the DORMANT state. Otherwise the subscriber repeats the algorithm (step 1).

A DORMANT or IDLE subscriber waits until the inbound channel is sensed idle for a period of b following EOM, signifying the end of round, and then operates as follows:

1. If its arrival buffer is empty it will move to (or remain in) the IDLE state and remain that way for the next round.
2. If its arrival buffer is full it will become the transmit buffer and the subscriber will
   - Move to the ACTIVE state
   - Transmit a short burst of unmodulated carrier and listen to the outbound channel for one round-trip delay.
   - Proceed with the algorithm for ACTIVE subscribers, starting at step (3).

Note that, following the end of round, after a subscriber transmits a reservation burst, the waiting period is one round-trip delay rather than b. This is necessary, in the worst case, to allow the end of the last message to propagate through the inbound channel and for the reservation burst to to propagate through the outbound channel.

The time separating two consecutive rounds would therefore be between one and one and a half end-to-end delays, depending upon the location of the last subscriber to transmit in the last round and the first one to transmit in the new round. A separation of one round-trip delay can be achieved at all times if, after the end of round, an active subscriber waits for a time necessary for the end of message to propagate from its receiver tap to the end of the inbound channel plus the time necessary for the reservation burst to propagate from the beginning of the outbound channel to its transmitter tap. This time is subscriber dependent but can be determined dynamically by each subscriber independently as it equals one round-trip delay minus the propagation delay between the subscriber's transmit and receive taps. Each subscriber can easily measure this.

The identification of the end of round and the resynchronization of the subscribers once the end of round is identified is the more complex part of the algorithm and directly affects performance. The longer it takes to resynchronize, the more performance degrades, but usually the less complex the algorithm. In the algorithm described above the time separating two consecutive rounds is between one and one and a half end-to-end delays, depending upon the location of the last subscriber to transmit in the the last round and the first one to transmit in the new round.

A. Adaptation of the algorithm for a BBS

Bidirectional broadcast systems (BBS) of the ETHERNET type do not enjoy the same physical ordering that a UBS does and, consequently, a logical equivalent must be established. Algorithms of that nature have been proposed before, e.g., MSAP [5] and BRAM.[6]

Consider the case where subscribers are identified by a number assigned to them sequentially according to their physical location on the cable. Subscribers normally include this number in the 'from' or 'source' field in all messages (as part of a higher level protocol). Assume that the completion of the transmission from the i-th subscriber occurs at time t. An active subscriber j, where $j>i$ will transmit its message starting at $t+(j-i)b'$, provided the channel is idle at that time. Here b' is the time required both for the carrier to propagate between the two most distant adjacent subscribers and to be detected at its destination. The time separating two consecutive messages within a round is bounded by $b=(M-1)b'$ where M is the total number of subscribers. An end-of-round is established when the M-th subscriber finishes transmission or declines to transmit in its turn. The interround idle period is therefore bounded by $1+Mb'$ which allows both for end-of-message propagation and for end-of-round detection.

IV. ANALYSIS

This section contains the performance analysis for the algorithm just described. In this analysis we assume that the time axis is slotted in slots whose duration equals one round-trip delay α (whisch we have normalized to $\alpha=1$. Each of the M subscribers may generate a message in a slot with probability σ. All messages are assumed to be of equal length T. We define the transmission period V to be the time required for reserving the channel (b) and transmitting the message (T). We also denote by "i-epoch" the time occupied by a round in which i subscribers transmit their message and the idle round-trip-delay that signifies the end of round. While the analysis is general, in the graphs we show the performance on a BBS so it can be meaningfully compared with other access methods (we chose $b=Mb'\approx1$). Performance on an actual unidirectional bus (where $b\ll1$) is therefore better than shown on the graphs, particularly for small values of T.

It is clear that the end points of the epochs, as well as the endpoints of the transmission periods constitute an embedded Markov chain, which is the basis of the analysis that follows.

Let Q be the steady-state one-step arrival transition matrix, i.e., $[Q]_{ij}$ is the probability of having j arrival buffers full at time $t+1$, given that i buffers were full at time t. Clearly

$$[Q]_{ij} = \binom{M-i}{j-i}\sigma^{j-i}(1-\sigma)^{M-j} \quad \text{for } j\geq i \tag{1}$$

$$[Q]_{ij} = 0 \quad \text{for } j<i$$

Let P be the steady state epoch transition matrix, i.e., $[P]_{ij}$ is the probability of having a j-epoch follow an i-epoch. Obviously $[P]_{ij}$ is the probability of having j arrivals within an i-epoch (of duration $iV+1$), given that all buffers are empty at the beginning of the epoch. Thus,

$$[P]_{ij} = [Q_{0j}]^{iV+1} = \binom{M}{j} \alpha_i^j (1-\alpha_i)^{M-j} \tag{2}$$

where

$$\alpha_i = 1-(1-\sigma)^{iV+1}. \tag{3}$$

Note that α_i represents the probability of an arrival buffer becoming full within an i-epoch.

Let π_i denote the steady state probability of an i-epoch, and $\pi = [\pi_0, \pi_1, \ldots, \pi_m]$. π will therefore be a solution to

$$\pi = \pi P \tag{4}$$

This solution cannot be given in closed form and for itself is not very interesting. It is, however, necessary for evaluating throughput and delay characteristics. An interesting special case is that of the low load, i.e., when σ becomes very small.

A. Average Epoch Length

The average epoch length is defined as

$$\bar{i} = \sum_{i=0}^{M} i \pi_i \tag{5}$$

Since the π_i are not given in closed form, the use of equation (4) will not yield a closed form of (5). An alternate approach used the consideration that, in a steady state, the average number of arrivals must equal the average number of departures. In this scheme the average number of departures is the average epoch length.

The average number of arrivals in an i-epoch is given by

$$\sum_{j=1}^{M} j \, \alpha_i^j = M \alpha_i$$

thus for the average epoch

$$M \alpha_{\bar{i}} = \bar{i} \tag{6}$$

substituting equation (3) into (6) we get

$$1-(1-\sigma)^{\bar{i}V+1} = \frac{\bar{i}}{M} \tag{7}$$

Equation (7) provides a relation between the average epoch length and the offered load (σ). This relation can be represented in a more general form.

Let

$$y = \frac{\bar{i}}{M}, \quad k = MV;$$

Equation (7) now becomes

$$(1-\sigma)^{ky+1} = 1-y \tag{8}$$

A set of graphs (on a logarithmic scale) for typical values of k are shown in figure 2. Conspicuous in these graphs is the rapid transition between a lightly loaded system and a saturated one. From an engineering standpoint, these graphs provide a valuable input for selecting the operating ranges and tradeoffs between the system parameters M, V, and σ. The transition range can be defined as the range between the two "knees" of the graph, i.e., between the two points where the curvature is maximized. As a first order approximation one can use the values of σ which correspond to $y=.05$ and $y=.95$. As we shall see later, these points also characterize the throughput and delay performance.

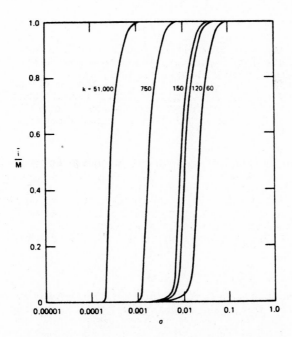

FIGURE 2   EXPECTED VALUE OF EPOCH LENGTH

Note also that equation (A7), Appendix A, indicates that, for light load

$$y = \frac{\bar{i}}{M} \approx \frac{\sigma}{1-k\sigma} \tag{9}$$

B. Throughput

The average throughput S is defined as the ratio of average success time to total time, or that portion of time (on the average) in which the system performs useful work, provided there is work to be done. It can easily be shown that, in the steady state, this can be reduced to

$$S = \frac{\sum_{i=0}^{M}\pi_i(iT)}{\sum_{i=0}^{M}\pi_i(iV+1)} = \frac{\bar{i}T}{\bar{i}V+1} \tag{10}$$

The value of $\bar{i}$ as taken from (8) can be substituted here to describe the dependency of the throughput on $M, \sigma,$ and T.

For the low load case, we substitute equation (9) into (10) and get

$$S = MT\sigma$$

which, as expected, indicates that throughput builds up linearly with the load.

Equation (10) also shows that S is a monotonically increasing function of $\bar{i}$, and hence of σ. Consequently maximal throughput is achieved at high load when σ reaches 1. Under these circumstances $\bar{i}=M$ and

$$S = \frac{MT}{MV+1} = \frac{T}{V+\frac{1}{M}} \approx \frac{T}{V} \tag{12}$$

Figure 3 shows S as a function of σ for $M=50$ and various values of T. Note especially the saturation effect, i.e., when a substantial increase in load results in only minor increase in throughput. The "knee" of these curves corresponds to the knee observed in the curve of $\bar{i}$ versus σ. It should also be recalled that these graphs represent the implementation of the round robin algorithm on a BBS, where the value of b is non-negligible. When implemented on a UBS, $V \approx T$ and hence (according to equation 12) S will reach 1 for high load.

C. Delay

Making use of Little's formula, the steady-state delay is the ratio of the average number in the backlog N and the average throughput S:

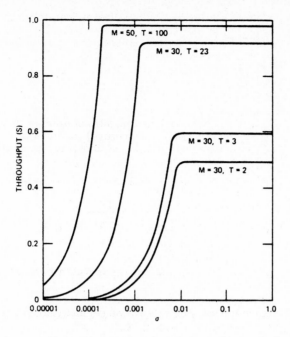

FIGURE 3 THROUGHPUT AS A FUNCTION OF ARRIVAL RATE

$$D = \frac{N}{S} \tag{13}$$

S is given in equation (10) and N is calculated next.

The average number in the backlog is the ratio of the sum of the backlogs over a long period of time to time itself. In steady state it can be shown to reduce to

$$N = \frac{\displaystyle\sum_{i=0}^{M} N_i \pi_i}{\displaystyle\sum_{i=0}^{M} (iV+1)\pi_i} \tag{14}$$

where N_i is the sum of the backlogs within an i epoch.

Within an i-epoch two separate processes take place--the arrival and departure processes. In the departure process one subscriber departs every transmission period V, decreasing the backlog by 1. During this epoch new messages arrive in the arrival buffer according to the arrival process. Each such arrival increases the backlog by 1. Since these processes are independent of one another, the total backlog is the sum of the two.

Figure 4 shows the departure process for an i-epoch. This epoch starts with i subscribers in the first transmission period of duration V. In the second

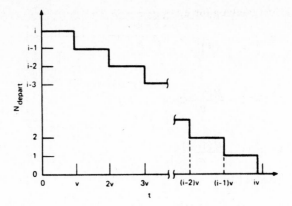

FIGURE 4   NUMBER OF SUBSCRIBERS IN THE
            DEPARTURE PROCESS OF AN
            i-EPOCH

transmission period the backlog will be $i-1$, in the next one the backlog will be $i-2$ until the i-th transmission period in which only one subscriber constitutes the backlog. The total departure backlog is therefore

$$N_{i,depart} = \sum_{j=1}^{i}(jV) = \frac{i(i+1)}{2}V \qquad (15)$$

To evaluate the arrival backlog, we define a random variable G_t representing the number of messages generated by time t from the beginning of an epoch (and within a single epoch). We then sum the expected value of G_t over an entire epoch to obtain the average arrival backlog.

For as long as t lies within the boundary of an epoch we have

$$Pr\{G_t = j\} = \binom{M}{j}\beta_t^j(1-\beta_t)^{M-j} \qquad (16)$$

where

$$\beta_t = 1 - (1-\sigma)^t$$

The expected value of G_t within a single epoch is

$$\overline{G_t} = \sum_{j=0}^{M} jPr\{G_t = j\} = M\beta_t \qquad (17)$$

The average arrival backlog for an i-epoch will therefore be

$$N_{i,arrive} = M \sum_{t=1}^{iV+1} [1-(1-\sigma)^t]$$

$$= M(iV+1) - \frac{M(1-\sigma)}{\sigma}\beta_{iV+1}$$

$$= M(iV+1) - \frac{M(1-\sigma)}{\sigma}\alpha_i \tag{18}$$

where α_i is defined in (3).

Using equations (15) and (18) we derive the total average backlog for an i-epoch

$$N_i = N_{i,depart} + N_{i,arrive} = \frac{i(i+1)}{2}V + M(iV+1) - \frac{M(1-\sigma)}{\sigma}\alpha_i \tag{19}$$

We substitute this result into (14) and then into (13) and receive the expected delay (in message length units)

$$D = \frac{1}{T}\left\{ MV + \frac{V}{2} + \frac{M + \frac{1}{2}\overline{i^2} - M\frac{1-\sigma}{\sigma}\overline{\alpha_i}}{\overline{i}} \right\} \tag{20}$$

where

$$\overline{i^2} = \sum_{i=0}^{M} i^2 \pi_i$$

$$\overline{\alpha_i} = \sum_{i=0}^{M} \alpha_i \pi_i$$

Under heavy load $\sigma=1$, $\overline{i}=M$, and $\overline{i^2}=M^2$ and the delay becomes

$$D(\sigma=1) = \frac{1}{T}\left[(MV+1) + \frac{(M+1)}{2}V \right] \tag{21}$$

where the first item is the length of the epoch in which the message arrived and the second is the average delay in the epoch in which the message is transmitted. This demonstrates that, under extreme load, delay is bounded.

For low load we substitute equations (A7)-(A9) and get $D=\frac{V+1}{T}$ which is intuitively expected.

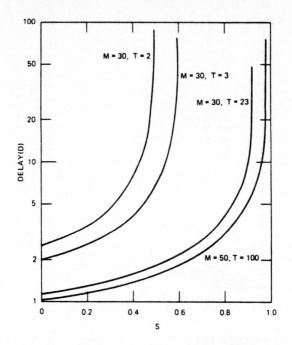

FIGURE 5   THROUGHPUT DELAY CHARACTERISTICS OF A UBS

Figure 5 shows throughput delay curves for several configurations. Note that all curves actually terminate, i.e., delay is bounded and that each curve is normalized to its own message length. The values we chose correspond to a system composed of a 2km cable with a nominal data rate of 10Mbs and message length of about 100, 150, 2000, and 10000 bits.

In figure 6* we plot the performance of the unidirectional algorithm against the performance of a nonpersistent CSMA-CD.[7] The system consists of 50 subscribers transmitting messages of 10000 bits over a 2 Km cable at a nominal data rate of 10Mbs. Several performance graphs for the CSMA-CD scheme are shown for various retransmission parameters.

Figures 7 and 8 compare the unidirectional scheme with that of an ETHER-NET like channel. [8] Figure 7 compares systems with 25 subscribers and message length of 256 bits (over a 2Km cable at 10Mbs). Figure 8 is similar to figure 7 except for the message length which is increased to 2048 bits. In both graphs we show the performance of the 1-persistent channel for various retransmission parameters.

---

* Data for figure 6 are taken from reference[7] and data for figures 7 and 8 are taken from reference[8]. Refer particularly to [8] for explanation of the capture effect.

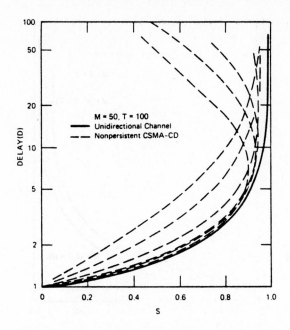

FIGURE 6   COMPARISON BETWEEN UBS AND NONPERSISTENT CSMA-CD

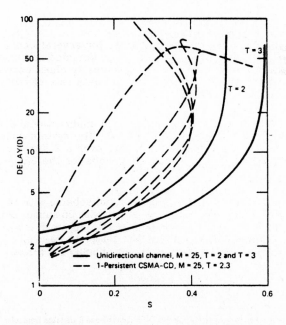

FIGURE 7   COMPARISON BETWEEN UBS AND 1-PERSISTENT CSMA-CD

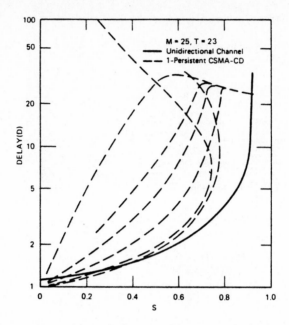

FIGURE 8   COMPARISON BETWEEN UBS AND 1-PERSISTENT CSMA-CD

These graphs clearly indicate that the unidirectional scheme performs better than both schemes in most load ranges except for very light loads. Recall, again, that these curves represent the implementation of the scheme on a BBS; an even better performance can be achieved by implementing the scheme on a UBS.

V. CONCLUSION

In this paper we presented and analyzed a round robin scheme with some very desirable characteristics. As a round robin scheme it has a bounded delay, which is a strict requirement for some applications such as packetized speech. The scheme is efficient in that the changeover time is not dependent on the number and relative position on the cable of the ready users. This performance of the algorithm is only lightly dependent on the end-to-end propagation delays, which makes it suitable for systems in which the message length is much shorter than end-to-end propagation delay. Performance analysis of the algorithm indicates that, in terms of throughput-delay, it is better than similar CSMA-CD algorithms over most load ranges.

Appendix: Small σ Analysis

We start with equations (2) and (3) and assume small values of σ. From equation (3) we get

$$\lim_{\sigma \to 0} \frac{\alpha_i}{\sigma} = iV+1$$

hence we assume that

$$\alpha_i \approx (iV+1)\sigma \tag{A1}$$

Substituting this into equation (2) we get

$$P_{i0} = (1-\alpha_i)^M \approx 1 - M(iV+1)\sigma = 1-\delta_i \tag{A2}$$

$$P_{i1} = M\alpha_i(1-\alpha_i)^{M-1} \approx (iV+1)\sigma = \delta_i \tag{A3}$$

$$P_{ij} = 0 \quad \text{for } j>1. \tag{A4}$$

Substituting (A2) - (A4) into (4) shows immediately that

$$\pi_j = 0 \quad j>1$$

so only π_0 and π_1 need to be calculated. Thus,

$$\pi_1 = \pi_0 P_{01} + \pi_1 P_{11} = \pi_0 \delta_0 + \pi_1 \delta_1$$

and along with the constraint that $\pi_0 + \pi_1 = 1$ we finally get:

$$\pi_0 = 1 - \frac{M\sigma}{1-MV\sigma} \tag{A5}$$

$$\pi_1 = \frac{M\sigma}{1-MV\sigma} \tag{A6}$$

From these basic results the following are derived

$$\sum_{i=0}^{M} i\pi_i = \frac{M\sigma}{1-MV\sigma} \tag{A7}$$

$$\sum_{i=0}^{M} i^2\pi_i = \frac{M\sigma}{1-MV\sigma} \tag{A8}$$

$$\sum_{i=0}^{M} \alpha_i \pi_i = \frac{\sigma}{1-MV\sigma} \tag{A9}$$

REFERENCES

1. F.A. Tobagi, "Multiaccess Protocols in Packet Communication Systems," *IEEE Trans. on Communications* **COM-28**(4) pp. 468-488 (April 1980).

2. D.G. Willard, "Mitrix: A sophisticated Digital Cable Communications System," in *Proc. of the National Telecommunications Conference*, IEEE (November 1977).

3. L. Kleinrock and F.A. Tobagi, "Packet Switching in Radio Channels: Part I - Carrier Sense Multiple-Access Modes and Their Throughput Delay Characteristics," *IEEE Trans. on Communications* **COM-23**(12) pp. 1400-1416 (December 1975).

4. R.M. Metcalfe and D.R. Boggs, "ETHERNET: Distributed Packet Switching for Local Computer Networks," *Communications of the ACM* **19**(7) pp. 395-403 (1976).

5. L. Kleinrock and M. Scholl, "Packet switching in radio channels: new conflict-free multiple access schemesfor a small number of data users," pp. 22.1-105-22.1-111 in *ICC Conf. Proceedings*, IEEE (June 1977).

6. I. Chlamatac, W.R. Franta, and K.D. Levin, "BRAM: The Broadcast Recognizing Access Mode," *IEEE Trans. on Communications* **COM-27**(8) pp. 1183-1189 (August 1979).

7. F.A. Tobagi and V.B. Hunt, "Performance Analysis of Carrier Sense Multiple Access with Collision Detection," pp. 217-244 in *Proc. of the Local Area Communication Networks Symposium*, The MITRE Corp. (May 1979).

8. N. Shacham and V.B. Hunt, *Performance Evaluation of the CSMA-CD 1-Persistent Channel Access Protocol in Common Channel Local Networks*, Telecommunication Sciences Center, SRI International, Menlo Park, CA. (Submitted to the International Symposium on Local Computer Networks, Florence Italy, April 1982).

LOCAL COMPUTER NETWORKS
P.C. Ravasio, G. Hopkins and N. Naffah (editors)
North-Holland Publishing Company
© IFIP, 1982

INTEGRATED SERVICES DIGITAL NETWORKS AND LOCAL COMPUTER NETWORKS: TOWARDS AN INFORMATION SOCIETY

FRANCO CAPPUCCINI

University of Rome
President of Consiglio Superiore Tecnico delle Poste
Telecomunicazioni ed Automazione, PTT Ministry
Rome, Italy

ABSTRACT

There is still a long way to go to get to an information society; in the 80s however public telephone networks and LANs will experience a remarkable develop – ment through the important contribution offered by electronics, thus furnishing more and more sophisticated computer based services to a variety of users.

The standardization of architectures, interfaces and protocols appears advantageous and is pursued by the PTTs for application on public networks, whereas LANs have a much more varied topologic and typologic form and non-standardized architecture and protocols.

The collaboration between the PTTs and the computer Companies in view of the standardization of the seven layers of the OSI architecture set up by ISO and CCITT may reveal itself to be, in the long run, fruitful in view of an information exchange between local networks and between these and public networks.

As an example of public networks planning in view of IDN, information is given on the Italian National Plan for Telecommunications.

1. INTRODUCTION

It is a current belief that this decade will be a time
of experiments and preparation which will allow us to
have a clear idea of what the information society we are
aimed at is going to be.

In fact all conditions for such a development exist: microelectronics is facing a transition stage from LSI to
VLSI, thus offering more and more powerful microprocessors and high capacity memories at decreasing cost per
integrated active element. Microprocessors are on the way
to become accessible even to the individual who can there
fore make use of an increasing computing power to apply
to processing and exchange of information of any type con
cerning industrial, office and home activities. The infor
mation exchange is made easier by specialized private telecommunication networks and by the public networks themselves which gradually integrate in digital form the tran
smission and switching functions (IDN).

In 1980 there were 500 million telephone sets in the
world and an equal number of television sets. This
gives an idea of the enormous potential which is offe
red to a telematics accessible to the public in general and also considering that data broadcasting, which
is now starting with teletext, is going to characterize
in this decade, together with direct satellite broadca
sting, an evolution of sound and television broadcasting
services.

The fact that the television set is going to become a

multifunction terminal makes it already possible to
foresee some form of integration between the interacti
ve videography service (videotex) and the broadcast vi
deography service (teletext). This integration, if pushed up to the level of telephone and broadcasting networks, may give also, to teletext that interactivity
which it hasn't got yet.

2. THE PROBLEM OF STANDARDIZATION

Telematics, considered as a more extensive form of the
words telecommunications and informatics, with the deci
sive contribution by microelectronics, has been representing for quite a time a remarkable issue from the in
dustrial, economic and social point of view for its intrinsic capability of penetration in any field of human
activities. It gives more room to the creative fantasy
of the designers, the possible limitations being represented more by the willingness on the part of the spe
cialized or general users to accept new services and
facilities than by their costs.
It would however be a mistake to consider telematics
simply as an addition of telecommunications plus informatics. In fact, the functions of communication and
information processing are so strictly connected and
correlated that, for the conception of complex systems,
they require the adoption of internationally standardized architectures, interfaces and protocols.
This is, on the other hand, a condition if these systems

have got to be able to exchange information, that is,
must be "open".

The concepts of open systems interconnection (OSI), ori
ginally introduced by the International Standardization
Organization (ISO) in a very general manner, find their
formalization in a seven layers architecture which only
standardize the modalities to communicate between corresponding layers belonging to different systems. The ways
of practical implementation within each layer are left
to the designer so that hardware can follow all technolo
gical developments in a flexible and independent manner.
Public telecommunication networks of every country are
institutionally open systems due to the needs of interna
tional traffic. The PTTs, through CCITT, have already
adopted the OSI architecture and have standardized protocols concerning the first three levels for circuit
switching (x 21) and for packet switching (x 25) which
are of interest for the public data networks. As for
the fourth level, which is of interest for teletex
service, ISO and CCITT are in a very advanced stage.
As for levels five to seven it is expected that some
of the several proposals put forward will be adopted
within this year.

There is no doubt that the PTTs, which have already
been engaged for a time in the gradual implementation
of the integrated digital network (IDN) as a step towards the total integration of services (ISDN), have,
also within themselves, every interest to make their
public networks open systems. This, in fact, favours

a transition towards ISDN which may last until the end
of the century. The PTTs will therefore be very active,
thorough CCITT and ISO in an early completion of the
standardization connected with the OSI architecture in
order to introduce the new services which shall have to
be compatible with 64 Kb/s switched digital connections.
A minor wave of initiatives seems to be found in the
field of LANs, probably for two reasons: because LANs
have anticipated public networks in the offer of new
high quality services, and because, for various reasons,
relevant systems have been designed as "closed".
In the USA, for example, IEEE is experiencing a delay
in its standardization process. Here is a quotation from
IEEE Spectrum, Jannuary 1982: "Manufacturers continue to
introduce LAN systems with unstandardized architectures
and protocols. The complete standard is scheduled to be
completed by this Spring. In the meantime there is
confusion".
In fact, LANs show a very diversified situation.
Three types of topology are largely used: star,
ring and bus.
Two typologies are currently used: one in base
band and one in radiofrequency band.
Data rates of 0.8 to 10 Mb/s with a capacity beyond
  1,000 terminals characterize baseband systems.
Data rates of 2.5 to 14 Mb/s with a capacity beyond
50,000 terminals are tipical of radiofrequency systems.
Even the concept of "local" varies substantially:

from 0.5 km to 8 km for base band systems and
from 7 km to 30 km for radiofrequency systems.
Digital PBX systems should also be considered: although they are slower than LANs they may offer valid alternatives in certain applications where data
and voice are constantly switched between terminals
and telephones.

      Due to the fact that a remarkable spread
of LANs is expected in this decade, together
with an upgrading of the public networks towards ISDN,
it seems natural to think of integration processes
of LANs between themselves and with the public networks, in an attempt to anticipate in some cases the
information society to which we have been referring
to. Although gateways allow an information exchange
between terminals belonging to types of networks which
are different even in data rate through conversion of
electric and software protocols, it appears to be convenient, at least on a European level, that an effective
collaboration policy between the PTTs and the computer
companies be established. Such a collaboration should
be aimed at standardizing the seven layers of the OSI
architecture in order to facilitate and extend computer applications for business and home use.
It should not be overlooked that difficulties may be
encountered in the collaboration between organizations
which are so large and different for tradition and scope. There is however a strong belief in the fact that
every effort should be made, because the advantages of-

fered by international standardization are of such an
importance for everybody, users, manufacturers and operating agencies that they do not require any further
comment.

3. THE ITALIAN NATIONAL PLAN FOR TELECOMMUNICATION SERVICES

In order to give a practical example of the actions
undertaken by the PTTs to cope with new services, information is given on the Italian National Plan for
the expansion and enhancement of Telecommunication
Services (NPTS).
The NPTS was approved by the Government at the end
of March this year and covers the whole decade. It was
prepared by the PTT Ministry taking also into account the
individual plans of the national telecommunications Agencies
which had been previously approved by the Ministry itself
according to the existing laws and regulations. Other Mi-
nistries cooperating in the Plan were those of Government
Shares (Partecipazioni Statali) and Industry.

The total investment for all telecommunication ser_
vices exceeds 30,000 billion lire at 1980 value.   The
largest part of it is devoted to integrate transmission
and switching in digital form with the aim of arriving at
a later stage at network in which all services (voice,texts
images, data) can be easily handled; and this would be
the Integrated Services Digital Network (ISDN).

A few figures can give a better idea of the NPTS.
The number of telephon subscribers in 1990, referred

to the end of 1981, will have a 1.6 increase bringing the total number of subscribers to over 22 millions with a density per 100 inhabitants approaching 39. The correspon ding figure at the end of the previous decade was 21.4, the comparison between the two figures gives an idea of the paramount importance NPTS attaches to the expansion of the telephone service.

As for transmission, the total number of circuits will experience a twofold increase at the end of the decade and digital technics will be predominant at the beginning in the urban and district areas.

The request for new electro-mechanical exchanges will pratically come to an end in 1990; by the end of 1984 digital lines will be 22% and 70% for local and tran sit exchanges respectively.

Data services subscribers amounted to 74,000 by the end of 1980, 24% of which on the switched telephone net-work and 76% on leased telephone or telegraph lines.

Within the framework of IDN the National Plan for Telecommunications allows the practical implementation, starting from 1982, of a public data network emboding cir cuit and packet switching and organized in two levels.

An upper level (primary network), with specialized data exchanges for circuit and packet switching located in a few large geographic areas. These exchanges would in fact be mainly devoted to national and international interconne- ctions.

A lower level (secondary network), with exchanges for circuit switching (voice and data), packet adaptors-concen trators etc. the geographical distribution of which being at the beginning dependent upon the number and distribution of subscribers.

In the light of this evolution it is expected that in 1990 the number of subscribers will be around 330,000, 40% of which making use of the public data network and the rest equally distributed between leased lines and the switched telephon network.

In the upgrading process of the public telephone and data networks towards IDN it is worth mentioning a number of services which are already in the field trial stage with the cooperation of the national telecommunications Agencies, the equipment manufacturers, the software houses and the in formation providers.

Following a similar pattern currently adopted by CEPT, the aim of these activies is twofold: on the one hand to evaluate the user's reactions and needs, on the other hand to advance in the process of standardization of terminal e- quipment for home and business use in the light of the ISO- CCITT open system interconnection architecture.

- Videotex (videotel) experiment is now starting involving about 1000 terminals (80% business, 20% home) and more than 40 information providers. The standard previsionally adopted is the "UK Prestel", while decisions for the opera- tional standards are pending.
- Teletext (televideo) is at present in the stage of evalua ting users' reactions by means of the transmission of a maga zine containing about 50 pages made up with alphanumeric and graphic information on several subjects with some sort

of limited   updating possibilities. In order to allow the
largest part of viewers to take part in the experiment the
information is not transmitted in coded form but as a conventional video signal. No decision has yet been taken on
the technical standards; however the largest possible compatibility with videotex is strongly pursued.
Electronic mail of the first generation (post office - to
post office) is now commercially available among 10 cities.
Groups 2 and 3 facsimile terminals are used, which are con
nected to the telephone network.
This is part of a larger experiment involving also alpha
numeric terminals and the telex network. In this way
a complex network is available allowing written message exchange among users of the telex, data and tele
phone networks on the one hand and among facsimile
users on the telephone network and users of the Post
Office facilities referred to above on the other hand.
It should be duly considered that the integration of
the Postal and Telecommunication networks can be poten
tially easier in Italy due to the fact that both services are under the regulatory action of the same Ministry.
Videoconference is at an early stage of experiment be
tween Milano and Roma making use of 2 Mb/s digital li
nes and of analogue to digital conversion with redundancy reduction.
For the sake of completeness a mention should also be
made of that part of the National Space Plan 1982-1986
which concerns the preoperational communication satellite

ITALSAT to be launched in 1986-1987.

This satellite, operating in the 20/30 GHz band, aims at the maximum of integration with the terrestrial network, thus anticipating the operational satellite of the 90s.

It will carry two main payloads: a telephone payload, including multispot antennæ and on board regeneration and switching for a point to point type of service at a total bit rate of 120 Mb/s; a special services payload (computer data, electronic mail, video conference, high speed facsimile etc) for a point to multipoint type of service at a total bit rate of 25/32 Mb/s.

ITALSAT programme is also strictly related with the introduction of fiber optics cables into the public telecommunication networks according to NPTS.

It has been pointed out at the beginning that the Italian Telecommunication environment is characterized by a plurality of Agencies: this is, per se , a positive factor towards liberalization and/ or deregulation but there is still a need for a clearer definition of the sphere of action of the Agencies themselves in order to make the best use of the technical and financial resources available.

This essential task is within the responsibilities of the PTT Ministry and according to a statement by the Government all issues should be considered and settled in the course of the present year.

LOCAL COMPUTER NETWORKS
P.C. Ravasio, G. Hopkins and N. Naffah (editors)
North-Holland Publishing Company
© IFIP, 1982

TELEMATICS AND LOCAL COMPUTER NETWORKS

LUIGI MERCURIO

Amministratore delle Delegato of OLTECO
Ivrea, Italy

INTRODUCTION

In the last years the term Telematique or Telematics was coined to indicate the increasing interconnections between computers and telecommunication systems.

This process, supported both by user demand of new services and by the dramatic technological evolution, is only at its beginning, nevertheless it has relevant impact on the way we look at the computer and communication systems and on their impact on the organisations of society.

Discussions are actively going on regarding the impact of such a process on the organization of our society. There are optimistic views emphasising the advantages of telematics as well as pessimistic views underlaying the possible risks of the computerisation of the human organization.

The debate has started and will last, I believe, for all the 80's with an increasing number of actors.

Nevertheless a generally agreable conclusion can be reach; we are facing an evolutionary change on our life as big, if not bigger, than the industrial revolution. And, still more important, we are aware that it is going to happen.

We are therefore in a position to manage and to drive such a process toward the wanted goals.

Computer systems are evolving.....

The technological trend is changing the architecture of computer systems from centralized toward decentralized or distribuited systems.

Intelligent, autonomous systems are going to be the basic building blocks of tomorrow's computer systems, which will expand their presence in the society.

This trend is demonstrated by the increasing part of the "computer" market acquired by small systems.

Fig. 1) clearly shows this trend. The computer market share of mainframes is decreasing from the 83% in the middle 70's to 36% in the middle 80's. While small system are increasing their market penetration; for example, desk top computers and personal computers, whose market share was negligible in the middle 70's, are going to acquire the 20% of the market in the 85'. The mini share is also growing from some 10% to about 20% in the decade.

This is the result of the large market expansion made possible by the presence of low cost computer systems which on the one hand allow small users to buy computers and on the other hand allow, in large organizations, the implementation of decentralized or distributed architectures.

There is a rational path, which goes from the first generation batch systems to the network of interconnected personal computers, passing through the time sharing systems, real time system, distributed hierarchical networks and so on.

There are two aspects to the demand for communication caused by the increasing presence of small computers . From one side the need to share complex expensive equipment such as a large data base, large printing capabilities and so on, and on the other side the demand and the potential of new computer based applications.

Furthermore, large organisations, while willing to allow decentralization of computing, are also going to maintain centralized control over the overall organisation, require communication capabilities in order to collect and summarize, in real time, data which is stored in the decentralized facilities.

But is the technological evolution the only driving force in this process?. The answer is, according to me, "no". The evolution, we are facing, is in fact the result of two convergent factors:the technological evolution and, more important, the social changes we are experiencing.

Modern organisations are facing and managing tasks even more complex which require to be handled using a new organizational model, in which a new level of decentralization of responsability and higher level of delegation are required.

The organization is therefore evolving, changing the mode in which control and management is performed.

The existing centralized, highly hierarchical computer systems, with the related organizational models can only be adapted with difficulty. There are at least two arguments to discuss in this respect: a technical one and an organizational one.

From a technical point of view the information and the tasks to computerize are growing at an impressive rate, putting on the computer systems requirements in terms of throughput,reliability, availability and, generally speaking, performances that cannot be satisfied, in a cost effective manner, with conventional centralized architectures.

On the other side the management of complex computer centers demands a management which is highly vertical and hierarchical in contrast with the need of decentralization.

The power acquired by such a group can grow above the desired threshold, the cost of personnell handling computer centers is growing at very high rate. All the organization will find itself dependent on a structure hardly "controllable" and, sometimes, not dependable.

Such a structure will be a focal point of failure in the overall organization, a fault can have a dramatic impact on the overall system.

Finally, the higher level of knowledge about computers and the higher professionality of people involved in the use of the computer systems itself is another factor pushing for decentralization.

But decentralization or distribution does not mean anarchy or confusion. Every organization wants and must retain control over its computerized facilities, most of all when they are going to be more and more important for the behaviour of the overall system.

Communications are therefore going to play an increasing by important role.

Telecommunications are evolving also.....

Telecommunication are also changing.

Again this change is supported by the evolution of technology and by radical change in the political role of telecommunications.

The evolution of telecommunication systems is, if possible, still more impressive. New services are announced by private and public carrier and telecommunication companies, which are upgrading at animpressive rate the number and the quality of communication systems.

This fact will open new opportunities and will raise new problems for the potential impact the new services, announced and expected, will have on every-day-life.

Restricting the scope to the data network or to the "professional" market of telecommunications, we can say that the ongoing evolution can be summarized as a transition from a raw point-to-point link, allowing the transmission of bare information (bits) from a transmitting to a receiving device; to a complex, self defined product, such as a network connecting many different addressable services to different access point (terminals).

Communication networks are therefore going to be well defined products on their own right. They will supply a set of facilities for communication independently of the kind of the interconnected systems and from the application they are supporting.

In fact a user-application can be depicted as in fig. 2). The user through a TERMINAL can access COMMUNICATION service to reach PROCESSING facilities supplying services and DATA BASE systems.

The COMMUNICATION, therefore the networks, is an important component in the overall chain.

Generally speaking, the driving force in the telecom market evolution can be summarized by:

. Technology – More and more communication systems building blocks are going digital, taking advantages of LSI and VLSI technologies.Furthermore,long haul communication are supported by satellite systems in a cost effective manner allowing large amount of information to be transported over long distances at very high rate.

.   Deregulations – Many countries are going to make a less
    restrictive regulations on telecom market allowing new partici-
    pants.As a first result of competition, we will have an explosion
    of new technologies and a severe cost reduction in many services.

.....Computer and Telecom trends are convergent.

It seems therefore that the evolution of computers and telecommunication technologies is taking place in a convergent manner, each one
supporting and integrating the other.

Distribution of processing power is possible, and it is supported by
the possibility of low cost, efficient interconnection; interconnections
and sophisticated telecommunication systems can be built taking
advantages of cost reduction of processing power.

Thus this is a self supporting process: the systems of tomorrow will
be an intelligent mixing of processing and switching capability with
a great potential for the user-community to implement and invent
even more complex and sophisticated services.

There will exist a world wide extended communication network in
which different technologies coexist and support communication of
almost any form of information in an integrated manner.

In this scenario of Telematics a role will be played by local
communication systems, such as voice and data PBX, local networks,
TV cable networks, etc.

They will represent the peripheral arms of the complex, world-wide
telematics network.

This is one of the reasons that put local networks in the focus of the
attention in today's debate and that motivate, I guess, this I.F.I.P.
Symposium.

I see local networks as a part of a more complex internetwork environment, they will be one of the basic building blocks of more complex distributed systems.

Local networks are to be regarded as the basis of the future computer systems, connecting a wide variety of non homogeneous, functionally different systems. Word processing, personal computers, large shared resource, typewriters and terminals will be interconnected by local networks allowing easy communication and easy access to local services as well as easy access to external public or private networks.

Loosely coupled distributed system are the natural result of the evolution of computer and communication technology and of their merging.

LOCAL DISTRIBUTION IN THE SCENARIO OF TELEMATICS

As said before, a substantial role will be played in the scenario of telematics by local distribution systems.

By local distribution systems I mean the set of telematic systems supporting both processing and switching of information in a geografically concentrated area:

.   Digital PABX

.   Local networks

.   Message switching systems

Every one of these systems will play a role, the user needs demand for an intelligent and integrated use of different technologies to build up really effective local distribution system. The key goals, that such a system must reach, are the following:

.   Integration –
    The local distribution system should support processing and

switching of different type of information: voice, data, images.
Local networks are moving toward PABX for voice switching.
Efforts and studies are going-on as the session on voice
transmission on LCN shows.
On the other hand PABXs are going to switch data as well as
voice.

.   Openess –
The local distribution system does not lock in the user with a
single supplier of equipment, but must provide for multivendor,
multifunctional environments.

.   Distribution –
The local distribution system should be able to support intra-
building connection as well as interbuilding, city wide communication.

.   Interconnectivity –
A local distribution system does not make any sense in a stand
alone role. It must be able to connect to a wide variety of long
haul communication networks: PSTN, PDN, Telex, Teletex.

.   Effectiveness –
The local distribution systems are to be effective. This means
they must provide cost effective connection, they must be
reliable,they must be manageable.

A system, which has these characteristics can be considered in
different environments: office automation, factory automation, home
automation. Most of the technical requirements for these systems are
in fact at least convergent.
A rigourous policy of standardization and modularization is mandato-

ry to reach the final goal. I believe, nevertheless, that the real world will be less linear and less rational. I see the coexistence of different technologies and different standards somewhere and somewhat diverging, but at the end I strongly believe that the market will impose the convergence and the interconnection of different systems.

It is today's task to work in a direction which will make such a convergence easy and effective.

I guess that the pannel discussion, planned in the programme of this Symposium, will give a clear perspective of the status of the art on this critical sector.

THE LOCAL DISTRIBUTION MARKET

The potential market for local distribution systems is enormous. We can include in such a market different existing market sectors as well as new market places which are defined by the new technologies:PABX, CATV systems, Office Automation, Factory Automation should be included in local distribution market.

The equipment, which should be connected to local distribution, includes terminals, teletypes, typewriters, personal computers, minicomputer, metering and measurement instruments, telephones, word processing systems, business systems, televisions, cash registers and so on.

In the next decades most of the electronics devices, that we are used to thinking in a stand alone or monofunctional mode, will change to be multifunctional and someway connected to local distribution systems.

For example, I should be able to use my home television set to send messages around the world, or I should be able to use my sophisticated executive workstation to send a message to my wife when

I am leaving the office to go home.

The technology is there, the need is there, the potential application understood, it is going to happen. The problem of today should be cost, the advent of VLSI technologies can help in solving it.

VLSI is going to be applied to LAN and PABX quite soon, many silicon companies are working on that and in the Symposium program there is a session discussing it as far as LAN are concerned.

Looking at the present the market for local distribution is characterized by two main factors: PABX and Local Networks.

Both the markets are in evolution. The PABX market is now of course predominant. It size world wide, including key systems is about 6,000 Milion of $. The forecast average expansion rate, in the next 5 years, is of 6.5% for PABX's, 11% for Telephone Instruments and of 7% for Key Systems.

The PABX market is changing and the PABX's will play a major role in local distribution systems. The driving force in the changes are at the present the following:

. Technological Evolution –

   PABX's are going digital. All the new announced PABX since the 1980 are digital. Most of them are able to switch interactive voice and data.

   Fig. 3) shows the cost trend for PABX's line.

. Reduction of the average PABX life time.

   The PABX have been, in the past, long life products with an average life cycle of 15 to 20 years.

   This is going to change, due to the cost reduction and the competitiviness in the market which, by introducing new features and new services, make PBX obsolete faster.

. Deregulation –

The deregulation, mostly in the USA, will encourage new participants to go into the PABX market, introducing a higher rate of innovation in a market which has been in the past decades static and conservative.

All those factors are going to make the PABX a machine more sophisticated with respect to the one we know today; the PABX will incorporate processing power allowing protocol conversion and multi-form information switching.

As a final result, the PABX will be an information switch which can represent one of the peripheral nodes of the telematics systems.

The local network market is now in an embryonic stage, it represents some million of dollars a year, which means few hundred installations. Mostly up to now it has been a test bed market, users are experimenting with local networks, they are trying to find out which technology (baseband or broadband) is most suitable for their needs, they are developing applications.

Marketing forecasts for local networks are quite different and difficult to criticize. There are different views which range over a couple of orders of magnitude.

Fig. 4) shows the potential of the market, it is crystal clear how different are today's forecasts.

In Fig. 5) our estimate of Western European potential market and sales for Ethernet type local network are shown.

The bottom line of the potential market shows that there is a leading-edge user market until the '83/'84, while between '83 and '84 there should start a general market penetration with rapid market growth starting in 1984/85.

Our estimates show for Ethernet type Local Network a compound annual growth rate of about 15 to 20%, while the actual market penetration should be somewhere between 25 to 50% of the potential market. Our estimate also shows that Ethernet type Local Network will represent in the short terms somethings between 40 and 60% of the European market.

POTENTIALS AND HANDICAPS OF LOCAL NETWORKS

Local networks will play, without doubt, a primary role in the local distribution market. I will briefly outline hereafter the potential and the requirements for local computer network and the troubles which exist in their market penetration.

The two main transmission techniques available today, baseband and broadband, are capable of supporting most of the known requirements in terms of throughput and distribution.
Despite the debate between baseband and broadband supporters, I believe that baseband and broadband will coexist and that they are destinated to respond, in an optimal way, to different needs.

Fig. 6) shows our estimate of the cost trend for connection to baseband and broadband backbones as a function of the frequency and time. According to our estimate, the cost of baseband connection will be for the next year significantly less than the cost of broadband connections, mostly at high frequencies per channel. This allows room for baseband systems, in all those cases in which the geographical distribution of the local communication systems is of some (2 – 3) Km and the interactive video integration is not a requirement. Additional broadband cost will be supported by the user everytime he needs larger geographical distribution (10–30 Km) and interactive video integration.

Fig. 7) shows our estimate of market sharing and applicability of baseband and broadband systems.

In other words, we believe that baseband will find a substantial market in intrabuilding high throughput networks, while broadband will represent the most part of city wide extended communications systems. From a different point of view one can see a hierarchy of systems as depicted in Fig. 8) in the Telematic networks.

The different technologies, together with the different characteristics of access protocols, give to local net the potential to be useful for different application environments.

This potential can be exploited and local networks will reach wide commercial acceptance only if today's pragmatic problems can be solved.

Among them one of the most important is standardization. Despite the fact that different standardization bodies are working on the subject, we do not see in the next future a suitable and effective standard to be widely accepted. This is true for at least two reasons:

.   it seems that the consensus on possible solutions is still fragile, different views coexist and compromise, making proposed standards complex and involute.

.   The standardization bodies are mostly working on data link layer standard. It is crystal clear that no integrated multivendor systems can be built on top of such a low level standard.
    This will produce, in fact, a common wire without a common language to speak.

The need for standardization is central to local networks. Only a clear, standardized environment will allow interconnectivity of both systems in local networks and of local networks in an internet environment.

None of today's computer suppliers, in fact, will be able to support all the requirements of the users and, on the other hand, it is mandatory to allow users to build up complex systems in which different components will really interact.

Effective gateway functions, protocol conversions addressing policies and schemes are not yet implemented. To size down the problems arising in this area it is mandatory to have a small set of well defined protocols to refer to. It seems to me that we can have a good outline of experiences and problems of gatewaying in the related session.

On the other side, when a complex, multivendor systems is sold and installed someone must be able to support users with installation, maintenance and monitoring tools and procedures.
Up to now local networks have been installed in R&D departments of leading edge organisations, universities and so on. No real experience exists for real commercial applications. Potential regulatory problems can arise in different areas, anti fire regulations, PTT's regulation, Union relationship, RF emission regulations and so on.
Furthermore; the fact that a local distribution system is going to be the real kernel of the computerized facilities in an organization, maintenance is a key issue to solve. Real time monitoring and tuning tools, fault isolation procedures, on line maintenance, are requirements not yet fullfilled by the LCN suppliers.

Last, but not least, applications. Most of the existing LAN are either embedded in a single supplier distribuited system or they merely represent a connection link.

Applications built making use of local networks and allowing vertical integration of different existing stand alone systems are not yet developed. The session on LAN application will give, I think, interesting ideas and stimulus to the Symposium attendees.

Today's available applications solve only terminal distribution or at most homogeneous computer to computer communication. Real distributed message switching systems, distributed data base environment and distributed network wide operating system are not yet available on the market, and we will see what is the state of the art in this field in the operating system sessions.

In conclusion the scenario is such that the local network technologies seems to be well known and have reached a level of maturity that allow them to go in the general market.

The solution of the existing problems can be implemented and I believe that the presence of LAN on the market opens new opportunities to have applications developed and the other pragmatic problems solved.

I hope to see in the next year some Symposium or workshop of the IFIP Working Group 6.4 of the Technical Committee 6 discussing experience and real application of networks.

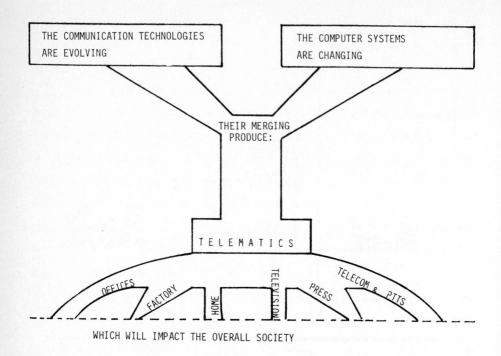

WHICH WILL IMPACT THE OVERALL SOCIETY

THE COMPUTERS ARE CHANGING	THE COMMUNICATIONS ARE EVOLVING

- TECHNICAL

    - CENTRALIZED VS DECENTRALIZED
    - LARGE VS MEDIUM/SMALL

- POLITICAL

    - ORGANIZATIONAL
    - COMPLEXITY OF TASKS
    - HIGHER PROFESSIONALITY
    - HIGHER DELEGACY

- RAPID TECHNICAL EVOLUTION
  (ANALOG → DIGITAL → VLSI)

- MARKET EVOLUTION: THE NETWORK
  WILL BE A SELF DEFINED PRODUCT

- DEREGULATION:

    - COMPETITIVENESS
    - NEW SERVICES
    - COST REDUCTION

IN FACT .....

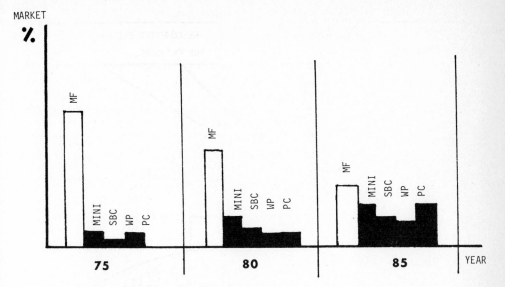

Figure 1.   COMPUTER MARKET EVOLUTION

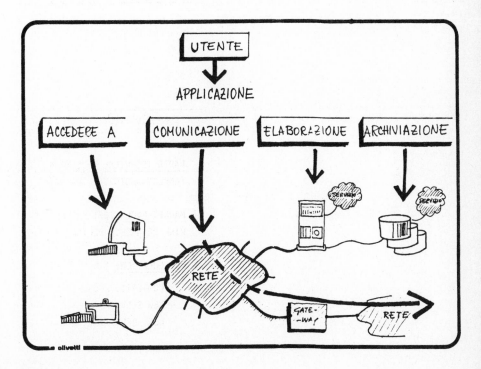

Figure 2.

THE COMPUTER MARKET AND TECHNOLOGY TREND
IS CONVERGENT WITH THE TELECOM TRENDS:

- DISTRIBUTED PROCESSING ARCHITECTURES
- LOW COST COMMUNICATIONS
- INTELLIGENT SWITCHING

AGAIN

(PROCESSING + SWITCHING) + PROCESSING = TELEMATICS

LOCAL DISTRIBUTION SYSTEM WILL PLAY AN IMPORTANT
ROLE IN THE TELEMATICS

LOCAL DISTRIBUTION SYSTEMS

- PABX
- LOCAL NETWORKS
- MESSAGE SWITCHING
- CABLE TV NETWORKS

WILL EVOLVE TO GUARANTEE:

- INTEGRATION
- OPENNESS
- DISTRIBUTION
- INTERCONNECTIVITY
- EFFECTIVENESS

LOCAL COMPUTER NETWORKS
TWO MAIN ACTORS

P A B X

- PABX EVOLUTION
  (ANALOG — DIGITAL)
- REDUCTION OF LIFE TIME
- DEREGULATION

L O C A L N E T W O R K S

- EMBRYONIC MARKET
- LEADING EDGE USERS AND
  TEST BEDDING FOR THE BEGINNING
- GENERAL MARKET PENETRATION
  STARTING 83-84

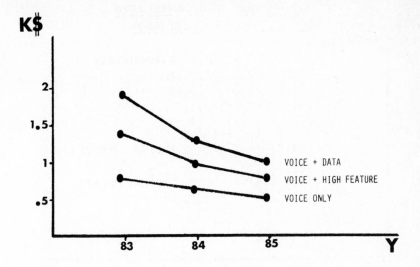

Figure 3. PABX COST PER LINE (TREND)

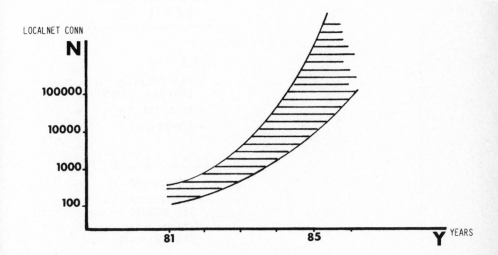

Figure 4. NUMBER OF CONNECTIONS

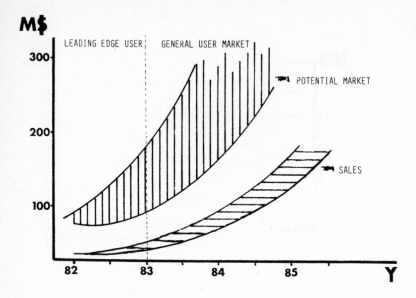

Figure 5.   POTENTIAL EUROPEAN LOCALNET MARKET & SALES

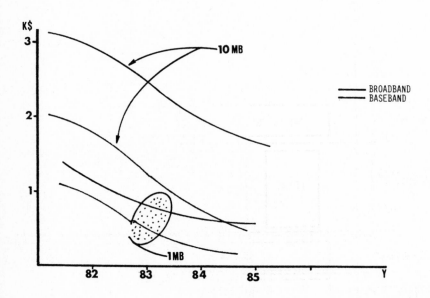

Figure 6.

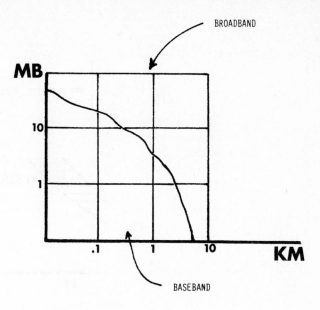

Figure 7.

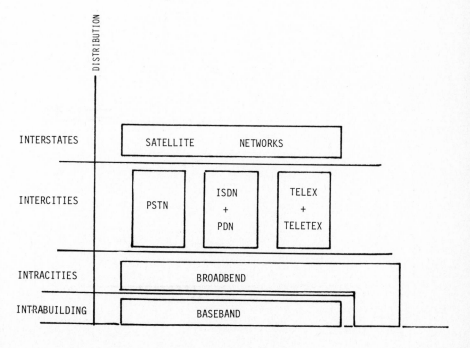

Figure 8.

AUTHOR INDEX